ANALYTICAL CHEMISTRY

ANALYTICAL CHEMISTRY

METHODS OF SEPARATION

ROBERT V. DILTS
Vanderbilt University

D. VAN NOSTRAND COMPANY
NEW YORK   CINCINNATI   TORONTO   LONDON   MELBOURNE

D. Van Nostrand Company Regional Offices:
New York   Cincinnati   Millbrae

D. Van Nostrand Company International Offices:
London   Toronto   Melbourne

Published by D. Van Nostrand Company
450 West 33rd Street, New York, N. Y. 10001

Published simultaneously in Canada by
Van Nostrand Reinhold Ltd.

10 9 8 7 6 5 4 3 2 1

PREFACE

The need for revision of the traditional analytical chemistry course has become increasing obvious during the last few years. Most of the introductory courses in quantitative analysis do not adequately reflect the modern techniques and instrumentation that are used today in industrial and academic laboratories. Generally, students are not introduced to modern analysis until their senior year. My goal in writing this text is to present contemporary methods of analytical chemistry to students fairly early in their undergraduate careers. Only freshman chemistry and some familiarity with organic systems are prerequisites for this text. Students majoring in chemistry, engineering, or premedical studies will find this approach helpful in their later studies and in their professional careers.

The text presents the important methods of separation—extraction, ion-exchange, and all forms of chromatography—within the theoretical framework of equilibrium principles. The discussions emphasize basic equilibrium concepts and general techniques rather than specific chemical systems. Worked examples and descriptions of current applications are always included. When appropriate, realistic experiments are presented that apply the separation methods. The basic laboratory skills of volumetric, gravimetric, and colorimetric analysis are also taught by using them in these experiments for quantitative determination of the separated components. Thus, classical analysis is learned by application in realistic laboratory situations, rather than in contrived exercises.

In keeping with the relevant tone of the text, research accounts in current journals are cited whenever possible. Discussions and experiments exemplifying contemporary analyses for drugs and other modern compounds have been included. Inorganic, organic, and biochemical systems are frequently used to illustrate techniques.

In order to reinforce the many principles presented, a large number of problems have been included at the end of each chapter. These problems cover useful numerical computations as well as critical evaluation and comparison of analytical techniques.

Nashville, Tennessee   Robert V. Dilts

Acknowledgments

I would like to acknowledge the encouragement, and actual assistance that I received during the development of this book. To do this adequately is difficult since many influences and contributions that produce a manuscript are not overt, but subtle suggestions that lead to and then along particular pathways. First, I am indebted to N. Howell Furman, who first stirred my interest in separation methods. His kindly manner, depth of knowledge, persuasive encouragement, and familiarity with applications of analyses led me to appreciate the importance of the separation step to any analytical procedure.

My colleagues at Vanderbilt University, especially Larry C. Hall, suggested many years ago that the traditional sophomore analytical chemistry course be re-oriented so as to keep the subject in the chemistry curriculum as a viable and profitable course. They encouraged me to design a course that would be of value in the latter portion of this century to science-oriented students selecting the course. The tolerance, criticisms, and interest of the students who were in the classes as the course was developed and matured were very beneficial. Throughout the years many graduate students worked as teaching assistants in this course and helped refine the material and work the bugs out of the laboratory experiments. Ron C. McNutt, Donald J. Mitchell, Gale C. Clark, and Caleb W. Holyoke, Jr. were especially valuable to me in this respect. The list of people who encouraged me to write up the material from the course into a textbook is lengthy, and in order not to offend anyone by inadvertent omission, will not be included here.

I would like to express my appreciation to the members of the Chemistry Department of the University of Kansas for their interest, patience, and hospitality during my stay there to write this manuscript. Clark E. Bricker's friendship, encouragement, advice, and suggestions were of outstanding value to me over the years, but especially valuable during the production of the manuscript. The science librarians at both the University of Kansas and Vanderbilt University were patient, extremely helpful, and understanding in assisting me to assemble the material.

I would like to thank Mary Pat Barr, Carol Robinson, Marnelle Creasey, Martha Holyoke, and George Reynolds for their work in typing and assembling the manuscript. Jim McCord provided unparalleled assistance through his meticulous reading of the entire manuscript and his extensive suggestions for its improvement. Stephen Daugherty is to be thanked for taking many of the photographs used.

Thomas W. Martin, Mary Bobo, and Mark M. Jones of the Vanderbilt University Chemistry Department facilitated the production of the manuscript in countless direct and indirect ways, for which I am extremely grateful.

I thank all of those mentioned and alluded to above, as well as the many other individuals who assisted in producing this book.

R.V.D.

CONTENTS

CHAPTER 1

THE SINGLE-PAN
ANALYTICAL BALANCE

THE OPERATION AND THEORY OF THE BALANCE

The ultimate measurement in analytical chemistry is that of mass. Weighing is an essential and integral part of all analytical procedures. The mass of containers, samples, reactants, and products must be established accurately and precisely. *Calibrated glassware* is standardized by weight measurements. *Standard solutions* are prepared from accurately known weights and volumes. Separation methods involve both precisely measured masses and volumes. For quantitative analysis, an accurate knowledge of the masses of chemicals is crucial. To obtain this requisite accurate measurement of the mass of objects, the analytical balance was developed.

For centuries balances consisted essentially of a beam, two pans, and some means for detecting any imbalance. Refinements of the details of careful construction naturally were made. About 1886 a balance was designed which consisted of a fixed weight attached to one end of the beam and both the pan and set of weights suspended from the other end. On this balance both the object and the accurate weights are compared against the same reference, on the same arm of the beam. This variant of conventional balance construction was ignored. In 1946, Erhard Mettler of Switzerland developed what is known now as the *single-pan balance*. The single-pan balance also has a counterweight at one end of a beam, with both the pan and set of weights at the other end. Fig. 1–1 is a schematic drawing of the balance developed by Mettler. Because weighing by substitution is intrinsically more accurate, and Erhard Mettler incorporated many convenient features in his design, this time the single-pan balance caught on. Any lingering reservations about the superiority of substitution weighing were dispelled in 1960, when, after extensive and exhaustive testing, the U.S. National Bureau of Standards recommended the use of the single-pan balance instead of the two-pan balance.[4] Today the single-pan analytical balance is found in almost all laboratories.

The function of an analytical balance is to compare the mass of an object against the accurately known mass of some standard (called weights). Mass, not weight, is compared. Weight is the force of gravity acting upon mass. Since the

1

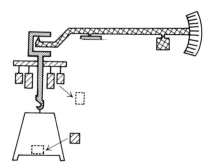

Fig. 1-1. Schematic diagram of a single-pan balance. (*Courtesy of Mettler Instrument Co.*)

force of gravity varies with both altitude and latitude, some means of negating this variation in its force must be found; otherwise, an object when weighed in Mexico City would have a different weight than it would have in London. By comparing the mass against a known mass of some substance, variations in the effect of gravity are cancelled. Gravity is assumed to be the same at both ends of the short beam of the balance.

The object to be weighed, A, is placed in the pan at one end of a balance beam. The length from the fulcrum to point of application of force is d_A. Weights, W, are added to the other pan until the initial position of equilibrium is regained. When this is attained, the mass of the object will be equal to the mass of the weights, provided that the arms of the balance beam are identical. Figure 1–2 shows this diagrammatically.

The torque on the lever on the object side is equal to the force applied times the distance through which it acts, $\text{Torque}_A = F_A \times d_A$. The torque on the lever on the weights side is equal to the force of the weights times the distance through which it acts, $\text{Torque}_W = F_W \times d_W$. When the beam of the balance has reached equilibrium, these two torques exactly balance one another so that

$$\text{Torque}_A = \text{Torque}_W$$
$$F_A \times d_A = F_W \times d_W \tag{1--1}$$

Force is the mass of the substance, m, times the effect of gravity, g, on it. Substituting in (1–1)

$$m_A \times g \times d_A = m_W \times g \times d_W \tag{1--2}$$

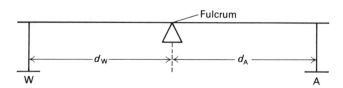

Fig. 1-2. Lever forces on a balance beam.

Assuming that gravity will have the same magnitude at both ends of the balance beam, g cancels out, leaving

$$m_A \times d_A = m_W \times d_W \qquad (1\text{--}3)$$

which is the fundamental equation for a balance based on the principle of levers. When $d_A = d_W$ then $m_A = m_W$. In the single-pan balance, no assumption is made about the balance arms being of equal length: the weights and objects are both on the same arm; d_A is d_W.

The single-pan balance is based on the method of weighing by substitution introduced by Borda. A balance beam whose fulcrum is not necessarily at its center has a pan and a set of weights suspended from one end and a rough tare or counterweight attached to the other (see Fig. 1–1). Equation (1–3) applies, but $d_A \neq d_W$ and $m_A \neq m_W$. When the object to be weighed is placed on the pan the two torques no longer balance one another, the object plus the weights produce a larger torque. To restore the beam to its initial equilibrium position, weights equal to the mass of the object are removed from the beam. The torques are equal again, only this time the counterweight is balanced by the object plus the remaining weights. Hence, in weighing an object on a single-pan balance, the amount of weight on the beam is always the same. Sometimes it is due only to weights, other times it is due to some weights and an object. This constant load is an important feature of the single-pan balance.

When discussing balances and weighing, certain terms are used that have precise scientific meanings, defined by the Committee on Balances and Weights of the American Chemical Society in 1954.[3]

Capacity. The capacity of a balance is the heaviest weight placed on one pan for which the balance can be brought to equilibrium on scale.

Readability. The readability of a balance is the smallest fraction of a division to which the index scale can be read with ease, either by estimation or use of a vernier or other device. The readability of a balance normally should be expressed in divisions. The readability limits the number of decimal places because in scientific measurements (see Chapter 4) only the last decimal place can contain any uncertainty.

Precision. Precision is the agreement between repeated measurements of the same mass. The precision of a balance is expressed as the standard deviation (see Chapter 4) of repeated weighings of the same object. The precision obtainable when using a balance depends not only on the balance, but on the skill of the operator, the method of weighing, and the surrounding conditions. A statement of precision should include a statement of the procedure used and conditions under which the precision was measured.

Accuracy. Accuracy is the agreement between the result of a measurement and the true value of the quantity measured. The factors which influence the accuracy of a weighing are discussed below.

Sensitivity. Sensitivity is the change in the response with the change in the quantity measured. In terms of the single-pan balance, sensitivity means the number of scale divisions per unit mass. The sensitivity of a two-pan balance varies with load, usually decreasing as the weight increases. The single-pan balance always operates with a constant load—the capacity of the balance—so that it has a constant sensitivity.

Sensitivity Reciprocal.   The sensitivity reciprocal is the change in weight required to change the equilibrium position by one division at any load within the capacity of the balance. It is expressed in mass units per division.

In practice, when weighing on a balance, enough weights are never removed to return the system to its original rest point (equilibrium position). It would be too tedious a chore. Enough weights are removed to return close to it (any arbitrary position will do), and then the remaining weight is measured using the sensitivity of the balance. The angle between the initial and final beam positions can be related to weight, so that the expression

$$m_A = m_W + \theta/S \tag{1-4}$$

gives the weight. m_A and m_W have been defined earlier, θ is the angle between the two equilibrium positions, and S is the sensitivity of the balance. The sensitivity of the single-pan balance is constant so that the angle (in scale divisions) by which the beam differs from its initial rest point can be graduated directly in weight units. One of the major conveniences of the single-pan balance is this direct reading of the mass on an optical scale.

The single-pan balance is independent of the characteristics of the balance arm—its length, weight, and bending—since both weights and object are suspended from the same arm. The length of the beam arm supporting the pan and weights is much shorter than the other arm to minimize its weight, thermal expansion, bending, and other properties that might affect the measurement.

With only one balance pan, opportunities to change its weight or harm it are less frequent than if there were two. Pan swinging occurs only half as frequently too. Since there are only two knife edges, it is quite simple to adjust them to be parallel and coplanar (both are essential to proper functioning of a balance). Wear and tear on knife edges is much less and has less effect on balance performance. The error in replacing the beam on the knife edges after arresting it is eliminated in the single-pan balance.

The balance case is designed so that the beam and weights are isolated from the pan compartment. They are not open to the laboratory atmosphere. Because of this design feature, there are fewer temperature gradients within the balance case and these cause less error.

A single-pan balance is much faster to use because of the direct-reading of all weight, the weight-removal mechanism, and the air-damping. A weighing can be completed in 30 seconds.

A single-pan balance always is under maximum weight—its capacity—so that it always operates at minimum sensitivity. In its investigation, the National Bureau of Standards[4] showed that this minimum sensitivity is so large that any arguments about diminished sensitivity are specious. Frictional effects on the knife edges were so slight that it was impossible to measure them. The increase in wear on the knife edges by operating at full capacity is overcome by constructing knife edges from longer pieces of sapphire.

Table 1–1. CATEGORIES OF ANALYTICAL
BALANCES

Classification	Capacity	Precision
High capacity	1000 g	1 mg
Analytical	160–200 g	0.1 mg
Semi-micro	75–100 g	0.01 mg
Micro	10–30 g	1 μg
Ultramicro	10 mg	10 ng

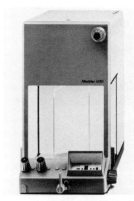

Fig. 1–3. Typical single-pan balances. (*Courtesy of Mettler Instrument Co.*)

Analytical balances are classified into five categories depending on their capacity. The construction necessary for handling each capacity determines the minimum weight-change detectable. Table 1–1 gives these categories. Fig. 1–3 shows three models of single-pan analytical balances available.

Construction Details

Fig. 1–4 shows a diagram of a single-pan balance, while Fig. 1–5 is a photograph of the beam compartment of a single-pan balance. The balance is not really so complex as it appears at first glance. The essential components are: (1) beam (including the counterweight and readout scale), (2) the weights and their removal mechanism, (3) the pan and pan arrest, (4) the air damper, and (5) the readout system.

Beam

The beam of a single-pan balance is constructed with unequal arms of solid chrome steel. Fig. 1–6 shows the beam and weights. The beam arm supporting the pan and weights (A in Fig. 1–6) is shorter than the arm holding the counterweight. The fulcrum is a synthetic sapphire prism, 1.5 cm long, resting on one edge on a

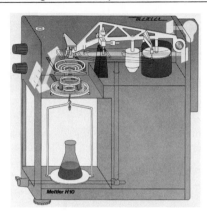

Fig. 1-4. The modern analytical balance. (*Courtesy of Mettler Instrument Co.*)

Fig. 1-5. The beam compartment. (*Courtesy of Mettler Instrument Co.*)

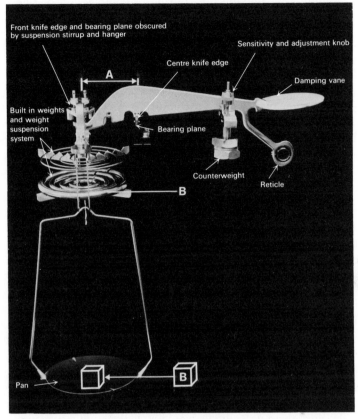

Fig. 1-6. The beam and weights. (*Courtesy of Mettler Instrument Co.*)

sapphire polished plate. When not in use the beam is held off the plate (arrested) by an elaborate mechanism. This mechanism carefully and smoothly lowers the beam exactly into place when the balance is used. At the pan end of the beam, a stirrup rests on the edge of a second sapphire prism. From this stirrup hangs not only the balance pan, but also the set of weights (see Fig. 1–6).

The beam arm containing the counterweight is much longer than the arm holding the pan, so that the counterweight can be lighter than the weights (see Equation 1–3). The counterweight is a heavy steel bolt, attached directly to the arm. Also attached to this end of the beam and contributing to some of the counter-weight are: the piston of the air damper; the arm containing the accurately marked glass scale of the readout system; and the adjustable thumbscrew to correct the position of the balance when it cannot be zeroed.

Weights

The weights consist of sequences of austenitic stainless steel rings suspended on racks in an elaborate assembly on the end of the beam. The weight denominations are 10, 20, 40, 80 g; 1, 1, 2, 5 g; and 0.1, 0.1, 0.2, 0.5 g, which give the balance a capacity of 160 g. Knobs on the front of the balance case, when turned, move arms that carefully raise the appropriate ring or combination of rings from the beam arm. The quality of the weights in most balances usually meets standards of type II-S-2 or II-P-3 (see p. 10).

Pan

The pan, made of lightweight corrosion-resistant alloy, is hung below the weights on a hook on the stirrup. Protruding from the bottom of the weighing chamber is the pan brake mechanism. The pan brake consists of a fine needle, which lightly touches the bottom of the pan to stop swinging. The pan brake is coordinated with the beam arrest mechanism; when the beam is released, the pan brake falls, allowing the pan to move unfettered to its equilibrium position.

Damping

The motion of a balance beam-pan-weights system is in damped harmonic oscillations. Each swing has a slightly smaller amplitude than the previous one. Eventually the system comes to rest at its equilibrium position. Because this takes at least ten minutes, it never is allowed to occur. Single-pan balances brake the oscillations to reach equilibrium within a few seconds by means of air damping (Fig. 1–7). A vane, V, on the end of the balance arm extends into a closed cylinder, D, (called the dashpot). The only opening in the dashpot is the slit through which the vane enters. The vane has a diameter slightly smaller than the inner diameter of the dashpot and a notch, N, in the circumference. When the beam moves, the vane moves through the dashpot compressing the air in front of it; its motion is braked by the resistance of the air. Air inside the dashpot rushes through the notch from one side of the vane to the other in order to equalize any pressure differentials. If allowed to develop, these differentials would alter the equilibrium position of the balance beam.

Readout System

On a single-pan balance the weight of an object is read directly through windows on the front of the balance case. The numbers for whole gram weights (and, on certain models, tenths of grams) are on scales attached to the weight-removal

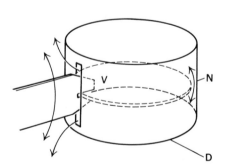

Fig. 1-7. Air damper.

lever system. They appear as the knobs are rotated. The numbers for tens of milli-grams, milligrams, and tenths of milligrams, however, because of the constant sensitivity, are obtained by the second term of Equation (1–4) and projected on the readout screen. The difference between the initial and final rest points is measured optically in scale divisions marked in milligrams.

A compartment in the rear left corner of the beam chamber contains a light bulb (see Fig. 1–5). The end of the beam is a disc upon which a scale has been etched accurately. The light from the bulb passing through this disc is manipulated through a lens-mirror system to the front of the balance case, where it is projected upon a frosted glass plate. Hundreds and tens of milligrams are read directly from the position of this projected scale. In the light path, on the right hand side of the balance case, is a moveable lens attached to a knob on the outside of the balance case (see Fig. 1–5). Movement of the knob rotates the lens which moves the image of the scale on the beam arm up or down on the frosted plate at the front of the balance. This zero-adjust knob in no way affects the equilibrium position of the beam; it merely calls wherever it rests, zero.

Initially, with no object on the pan, this lens is rotated to match the 0-line of the movable image against the 0-line of the fixed scale. Once this zero adjustment has been made, any change in the position of the lens during a weighing will shift the zero point an unknown amount. According to the balance model, the last decimal places are obtained by (*a*) interpolation using a vernier; (*b*) insertion of a second movable lens in the light path, whose rotation moves the image of the printed scale to another position. The distance moved is measured either on a movable scale or digitally. Fig. 1–8 shows the vernier and the digital readouts.

There are at least thirteen manufacturers of single-pan analytical balances at the present time. These balances have capacities between 160 and 200 g. The optical scale extends for 1000 mg. The reproducibility of the weight readings varies between 0.01 and 0.3 mg, depending upon the model and readout system.

Some balances are manufactured with the capability to tare for the weight of a container. Taring is achieved by hanging a second, smaller set of weights on the beam. The weight of the container is removed from this set of weights. The last decimal places of the weight of the container are adjusted optically.

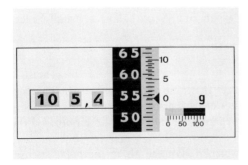

Weight = 105.4554g

(*a*)

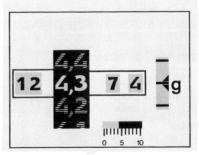

Weight = 124.374 g

(*b*)

Fig. 1-8. Typical balance readouts. (*Courtesy of Mettler Instrument Co.*)

ERRORS IN WEIGHING

The weight of any object obtained by a balance contains some uncertainty. The part of this uncertainty due to the normal random errors of balance and operator performance cannot be avoided. The remaining errors can be detected, minimized, and, in many cases, avoided completely. Most analytical weighings are by difference; that is, both the container and the container plus sample are weighed. The weight of the sample is obtained by subtraction. Errors in both weights that are identical and due to the same cause will cancel out. However, reading errors, weight errors, and random errors are increased since two weighings are made instead of just one.

Errors in the Weights

The weight of the chrome steel rings of the single-pan balance is extremely close to the specified value, but there will be a small difference from it. The magnitude permitted for this difference will depend upon the quality of the weights. The control of the accuracy of weights used in the United States is exercised by the National Bureau of Standards. They have authorized the American Society for Testing Materials to establish standards for all weights. The ASTM has recommended that various categories of weights be established and proposed the norms and weight tolerances for each category.[2] The ASTM report assigns all weights a type based on their physical design. Type I weights must be constructed out of only one piece of metal. Type II weights can be made in two pieces, so they may contain a cavity to hold weight adjusting material. Weights also are classified into four grades—S, O, P, and Q—on the basis of the physical properties of the materials from which they are constructed. The requirements for S are more stringent than those for O, and so on. The properties are density, surface area, surface finish, surface protection, magnetic properties, corrosion resistance, and hardness. Weights also are categorized into classes—1 through 6—depending upon the weight tolerances permitted. The smaller the class number, the smaller the permitted tolerances. Table 1–2 lists the ASTM type, grade, and class specifications for weight sets according to their intended applications.

Table 1–3 lists the tolerances for Class 2, 3, and 4 weights, which, as can be seen from Table 1–3, are most commonly employed in analytical laboratories.

The built in weights of most single-pan analytical balances usually meet standards of type II-S-2 or II-P-3.

Temperature Difference

When the object being weighed is not at the same temperature as the balance, an error is introduced in the weight of the object. This is due primarily to what is called the *sail effect* although thermal expansion changes the rest point of the balance.

When the object being weighed is warmer than the air in the balance case, convection currents are set up. The warm air over the object rises and circulates through the weighing compartment, forcing the pan to rise slightly, so that the weight of the object appears to be less than it actually is. This is what is known as the

Table 1–2. ASTM RECOMMENDED WEIGHTS FOR BALANCES

Application	Type	Grade	Class
Reference Standards used for calibrating other weights	I	S	1, 2, 3, or 4[a]
High precision Standards for calibration of weights and precision balances	I or II[b]	S or O[b]	1 or 2[c]
Working Standards for calibration and precision analytical work	II	S or O	2
Laboratory weights for routine analytical work	II	O	2 or 3
Built-in weights, high quality analytical balances	I or II	S	2
Moderate precision laboratory balances	II	P	3 or 4
Dial scales and trip balances	II	Q	4 or 5
Platform scales	II	Q	5 or 6

SOURCE: Ref. 2.

[a] Primary Standards are for reference use only and should be calibrated. Because the actual values for each weight are stated, close tolerances are neither required nor desirable.

[b] Because working standards are used for the calibration of measuring instruments, the choice of tolerance depends upon the requirements of the instrument. The weights are usually used at the assumed nominal values and appropriate tolerances should be chosen.

[c] Type I and Grade S will have a higher constancy but will probably be higher priced.

Table 1–3. ASTM TOLERANCES FOR ANALYTICAL WEIGHTS

Denomination	Individual Tolerance, mg		
	Class 2	Class 3	Class 4
100 g	0.50	1.0	2.0
50	0.25	0.60	1.2
30	0.15	0.45	0.90
20	0.10	0.35	0.70
10	0.074	0.25	0.50
5	0.054	0.18	0.36
3	0.054	0.15	0.30
2	0.054	0.13	0.26
1	0.054	0.10	0.20
500 mg	0.025	0.080	0.16
300	0.025	0.070	0.14
200	0.025	0.060	0.12
100	0.025	0.050	0.10

SOURCE: Ref. 2.

sail effect. This error occurs if an object that has been heated is not left in the desiccator sufficiently long enough to cool to room temperature, or if the air in the balance room is cooler than the air in the laboratory where the object has been stored. A heated object cools to room temperature asymptotically. It requires about an hour and a half for an object to cool from red heat to room temperature in a desiccator. In a study of the cooling of porcelain crucibles in a desiccator, Agterdenbos[1] found that each degree difference in temperature between the crucible and the balance corresponded to a 0.16 mg difference in weight. Thus a crucible that was only 2°C warmer than the balance would have a 0.3 mg error, and one 5°C warmer would appear to weigh 0.8 mg less. This study was made on a two-pan balance; the error on a single-pan balance is less because there is no coupling of effects between the two pans, and the beam is physically isolated from the weighing compartment.

Thermal expansion changes the rest point of the balance and the value of the scale divisions on the optical readout. The light bulb in the beam chamber heats the chamber when it is on. To minimize this heating, the beam should be kept arrested as frequently as feasible.

The heat from one's body is sufficient to cause a slight temperature difference in the balance. Therefore one should not hover over the balance or lean too closely to it too long. Hands should never be inserted inside the weighing chamber—use tongs or forceps.

An object will be cooler than the balance when the object has been stored in a refrigerator or when the laboratory temperature is lower than that of the balance room. In this case the sail effect operates in the opposite direction, causing an erroneously heavy weight to be recorded. If the humidity is high, moisture is apt to condense on the cooler object, also causing an apparent increase in the weight of the object.

Weight Changes in the Object

Occasionally the object being weighed will undergo a change in its weight during the process of weighing. Under normal conditions, using single-pan balances, the length of time for a weighing is very short, so that weight changes in the sample and container are negligible.

Certain materials, such as Fe_2O_3, CaO, Al_2O_3, rapidly adsorb moisture and/or carbon dioxide from the air. Attempts to weigh these chemicals in open containers are futile for they continually increase in weight. Closed containers, for example, stoppered weighing bottles and crucibles with lids, prevent chemicals stored in desiccators from adsorbing moisture during weighing.

Students frequently attempt to weigh volatile liquids such as acetone, methyl or ethyl alcohol, benzene, and others, in open or partially open containers in the analytical balance chamber. Not only are the fumes corrosive to the balance case, pan, and beam, but it is impossible to obtain a steady reading. The rapid evaporation causes the weight to decrease continuously. When such liquids must be weighed, use tightly closed containers.

A beaker, weighing bottle, or crucible containing an undried sample has a film of adsorbed moisture on its surface. The extent (and hence weight) of this film depends upon the humidity of the surroundings. When an object is taken from a humid room to a dry one (say, from an unair-conditioned laboratory to an air-conditioned balance room) some change in the weight of the surface film occurs which shows up as weight of the object. An undried object should be allowed to establish equilibrium with the air in the balance before trying to weigh it.

Buoyancy

According to Archimedes' principle, any object immersed in a fluid will be buoyed up by a force equal in the weight of the fluid displaced. Since air is indeed a fluid, objects weighed in air are buoyed up by, and hence appear lighter because of, the air they displace. To obtain the true weight of an object, a correction for this buoyancy must be applied. When weighing by difference, the volume of the container subtracts out making the buoyant effect negligible. When a single weighing of an object of large volume (such as a Dumas bulb or volumetric flask) is made, corrections for buoyancy must be considered for they can be appreciable.

The formula for correction of the weight of an object obtained on a single-pan balance to its weight in vacuum involves the differences in the volumes (densities) of the weights and counterweights, as well as the volume (density) of air displaced by the object weighed.

$$W_{\text{ob}} = W_{\text{a}} + W_{\text{a}} d_{\text{air}} \left(\frac{1}{d_{\text{ob}}} - \frac{1}{d_{\text{w}}} \right) \qquad (1\text{--}5)$$

W_{ob} is the weight of the object *in vacuo*, W_{a} the apparent weight of the object in air, d_{air} is the density of air, d_{ob} the density of the object being weighed, and d_{w} is the density of the weights used. The chrome stainless steel weights used in single-pan balances have a density of 7.76 g/cm^3. The density of air varies with humidity, temperature, and altitude. The usual density used is for sea level, at 50% humidity and 20°C—1.20 mg/cm^3. It should be noted that at an altitude of 5000 ft and 25% relative humidity the density of air falls to 1.00 mg/cm^3 at 20°C.

Electrification of the Object

When an insulator, such as glass or porcelain, is wiped with a dry towel, a charge of static electricity develops on its surface. Borosilicate glass is more susceptible to acquiring a charge of static electricity than is ordinary soft glass. When such a charged object is placed on the metal pan of the balance it induces charges throughout the weighing chamber. The weighing chamber of most single-pan balances is constructed of enameled cast-aluminum and glass. These induced charges cause erratic balance behavior and error in the weight of the object. The magnitude of this error will, of course, depend on the extent of electrification but it has been known to be as large as 0.1 g. This error is especially prevalent in low humidity; it usually can be ignored when the humidity of the room is over 50%.

Errors due to electrification can be avoided by drying objects in an oven or over a flame, rather than with a towel, and allowing them to cool.

CARE OF AN ANALYTICAL BALANCE

An analytical balance will function properly and last for decades if it is cared for correctly. The following precautions should be taken when using these balances:

1. Make sure the balance is level before using it. The air bubble of the oil-drop level on the balance case should be in the center of the circle. When it is not, adjust the legs of the balance until the balance is level. The optical scale of single-pan balances will not zero when the balance is tilted too much.

2. Make sure that the beam arrest, pan arrest, and optical readout are functioning properly. If they are not, call an instructor to make the necessary adjustment or repairs; never attempt to adjust the balance yourself.

3. Make sure that the weight of the object does not exceed the stated capacity of the balance. The capacity is printed on the faceplate of the balance, near the readout.

4. Keep the balance scrupulously clean.
    (a) Brush the balance pan with a large camel's hair brush before using. This will remove any dust or lint that might have settled on it since the last use.
    (b) Weigh chemicals in some sort of a container (weighing bottle, weighing paper, cups, or other convenient receptacle). Never place chemicals directly on the balance pan.
    (c) Weigh highly volatile materials (such as iodine, or benzene) in closed containers because their vapors are corrosive to the balance parts.
    (d) Remove the container from the weighing chamber before adding or removing chemicals. This way, chemicals cannot be spilled inside the balance case.
    (e) Wipe up immediately any chemicals that might have been spilled on the pan or on the bottom of the weighing compartment.
    (f) Close the doors of the weighing chamber after using the balance to prevent dust and dirt from entering when it is not in use.

5. Close both doors of the weighing chamber before releasing the beam.

6. Sit directly in front of the balance case, with the readout scale at eye level to avoid an error due to parallax. Obviously, this is not necessary if the balance has a digital readout.

7. Arrest the beam completely when placing objects on the pan or removing them from the pan. Most single-pan balances have a partial arrest position that is used when selecting the proper weights.

8. Place the object to be weighed in the center of the balance pan. Centering of the object minimizes swinging of the pan. This gives clearer and steadier readings on the optical readout.

9. Record the weight of the object directly into the laboratory notebook. Do not record weights on loose scraps of paper, for these have a notorious ability to become lost. Label all weighings clearly so that guessing as to which weight goes with what object and was made on what date is not necessary.

10. Remove all objects from the balance compartment, and close it after completing a weighing. Turn all knobs back to zero; this action returns all weights to the beam.

11. Replace the protective cover on the balance when finished using it.

Instructions for Weighing on a Single-Pan Balance

The following instructions were written for the operation of a Mettler H6 single-pan balance. Slight modifications will be necessary for application to other models or balances from other manufacturers. The sequence of operations below does not differ from balance to balance, so it can serve as a guide for any balance.

1. Remove the plastic cover carefully so as not to break the magnifying lens.
2. Dust the balance pan with the brush in the balance.
3. Check that all three weight knobs are set at zero.
4. Rotate the knob on the left side of the balance case (beam arrest) counter-clockwise to release the beam completely.
5. Turn the knob on the right side of the balance (zero adjust) until the "00 line" on the green-backed scale lies exactly in the center of the double black prongs. Do not touch this knob again.
6. Turn the beam arrest knob to the *up* position to arrest the beam.
7. Place the object to be weighed on the pan.
8. Estimate the weight of object to nearest 10 g and set the left knob on the front of the balance to that weight.
9. Rotate the beam-arrest knob clockwise (toward front of balance) to release the beam partially.
10. (a) If the 00-line on the green scale rises above the 00-line on the silver scale, the weight is too light (you took off too much). Arrest the beam and remove 10 g of weight by turning the knob.
    (b) If the 00-line on the green scale is below the 00-line on the silver scale the weight is too heavy (you took off too little). Arrest the beam, and add 10 g by turning the weight knob. If now the 00-green line rises, the first 10 g reading was correct. If not, move the 10 g knob to the next higher 10 g weight.
11. Turn the unit weight knob at the right front of the case counterclockwise: 9, 8, 7, and so on, until the 00-line on the green scale falls below the 00-line on the silver scale. This is the correct weight position.
12. Turn beam-arrest knob counterclockwise to release the beam completely.
13. Read the four decimal places as follows:
    (a) The first two from the black line on the green-backed scale that is closest to, but below, the center of the double black prongs.
    (b) Turn the knurled, upper-right knob on the front of the balance case until the line chosen in step 13(a) lies exactly in the center of the double black prongs.
    (c) Read the last two decimal places off the silver scale. Each line represents 0.1 mg; so if it reads 23, this is 2.3 mg.
14. Arrest the beam and return all the weight knobs to the zero position.
15. Close the side doors, and replace the plastic cover.

EXPERIMENT I-I
The Balance

A.   Trial Weighings

Weigh separately a weighing bottle and its top. Record the weight of each in your laboratory notebook. Reweigh the bottle and the top of it together. Record their combined weight. Compare the sum of the weight of the bottle and its top with the combined weight of the two. They should agree within $\pm$ 0.0002 g. If they do not, repeat the weighings. If they still do not agree, check with the laboratory instructor to determine whether your procedure or readings are wrong.

B. Weighing an Unknown

Obtain an unknown (Note) from the laboratory instructor and weigh it. Report the weight of this object to the instructor, and make sure that he approves the value before proceeding to weigh anything else.

NOTE

Any moderately heavy object that is numbered will make an excellent unknown. Weighing bottle tops, numbered with a diamond stylus, has proven to be satisfactory since they do not change weight appreciably over periods of five to ten years.

PROBLEMS

1. The rate of cooling of a porcelain crucible in a desiccator can be expressed by the equation:

$$\log \Delta T = \log \Delta T_0 - kt$$

where ΔT is the difference between the temperature of the crucible–desiccator system and room temperature at time t; ΔT_0 is the initial difference between the temperature of the crucible–desiccator system and room temperature; and k is a constant representing the rate of heat loss for the system, 0.017°C/min. What will be the error in weight of a 18.4976 g crucible, heated to 110°C in an oven, and then cooled in a desiccator? Assume that the crucible–desiccator system has a temperature of 50°C at time zero and that room temperature is 22°C. The error in weight due to thermal effects has been found to be 0.16 mg/°C temperature difference.
    (a)   After twenty minutes in the desiccator?
    (b)   After thirty minutes in the desiccator?
    (c)   How long should the crucible be left in the desiccator in order to have only a 0.16 mg error in its weight?
2. (a)   A 30-ml weighing bottle, when weighed with a sample in air weighs 29.4685 g. The density of this bottle is 1.02 g/ml. What is the correct weight, *in vacuo*, of the bottle plus the sample?
    (b)   Some of the sample is removed from the bottle, which upon reweighing has a weight of 28.8775 g. What is the correct weight of the bottle and its contents *in vacuo* now?
    (c)   The apparent weight of the sample in air is 0.5910 g. What is the correct weight of the sample *in vacuo*?
3. Martha, a hasty and thoughtless chemistry student, does each of the following while weighing on an analytical balance. What, if anything, is wrong with each? When possible, state the effect on the weight obtained.
    (a)   The zero on the optical scale of her balance can not be brought to coincide

with the zero on the etched scale. Therefore, she uses 3 as the reference point, both at the beginning and at the end of the weighing.

(b) In order to avoid the bother of having to take it off each time, she leaves the top off the weighing bottle and dried sample when weighing out samples.

(c) Having mislaid her crucible tongs, she handles the object to be weighed with her fingers.

(d) Since she was taught not to put her hands in the pan compartment of the balance, she leaves the weighing bottle on the balance pan, while she reaches in with a spatula to remove sample from it.

(e) While doing the freezing point depression experiment, she attempts to weigh the unstoppered tube of benzene.

(f) Because it is more convenient, she always places the balance beam in the partial release position while adding or removing weights.

(g) Since she is disorganized and usually behind in her work, she only leaves her objects in the desiccator thirty minutes to cool, instead of forty-five minutes to an hour.

(h) When she finishes with a weighing, she meticulously sets every weight knob on the balance back to read zero.

4. 95.0 g of chromatographic grade alumina (density = 3.05 g/cm^3) is weighed out (in a weighing cup, of course) in air. What correction should be applied to this weight to obtain its weight *in vacuo*?

5. A styrofoam ball (density = 0.0359 g/cm^3) weighs 13.8146 g in air. What is its correct weight *in vacuo*?

REFERENCES

1. Agterdenbos, J., *Anal. Chim. Acta*, **15**, 429 (1956).
2. ASTM committee, preliminary draft of *ASTM Specifications—Laboratory Weights and Precision Mass Standards*, subject to revision before final adoption, 1973.
3. Macurdy, L. B. *et al.*, *Anal. Chem.*, **26**, 1190 (1954).
4. Peiser, H. S., *Natl. Bur. Standards, Misc. Publ.*, **235**, 45 (1960).

CHAPTER 2

LABORATORY APPARATUS

DESCRIPTION OF LABORATORY EQUIPMENT

In order to effect separations and to analyze the separated components certain somewhat specialized laboratory apparatus is used. This apparatus, designed to be used for one specific function, is more accurate than normal equipment and frequently must be calibrated for meaningful use. Most of the equipment used for quantitative analyses is more expensive than routine laboratory equipment. In order to furnish reliable data, this equipment must be treated carefully and used intelligently. To aid us in this proper use, let us look at the function, requirements, design, and care of these pieces of apparatus.

Burettes

A *burette* is a long tube of glass of constant diameter that is used to measure very accurately volumes of liquids, normally during the titration of some solute (see Fig. 2–1). A burette is graduated to enable a volume of liquid to be measured with an accuracy of 2 parts per thousand or less. The bottom of a burette is drawn down to a fine tip so that the flow of liquid from the burette will not be too rapid. A stopcock to control the flow of liquid from the column is incorporated below the calibrated section of the tube, yet above the fine tip. Although stopcocks traditionally were made of ground glass, recently Teflon stopcocks have become more favored. Teflon stopcock plugs are virtually unbreakable and do not need to be greased. Burettes are supplied with metal or plastic clips to prevent the stopcock plug from falling out. Burettes also have glass or plastic caps that fit loosely on the top of the tube to prevent dust from contaminating the standard solution contained in the burette. Burettes are used to measure variable volumes of liquids, never for storing them.

To avoid chaos, the National Bureau of Standards has established criteria for the design and manufacture as well as the tolerances for the markings on burettes. The latest criteria are given in National Bureau of Standards Circular 602. Table 2–1 lists characteristics of the most commonly encountered burettes: their capacities, their markings, and their tolerances. Tolerances designated as Class A are the ones specified by the National Bureau of Standards.

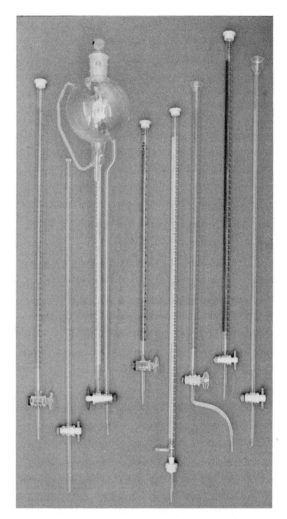

Fig. 2-1. Burettes. (*Photograph by Stephen Daugherty.*)

Table 2–1. TOLERANCES FOR BURETTES

		Tolerance	
Capacity, ml	Smallest Graduation, ml	Class A, ml	Class B, ml
10	0.05	0.02	0.04
25	0.10	0.03	0.06
50	0.10	0.05	0.10
100	0.20	0.10	0.20
Microburettes			
5	0.01	0.01	0.02
10	0.02	0.02	—

Burettes and other calibrated glassware should never be heated, since heating will destroy the calibration. The expansion of glass is not reversible, so upon cooling, different volumes result.

Chromatographic Columns

Columns for liquid chromatography consist of long, constant-diameter tubes of glass or plastic that are tapered down at the bottom to dimensions capable of extending through rubber stoppers. The length and diameter of chromatographic columns vary according to the capacity of the required separation. Frequently, chromatographic columns have fritted glass discs built into them just above the taper in order to prevent the powdered solid packing from passing through the column. Many chromatographic columns have stopcocks (preferably of Teflon) at the bottom to regulate the flow of eluting solvent, although rubber tubing and a Hoffman clamp can be used quite successfully.

Columns for gas chromatography consist of long (2–100 ft), small-diameter ($\sim\frac{1}{8}$–$\frac{1}{4}$ in) copper, glass, or stainless steel tubes. These tubes are coiled or bent to fit into an air bath. They have no gas valves for the gas flow is regulated elsewhere. Fig. 2–2 shows typical chromatographic columns, with and without stopcocks.

Chromatographic Jars

The jars used during elution of paper and thin-layer chromatograms vary in size and details of construction. The properties of the jars are determined by the nature of the method being used, the development techniques, and the size of the

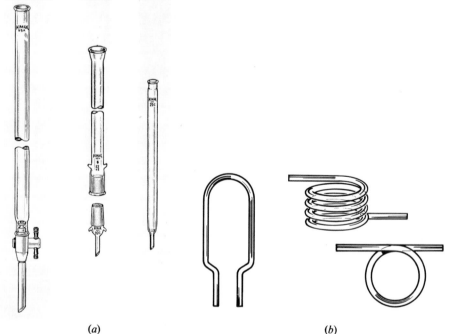

(a)   (b)

Fig. 2-2. Typical Chromatographic Columns: (a) liquid (*Courtesy of Kimble Products*); (b) gas (*Courtesy of Hewlett-Packard*).

sample being separated. A complete discussion of development chambers is given in Chapter 10 for paper chromatography and Chapter 11 for thin-layer chromatography.

Desiccator

A *desiccator* is a tightly closed container which provides an atmosphere of very low humidity for the cooling and storage of analytical samples. Desiccators normally are constructed of heavy glass, plastic, or aluminum metal. A thin layer of drying agent (desiccant, see Chapter 3) about 2–3 cm thick is placed on the bottom of the desiccator. This layer of desiccant is covered with a protective screen so that the objects will not come in contact with the desiccant. A plate (porcelain, plastic, or metal) with holes through which the object to be cooled can be set fits on top of the metal screen. The removable lid is usually greased to provide an air-tight seal. Fig. 2–3 shows some typical desiccators.

Drying Ovens

The extraordinarily large surface area of finely divided solids can adsorb considerable quantities of water from the atmosphere. In order to obtain accurate quantitative results in an analysis, the powdered sample must be freed from this adsorbed water. Customarily, this is done by placing the sample, in an open container, in a drying oven. Fig. 2–4 shows a typical drying oven capable of holding many samples. The temperatures of these electrically heated ovens can be regulated anywhere between 0 and 300°C. Samples are usually dried above 105°C, but temperature-sensitive samples and precipitates may be dried at temperatures less than 100°C. Alumina and silica gel, used in adsorption chromatography, can be activated in drying ovens. Alumina and silica gel thin-layer chromatographic sheets are activated in drying ovens. The amino acid–ninhydrin color reaction is hastened by drying the chromatographic paper in the oven.

Filter Crucibles

Many precipitates cannot or need not be filtered through paper. When filter

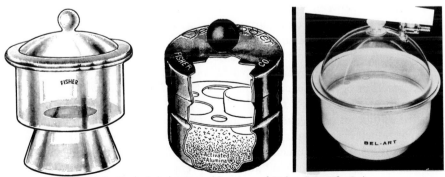

Fig. 2–3. Typical desiccators. (*Courtesy of Fisher Scientific Co.*)

Fig. 2-4. A drying oven. (*Courtesy of Fisher Scientific Co.*)

paper is used, it must be destroyed before the precipitate can be dried and weighed. This destruction is avoided by using a filter crucible to remove the precipitate from the mother liquor. Suction is always used to speed up the filtration process with filter crucibles.

Filter crucibles are constructed of glass, porcelain, or alundum. They come with capacities between 8 and 50 ml. The bottom of each of these crucibles is a porous mat, permanently built into the crucible. There are three pore sizes of these mats available: *fine*, maximum pore radius of 3 μ; *medium*, maximum pore radius of 4.4 μ; and *extremely coarse*, maximum pore radius of 50 μ. The walls of Selas porcelain filtering crucibles are constructed of glazed nonporous porcelain, whereas the filter bottom is of unglazed, porous porcelain. *Alundum (fused alumina) crucibles* are made entirely of porous alundum. *Gooch-type glass filter crucibles* are constructed with borosilicate glass walls and fritted glass filter bottoms. Fig. 2-5 shows examples of all three types. Corrosive liquids (for example, NaOH) are filtered through ordinary Gooch crucibles containing removable asbestos fiber mats.

After being filtered, precipitates are not removed from filter crucibles but are dried in them. Glass crucibles are good for precipitates that do not have to be dried

(a)   (b)   (c)

Fig. 2-5. Filter crucibles: (a) Selas porous porcelain; (b) alundum, [(a) and (b) *Courtesy of Fisher Scientific Co.*]; (c) Gooch-type fritted glass (*Courtesy of Kimble Products*).

over 110°C, although they can be heated in a furnace to 500°C temperatures. Porous porcelain crucibles may be heated up to 1300°C, whereas alundum crucibles may be heated to 1450°C.

In order to obtain good filtering and long life from filter crucibles, they must be treated with care. The mats should not be scratched, since abrasion will weaken them. Chemicals which attack unglazed glass or porcelain should not be filtered through the crucibles, for example, sodium hydroxide or other strong alkalis, hydrofluoric acid or other fluorides, and phosphoric acid. The mats are capable of withstanding up to 15 lb/in^2 pressure but should not be used at higher pressures.

The mats in new filter crucibles should be washed, using suction, with hot hydrochloric acid before use. This washing is followed by rinsing with water and then deionized water. The cleaning of crucibles after use ordinarily is based on the nature of the precipitate contained in them. Frequently ordinary soap and water will suffice. Dichromate cleaning solution should be avoided, since it stains the mats. Naturally, cleansing powders containing insoluble abrasives should be kept scrupulously out of the crucibles. Many organic precipitates or metal chelates can be dissolved with carbon tetrachloride or chloroform. Copper and iron oxides can be removed with hot hydrochloric acid plus potassium chlorate. Nitric acid will remove mercury, silver and other metal residues. Silver chloride is best removed using ammonia, while manganese dioxide will dissolve readily in concentrated hydrochloric acid. When washing filter crucibles, the wash liquid must be drawn slowly through the mat. This wash liquid must be thoroughly removed by rinsing, using suction with large amounts of wates and deionized water.

Filter crucibles are held in filtering flasks by filter crucible holders of various designs (see Fig. 2–6). The flasks are shaped like Erlenmeyer flasks, but constructed of heavy-walled glass or polypropylene (see Fig. 2–7). A nipple on the side of the flask near its top permits connection of heavy-walled rubber tubing and a safety trap to a water aspirator.

Glass Hooks

Containers used to dry samples and precipitates in the oven should be open to the atmosphere, so that the adsorbed water can escape. The container should have a watch glass on top of it, however, so that dirt or other contaminants do not fall into it. This dilemma is solved by placing the watch glass on top of glass hooks. An opening is thus created around the circumference of the beaker. Fig. 2–8 shows

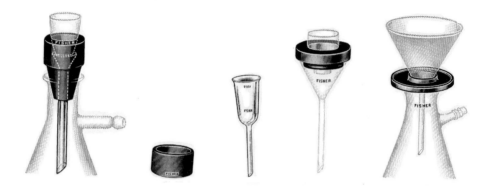

Fig. 2-6. Filter crucible holders. (*Courtesy of Fisher Scientific Co.*)

Fig. 2-7. Filtering flasks. (*Courtesy of Kimble Products.*)

Fig. 2-8. Glass hooks.

two kinds of glass hooks. These hooks either can be made by each student at the beginning of the course or purchased commercially.

Hot Plates

Hot plates are used when a broad heating surface is needed to heat samples during dissolution. They are used to evaporate flammable solvents and to heat at temperatures lower than conveniently obtained with a flame. Combination magnetic stirrers and hot plates are excellent when titrating at slightly elevated temperatures (for example, at 35–40°C) such as is recommended in many titrations with EDTA.

Meniscus Reader

Reading the position of the meniscus of a liquid in a burette, pipette, or volumetric flask can be quite a puzzling task. Exactly where it is and what portion should be read causes concern to novices. The meniscus of a liquid that wets glass should be read at the lowest point on the meniscus. In order to establish this point clearly, it is necessary to put something dark behind and below the meniscus and something white above the meniscus. This makes the profile of the meniscus dark and clearly visible against a white background.

A meniscus reader may be made by the student with a black fiber-tip pen and file card or purchased commercially. The commercial meniscus reader shown in Fig. 2–9 is made from a small piece of plastic, the lower portion of which is black,

Fig. 2-9. A meniscus reader and its proper use. (*Courtesy of Fisher Scientific Co.*)

the upper portion of which is white. When used properly, the dividing line between the black and white is placed at the bottom of meniscus, with the black half down.

Phase-Separating Paper

During an extraction, both of the immiscible phases tend to become slightly cloudy because of the dispersion of small droplets of the opposite phase in them. In order to perform accurate colorimetric or other measurements upon each phase, these dispersed droplets must be removed. The most rapid and convenient method for filtering out these droplets involves the use of phase-separating paper. This silicone-treated paper allows the organic liquids to pass through, while retaining small droplets of water. It is used in a small funnel, just as regular filter paper. When phase-separating paper is not available, ordinary filter paper can be used to filter out liquids. When wet with water, ordinary paper will retain the droplets of organic liquid, allowing water to pass through. When wet with an organic liquid, ordinary paper will retain the droplets of water, allowing the organic liquid to pass through.

pH Meters

One of the most convenient methods of measuring the hydrogen ion concentration (or activity) of a solution is by means of the pH meter. A pH meter is a vacuum-tube voltmeter, whose scale has been marked in pH units instead of volts, that measures the voltage drop across two electrodes immersed in a solution. One of these electrodes has a constant potential (the reference electrode) and the other electrode has a potential that depends upon the concentration (or activity) of hydrogen ions in a solution. Fig. 2–10 shows a currently available pH meter.

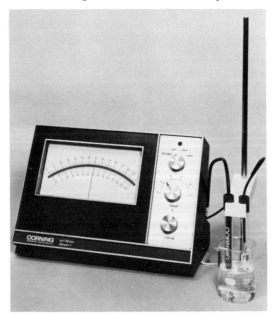

Fig. 2–10. A pH meter. (*Courtesy of Corning Scientific Instruments.*)

The potential of any electrochemical system that depends upon the hydrogen ion activity in a solution can be used as the basis for a pH-sensitive electrode (the indicating electrode). The hydrogen, quinhydrone, and antimony electrodes all involve half-reactions containing hydrogen ions. The most rugged, convenient, and accessible pH-indicating electrode is the *glass electrode*.

Fig. 2–11 is a sketch of a commercially available glass electrode. This electrode consists of a glass tube, one end of which is a thin-walled bulb blown from a special glass. This glass bulb is about 0.01 mm thick. The bulb exchanges cations from its surface for hydrogen ions in any solution. This exchange of ions establishes an electrical potential at the outer surface of the glass bulb—an *interface potential*. The magnitude of this potential depends upon the number of hydrogen'ions that are present in the solution into which the electrode is dipping. Inside, the glass bulb contains a 0.1 M HCl solution. The inner surface of the glass bulb exchanges ions in the same way that the outer surface does, but since it is always in contact with a solution of a constant hydrogen ion activity, its interface potential is constant. The potential difference between the inner and outer surfaces of the glass is measured against reference electrodes. The inner reference electrode is a piece of silver wire, coated with a thin film of silver chloride and dipping into the 0.1 M solution of HCl. The potential of this electrode is given by:

$$E = E°_{AgCl–Ag} + 0.0591 \log (1/[Cl^-])$$

for the reduction reaction:

$$AgCl\ (s) + e^- = Ag(s) + Cl^-$$

where $E°_{AgCl–Ag}$ is the standard reduction potential for this silver–silver chloride electrode. Since the chloride ion concentration is constant (at 0.1 M) the potential of the electrode is constant.

The reference electrode for measuring the outer electrode surface potential is separate from the glass electrode. (Actually, combination electrodes are com-

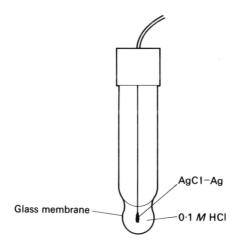

Fig. 2-11. Sketch of a glass electrode.

mercially available which have both calomel and glass electrodes, but this discussion will focus on separate glass and reference electrodes). This self-contained system, a half-reaction, has a known, fixed, and stable potential because the concentrations of all species present are known and kept constant. Many half-reactions are usable for reference electrodes, but the most rugged and widespread reference electrode is the *calomel*, based on the reduction of mercurous chloride to metallic murcury.

$$Hg_2Cl_2(s) + 2e^- = 2Hg°(l) + 2Cl^-$$

The potential for this reduction is given by:

$$E = E°_{Hg_2Cl_2-Hg} + \frac{0.0591}{2} \log (1/[Cl^-])^2$$

where $E°_{Hg_2Cl_2-Hg}$ is the standard reduction potential for the reaction. When the chloride ion concentration of a solution is fixed at some value the potential of the electrode is established and will be constant. There are three concentrations of chloride ion commonly used, giving rise to three calomel electrodes. When 0.1 *M* KCl is the filler solution, we have the 0.1 *M* calomel electrode; when 1.0 *M* KCl is the solution, we have the 1.0 *M* calomel electrode; and when the solution is saturated KCl, we have the saturated calomel electrode. Fig. 2–12 is a sketch of a saturated calomel electrode. Because of its ruggedness and ease of preparation the saturated calomel electrode (SCE) is the most commonly used reference electrode for routine work. pH meters measure the potential difference between a glass and SCE reference electrode.

Thus, the electrochemical cell whose potential is being measured by the vacuum-tube voltmeter can be written:

$$Ag(s),AgCl(s)|HCl (1\ M)||glass|| \text{ unknown } [H^+]|KCl(sat'd)|Hg°(l),Hg_2Cl_2(s)$$

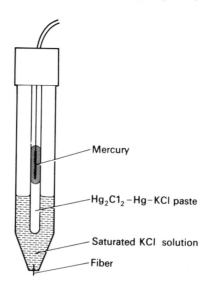

Fig. 2-12. A saturated calomel electrode.

Combining the Nernst equation expressions for all four potentials into one expression for the potential of the cell:

$$E_{cell} = E' + 0.0591 \; \log([H^+])$$

Because of the strain in the glass surface caused by the curvature of the bulb and the day-to-day variations in the nature of the surface, an asymmetry potential is included in the term E' above. The value of this asymmetry potential is unknown. Therefore, before use each time, the pH meter must be calibrated or standardized. This calibration is achieved by immersing the glass and calomel electrodes into a buffer of very accurately established pH (the best are available from the National Bureau of Standards). A variable potentiometer in the electrical circuit of the vacuum tube voltmeter is adjusted until the pH meter needle reads the known pH value of the standard buffer. The potentiometer is then fastened and not changed until the next time the meter is calibrated. Since the asymmetry potential will vary with time, a pH meter should be standardized every time it is used. When a pH meter is used continuously for long periods of time, the standardization should be checked every two hours.

The operating instructions for the Corning Model 7 pH meter are given in Chapter 3.

Pipettes

A *pipette* is a piece of glass tubing, tapered to a narrow tip at one end and containing a bulb in the middle. Pipettes are designed to transfer very accurately measured volumes of liquids from one container to another. Liquid is sucked into the tube through the open end. The lower end is tapered to a fine tip in order to permit accurate regulation of the flow of liquid from the pipette. Fig. 2–13 shows designs of some pipettes commercially available.

Pipettes designed to deliver only a single volume of liquid are called *transfer pipettes*. These are usually marked with only a single calibration line and stamped TD (to deliver). Pipettes designed to deliver variable volumes of liquid are called *measuring pipettes*. These are marked with many graduations and also are stamped TD (to deliver). All pipettes are stamped with the temperature (usually 20°C) at which the volume is to be measured.

As was seen for burettes, and is true for all calibrated glassware, the National Bureau of Standards attempts to exercise some control over the quality of the pipettes in use. Their established tolerances for pipettes are given in Table 2–2. The National Bureau of Standards will calibrate a pipette only if it falls within its tolerances and other specifications.

Rubber Policemen

The quantitative transfer of a precipitate from the vessel in which it was formed to the filtering apparatus is a very necessary operation in gravimetric analysis. In order to achieve complete transfer, especially of the last particles, a rubber policeman is necessary. A *rubber policeman* is a piece of rubber tubing that is crimped at one end. The end of this crimped section is cut off diagonally (see

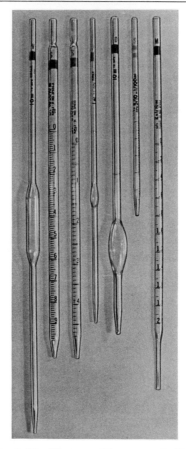

Fig. 2-13. Pipettes. (*Courtesy of Kimble Products.*)

Table 2–2. NBS TOLERANCES FOR PIPETTES

Capacity, ml	Limit of error of Total or Partial Capacity Transfer Pipettes, ml	Measuring Pipettes, ml
2	0.006	0.01
5	0.01	0.02
10	0.02	0.03
30	0.03	0.05
50	0.05	0.08
100	0.08	0.15

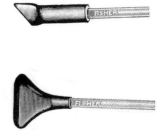

Fig. 2-14. A rubber policeman. (*Courtesy of Fisher Scientific Co.*)

Fig. 2–14). When used, the rubber policeman is placed on the end of a glass rod. The policeman is used to scrape, push, or otherwise cajole the particles of precipitate out of one vessel into the other. Its function and use are completely analogous to that of a rubber spatula found in the kitchen.

Separatory Funnel

A *separatory funnel* is a conical or cylindrical glass vessel, with a stopper at one end and a stopcock at the other. Separatory funnels are primarily used in extractions. Vigorous shaking produces extensive contact between the two liquid phases. After this, placing the funnel in an iron ring enables complete separation of the two liquid phases to occur. Separatory funnels can also serve as reservoirs for the eluting solvent in liquid chromatography. (For some odd reason, when used for this purpose, a separatory funnel is called a *dropping funnel*.) Fig. 2–15 shows a typical conical separatory funnel. Conical separatory funnels are called pear-shaped or *Squib separatory funnels*. Cylindrical separatory funnels are called cylindrical separatory funnels.

While shaking, the funnel is inverted occasionally and the stopcock opened (venting) in order to prevent a pressure buildup from the volatile vapors. After shaking and venting, the funnel is hung in a ring stand until the two phases separate physically. Then the stopper is removed, the stopcock opened, and the lower phase drained into the receiving vessel.

Spectrophotometers

The function of a spectrophotometer is to measure accurately the intensity of light that is absorbed by a substance. While light absorption by gases and solids is extremely important and useful, most analytical procedures are restricted to light absorption by solutions, so this section will be limited solely to a discussion of that. The inclusion of *spectro* in the term means that these instruments are capable of measuring the relative intensity of light absorbed at various different wave lengths, not simultaneously, of course, but successively.

The essential components of any spectrophotometer are: (1) a source of radiation, (2) an optical system for manipulating the light through the instrument, (3) a monochromator, (4) the sample cell, and (5) a detector. Let us look, very

Fig. 2-15. Squibb separatory funnel. (*Courtesy of Kimble Products.*)

cursorily, at the specific components used in the more inexpensive spectrophotometers encountered in undergraduate and clinical laboratories.

The customary source of white radiation is the *tungsten filament light bulb.* This operates at a temperature of 2870°K, where it has a spectral emission between 350 and 2500 nm. Only eleven percent of the total output falls in the visible region. The intensity of the radiation increases continuously, but not linearly. The lamp is operated at 4–8 V, and at 80–250 W. The intensity of the output can be no steadier than the power that is supplied across the tungsten filament. The emission intensity varies as the fourth power of the applied voltage, so that a very constant source of voltage is required to obtain stable output readings. Usually a constant voltage transformer or constant voltage source is used to power the tungsten filament.

A monochromator is used to disperse the white light emitted by the tungsten filament into its component wavelengths. The monochromators commonly used are slits and either quartz prisms or *replica diffraction gratings.* Since replica gratings have definite advantages and are more inexpensive than prisms, most low priced instruments now employ diffraction gratings and slits as the means of obtaining monochromatic radiation. A diffraction grating consists of a flat glass plate coated with aluminum upon which are ruled 15,000–90,000 parallel lines per inch. By means of destructive interference, the white light reflecting from the rough surface of the ruled grating is dispersed as separated wavelengths. By rotating the diffraction grating, the different wavelengths can be focused at the exit slit. Original gratings are rare, delicate, and exceedingly expensive. But replica gratings can be made very inexpensively. A thin layer of collodion is coated on the surface of a diffraction grating and allowed to dry. The dried film is carefully peeled off the original, aluminized, and then used in the low-priced spectrophotometer. Naturally the quality of these replica gratings is not too high, but they are quite sufficient for most purposes. The main advantage of a diffraction grating as a monochromator lies in the fact that it gives a linear dispersion; that is, the wavelengths are uniformly spread out over the entire wavelength region.

For the most part, the sample cell is a neglected component of the spectrophotometer, and therefore it causes considerable problems. Cylindrical cells should be avoided because of their lens properties that intensify the light in certain regions on the detector surface. Cylindrical cells give irreproducible readings, for it is almost impossible to reposition the cylindrical cell in the cell holder exactly (horizontally, vertically, and rotationally) each time. Consequently, cells for a spectrophotometer should be rectangular, with flat, parallel entrance and exit windows. The sides should be fused rather than glued together, so that any solvent can be used in them without having to worry about the cell falling apart. The cells should be marked so that they can always be inserted into the cell holder with exactly the same orientation, so as to keep the reflected and scattered radiation constant. The cells should be of accurately known dimensions; they usually come in fixed thicknesses, 1.0, 2.0, 10.0 cm, and so on. Cells for absorption measurements in the visible region can be made from Pyrex, which is transparent between 420 and 1800 nm. Vycor is transparent between 350 and 1800 nm. When working down into the ultraviolet region, the cells used must be made of silica, which is transparent down to about 220 nm. *Matched pairs of cells* consist of two cells which give identical readings when the same solution is placed in either cell. Matched cells have identical path lengths and reflect and scatter light to the same extent. For accurate work a pair of matched cells must be used; one for the blank and one for the solution being measured.

The usual detector is the phototube. A phototube contains two electrodes in an evacuated glass envelope. The cathode is a half-cylinder of metal, coated on its inside with a layer of a photoemissive substance. Usually an alkali or alkaline earth metal oxide is used because of its low work function. The anode is a piece of wire kept about 90 V positive to the cathode. When a photon strikes the coating on the cathode, an electron is emitted. This electron is attracted to the anode, causing an electric current to flow. The magnitude of the current is proportional to the number of electrons emitted, which, of course, is dependent upon the number of photons striking the cathode. Thus, the current flowing through the phototube is a measure of the intensity of the light striking the surface of the cathode. Phototubes do not respond to all wavelengths of light because of the energy differences of the photons of different frequencies. The wavelength response of the coating on the cathode depends upon its chemical identity. Two phototubes must be used in order to span the energy spread of the visible region. One has a coating that is sensitive from 350 to 625 nm. The second is sensitive to wavelengths greater than 625 nm. The sensitivity of the phototube's response is not constant throughout each wavelength region, but varies according to the wavelength. Thus the phototube response must

Fig. 2-16. The Bausch and Lomb Spectronic 20 Spectrophotometer: (1) Sample holder, (2) meter, (3) wavelength scale, (4) wavelength control, (5) light control, (6) power switch/zero control. (*Courtesy of Bausch and Lomb.*)

be standardized at each wavelength. Absolute light intensity readings are extremely difficult to determine, so only relative intensities are usually measured.

The electric current flowing from the detector is passed through an amplifier and then to an ammeter. In a spectrophotometer the scale of the ammeter is marked in either percent transmission or in absorbence.

One very widely used, inexpensive spectrophotometer is the Spectronic 20, manufactured by Bausch and Lomb and pictured in Fig. 2–16. The optical diagram from this instrument is shown in Fig. 2–17. Light from the tungsten lamp, after passing through the entrance slit, is focused on the replica diffraction grating. The

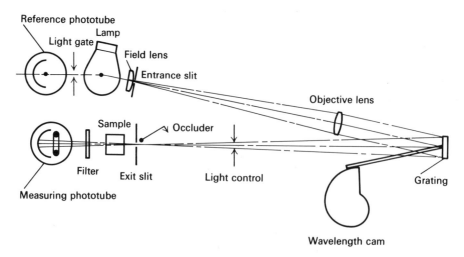

Fig. 2-17. Optical diagram of Bausch and Lomb Spectronic 20 Spectrophotometer. (*Courtesy of Bausch and Lomb.*)

appropriate wavelength is selected by rotation of the wavelength cam, which rotates the grating. The wavelength of light selected passes through the exit slit, through the sample in its square cell, and strikes the phototube. A piece of metal, called an *occluder*, is positioned across the bottom of the sample holder so that no light can strike the phototube when there is no sample cell in the cell holder. Insertion of the cell pushes the occluder out of the light path, allowing the light beam to enter the cell, be absorbed, and then emerge. The Spectronic 20 operates over a wavelength region between 340 and 950 nm, changing phototubes at 625 nm. Because a replica grating is employed, the 20 nm bandwidth is constant over the entire spectral gion. Reading on the meter are reproducible to within ±3 percent.

Operating instructions for the Bausch and Lomb Spectronic 20 Spectrophotometer are given in Chapter 3.

Syringes

Reproducible and accurate measurement of the small volumes of liquids required for paper, thin-layer, and gas chromatography is impossible to achieve with an ordinary pipette or burette. Introduction of liquid samples to a gas chromatograph involves puncturing a self-sealing rubber septum. This problem of delivering accurately a few microliters of liquid through a rubber septum is solved by using a hypodermic syringe. The most widely used are the *Hamilton syringes*, which have two inch long, fixed needles and tungsten wire plungers (see Fig. 2–18). Hamilton

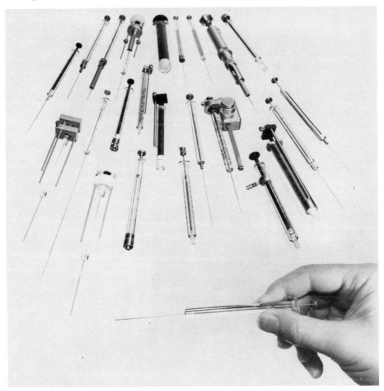

Fig. 2-18. Hamilton syringes. (*Courtesy of Hamilton Co.*)

syringes have volumes of 1.0, 10.0, 50.0, and 100.0 microliter which are marked with a precision of 1%. Frequently a guide is used to provide support and prevent bending of the fine wire plunger. Hamilton syringes are gas tight at 150 lb/in^2.

Volumetric Flasks

Solutions having exactly known concentrations are prepared in volumetric flasks. A specified amount of solute is dissolved by a solvent to produce the solution whose volume is accurately measured by a volumetric flask. Volumetric flasks are calibrated at a single, exactly known volume. Fig. 2–19 shows that their design is such that while the bulk of the solution is contained in the globular portion of the flask, a narrow neck permits precise adjustment of the volume to the calibration mark. This design makes adequate mixing of the solution difficult, so that the flask must be up-ended slowly about ten times or more for complete mixing. The National Bureau of Standards specifies design characteristics and has set tolerances for volumetric flasks. Table 2–3 lists the tolerances for volumetric flasks.

The volume of solution measured by a volumetric flask cannot be removed completely from the flask. Therefore, the normal volumetric flask is marked to contain (TC) a certain volume of solution. Some flasks are marked both to contain (TC) and to deliver (TD) a certain volume. Because of drainage, solution is left on the walls of the flask, so the TD mark is always higher up the neck than the TC mark. A flask that is marked TC should never be used as a volumetric measuring

Fig. 2-19. Volumetric flasks. (*Courtesy of Kimble Products.*)

Table 2–3. NBS TOLERANCES FOR VOLU-
METRIC FLASKS

Capacity, ml	Limits of Error, TC, ml
5.0	0.02
10.0	0.02
25.0	0.03
50.0	0.05
100.0	0.08
200.0	0.10
500.0	0.15
1000.0	0.30

Fig. 2-20. Weighing bottles. (*Courtesy of Kimble Products.*)

cylinder. Volumetric flasks used to have ground glass stoppers. Now they are manufactured with ground glass joints in their necks, but plastic stoppers are supplied.

Weighing Bottles

In order to weigh dried samples out of contact with the moisture in the air, a tightly closed container is used, which is called a *weighing bottle*. As Fig. 2–20 shows, a weighing bottle is merely a small cylindrical bottle with a ground glass stopper. Weighing bottles usually are made of glass and have thin hollow stoppers so as not to contribute too large a tare during weighing. The top of a weighing bottle is kept off, but alongside the bottle during drying in the oven and cooling in the desiccator. Whenever the bottle is removed from the desiccator, the top is put on it to keep out moisture. Inconvenient as it may seem, the top always should be kept on the weighing bottle while weighing out a sample, except when material is being removed from the weighing bottle.

Weighing Paper or Cups

The use of weighing bottles is not *de rigueur* when the chemical to be weighed

Fig. 2-21. Weighing cups and papers. (*Photograph by Stephen Daugherty.*)

has not been dried. In order to protect the balance pan, chemicals are never placed directly onto the metal pan. Beakers and glass dishes contribute much too large a tare when weighing out small samples. Various lightweight papers and cups are available which can be used to weigh small samples. Fig. 2–21 shows several examples of weighing cups which range from glazed paper circles, through glazed paper cups (such as used on chocolate candies or for baking cupcakes), to plastic or aluminum boats or dishes. All these containers are light-weight, have smooth surfaces so that powder particles do not remain on them, and are disposable after a single use. Almost all are inexpensive.

THE LABORATORY NOTEBOOK

The laboratory notebook should provide a conveniently accessible record of everything that was performed, observed, calculated, and concluded during an experiment. The idiosyncrasies of recording in the notebook depend on the character of the experimenter; however, there are certain basic types of information and certain customs that have become obligatory. Anyone who doubts the necessity of these should try reconstructing and explaining experiments on the basis of the material recorded in his notebook—two or three years after it was written down.

The laboratory notebook should be permanently bound. Pages from spiral bound or loose-leaf notebooks tear out too easily. Pages should never be torn out of the notebook. The page size and thickness of the notebook are determined by the nature of its usage. It is foolish to purchase a five hundred page notebook for a one-semester course in quantitative analysis. A small (7.5 × 10 in) notebook is a convenient size to record weights in a balance room. The pages of the notebook should be numbered consecutively. There should be a table of contents on the first pages, kept up to date at all times. All entries should be made in ink, since pencil is not permanent, becoming illegible with time.

Neatness and organization are prime requisites in keeping an intelligible notebook, but the laboratory notebook is a working record of what is going on in the laboratory, not a model of perfection. No one expects it to be, so do not copy material over into another book to make the notebook look prettier. Copying is not only a total waste of time, but is dishonest since the second notebook ceases to be the original record of the data, and is merely a transcription of it.

Sooner or later everyone who uses a laboratory notebook makes a mistake in recording data or interpreting it. This is normal human error, so it is not to be considered of major significance. Such mistakes are corrected, not obliterated. Usually a single line is drawn through the incorrect material. The correct material is placed above it, with the reason for the alteration stated. Two illustrations are given below.

9   misread burette
burette reading: 37.~~4~~3 ml

793   wrong atomic weight
%nickel: 1.~~487~~%

All material pertinent to the experiment, its understanding and proper interpretation should be recorded in the notebook. It is futile to copy lengthy and elaborate procedures into the notebook, however. If the experimental procedure is followed without deviation, merely cite the source, for example, Willard, Furman, and Bricker, p. 242. If slight deviations are made, cite the source of the procedure and then state the variations. If the procedure used is a major revision, then write it all down. Record all weights, temperatures, volumes, and instrument readings taken. Tabulated form (see p. 55, Chapter 3) is an efficient method for presenting numerical data. Make certain that the date upon which all pieces of data were recorded is apparent. This usually means placing a date in the upper right hand corner of each and every page of the notebook. All data on that page are understood to have been recorded that day. If any data on the page were recorded on another day, then several dates will appear on the page, above or beside the pertinent data. The date is an important piece of information, not only from a legal viewpoint, but also in explaining anomalous data or unexpected finds. The date obviously is significant when sampling water, soil, or streams for analysis.

Record all data, observations, and final results on the right-hand pages of the notebook. The left-hand pages are for scratch work, calculations, and so on. Paste all graphs on the left-hand pages.

Be sure to record all observations during the course of the experiments. Learn to be honest. Write down what actually did happen, not what should have happened, or what you thought should have happened. Be observant. Unfortunately for beginning students, practice is the best way to learn the difference between trivia and significant observations. It is better to record too much material, than to forget to record some necessary information.

Frequently, time alters one's approach to experimental data, causing shifts in emphasis, making different facets of an experiment the major ones. So, be sure everything that could be useful is recorded.

CHAPTER 3

LABORATORY OPERATIONS

GRAVIMETRIC TECHNIQUES

Drying of Samples

Many of the samples used for quantitative analyses are finely powdered solids. The enormous surface area of these solids (6 square meters per gram for particles that are 1 micron cubes) is covered with a layer of water adsorbed from the atmosphere. The exact amount of adsorbed water on the surface varies with the nature of the surface, the humidity of the environment, and storage of the sample, but the layer is between 10^{-4} and 10^{-5} mm thick and weighs between 0.1 and 0.01 g/m^2, depending upon conditions. In order to obtain the correct percentage of any component in the sample, therefore, this layer of water must be removed or an unknown variable will be involved in the weight of the sample. The most effective way to remove this water is to heat the sample in an open container in a drying oven at a temperature just above the boiling point of water. The powdered sample is placed in a weighing bottle which in turn is placed in the smallest beaker that will hold it. The beaker is marked with both the nature of the sample and the identity of the experimenter. Glass hooks are placed on the rim of the beaker, a small watch glass placed over them, and this assembly is placed in the drying oven. Fig. 3–1 shows the correct arrangement for placing a sample in the oven to be dried.

Most solids can be dried satisfactorily by heating at 105–110°C for one hour, although some solids require a drying time of two hours or longer. It is not good practice to dry samples in the oven for extremely long periods of time, for example, overnight, because some solids, especially organic materials, may begin to decompose when heated for long periods of time in the presence of moisture and dust. Sublimation, thermal decomposition, loss of entrained gases can all occur when samples are heated for long periods of time.

Desiccator

Dump the old desiccant out of a desiccator, degrease the lid, and wipe the walls of the container clean with a dry towel. Desiccators with ground-glass flanges

Fig. 3-1. Drying of a sample.

must be greased so as to provide an air-tight seal and prevent the lid from sliding off. A small amount of petroleum jelly is placed at two or three places around the flange of the body of the desiccator. The lid is returned to the desiccator and rotated with sure, deliberate movements to spread the grease evenly. When the lid is properly greased, there is no petroleum jelly dripping off the inner or outer edges of the rim; the glass flange will look uniformly greasy, with no light (dry) spots. The lid can be rotated only with difficulty. Two ways to check the proper greasing of a desiccator lid are: (1) Tilt the desiccator slightly and carefully. The lid should not begin to slide off the base. If it does, there is too much grease on the flange and some of the grease should be removed. (2) Gently try to remove the lid from the base by slowly pulling the lid up vertically. If it comes loose, then there is probably too little (or perhaps too much) grease on the flange. A properly greased desiccator can be picked up by the lid about an inch off the desk surface. *Be careful.*

After the lid has been greased properly, the desiccator is filled with desiccant. Table 3–1 gives a list of commonly used desiccants and their effectiveness. One factor, other than effectiveness, often considered during selection is the cost of the desiccant. Calcium chloride or Drierite are used most frequently in student desiccators because they are the cheapest, and while not the most efficient, they are certainly adequate. Magnesium perchlorate, the most highly efficient desiccant, is not widely used because of its high cost and the potential danger involved when drying and storing organic materials. Concentrated sulfuric acid usually is not used in beginning laboratories because of the hazards involved.

To charge a desiccator, the desiccant is poured slowly and carefully through a cone of paper onto the bottom of the desiccator, so that the desiccant does not come in contact with the sides of the upper portion. The desiccant is added until a layer of only 1–1.5 inches is formed. (Remember that it is the exposed surface area of desiccant that is effective in quick drying of the atmosphere inside the desiccator. Because of the conical construction of the bottom of most desiccators, the deeper the layer of desiccant, the less exposed surface.) After the desiccator is

Table 3–1. EFFECTIVENESS OF COMMON DESICCANTS

Desiccant	Residual Water, μgram/liter at 25°C
Magnesium perchlorate, anhydrous	0.2
Barium oxide	2.8
Alumina	2.9
Phosphorus pentoxide	3.5
Calcium chloride, anhydrous	67
Drierite ($CaSO_4$)	67
Silica gel	67
Ascarite (91.0% NaOH)	93
Calcium chloride	99
Sodium hydroxide	513
Barium perchlorate, anhydrous	599
Magnesium oxide	753
Mikohbite (68.7% NaOH)	1378

SOURCE: F. Trusell and H. Diehl, *Anal. Chem.*, **35,** 674 (1963).

filled (see Fig. 3–2), the screen is placed on the ledge in the desiccator, the porcelain or aluminum plate put on top of the screen, and the lid tightly placed on the desiccator.

The moisture inside a desiccator can be reduced to a sufficiently low level within thirty minutes after the desiccator has been opened. It takes forty minutes or more for an object heated at 105°C to cool to room temperature. Therefore, objects placed in the desiccator to cool must remain there at least forty minutes before they can be weighed. Be patient, for if shorter times are allowed, error is introduced since the object will not be at room temperature nor will the atmosphere inside the desiccator be dry.

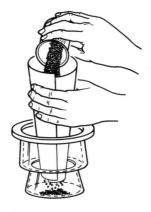

Fig. 3-2. Filling a desiccator.

Extreme caution should be exercised when placing into a desiccator objects (for example, crucibles) that have been heated in a muffle furnace or flame to extremely high temperatures ($>300°C$). The air inside will expand considerably at this temperature, causing the lid of the desiccator to pop off at best, or the desiccator to shatter. Therefore, either the lid should be left slightly ajar for the first minute or so, or gently lifted every three or five seconds for the first minute, to allow the expanded air to escape. Better still, allow the object to cool to about $150°C$ before putting it in the desiccator.

After samples have been cooled, they should be stored in the desiccator until they have been weighed, and in fact, until the analysis has been completed and the results accepted. During the initial cooling, tops of weighing bottles are left off, but when merely storing a sample, the top should be left on the weighing bottle for protection of the sample.

Weighing by Difference

A very rapid and efficient method of weighing a sample out of a weighing bottle into a beaker or Erlenmeyer flask is called weighing by difference. In this technique, the sample itself never actually is weighed. Rather the weighing bottle plus its contents are weighed before and after the sample is removed, the weight difference is assumed to be the weight of the sample taken out. Note that this technique assumes that all of the material removed from the sample bottle ends up in the beaker or Erlenmeyer flask; that is, not a single crystal is dropped or lost in any way.

Table 3–2. TYPICAL DATA FOR WEIGHING BY DIFFERENCE

Sample number	1	2	3
Weight of bottle and contents, g	22.4378	21.5251	20.6509
Weight after sample removal, g	21.5251	20.6509	19.6731
Weight of sample, g	0.9127	0.8742	0.9778

With the top on, the weighing bottle containing the entire amount of dried solid is weighed. Let us assume that it weighs 22.4378 g (see Table 3–2). Also assume that we are trying to weigh samples between 0.8–1.0 g. Using tongs or a paper, remove the bottle from the pan compartment of the balance, remove the top of the weighing bottle, and hold the bottle over the beaker into which the sample is to be weighed. Using a nickel spatula, remove a small amount of solid from the weighing bottle and place the solid directly into the beaker. Recap the weighing bottle and check its weight. Undoubtedly it will not weigh sufficiently less to have had the correct amount of sample removed. Repeat the removal process and check the bottle's weight again. Continue this process until the amount of sample removed falls within the desired range. The powder adhering to the spatula should be brushed into the beaker, using a camel's hair brush. Remember that solids are never returned to a weighing bottle once they have been removed, so proceed slowly and with caution. Should too much sample be removed, the sample must be discarded, the beaker washed and dried, and the entire process begun again. When the correct amount of sample has been removed from the weighing bottle, the exact weight of the bottle should again be recorded. In our example, let's say the bottle now weighs 21.5251 g. The difference between the initial weight of the bottle and its contents, and the final weight, in this case 0.9127 g, is the weight of the sample.

If, during removal of the solid from the weighing bottle, some solid is spilled on the table top, it is futile to pretend that it will have no effect on the results. The only possible move at this point is to discard the sample that is being weighed out and to start all over again with a new one.

After the first sample has been removed from the weighing bottle, the weight of the bottle plus the remaining contents becomes the weight of the bottle and contents for the second sample (see Table 3–2). The second sample is removed carefully from the weighing bottle in the same fashion as the first, and the weight of the bottle plus the remaining solid recorded. The third sample is obtained in the same way. Thus, by making only four weighings (assuming that none of the weighings have to be rejected because of carelessness), three samples can be obtained.

When liquids are being weighed by difference from ordinary closed containers, instead of from a weight burette, care must be taken to ensure that the dropper or pipette used to remove the liquid also is weighed; otherwise the drops of liquid remaining in the pipette will be considered as part of the sample, when, in actuality, they are not.

Precipitation

The best precipitates for gravimetric separations are those containing large, pure crystals. Such crystals can be obtained by careful and slow mixing of dilute solutions of the reagents. When two concentrated reagents are mixed together rapidly, the solution becomes so supersaturated that only new nuclei are formed. No crystal growth to speak of has time to occur. So, the resulting precipitate is colloidal. When, however, two dilute solutions of the reagents are mixed together slowly, the degree of supersaturation of the solution is very slight. Crystal growth has time to occur, making it unnecessary to form new nuclei. The resulting precipitate consists of large crystals.

A freshly precipitated solid is always contaminated. The process of incorporating weighable amounts of normally soluble impurities into a precipitate is called *coprecipitation*. Coprecipitation can be caused by two forces. Surface charges on the solid cause ions of the opposite charge to be adsorbed onto the precipitate. Ions in common with one of the ions of the precipitate are most favored for coprecipitation. The more insoluble the compound formed, the greater its adsorption. (For a lengthier discussion of adsorption see Chapter 7.) When a precipitate is formed rapidly, impurities are unable to escape from the neighborhood of the crystal growth, so they become entrapped in pockets or crystal defects of the particle. This process is called *occlusion*. Slow mixing of dilute solutions minimizes coprecipitation and allows time for soluble ions to diffuse away from the vicinity of crystal growth.

The following procedure should be followed when effecting a separation by precipitation:

1. Precipitate with a dilute solution of the reagent. Common sense should be used here to strike a balance between excessively large volumes of precipitant and high concentrations of solution.
2. Precipitate from as dilute a solution of substituent as practical. Again common sense should be used to balance concentration and volume.
3. Precipitate slowly—preferably drop by drop, from a medicine dropper. Be reasonable about the time used in adding the precipitant—add the individual drops rapidly. One drop every half-second makes a suitable rate of reagent addition for most precipitations.
4. Precipitate while stirring the solution rapidly and evenly. Smooth stirring ensures thorough mixing of components so that local pockets of high concentrations of reagents do not exist.
5. Precipitate from hot solutions. The solubility of most precipitates increases with increasing temperature. When solutions of a given concentration are mixed at an elevated temperature the degree of supersaturation is less than at room temperature. Since the rate of formation of a crystal of precipitate is proportional to the extent of supersaturation, this decrease in supersaturation will slow down the rate of crystal formation. When, as is the case for many precipitates, the temperature coefficient of solubility is very slight, heating will have an almost negligible effect on precipitate purity.

The ideal precipitant would be added to the reagent, molecule by molecule, uniformly throughout the solution of constituent. This ideal can be attained by a technique that is known as *homogeneous precipitation*. In homogeneous precipitation, a chemical that will not react with the substituent to be precipitated is added to the solution. When the solution is heated, the chemical hydrolyzes to form a compound that will react to form a precipitate. For example, thioacetamide, CH_3CSNH_2, does not react with metal ions. When mixed into a solution of metal ion, nothing happens. Upon heating, the thioacetamide is hydrolyzed to acetamide and hydrogen sulfide according to the reaction:

$$\underset{\displaystyle CH_3-\overset{\displaystyle S}{\overset{\displaystyle \|}{C}}-NH_2}{} + H_2O \rightarrow \underset{\displaystyle CH_3-\overset{\displaystyle O}{\overset{\displaystyle \|}{C}}-NH_2}{} + H_2S$$

The H_2S, of course, reacts with metal ions to form insoluble sulfide precipitates. In this fashion, the precipitant is added homogeneously throughout the solution, molecule by molecule.

Oxalic acid can be formed by the hydrolysis of dimethyl oxalate.

$$H_3CO-\overset{\displaystyle O}{\overset{\displaystyle \|}{C}}-\overset{\displaystyle O}{\overset{\displaystyle \|}{C}}-OCH_3 + H_2O \rightarrow HO-\overset{\displaystyle O}{\overset{\displaystyle \|}{C}}-\overset{\displaystyle O}{\overset{\displaystyle \|}{C}}-OH + 2CH_3OH$$

The oxalic acid molecules will precipitate calcium and rare earth ions. The sulfate ions used to precipitate barium and lead ions can be formed homogeneously by hydrolysis of sulfamic acid.

$$NH_2SO_3H + H_2O \rightarrow NH_4^+ + H^+ + SO_4^{2-}$$

When the precipitating agent is a weak base, competition for it in solution exists between the proton and the metal ion. In moderately acid solutions, the base is protonated, so no metal ion-reagent precipitate will form when the reagents are mixed. If the pH of this solution is raised ever so slowly, the protons of the reagent are neutralized, forming the conjugate base which is the precipitant. The conjugate base reacts molecule by molecule throughout the solution with the metal ions. The standard technique for precipitation with weak bases is to add the precipitating agent to an acid solution of the metal ion, and then to neutralize the acidity with a weak base such as ammonia. Thus, dimethylglyoxime is added to acid solutions of nickel ion. When its protons are removed by the acid–base reaction, a red precipitate forms.

$$C_4H_6N_2(OH)_2 \;+\; Ni^{2+} \;\xrightarrow{\;pH=4\;}\; \text{no reaction}$$
dimethylglyoxime

$$C_4H_6N_2(OH)_2 + OH^- \rightarrow C_4H_6N_2(OH)O^- + H_2O$$

$$2C_4H_6N_2(OH)O^- + Ni^{2+} \rightarrow (C_4H_6N_2OHO)_2Ni(s)$$

Analogous reactions occur when 8-hydroxyquinoline (C_9H_6NOH) is mixed with copper, zinc, or magnesium ion solutions at pH values around three, and then the pH of the solution is raised to eight or nine to precipitate the metal chelate.

This technique of precipitation by pH change also can be carried out homogeneously by adding to the initially acid solution of precipitant and metal ion, some compound that will decompose upon heating to form a base. Urea is used most frequently for this purpose.

$$\overset{\displaystyle O}{\overset{\displaystyle \|}{NH_2\!-\!C\!-\!NH_2}} + H_2O \rightarrow 2NH_3 + CO_2$$

Urea is added to the acid solution of dimethylglyoxime and nickel. This mixture is heated, just below boiling, for considerable lengths of time during which the urea hydrolyzes. The ammonia formed removes the proton from the dimethylglyoxime molecule. As the pH of the solution slowly increases, the dimethylglyoximate ion reacts to form the red nickel precipitate.

Chapter 5 contains instructions for the separation of nickel from other metal ions by precipitation as its dimethylglyoxime chelate, by both the conventional technique and by homogeneous precipitation.

Digestion (Aging of Precipitates)

A freshly formed crystal has an extraordinarily rough surface with hollows, jagged spires, and other imperfections. This surface is capable of, and does, adsorb onto its surface weighable amounts of soluble ions from the solution in contact with it (coprecipitation and postprecipitation). Regardless of how carefully the reagents were mixed, the particle sizes of the precipitate are not uniform so there are many small particles present. Some occlusion is bound to have occurred. All of these defects can be alleviated by allowing the precipitate to remain in contact with the mother liquor for an extended period of time. This self-purification by recrystallization is called *digestion*. During digestion, dynamic equilibrium occurs between the precipitate and the solution, wherein the surface of the precipitate dissolves, while more precipitate forms on the larger existing crystals. The surface energy of the precipitate is minimized during the process of digestion, which means that the total surface area of the precipitate is decreased. The irregular portions of the surface dissolve, while the fresh precipitate forms in the depressions. The smaller particles of precipitate dissolve while fresh precipitate forms on the larger particles. During this equilibrium dissolution–reprecipitation process, occluded impurities are liberated from their entrapment. Since the surface area of the solid is decreased, coprecipitation is minimized. The result of digestion is larger, purer crystals.

The process of digestion can be achieved by allowing the precipitate to stand overnight in the mother liquor. When time is short, digestion can be hastened by allowing the precipitate to stand in contact with the mother liquor at an elevated temperature (usually just below boiling) for an hour or two. (Why?)

Filtration

While precipitates can be filtered from the mother liquor using paper, it is much more rapid and convenient to use a filter crucible and suction filtration. The filter crucible is placed in an appropriately styled holder, which in turn is placed in the neck of the suction-filter flask. Pressure rubber tubing is connected from the nipple on the flask to a safety trap. The short end of the glass tubing in the trap is connected to the filter flask, the long end is connected to the water aspirator. Fig. 3–3 shows the proper arrangement.

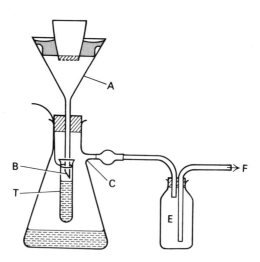

Fig. 3-3. Filtering by suction: (A) supporting funnel; (B) funnel tip, which extends below (C), the side arm of receiver; (E) safety bottle; (F) connection to the suction line; (T) test tube, held in place by a wire or a string, used to collect small portions of the washings for testing purposes.

After the water aspirator is turned on, the supernatant liquid from the beaker containing the precipitate is poured slowly down a stirring rod onto the center of the filter mat in the bottom of the crucible. After most of the mother liquor has been decanted off into the filter flask and tested for complete precipitation, the precipitate is stirred up with the liquid remaining in the beaker. The resultant slurry is poured slowly into the filter crucible. It is prudent not to fill the crucible more than about three-quarters full with liquid.

After the bulk of the precipitate has been transferred in this fashion to the filter crucible, the remaining crystals are conveyed with a stream of wash liquid from a wash bottle. A rubber policeman is used to push them up and over the lip of the beaker. The last remaining traces of the precipitate on the walls of the beaker are scraped down with the rubber policeman into a small amount of wash liquid. The precipitate at the bottom of the beaker is scraped into a small pile and, while wet, pushed off the lip into the crucible. Wash liquid is used copiously during the transfer to make sure that every single particle of precipitate is removed from the beaker.

Washing

The precipitate in the filter crucible must be washed free from all mother liquor and the coprecipitated ions on its surface. The wash solution used must be chosen intelligently so as not to ruin the analysis. Water is seldom used as the wash liquid, since many precipitates become colloidal and pass through the pores of the filter mat unless they are washed with an electrolyte.

The electrolyte selected as the wash solution should have an ion in common with the precipitate, if possible. The wash solution should not react with the precipitate or any possible impurities to form additional, contaminating precipitates. The wash solution should not complex or in any other way solubilize the precipitate. The electrolyte will remain on the surface of the precipitate after washing, so it should be a salt that will be readily volatilized during the drying process. Volatile acids and ammonium salts are frequently used for this reason. Chlorides and nitrates are also used as wash liquids. Sulfates and phosphates are avoided since their salts are not readily volatilized. Organic chelating agents, such as dimethylglyoxime and 8-hydroxyquinoline are not readily volatilized so they are not used in washing solutions. If the precipitate is to be dried only at 105°C, the electrolyte can be washed off inorganic precipitates with a final wash of alcohol–water.

When the solubility of the precipitate permits, the wash solution is usually heated. Since impurities are much more soluble in hot water than in cold, hot washing may be more efficient. Many precipitates, however, have solubilities that increase appreciably with increasing temperature, so that these precipitates cannot be washed with hot solutions.

Drying of Precipitates

After the precipitate has been washed free from impurities, the solvent and wash electrolyte must be removed from it—it must be dried. When the compound that was precipitated is to be weighed, all that is needed to dry it is to evaporate the wash solution from its surface. The crucibles containing the wet precipitate are placed in the smallest beaker that will hold them, glass hooks placed on the rim of

Fig. 3-4. Drying of crucibles and precipitates.

the beaker, and a small watch glass placed over the top. Fig. 3–4 shows the proper arrangement for drying precipitates in filter crucibles. The beaker, after being marked on its frosted glass disc with some identifying signs, is placed in the drying oven. Usually one hour is sufficient time to evaporate off all solvent. After drying, the crucibles and their contents are placed in the desiccator to cool before being weighed.

Constant Weight of Crucibles

During the drying of the precipitate the only weight change that should occur is due to the loss of the wash solution from the surface of the precipitate. The crucible, that is, the mat or walls, must not have anything on them that will be oxidized or volatilized during this drying process. If the crucible changes weight, this change would appear as weight of the precipitate, so that incorrect results would be obtained.

In order to prevent this, the crucible is brought to *constant weight* before the precipitate is filtered into it. The crucible is heated, cooled, and weighed under the identical conditions that will be used for the precipitate. This process of heating, cooling, and weighing the crucible is repeated until the weight of the crucible becomes constant, that is, the weight is identical within experimental error on two successive weighings. Since for most single pan balances the error in weighing is merely ±0.1 mg, the experimental error for two successive weighings thus becomes ±0.2 mg. Consequently, the crucible is reheated and reweighed until two successive weighings are within ±0.2 mg. (*Note:* The following data would not be acceptable as constant weight: 16.4398 g, 16.4394 g, 16.4397 g.) Usually there is some trend in weight changes during successive weighings—either a decrease in weight because substances such as dirt and grease are volatilized off, or an increase in weight because substances in the mat are oxidized. However, erratic changes in weight may occur if more than one process occurs simultaneously—a weight loss and a weight gain—and the rates of the two differ. Two or three successive weighings should be adequate for attaining constant weight.

In order to ensure that all of the solvent and volatile wash electrolyte have been removed from the precipitate, the crucible and the precipitate are also brought to constant weight at the end of the determination.

Occasionally the chemical identity of the precipitate is not suitable for weighing, and the precipitate must be transformed by heating (oxidizing) into some other form. This usually is an oxide, but not necessarily so. This transformation cannot be done at 105°C in a drying oven, but can be performed in a muffle furnace at temperatures up to 1200°C. It is especially important that precipitates heated at these elevated temperatures be brought to constant weight, since this ensures that the chemical, thermal transformation has been completed.

VOLUMETRIC TECHNIQUES

In order to measure accurately, volumetric glassware must be scrupulously clean. Cleanliness can be ascertained by wetting the surface and observing whether an unbroken film of liquid drains over the surface (clean), or whether droplets of liquid form, indicating the presence of grease and dirt.

The glassware may be cleaned with laboratory detergent and a brush, followed by thorough rinsing with tap water, and final rinse with deionized water. While dichromate–sulfuric acid cleaning solution must be used on persistent and stubborn contaminants, its use should be avoided when possible because chromate ion is very strongly adsorbed onto glass surfaces, and extraordinary amounts of rinsing are required to remove it.

The liquid film coating the inside of a piece of volumetric glassware should be of the same chemical composition and concentration as the solution whose volume is to be measured. In order to achieve this, the piece of glassware must be rinsed with small portions of the solutions before filling. A few milliliters of the solution to be placed in the container are poured into it, the solution is swirled around so as to coat all the surface completely, and then the liquid is discarded. This process is repeated twice more; only then can it be assumed safely that the film has the same concentration as the bulk liquid.

Use of Volumetric Glassware

Volumetric Flasks

The solute to be dissolved is placed in the volumetric flask, care being taken to make sure that none remains on the ground glass neck. The solvent is added until about three-quarters of the bulb is filled, and then the flask swirled until the solute has dissolved. Additional solvent is added to raise the level of the solution up to the top of the bulb, and again the flask is swirled uniformly to mix the solution as thoroughly as possible. Additional solvent is added until the level of the solution is just below the graduation line. At this time the liquid on the upper portion of the neck is allowed to drain down for at least 30 seconds and preferably a minute.

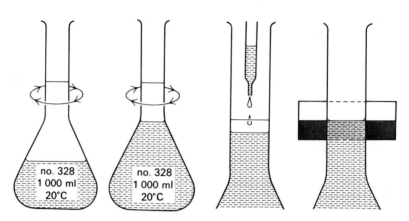

Fig. 3-5. Filling a volumetric flask to the mark.

Very carefully, the remaining solvent is added drop by drop from a medicine dropper, pipette, or burette to the flask. A meniscus reader is placed behind the graduation mark, and solvent is added until the bottom of the meniscus is just tangent to the graduation mark on the neck of the flask. Fig. 3–5 shows the proper level.

After the level of the liquid has been carefully adjusted, the contents of the flask must be mixed thoroughly. This is best done by slowly upending then righting the flask, and allowing it to remain in both the upright and inverted positions until the bubbles of air have reached the top. At least ten inversions are required for complete mixing. It is possible that during mixing some of the liquid will wet the ground glass joint, so do not be disturbed if the level of the liquid in the flask after mixing is just slightly below the mark. If the swirling was done properly earlier, in the bulb of the flask, any change in volume due to dissolution of the solute will have been accounted for.

When the solution has been measured and mixed, transfer it to a clean, dry, stoppered, nonreactive container for storage.

Pipettes

Pipettes are used to transfer exact volumes of liquids. To use, immerse the narrow tip of a pipette into the liquid to be transferred. Be sure that the immersion is sufficiently deep, so that when the liquid is removed, the tip will still be under the surface of the liquid. Slowly, using a suction bulb, draw the liquid up into the pipette, until the level is a few millimeters above the capacity mark on the stem. Quickly remove the suction bulb and place the forefinger tightly over the open end of the pipette, holding the upper stem with the thumb and middle finger. Remove the tip of the pipette from the solution and with a paper tissue wipe any drops from the outside of the tip. Slowly and carefully release the pressure of the forefinger on the end of the pipette until the solution begins to flow out the tip. Allow the solution to drain out until the bottom of the meniscus is tangent to the capacity mark on the neck of the pipette. Stop the flow by increasing the pressure of the forefinger. Touch the tip of the pipette to the glass wall of a waste container to remove any drop of

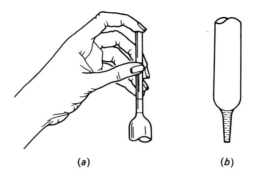

(a)   (b)

Fig. 3-6. Use of a pipette: (*a*) correct holding position,
(*b*) liquid remaining at the tip.

liquid hanging on the end. When properly filled, the pipette should have the liquid meniscus tangent to the marking on the stem, no drops hanging at the tip or outside of the pipette, and no air bubbles in the calibrated section.

Place the tip of the pipette in the container into which the solution is to be transferred. Remove the forefinger from the upper end so as to allow the solution to flow out of the narrow tip of the pipette under gravity. Do not blow or force the liquid out with pressure! The National Bureau of Standards has set the minimum delivery times for pipettes at 20 seconds for a 10-milliliter pipette and 30 seconds for a 50-milliliter pipette. When the liquid level nears the bottom of the pipette, touch the tip of the pipette to the side of the container and allow the remaining liquid to flow down the side. After liquid flow has obviously stopped, leave the pipette in contact with the wall for about 30 seconds for drainage of liquid from the walls of the pipette. Make certain that the flow of liquid has stopped before removing the pipette from the wall of the container.

Transfer pipettes are calibrated to have an amount of liquid remaining in the tip. After draining the solution from the pipette, this liquid must remain in the tip in order to measure the correct volume. Do not attempt to remove it! Fig. 3–6 shows how to hold a pipette and a close-up of the tip after the correct volume of liquid has been transferred.

Burettes

Burettes are made to measure and deliver variable volumes of liquids very accurately. In order to be used properly, the stopcock in the burette must be liquid-tight yet free-turning. When the stopcock is made of Teflon, the nut at the narrow end should be tightened as much as is compatible with smooth controlled rotation of the stopcock. Ground glass stopcocks must be greased properly.

Before greasing the stopcock of a burette, remove the metal clip and the plug and with a towel dry the plug and the bore thoroughly. Water on either will form channels when the stopcock is greased, causing leaks. Squeeze onto your finger a very small glob (just smaller than the head of a map pin) of stopcock grease. Smear some of this around both the wide and narrow ends of the plug and a smaller amount in the middle. Insert the plug into the bore in the burette and rotate the stopcock until the grease has spread evenly over the entire surface of the stopcock. When the stopcock is greased perfectly, its surface will appear uniformly wet (free from streaks that are lighter), there will be no grease in the openings of the hole through the stopcock, the stopcock will turn easily, yet not too freely, and, when listened for, the sound of rasping glass will be absent.

After the stopcock of the burette has been adjusted properly, the burette should be tested to see that its stopcock does not leak. Fill the burette with deionized water to a height above the zero mark. (Be sure to fill the tip of the burette too!) Allow the burette to stand in a vertical position in a burette clamp for ten to thirty minutes. If water leaks out, either around the stopcock itself or from the tip of the burette, drain the burette, redry and regrease the stopcock, and test again. Only when it does not leak is it ready for use.

To wet the burette walls with the liquid that is to be dispensed from it, place five to ten milliliters of this solution into the burette, hold the burette nearly horizontal, and rotate it so the solution covers the entire inner surface. Hold the burette vertically, open the stopcock, and allow a few milliliters of solution to flow through the tip of the burette. Pour the rest of the solution down the sink. Repeat this process twice. Carefully pour the solution through a small glass or plastic funnel into the burette to a level several centimeters above the zero mark. Drain the solution through the tip of the burette to just below the zero marking, making sure that no air bubbles remain in the tip or stopcock. Wait about ten seconds for drainage of the solution on the walls of the burette. (For a typical burette under normal conditions of use, the drainage volume after two hundred seconds is less than 0.01 ml.) Touch the tip of the burette to the side of the waste beaker to remove any drops hanging. Read the volume using a meniscus reader, with its dividing line placed at the bottom of the meniscus. Burettes are read downward from the zero marking, with readings estimated to the nearest tenth of a division. Thus, a fifty milliliter burette, marked in tenths of milliliters, can and should be read to the nearest hundredth of a milliliter by interpolating between the markings. Record the initial burette reading.

Draining the volume of solution from a burette should be done as rapidly as required by the specific experimental conditions. Frequently the stopcock can be opened completely, and the liquid allowed to flow out as fast as possible. The National Bureau of Standards states that the minimum delivery time for a 50-ml burette must be 90 sec, and they are calibrated at this rate of outflow. During a titration the stopcock is opened only partially so as to impede the flow of liquid to a rapid flow of discrete drops. After the solution has drained from the burette, its tip is touched to the inside wall of the receiving container to make sure that all of the liquid measured ends up in the desired container. Wait at least ten seconds for drainage—the exact length of time depends upon the volume of solution measured and the rate of outflow. To check for complete drainage, read the burette when you think it is time, then, about ten seconds later read the burette a second time. When the two burette readings are identical drainage has ended.

Hamilton Syringes

Hamilton syringes are very delicate pieces of equipment used to measure microliter volumes of solution. These syringes must be handled very carefully to avoid bending either the needle or the plunger. The use of a guide is recommended to minimize the danger of bending the plunger during injection of a sample.

Place the syringe tip into the solution to be sampled. Gently slide the plunger up and down to dislodge air bubbles, and finally draw the plunger up easily so as to withdraw a volume larger than required. Invert the syringe so that its tip points upward, and slowly push the plunger to the marking for the desired volume. Wipe off the excess solution that has run out the tip.

The injection process should be effected with decisiveness and as rapidly as possible. For use in gas chromatography, rapidly insert the point of the needle through the rubber septum of the sample injection port. Without hesitation, inject all of the sample quickly into the port. Instantly withdraw the point of the syringe after all of the sample has been injected.

Titration

A *titration* consists of accurately measuring the volume of a standard solution that just reacts completely with an accurately measured equivalent amount of an unknown sample. A *standard solution* is one of accurately known concentration. The titration must be performed slowly and carefully to avoid adding an excess of the solution in the burette (the *titrant*) to the solution in the titration vessel (the *titrate*). The purpose of a titration may be to determine the concentration of the solution in the burette (to standardize it) or to determine the amount of some constituent in the titrate.

The sample to be titrated is placed in an Erlenmeyer flask. Solids are weighed by difference into the flask, liquids are measured with a burette or pipette. An Erlenmeyer flask is used because the solution can be swirled in it more conveniently and with less splashing. Solvent is added to dissolve the sample. The solution is mixed thoroughly. The burette is filled with the titrant, the cap is placed on the burette, and the initial volume read and recorded (see Table 3–3). The indicator to be used to detect the end point of the titration is added to the solution. Visual indicators (dye solutions) may be used for pH, oxidation–reduction, precipitation,

Table 3–3. TYPICAL DATA FOR THE TITRATION OF ZINC WITH $0.01000\ M$ EDTA

Sample	1	2	3
Weight bottle and contents, g	24.3295	24.1811	24.0197
Weight bottle after sample removal, g	24.1811	24.0197	23.8641
Weight sample, g	0.1484	0.1614	0.1556
Final burette reading, ml	41.42	44.81	43.22
Initial burette reading, ml	0.06	0.02	0.15
Total volume titrant, ml	41.36	44.79	43.07
Number millimoles Zn titrated	0.4136	0.4479	0.4307 millimoles
Percentage of Zn in sample	18.22%	18.14%	18.09%
Average percentage of Zn		18.15%	
Standard deviation		0.06%	
Relative standard deviation		3.3 p.p.t	

and chelatometric titrations. Alternatively, a pair of electrodes consisting of a suitable indicator and reference electrode may be used.

The flask containing the titrate solution and indicator is placed on the base of the titration stand. The tip of the burette is lowered two or three centimeters inside the neck of the flask. When using color indicators, a titration stand with a white porcelain base, or a piece of white paper underneath and behind the titration vessel enhances perception of the color change at the equivalence point. Fig. 3–7 depicts a titration.

During a titration, the stopcock of the burette is manipulated with the left hand. The markings on the burette face the experimenter, and the knob of the stopcock is turned to the right side of the burette. The stopcock is grasped so that its narrow end is toward the palm of the left hand. The fingers reach around the sides of the stopcock and grasp the knob to turn it (see Fig. 3–7). This technique may feel awkward initially, but with a bit of practice it becomes a comfortable arrangement. Grasping and manipulating the stopcock in this fashion fends off disaster. Normal motion of the arm pulls the hand away from the torso, use of one's left hand pulls the stopcock tighter into the burette. If the right hand were used, this natural movement of the arm would pull the stopcock out of the burette, ruining the titration. Metal clips or guards on the stopcock merely hold it in the burette; they do not hold it tightly in place. It can still be pulled loose, allowing the titrant to leak out.

Initially the outflow of titrant is adjusted to a rate about half-way between discrete drops and a steady stream. The Erlenmeyer flask sits on the base of the titration stand as the titrant is added. The flask is moved with the right hand in a

Fig. 3-7. Titration technique.

continuous and gentle circular motion. This motion swirls the solution with a uniform rotation. The swirling should not splash the solution onto the sides of the flask. The rate of addition of titrant and swirling of the flask should be synchronized so that no excess of titrant builds up in the flask. When a magnetic stirrer is used to stir the contents of the flask, its rate should be adjusted so that: (1) the solution does not splash up on the sides of the flask, and (2) the cavity at the center of the flask, over the stirring bar, is not deep.

The titrant is added at this rate until the end point of the titration is approached. When using a visual indicator, slow down when the color change that occurs at the point of entry of the titrant into the titrate solution begins to persist for longer periods of time, or begins to be disseminated throughout the solution before finally disappearing. When using a vacuum-tube voltmeter to measure the potential (or pH) of the solution, slow down when the rate of change of potential (or pH) with titrant addition begins to increase rapidly. Interrupt the titration to wash down the sides of the flask and the tip of the burette with the solvent. Don't get carried away, just use a little bit of wash liquid!

From here on, until the end point is finally reached, the titrant is added drop by drop. Wait after the addition of each drop until the reaction has taken place (that is, the color reverts to its initial hue or the meter reading becomes stationary). Immediately before the end point it probably will be desirable to add fractions of whole drops. Drop fractions can be added to the titrate in either of two ways: (1) The stopcock is turned so slightly that only a portion of a drop emerges onto the tip, or (2) the stopcock is rotated so rapidly that only a fraction of a drop has time to emerge from the burette tip. This drop fraction is then transferred from the tip of the burette with some solvent from a wash bottle. Alternatively, the tip is touched with the end of a stirring rod, which transfers the solution to the stirring rod. The end of the stirring rod is then immersed in the titrate solution.

When it appears that the end point has been reached, the sides of the flask are washed down a final time to make sure that any of the sample that may have splashed onto the walls is titrated. The tip of the burette is washed off into the flask to ensure that all of the titrant that has been measured out of the burette actually gets into the titrate solution.

The *end point* is that point at which the desired pH or potential reading is reached on the vacuum-tube voltmeter, or when the indicator color change has permeated the entire solution and persists for thirty seconds or more. At the end point there should be no drop of titrant hanging on the tip of the burette, the Erlenmeyer flask should have been washed down with solvent, and the indicator should just have changed color or reached the desired value. Titrant addition is over.

Wait about ten seconds for the titrant to drain down the walls of the burette, and then read the burette—again to the nearest tenth of a division. Record this volume in your laboratory notebook. Table 3–3 contains typical titration data for the titration of zinc with standard 0.01000 M EDTA.

Extraction

The separatory funnel used for extractions preferably should have a Teflon stopcock since most organic liquids are excellent solvents for stopcock grease.

Because the purpose of an extraction is the transfer of solutes from one liquid phase to a second liquid phase, intimate contact of the two extensive liquid surfaces is essential. To achieve this contact, vigorous shaking of the two phases in contact with each other is vital. Since the physical transfer across the phase boundary is not instantaneous, this shaking must be lengthy.

The stopcock on the separatory funnel should be checked to make sure that it is greased properly or tightened appropriately so that it does not leak. See the section on the burette, p. 53, for instructions on greasing a stopcock and checking for leaks.

Selection of the correct sized funnel is done on the basis of the total volume of liquid to be contained in the funnel. During an extraction, the funnel should never be more than half-filled or mixing is impaired. The solution to be extracted is placed in the funnel with the stopcock closed, of course. The extracting solvent is added, and the stopper placed on the funnel. The funnel is inverted so that the stopcock is at the top, and shaken very gently once or twice. Volatile organic solvents build up pressure inside the funnel, which must be diminished without losing any of either solution. With the funnel still turned upside down, open the stopcock to relieve the excess pressure. (This process is called *venting*.) Close the stopcock and shake gently again. Again vent to decrease the pressure. Continue to shake and vent until there is no pressure buildup during shaking.

Shake the flask vigorously for a minute or two. Allow the liquids to rest, separating from one another, for about thirty seconds. Shake again for a minute or two. Continue shaking and resting until distribution equilibrium has been attained—usually three or four minutes.

Hang the separatory funnel, stopcock pointed down, in an iron ring on a ringstand. Allow the two liquid phases to separate completely. This will require several minutes, but be patient. When the two liquid phases have separated completely, remove the lower one. The separatory funnel is designed for the removal of the bottom (more dense) liquid, so that even when the upper layer is desired, the lower liquid is removed first.

Remove the stopper from the top of the funnel. Insert the stem of the funnel into the receiving vessel. Slowly open the stopcock, allowing the lower phase to drain down through it into the receiver. No mixing of the two liquids should occur during the separation process. Drain the liquid from the funnel until the interface between the two phases reaches the stopcock. When the lower phase is the one that is wanted, drain it out slowly until the interface is at the bottom of the stopcock bore and then rapidly close the stopcock. When the upper phase is the desired one, close the stopcock as soon as the interface reaches the top of the stopcock bore and then pour the upper phase out of the top opening of the funnel.

Liquid adhering to the inside of the stem of the funnel can be rinsed out with the appropriate solvent, adding the rinse to the bulk of the lower phase.

CHROMATOGRAPHIC TECHNIQUES

Column Preparation

If the chromatographic column does not have a sintered glass plate at the bottom of the wide portion to prevent the packing from running out, a glass wool plug must be inserted for this purpose. A *glass plunger*—a piece of glass rod about half again as long as the column with one end flattened to a circle—is a useful tool when packing chromatographic columns. With the plunger, gently shove a small plug of glass wool down the column to the constriction. Tamp the glass wool loosely into place. This glass-wool wad should be sufficiently dense to prevent any solid from passing through it, but loose enough so as not to impede the flow of liquid through it. It should not be more than a few milliliters thick under any circumstances.

Most chromatographic packings are 100–200 mesh, that is, particle sizes between 0.074 and 0.149 mm. Since these particles can pass through the glass wool plug, a 1 mm layer of sea sand is poured on top of the glass wool.

Dry Packing

Often alumina and other adsorbants are packed dry into the chromatographic column and then wetted. Dry packing sounds extremely simple. The desired amount of dry packing is poured slowly and continuously through a small funnel into the column. As the packing is poured into it, the column is tapped gently but continuously with a ruler or wooden pencil. The tapping of the column is continued until the packing has settled completely and the desired column height has been obtained. Packing a column is an art that is only mastered after much practice, so the first few times some distortion of the separating bands is liable to occur.

The top layer of adsorbant must be protected so that it is not disturbed during sample and eluent addition. This protection can be accomplished either by pouring a 2–5 mm layer of sea sand atop the packing, or by covering the packing with a disc made from filter paper. Using a cork borer, from a piece of filter paper cut a disc that has a diameter just slightly smaller than the internal diameter of the column. Using the tamping rod, carefully push the disc to the top of the column and tamp it down firmly.

The packed dry column is wet by slowly pouring the solvent through the packing, using suction when necessary.

See Chapter 14 for the technique used to pack gas chromatographic columns.

Wet Packing

Chromatographic columns used for partition and ion-exchange chromatography are always packed wet. The cellulose, silica gel, or ion-exchange resin is soaked in the appropriate solvent until it is wet thoroughly and swelling has finished. Carefully decant off the supernatant liquid containing all the fine particles. Add fresh solvent, allow the heavy particles to settle, and again decant off the supernatant liquid containing the fine particles. Then add enough solvent to the wet solid to produce a thin, gruel-like slurry.

Place a small glass or plastic funnel in the neck of the appropriately sized chromatographic column that already has the wad of glass wool and sand at the bottom (or has a built-in sintered glass disc). Fill the column about one-fourth full with the solvent to be used. Pour about one-fifth of the slurry into the column. Using the glass plunger mix the packing with the solvent in the column to form a smooth slurry. Allow the packing to settle. Add a second fifth of the slurry to the column, stirring with rapid up and down motions of the glass plunger until a uniform slurry that contains a portion of the previously added packing is obtained. Allow the packing to settle. Repeat this procedure with the third, fourth, and last fifth of the slurry. This portionwise addition of the slurry while stirring is essential in order to eliminate striations so as to obtain a uniform column packing.

Gently tamp down the packing to give a compact but not solid column. Drain the solvent down to a level about 1 cm above the top of the packing. Add 2–5 mm of sea sand, or cut a disc of filter paper just slightly smaller than the diameter of the column and push it gently onto the top of the packing with the plunger. The sand or piece of filter paper is to prevent the upper layer of the packing from being disturbed during addition of sample and eluting agent.

Pass about fifty milliliters of solvent through the column in order to wash the packing and to assist it in settling completely. Drain this solvent to a level of about 0.5 cm from the top of the packing. At no time should the surface of the solvent be allowed to fall below the surface of the packing or air will enter the column, coat the particles, and prevent equilibrium from being achieved.

Sample Addition

For a successful chromatographic separation, the sample must be added to the top of the column as a small, concentrated band. In order to achieve this, considerable care must be taken during addition of the sample.

Pipette an aliquot of the sample onto the top of the column in such a manner that the powdered solid at the top is not disturbed. This is done by placing the tip of the pipette against the inside wall of the column, just above the sand or piece of filter paper. As the aliquot of sample drains from the tip, run the tip of the pipette around the inside of the column, being careful not to touch the packing. The solvent should be draining very slowly from the chromatographic column during sample addition. Allow the sample to drain down onto the column to a level within 1 mm of the packing surface. Rinse the inner wall of the column with 1 ml of the pure solvent, allowing this liquid to drain to 1 mm above the top of the solid packing. Repeat the washing with a second and third 1-ml portion of the solvent, draining each aliquot down to within 1 mm of the solid surface before adding the next. This washing should be sufficient to wash all of the sample onto the column, but it may not be. If not, continue washing with 1-ml portions of solvent until the supernatant liquid above the top of the column is colorless (when working with colored samples).

Development

The apparatus for the development of the column is shown in Fig. 3–8. An appropriately sized separatory funnel serves as the reservoir for the eluting agent. The tip of this funnel should extend inside the top of the column. The rate of flow of eluate from the chromatographic column is adjusted by the stopcock or Hoffman clamp at the bottom of the column. The rate of flow of eluting solvent into the top of the column is controlled by the stopcock of the separatory funnel until the liquid level in the column remains constant, preferably about five or more cm above

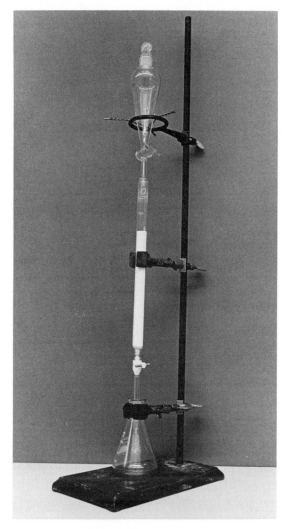

Fig. 3-8. Apparatus for development of a chromatographic column. (*Photograph by Stephen Daugherty.*)

the surface of the packing. The rate of addition of eluting agent from the separatory funnel then becomes equal to the rate of elution.

Frequently, a chromatographic column is packed so tightly that the eluting solvent cannot flow through the column under the influence of gravity at the specified rate—or often, at any rate at all. Then, coercion must be used to force the liquid through the column. Solvent can either be pushed or pulled through.

Suction provides the most convenient method for increasing the rate of eluate flow. The suction flask arrangement shown in Fig. 3–3 is attached to the bottom of the chromatographic column with the tip of the column extending into the receiving test tube. Fig. 3–9 shows the proper arrangement of this. When the desired amount of eluate has been collected in one test tube, the suction line is opened while the

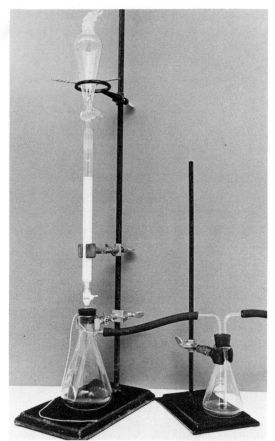

Fig. 3-9. Apparatus for using suction to increase elution rate. (*Photograph by Stephen Daugherty.*)

test tube is replaced with another one. Suction cannot be used with volatile eluents such as ether, benzene, or methanol.

Pressure can be applied to the top of the column to speed up the flow of eluent. Under pressure the reservoir of solvent must be removed which means closer attention must be paid to the column. Pressure apparatus consists of a squeeze-bulb attached to a piece of glass tubing, which is inserted through a one-hole rubber stopper. The stopper is forced into the neck of the column, and the bulb squeezed to increase the pressure and hence flow rate (Fig. 3–10). Alternatively, where feasible, a stream of compressed air can be used to force the liquid through the column.

When using either of these two techniques, care must be used so as not to compress the solid packing so much that it forms a dam and impedes the flow of any liquid through the column. Gentle persuasion is best.

When an automatic fraction collector and a sufficiently large solvent reservoir are used, chromatographic development can be ignored for extended periods of time (hours or overnight). Normally, however, it is a prudent gesture to check on

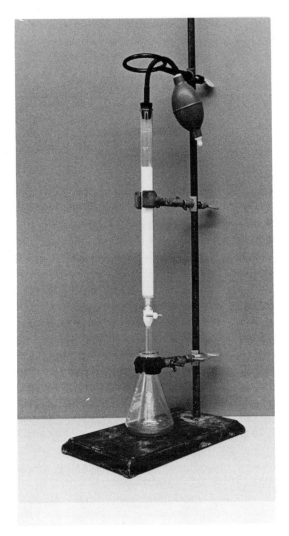

Fig. 3-10. Apparatus for using pressure to increase elution rate. (*Photograph by Stephen Daugherty.*)

the column operation every now and again. When suction or pressure must be used, almost constant attention is required to ensure no mishaps occur.

THE CORNING MODEL 7 pH METER

Many makes and models of pH meters are available for use in student and research laboratories. While it would be impossible and impractical to give detailed operating instructions for all of these, instructions for the operation of any one model are illustrative of the procedures and the cares that must be followed when using any of them. Consequently, operating instructions for the Corning Model 7 pH meter are given.

The Corning Model 7 pH Meter is a general-purpose instrument capable of pH and millivolt measurements. It employs a highly reliable solid-state chopper for zero drift and extremely stable operation. No warm-up period is required.

1. Plug the power line cord into a 3-prong power outlet supplying 105–125 V ac at 60 cycles.
2. Set the Function Switch to STANDBY position. If the meter needle does not read zero, mechanically zero the meter with a screwdriver using the Mechanical Zero Adjuster.
3. Plug the pH glass and reference electrodes into the input and reference connectors on the back of the pH meter. Both electrodes should have been wetted previously. The glass electrode should have been soaked in 0.1 M HCl for at least two hours before using. Dry both electrodes with an absorbant tissue before immersing in any solution.
4. Immerse both electrodes, so that their tips are covered, in a buffer solution of known pH. The buffer used should have a pH value as close as possible to that of the sample to be measured.
5. Measure the temperature of the buffer solution and set the Manual Temperature Compensator to this value.
6. Set the Function Switch to the pH position.
7. Adjust the Calibration Control until the meter reads the pH value of the buffer solution. (Be sure to use the pH value which corresponds to the temperature at which the measurement is made. See the chart on the bottle.) Return the Function Switch to the STANDBY position.
8. Remove the electrodes from the buffer solution by sliding the Electrode Holder up the Support Rod. Rinse them off with distilled water to prevent carry-over of the buffer solution. Wipe the electrodes dry with an absorbant tissue.
9. Lower the electrodes into the unknown sample solution.
10. Check that the temperature of the sample solution is the same as that of the buffer solution used for the standardization. If it is not, adjust the Manual Temperature Compensator to the new temperature. Set the Function Switch to the pH position.
11. Read the pH value of the sample. The relative accuracy of the reading is 0.05 pH and the repeatability is ± 0.02 pH. Return the Function Switch to the STANDBY position.
12. Remove electrodes from the sample solution. Wash the electrodes with distilled water and reimmerse in the beaker of 0.1 M HCl, disconnect the power line plug, check that the Function Switch is on STANDBY, and place the plastic dust cover over the instrument.

THE BAUSCH AND LOMB SPECTRONIC 20 SPECTROPHOTOMETER

While there are innumerable colorimeters and spectrophotometers used in chemical and biochemical laboratories, the Bausch and Lomb Spectronic 20 is encountered so frequently in student and clinical laboratories that operating instructions for it not only provide the illustration of the operation of any spectro-photometer, but also will be practical. See Fig. 2–16 for numbering.

1. Turn the instrument on by rotating the left-hand knob on the front of the instrument (6) clockwise until the pilot light (if there is one) glows.
2. Allow the instrument to warm up for at least five minutes before attempting to use it.
3. Rotate the wavelength control knob [right-hand knob on top of the instrument case, (4)] until the desired wavelength (in nanometers) is indicated on the wavelength scale (3).
4. Adjust the dark current knob [left-hand knob on front of instrument case (6)] until the meter needle reads 0 on the % Transmittance scale or ∞ on the Absorbance scale. Because a voltage is applied between the cathode and the anode of the phototube, and the coatings have low work functions, some electrons will be drawn from the coating to the anode, even when no light is striking this cathode surface. This current, called the *dark current*, must be compensated for in order to obtain accurate instrument readings. This com-pensation is accomplished by arbitrarily setting the meter on the instrument to read zero while this current flows. The current is thus "bucked out" by a potentiometer.
5. Insert the cuvette containing the reagent blank or solvent into the sample holder (1) and close the lid to eliminate outside light from the cell compart-ment.
    (a) When using square cuvettes, be sure that the frosted glass side is facing the front of the instrument. The clear glass sides should have been wiped free from stains and lint.
    (b) When using matched test tubes, be sure to set the index line on the test tube opposite the index line of the sample holder. This matching reproduces, insofar as it is possible with round containers, the insertion setting of the test tube. To avoid any possible scratching of the test tube in the optical path, insert the tube with the index line at right angles to the index line on the test tube holder in the instrument, and then rotate the tube until the two lines match.
6. Adjust the light control knob [right-hand knob on the front of the instrument case, (5)] until the meter needle reads 100 on the % Transmittance scale or 0 on the Absorbance scale.
    (a) The emission intensity of the tungsten filament, the absorption of light by the reagent blank, and the phototube response all change when the wave-length of light is changed. Therefore, the meter reading will vary from wave-length to wavelength when the reagent blank is placed in the cell compartment. In order to compensate for this variation, the meter arbitrarily is set electrically to full-scale reading, using the amplifier circuit of the instrument.
    (b) This setting of the dark current (0) and reagent blank (100%) on the spectrophotometer must be done before each and every reading is taken because drifting of the electrical components of the instrument, changes in the emission characteristics of the tungsten filament with time, and changes in the absorption of the solvent and reagent with wavelength occur.

7. Replace the blank with the unknown sample. Without any further adjustments of anything, read the Absorbance or % Transmittance directly from the meter. Read the meter scale to the nearest tenth of a division.

8. When finished, turn off the instrument and replace its dust cover. Return immediately all cuvettes or matched test tubes to the stockroom.

THEORY OF LIGHT ABSORPTION

One of the most convenient, accurate, and sensitive methods for measuring the concentration of solutes in dilute solutions is by colorimetry or spectrophotometry; that is, by measuring the amount of light (energy) the molecules or ions absorb from a beam of white light. The term *colorimetry* applies when white light or the broad wavelength bands passed by gelatin or interference filters is passed through the sample solution and its decrease in intensity measured. As was mentioned earlier, the term *spectrophotometry* is appropriate when the beam of radiation passed through the absorbing solution is very narrow (only a few nanometers wide) and the wavelengths selected for use can be varied continuously and conveniently.

A molecule or ion absorbs from a beam of electromagnetic radiation shining on it, only that wavelength that corresponds to (or can cause) an energy change in the species. In the visible and ultraviolet region of the spectrum (ultraviolet region—100–400 nm, 12.0–3.2 electron volts; visible region—400–750 nm, 3.2–1.6 electron volts) this energy change corresponds to the excitation of an outer electron from a lower to a higher energy level within the molecule or ion. The amount of radiation absorbed depends upon the probability of a photon hitting the molecule or ion and the probability that once it does hit the molecule that it will cause the electron to be excited. The color of light absorbed is not the color seen by the eye, but its complement (Table 3–4), for the eye sees only transmitted, not absorbed, light.

Let us shine a narrow beam of monochromatic (only one wavelength) radiation through a container holding the sample solution (see Fig. 3–11). Call I_0 the initial intensity of the light. When the beam of light strikes the glass surface of the container some ($\sim 3\%$) of it will be scattered. Call this scattered light I_S. The beam passes through the glass (where, at the wavelength selected, none is absorbed) and then through the sample solution. In the solution some light is absorbed by the molecules or ions. Call this absorbed light I_A. The light hits the other glass surface where more of it is scattered (another 3% or so), which is included in the term I_S. The beam then passes through the glass again and on to the detector. The light emerging from the sample container, that is, the light transmitted by the solution, has an intensity called I_T. Summing up:

$$I_0 = I_S + I_A + I_T \qquad (3\text{–}1)$$

As we shall see later, I_A is determined by the concentration of the molecules or ions in the light path. I_A is the term that we want to measure, because, conversely, knowing it we can calculate the number of molecules or ions in a given volume of solution (concentration). Unfortunately, there is no known method for directly measuring I_A, so we must be content to arrive at its value indirectly. Both I_0 and I_T can be measured, so that:

$$I_0 - I_T = I_S + I_A$$

Table 3–4. WAVELENGTHS AND COLORS

Wavelength Range, nm	Color Absorbed	Color Transmitted
400–450	Violet	Yellow-green
450–480	Blue	Yellow
480–490	Green-blue	Orange
490–500	Blue-green	Red
500–560	Green	Purple
560–575	Yellow-green	Violet
575–590	Yellow	Blue
590–625	Orange	Green-blue
625–750	Red	Blue-green

While I_S can be measured, it is very inconvenient to do so directly. The light loss due to scattering is compensated for electronically. Once the adjustment is completed, conditions are kept constant so that the amount of scattered light does not change. This compensation is accomplished as follows: with a "blank" or non-absorbing solution ($I_A = 0$) in the spectrophotometer, the needle of the ammeter is set to read $I_0 = I_T$ by adjusting the amplifier in the spectrophotometer's detector circuit. After this amplifier setting anything that changes I_S makes all measurements of I_A wrong. Therefore, since I_S is different for each cell, the same cell or a "matched" cell must be used when measuring the concentration of the unknown solution.

Measurement of absolute light intensity, I_0 and I_T, in lumens, is one of the most tedious and time-consuming measurements in physics and is best avoided. Since I_0 changes with wavelength, absolute intensity measurements would have to be made at each wavelength. Since the characteristics of the tungsten filament deteriorate with time, absolute intensity measurements would have to be made each and every time the instrument was used. For spectrophotometry it is not necessary to measure absolute light intensities when the intensity of light transmitted by the solution is expressed as a fraction of the intensity that initially impinges on the cell. Thus, we don't use absolute intensities, merely relative ones.

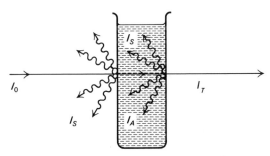

Fig. 3-11. Light strikes a sample cell.

With no light absorbing material in the light beam, the spectrophotometer scale is set to read no absorbance (Absorbance = 0, or 100% Transmittance) by means of the amplifier in the detector circuit. This makes I_0 become 100. All resultant measurements of I_T are expressed as a fraction of this value. This fraction is called the *transmittance, T*, of the sample.

$$T = \frac{I_T}{I_0} \tag{3-2}$$

The fraction converted to a percentage is called the *percent transmittance, % T:*

$$\% \, T = 100 \, T = 100 \, \frac{I_T}{I_0} \tag{3-3}$$

Beer's Law

When a beam of monochromatic radiation passes through an absorbing solution of thickness X, a certain fraction (I_A/I_0) of the incident radiation will be absorbed. If the beam which emerges from this solution, having an intensity now of I_T, is in turn passed through a second layer of the same solution of the same thickness X, the same fraction of the light will be absorbed. Therefore, the intensity of the light beam diminishes exponentially as it passes through a solution, each small layer of thickness X absorbing the same fraction of the light incident on it, so we can write:

$$I_T = I_0 e^{-kX} \tag{3-4}$$

where k is a proportionality constant representing the probability that a photon will hit an absorbing ion or molecule and that once it strikes it has the right energy to be absorbed.

If the thickness of the solution is kept constant, but the number of absorbing species, N, in the light path is doubled, then the intensity of light that is absorbed from the incident beam will be doubled. If this number of absorbing species is in turn doubled, then the intensity of light absorbed will be twice that of the previous solution or four times the initial absorption. Therefore, the intensity of light decreases exponentially as the number of absorbing species in the light path increases, so we can write:

$$I_T = I_0 e^{-k'N} \tag{3-5}$$

where k', a different number from the k above, has the same significance. N can be expressed in terms of the concentration of absorbing species, C, and the length of the light path, b, through the container. Combining Equations (3-4) and (3-5) and substituting in for N:

$$I_T = I_0 e^{-kbC} \tag{3-6}$$

Which, when converted to powers of ten rather than of e, gives:

$$I_T = I_0 10^{-abC} \tag{3-7}$$

where, a, the probability of absorption occurring, now includes the conversion from natural to decimal logarithms. Taking the logarithm of Equation (3–7)

$$\log (I_T/I_0) = -abC \qquad (3\text{–}8)$$

The inclusion of the minus sign in Equation (3–8) is cumbersome and awkward in practice, so let's get rid of it by inverting the logarithmic term:

$$\log (I_0/I_T) = abC \qquad (3\text{–}9)$$

This logarithmic term is given the symbol A and is called the *absorbance* of the solution. Substituting into Equation (3–9) produces the now accepted form for writing Beer's law:

$$A = abC \qquad (3\text{–}10)$$

where the symbols are those recommended by the Committee for Nomenclature in Applied Spectroscopy 1952.[1] a is called the *absorptivity* and varies in magnitude with wavelength as is shown in Fig. 3–12. C can have any convenient units. b, the cell thickness, is usually in centimeters for solution measurements. A is the logarithm of a fraction and hence, dimensionless. Therefore, the units of a depend upon those selected for C. When C is expressed in moles/liter, a is called the *molar absorptivity* and has the units square centimeters/mole.

Comparison of Equations (3–2), (3–9), and (3–10) show that the relationship between transmittance and absorbance is:

$$A = \log (1/T) = \mathrm{p}T \qquad (3\text{–}11)$$

A plot of the change in the absorbance of a solution at a fixed wavelength as a function of the concentration changes in a solution is called a Beer's law plot. Fig. 3–13 shows that these Beer's law plots should be straight lines, of slope ab that intersect the origin. Since the slope of the graph depends upon the absorptivity, a, of the solution, plots measured at different wavelengths will have different slopes. Fig. 3–14 shows three different Beer's law graphs, one for each of the three wavelengths of Fig. 3–12. In order to obtain the maximum sensitivity, that is, the greatest change in the absorbance for a given change in the concentration of the solution, absorbance measurements usually are taken at the wavelength where the absorbance is a maximum, λ_{max}.

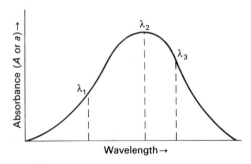

Fig. 3-12. A typical visible spectrum.

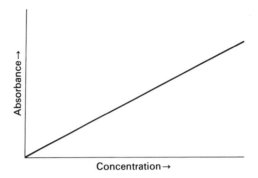

Fig. 3-13. A typical Beer's law plot.

Equation (3–10) indicates that Beer's law will hold at any wavelength, since wavelength is not included in its statement. Therefore, when there is a second substance present in the solution that will cause an interfering absorption at the wavelength of maximum absorbance, measurements can be made at other, less sensitive, wavelengths. Fig. 3–15 shows this more clearly, when it is desired to measure the absorption of substance 1. Measurement at the λ_{max} for substance 1 will cause errors since substance 2 also absorbs radiation at this wavelength. Erroneously high absorbance readings will result. By selecting λ_s as the wavelength at which Beer's law is used, a linear, an accurate calibration curve can be obtained.

The total measured absorbance of a solution at a selected wavelength is the sum of the individual absorbances of all substances present in the solution that will absorb radiation of that wavelength. Thus, for the spectra shown in Fig. 3–15, the total measured absorbance of the solution at λ_{max} is

$$A_T = A_1 + A_2$$

or in general for any solution:

$$A_T = A_1 + A_2 + A_3 + \ldots + A_n \tag{3–12}$$

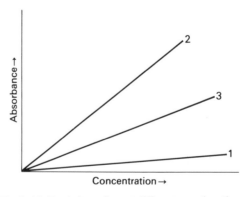

Fig. 3-14. Beer's law plots at different wavelengths.

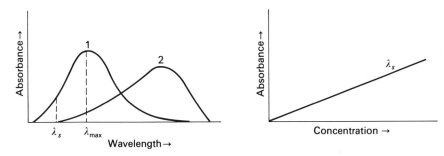

Fig. 3-15. Use of Beer's law in the presence of an interference.

This additivity of absorbances can be used to analyze mixtures of compounds which absorb at the same wavelength. Consider the case of two blue dyes, methylene blue and victoria blue B, which have the absorption spectra shown in Fig. 3–16. There is considerable overlap of the two spectra, with the wavelength of maximum absorbance for victoria blue B at 610 nm, and that for methylene blue at 625 nm. At either of these two wavelengths, the measured absorbance will be:

$$A_T = A_{\text{vbB}} + A_{\text{mb}}$$

at 610 nm, substituting in from Beer's law:

$$A_{610} = A_{\text{mb}_{610}} + A_{\text{vbB}_{610}} = a_{\text{mb}_{610}} b C_{\text{mb}} + a_{\text{vbB}_{610}} b C_{\text{vbB}}$$

at 625 nm, substituting in from Beer's law: $\qquad$ (3–13)

$$A_{625} = A_{\text{mb}_{625}} + A_{\text{vbB}_{625}} = a_{\text{mb}_{625}} b C_{\text{mb}} + a_{\text{vbB}_{625}} b C_{\text{vbB}}$$

The values of the molar absorptivities $a_{\text{mb}_{610}}$, $a_{\text{mb}_{625}}$, $a_{\text{vbB}_{610}}$, and $a_{\text{vbB}_{625}}$ can be obtained by measuring the absorbances at each of the two wavelengths of a pure solution of known concentration of victoria blue B and of a pure solution of known concentration of methylene blue. Then from Beer's law for these solutions

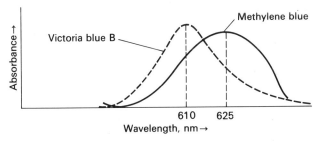

Fig. 3-16. Spectra for victoria blue B and methylene blue.

the four molar absorptivities can be calculated. Actually what is calculated by this process is *ab* since

$$ab = \frac{A}{C}$$

If *b* is known, it can be inserted in the above equation and *a* found. If all known and unknown solutions are measured in the same cell, *b* need not be known. Since it is constant for all solutions, the product *ab* can be used in Equation (3–13). The only unknowns now remaining in Equation (3–13) are the concentrations of the two dyes. Since we have two equations with only two unknowns, these can be solved easily enough. In practice, mixtures containing up to five absorbing species have been analyzed this way.

Equation (3–10) (Beer's law) seems to be independent of temperature because it does not include a temperature term. To a first approximation this is true. This is deceptive, since all the terms in Equation (3–10) are temperature dependent. The path length through the cells used to hold the unknown and standard solutions increases with increasing temperature. The concentration of solutions decreases with increasing temperature for the volume of the solution increases. The probability of an electronic transition is temperature dependent. Thus, Beer's law should always be applied at the same, constant temperature. The exact value does not matter, as long as it does not vary throughout the measurements.

There are no known true deviations from Beer's law. That is to say, every time a series of solutions does not appear to obey Beer's law, the deviation from linearity can be explained by other means—as for example, equilibria, instrument deficiencies, interferences, and concentrations too large. There are, however, upper limits of concentration, above which there are just too many absorbing centers per unit volume for Beer's law to be obeyed. At high concentrations, absorbances are lower than those predicted from Beer's law. The resultant downward curvature in the Beer's law plot is called a negative deviation from Beer's law (see Fig. 3–17).

Beer's law is used both mathematically and graphically to measure the concentration of an unknown solution. For either method, a pure (standard) solution of the absorbing species is required. When only an occasional concentration measurement is needed it probably is more convenient to use the mathematical

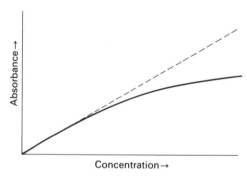

Fig. 3-17. Graph exhibiting a negative deviation from Beer's law.

approach, whereas for routine concentration measurements on hundreds of samples the graphical method is simplest. The graphical method is always more accurate for the slope of the line (*ab*) is the average of the absorptivities at all concentrations, and hence is more accurate and statistically more reliable than any single measurement of the absorptivity.

To use Beer's law mathematically, measure the absorbance (A_S) of a standard solution of the species whose concentration is to be measured in the unknown. From this measured absorbance and the known concentration (C_S), calculate the value of *ab* in Beer's law.

$$ab = \frac{A_S}{C_S} \qquad (3\text{--}14)$$

Measure the absorbance of the unknown solution, A_U, in the same spectrophotometer cell. The concentration of the substance in the unknown can be calculated by substituting Equation (3–14) in Beer's law.

$$C_U = \frac{A_U}{ab} = \frac{A_U C_S}{A_S} \qquad (3\text{--}15)$$

To use Beer's law graphically, prepare at least three solutions of different concentrations of the pure solute. Measure the absorbance of each of these solutions. Draw a Beer's law graph (Fig. 3–13) from these concentration and absorbance data. Use the Method of Least Squares (Chapter 4) to locate the best straight line through the experimental points. The absorbance of the unknown solution is measured at the same wavelength at the same temperature, and in the same cell. From this measured absorbance, the concentration of the species in the unknown is read off the Beer's law graph.

REFERENCE

1.   Hughes, H. K., *et al.*, *Anal. Chem.*, **24**, 1349 (1952).

CHAPTER 4

ERRORS AND THE USE OF STATISTICS IN ANALYTICAL DATA

ACCURACY AND PRECISION

The numerical value obtained in every scientific measurement contains some degree of uncertainty. In very accurate work the uncertainty may be extremely small, but it is still present. This uncertainty is called the error of the measurement. When discussing the errors present in a set of analytical data, there are two different aspects to be considered. The first of these is the *accuracy* of the data. Accuracy relates to the closeness of approach of a single measurement, or of the average of a series of measurements, to the true value. The true value is incapable of being measured exactly, but in many cases it can be estimated very closely. By using calibrated equipment, performing the work extremely carefully, executing a very large number of measurements, and then applying statistics to the results, reasonable approximations of the true value can be obtained. Frequently, the true value is estimated from the results of different analysts in different laboratories.

The second aspect of errors is called the *precision* of the measurement. Precision describes the closeness of approach of replicate results to a common value. Repeated measurements of the same quantity will usually not be identical, but will scatter around some common value. Precision describes the reproducibility or scatter of a series of measurements or results. Both the terms accuracy and precision have specific meanings and implications, so they should not be used interchangeably or carelessly.

To illustrate exactly what is meant by the two terms, accuracy and precision, let us examine two sets of data for the weight of a crucible. The data in set A were obtained by five different students each weighing the crucible on his own analytical balance, each using, therefore, a different set of weights. The second (set B) were obtained by having a sixth student weigh the crucible five times on his analytical balance, thus these data were obtained on the same equipment.

The crucible is then weighed by a skilled analyst, using ASTM II-S-1 weights, and applying all appropriate corrections to the weight obtained. He finds a value of 9.2474 g as the average of ten replicates, with no statistically significant trends

	Set A	Set B
Weight of crucible, g	9.2463	9.2483
	9.2480	9.2481
	9.2477	9.2484
	9.2489	9.2480
	9.2455	9.2483
Average weight, g	9.2473	9.2482

or deviations in the individual weights or in the mean. Thus, it is fairly safe to assume that this value is sufficiently close to the true value to be considered the "correct" weight of the crucible.

Let us now examine the data in sets A and B. The weights obtained in set B, by the one operator using the same equipment are less scattered, much closer to each other than those found in set A. We can say that the precision of these data is higher than the precision of the data in set A. The average of the weights obtained by the five students (set A) is closer to the true value than is the average of the weights in set B. (The origin of this could be due to an incorrect weight, a reproducibility incorrect procedure by the student, failure to allow for temperature differences, and so on.)

These data reveal an interrelation between accuracy and precision that is very important. Precise data need not necessarily be accurate data. A constant and reproducible error can be contained in each piece of data. The data in set A are misleading, for it is highly unlikely that poor precision will accompany good accuracy. While accuracy without precision is highly unlikely, and, as in the case of the data in set A, is obtained fortuitously, high precision does not guarantee high accuracy.

So far we have merely discussed accuracy and precision in general terms, observing that data that lie close to each other are more precise and averages that are closer to the true value are more accurate. Now let us look at some of the quantitative methods that have been used to express more exactly the precision and accuracy of scientific data. There are many methods for doing this, but those that are used in this book are the ones recommended by the Advisory Board of the publication *Analytical Chemistry*[1] and by statisticians.

Methods for the Expression of Accuracy

The usual expression of accuracy is merely the difference between the piece of data (or the average of a set of data) and the true value. This is known as the *absolute error* or the *mean error*. Generally, the absolute error by itself is of low information and of little use unless one knows the magnitude of the quantity being measured or calculated. Thus saying that there is a 3.0 mg low error in weighing a sample, while having some value, takes on a much greater significance if we know what the weight of the object is. It makes a difference whether the weight is 30 g or 30 mg. The error is usually negligible in 30 g, but is very significant in 30 mg.

Thus the accuracy of a measurement is usually expressed in relative terms, as a fraction of the true value. Unfortunately, the answer to many analytical calculations is a percentage. In order to avoid confusion, relative accuracy is not expressed as a percentage, but in terms of parts per thousand (p.p.t.). This is obtained by multiplying the fraction by one thousand, a procedure that is completely analogous to calculating a percentage. Thus:

$$\text{relative accuracy} = \frac{\text{absolute error}}{\text{true value}} \times 1000 \qquad (4\text{--}1)$$

and in case of the data in set A:

$$\text{relative accuracy} = \frac{-0.0001 \text{ g}}{9.2474 \text{ g}} \times 1000 = -0.01 \text{ p.p.t.}$$

and for the data in set B:

$$\text{relative accuracy} = \frac{+0.0008 \text{ g}}{9.2474 \text{ g}} \times 1000 = +0.086 \text{ p.p.t.}$$

It should be pointed out that as a general practice, relative accuracy and relative precision expressions are rounded off to the first decimal place. Note that the smaller the numerical value of the relative error (disregarding the sign) the more accurate the data are. Thus, as we have estimated earlier, the data in set A are more accurate than those in set B, because the absolute value of the relative accuracy is smaller.

Methods for the Expression of Precision

There are many different ways to express the precision of a set of data. Of these, only a few have any statistical basis, causing these expressions now to be recommended. Today these are the most frequently encountered terms. A couple of the terms below are listed for historical purposes. A student may encounter them in the older literature and should be aware of their meaning.

The Range, ω

This is merely the numerical difference between the highest and the lowest values of a set of results. For the data in set A,

$$\omega = 9.2489 \text{ g} - 9.2455 \text{ g} = 0.0034 \text{ g}$$

Use of the range is not particularly informative, for it tells nothing about the distribution of the data. The data could be distributed uniformly between the two limits, or they all could be clustered around one value, with just a single datum way off. The range is most frequently used for very small sets of data, that is, two or three items. The range becomes less informative as the number of pieces of data in a set increases. The range is more informative about the precision of a set of data than the average deviation when there are fewer than eight pieces in the set.

The other methods for expressing precision are based on the absolute difference between each particular piece of data and the average of the set. This difference is known as the *deviation* of a particular piece of data. A deviation has no sign, being obtained by subtracting the datum from the average of the set. Thus, for any given measurement, X_i, in a finite set of data whose average or arithmetic mean is m, the deviation is:

$$|X_i - m|$$

The *mean*, of course, is:

$$\frac{\sum_i X_i}{n}$$

where n is the number of pieces of data in the set. The deviations for the data in set A and set B are given below.

Deviation for Set A, g	Deviation for Set B, g
0.0010	0.0001
0.0007	0.0001
0.0004	0.0002
0.0016	0.0002
0.0018	0.0001

The Average Deviation, a

Prior to 1960 the average deviation was a very popular method for expressing the precision of a set of data. The only reason for its widespread use was that it is relatively easy to calculate. Statistically, the average deviation has no importance for it does not convey any useful information. It is employed infrequently now and its use should be discouraged. The average deviation is nothing more than the average of all of the deviations for the members of the set of data, taken without regard to sign. Or:

$$a = \frac{\sum_i |X_i - m|}{n} \tag{4-2}$$

Thus for the data in set A, the average deviation is

$$a = \frac{0.0010 \text{ g} + 0.0007 \text{ g} + 0.0004 \text{ g} + 0.0016 \text{ g} + 0.0018 \text{ g}}{5} = 0.0011 \text{ g}$$

and for the data in set B, the average deviation is:

$$a = \frac{0.0001 \text{ g} + 0.0001 \text{ g} + 0.0002 \text{ g} + 0.0002 \text{ g} + 0.0001 \text{ g}}{5} = 0.0001 \text{ g}$$

The Standard Deviation, s

The standard deviation is a meaningful statistical term used to express precision. If one should happen to have a set of data that contains an infinite number of pieces, then σ would be the parameter used to describe the standard deviation of the members of the set. Normally, however, scientists have only finite sets of data, and in fact, in analytical chemistry, usually only a very small set of data (two, three, four, or five members). Thus the symbol used for the standard deviation is s, indicating that we are treating only a limited set of data. From the way that the standard deviation is formulated, more weight is given to pieces of data having large deviations. This is appropriate, since they occur infrequently. The average deviation weighs all deviations equally. The standard deviation is the most frequently encountered method of expressing precision and will be used throughout this book. It is defined as the square root of the sum of the squares of the deviations divided by one less than the number of pieces of data in the set, namely:

$$s = \sqrt{\frac{\sum_i (X_i - m)^2}{n-1}} \tag{4-3}$$

The standard deviation for a finite set of data is obtained by dividing by one less than the number of pieces of data since this denominator represents the number of degrees of freedom the set of data possesses which are available for assessing error. Since the mean rather than the true value is used in calculating the deviations, and it is a property of the set that $\Sigma(X_i - m) = 0$, when one has selected $n-1$ values of the deviation, the last deviation cannot be arbitrarily selected, but is predetermined. Thus when calculating s for any set of data possessing the mean, m, only $n-1$ degrees of freedom show the effects of error.

The squares of the deviations for the data in sets A and B are:

	Set A $(X_i - m)^2$	Set B $(X_i - m)^2$
	100×10^{-8}	1×10^{-8}
	49×10^{-8}	1×10^{-8}
	16×10^{-8}	4×10^{-8}
	256×10^{-8}	4×10^{-8}
	324×10^{-8}	1×10^{-8}
Sum	745×10^{-8}	11×10^{-8}

Consequently, the standard deviation for the data of set A:

$$s = \sqrt{\frac{745 \times 10^{-8}}{4}} = 1.4 \times 10^{-3} \text{ g} = 0.0014 \text{ g}$$

and the standard deviation for the data of set B:

$$s = \sqrt{\frac{11 \times 10^{-8}}{4}} = 2 \times 10^{-4} = 0.0002 \text{ g}$$

The smaller the value of the standard deviation, the more precise the data. Notice that the numerical value of the standard deviation is greater than that of the average deviation, for the data in both sets. This is due to the increased weight given to the values with larger deviations.

The Variance, s^2

For certain statistical tests it is more convenient to use the square of the standard deviation, instead of the standard deviation. This term is called the variance, and it is defined as the sum of the squares of the deviations divided by one less than the number of pieces of data. Or:

$$s^2 = \frac{\sum\limits_i (X_i - m)^2}{n-1} \tag{4-4}$$

The variance of the data in set A is 1.86×10^{-6}, and the variance for the data in set B is 3×10^{-8}.

Relative Standard Deviation (Coefficient of Variation)

As was pointed out above, when discussing accuracy, the absolute value of the standard deviation *per se* is of limited value. Usually the value of the mean of the data set is given along with the standard deviation, which does enable one to estimate the relative magnitude of the standard deviation. When the standard deviation is expressed as a fraction of the mean of the set of data, a better feeling for the proportionality of the error is obtained. The relative standard deviation is nothing more than the standard deviation divided by the mean of the set. Again this is expressed as parts per thousand in order to avoid the possible confusion by the use of percentage values.

$$\text{relative standard deviation} = \frac{s}{m} \times 1000$$

For the data in set A:

$$\text{relative standard deviation} = \frac{0.0014 \text{ g}}{92.473 \text{ g}} \times 1000 = 0.15 \text{ p.p.t.}$$

and for the data in set B:

$$\text{relative standard deviation} = \frac{0.0002 \text{ g}}{9.2482 \text{ g}} \times 1000 = 0.02 \text{ p.p.t.}$$

Thus, once again it is found that the data in set B are more precise than those in set A. The smaller the numerical value of the relative standard deviation, the more precise the data set is.

Probable Deviation, p

The probable deviation is only used as a means of expressing precision when there is a very large number of pieces in the set of data (that is, more than one hundred). The probable deviation is the most frequently occurring deviation. When all of the positive deviations are arranged sequentially, the probable deviation is that deviation so chosen that there are as many deviations with magnitudes greater than it as there are positive deviations with a magnitude smaller than it. The same value should be obtained by performing the identical manipulation on all the negative deviations. Statistically it is readily obtained from the standard deviation

$$p = 0.67 \, s \tag{4-6}$$

Confidence Limits or Interval

This is a statistical term used to define the distance on either side of the mean value of a set of data, within which one may expect to find, with a stated probability, the true value. Thus the 95% confidence interval or limits is the distance on either side of the average within which the true value will be found 95% of the time. Going to 99% confidence limits, increases the probability of including the true value, but naturally it must be a broader region than the 95% confidence limits.

Confidence limits are defined from the *t test* (see below) as

$$\text{confidence interval} = \pm \frac{ts}{\sqrt{n}} \qquad (4\text{--}7)$$

where n is the number of pieces in the set of data and t is a number depending upon the number of pieces of data and the confidence level desired. Values of t are tabulated in statistics books. A selected portion of such a table is given in Table 4–2 for 1–10 pieces of data and 90, 95, and 99% confidence levels. For most analytical work 90 or 95% confidence is sufficient, although for very accurate work, 99% confidence levels are used.

For the data in set A at 95% confidence:

$$\text{confidence interval} = \frac{(2.78)(0.0014 \text{ g})}{\sqrt{5}} = \pm 0.0017 \text{ g}$$

so the true value lies within 9.2473 ± 0.0017 g at 95% confidence level. For the data in set B for 95% confidence:

$$\text{confidence interval} = \frac{(2.78)(0.0002 \text{ g})}{\sqrt{5}} = \pm 0.0002 \text{ g}$$

and the true value lies within 9.2482 ± 0.0002 g 95% of the time. (Since we have already said that the error in set B was not a random error, but a systematic one, it is not to be expected that the true value in the case of set B will be statistically predictable.)

Note that the 99% confidence interval for set A is ± 0.0029 g and that for set B is ± 0.0004 g.

Classification of Errors

In looking over the errors that are apt to occur during a chemical analysis, one sees that they are of two major types, those of known origin that can be corrected for and those whose origin is unknown. On this basis, errors are generally divided into the two categories—*determinate* or *systematic errors* and *indeterminate* or *random errors*. The borderline between the two categories is vague and blurry.

Determinate Errors

Determinate or systematic errors are those errors whose source can be identified.

Their behavior and their effect on the results are understood. It may not be possible to prevent determinate errors, but they usually can be corrected for. Further subdivision of determinate errors is based upon their source; whether the error lies in the chemistry of the experiment, the equipment used, or the person carrying out the experiment.

Equipment errors are ascribed to deficiencies in the quality of the apparatus used in carrying out the experiment: instruments, glassware, reagents, and so forth. The zero point of a pH meter may be wrong, burettes may not be calibrated properly, the balance is not functioning properly, a reagent contains a reactive impurity, a solvent is impure. These are usually eliminated by fixing the instrument, calibrating the meters and glassware, using high purity reagents, and other means. When the source cannot be located or eliminated, an appropriate correction factor may have to be applied.

Personal errors can be caused by poor laboratory technique, judgement, or bias. The major errors here are blunders and they are physical in nature, such as letting a chromatographic column run dry, not waiting for a sample to reach the balance temperature before weighing it, spilling of material during quantitative transfers, and incomplete mixing of solutions. Personal errors may be the largest source of error with beginning students, but they should decrease with increasing expertise. An experienced and skillful operator will still have some sources of error attributable to him, however. These may be due to errors in personal judgement or due to prejudice. The meniscus on a volumetric flask may be read too high, an indicator may be always allowed to turn just a little too much, a meter may be read just slightly high or low. Prejudice is involved when the experimenter has some idea as to the result to be expected and reads a burette or meter in such a fashion as to get closer to it, rather than obtaining a truly independent reading.

Errors in method are chemical or physicochemical in nature and lie in a property of the system being studied. Examples include the solubility of a precipitate in the mother liquor or wash liquids, incomplete reactions, coprecipitation, air oxidation, solvent evaporation, and others. For skilled experimenters, these errors are apt to be the most serious. They usually can be removed only by changing to a method of analysis that involves different chemistry. They can be corrected by running blanks and then applying appropriate correction factors.

Determinate or systematic errors are not amenable to treatment by statistics.

Indeterminate Errors

Indeterminate or random errors are those that are caused by unknown or uncontrolled factors. Once the source of a random error is known, it becomes a systematic error. This class should be truly random in nature, causing results that are high just as frequently as they are low. Random errors cannot be corrected, because they are due to the normal fluctuations in the behavior of the equipment or of the experimenter. The equilibrium position of a balance will vary ever so slightly from weighing to weighing, the movement of a meter will cause the needle of a pH meter or of a spectrophotometer to give slightly different readings each time, an experimenter will read the meniscus on a burette a bit differently each time, drainage through a chromatographic column packing will be slightly different each time, causing different R_f values. These are the normal, daily fluctuations in performance and occur in a random fashion.

Indeterminate errors can be treated by statistical methods and it is only indeterminate errors for which statistical treatment is valid.

The Normal Law of Distribution of Indeterminate Errors

The distribution of indeterminate errors is expected to follow the normal distribution (Gaussian) law. This law is given by the equation:

$$Y = \frac{1}{\sigma(2\pi)^{\frac{1}{2}}} \exp\left\{-\tfrac{1}{2}\left(\frac{X_i - m}{\sigma}\right)^2\right\} \tag{4-6}$$

where Y is the frequency of occurrence of a deviation of a particular magnitude, σ is the standard deviation, X_i is the experimental datum, m is the mean of the set, and thus $X_i - m$ is the deviation of the value. This exponential relationship between a deviation caused by a random error and the frequency with which it occurs, strictly speaking, is valid only for extremely large numbers of pieces of data. For smaller sets of data, such as are normally encountered in analytical laboratories, the scatter of deviations will not follow this relationship. By considering these data as only a few points, which are a part of a much larger set of data which does obey a Gaussian distribution, statistics and statistical tests can be applied successfully to small sets of data. A graph of the frequency of occurrence of a deviation, Y as a function of the magnitude of the deviation gives the familiar bell-shaped normal distribution curve. Fig. 4–1 is such a graph.

Fig. 4–1 shows where the mean, m, the average deviation, d, the standard deviation, s, and the probable deviation, p, fall in a normal distribution. The standard deviation occurs at the inflection point of rising and descending portions of the curve. Sixty-eight percent of the area of the normal distribution curve lies

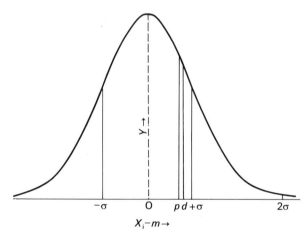

Fig. 4-1. The normal distribution curve.

between $-\sigma$ and $+\sigma$. This means that two out of three pieces of data deviate from the mean by only one standard deviation or less.

Two features of the normal distribution curve should be pointed out. First, the curve is symmetrical. That is to say, positive and negative deviations occur with equal frequency (probability). Second, small deviations occur more frequently than large deviations. Or, to phrase it another way, the larger the deviation, the less apt it is to occur. A corollary of this, however, is that although small deviations occur most frequently, large deviations do have a finite probability of occurring. This feature of the error curve takes on importance when deciding whether or not to reject a piece of data that is not very close to the rest of the data of the set (see below).

STATISTICAL TESTS OF DATA

The F Test

A problem frequently encountered in evaluating analytical data involves judging whether or not the precision of two sets of data is essentially the same. Do two different analytical methods give data with roughly the same precisions, or is one method considerably less precise than the other? The F test is used to compare the precision of two sets of data. F is the ratio of the variances for each set; the ratio so set up that it is always greater than one ($s_1^2 > s_2^2$):

$$F = \frac{s_1^2}{s_2^2} \tag{4-7}$$

In the F test, after the value of F has been calculated from the two sets of data, the value is compared with that given in a table of statistical F values. When the calculated F is larger than the tabulated value, the data in set 1 are indeed less precise than those in set 2, at the specified confidence level. Table 4–1 gives values for F at

Table 4–1. VALUES OF F AT 95 PERCENT CONFIDENCE LEVEL

$v_2{}^b$	$v_1{}^a$									
	2	3	4	5	6	7	8	9	10	∞
2	19.00	19.16	19.25	19.30	19.33	19.36	19.37	19.38	19.39	19.50
3	9.55	9.28	9.12	9.01	8.94	8.88	8.84	8.81	8.78	8.53
4	6.94	6.59	6.39	6.26	6.16	6.09	6.04	6.00	5.96	5.63
5	5.79	5.41	5.19	5.05	4.95	4.88	4.82	4.78	4.74	4.36
6	5.14	4.76	4.53	4.39	4.28	4.21	4.15	4.10	4.06	3.67
7	4.74	4.35	4.12	3.97	3.87	3.79	3.73	3.68	3.63	3.23
8	4.46	4.07	3.84	3.69	3.58	3.50	3.44	3.39	3.34	2.93
9	4.26	3.86	3.63	3.48	3.37	3.29	3.23	3.18	3.13	2.71
10	4.10	3.71	3.48	3.33	3.22	3.14	3.07	3.02	2.97	2.54
∞	3.00	2.60	2.37	2.21	2.10	2.01	1.94	1.88	1.83	1.00

[a] v_1, number of degrees of freedom for larger variance.
[b] v_2, number of degrees of freedom for smaller variance.

the 95% confidence level. v_1 is the number of degrees of freedom of data of the set having the larger variance, and v_2, therefore, is the number of degrees of freedom of the set of data having the smaller variance.

Consider the data obtained during a determination of the equivalent weight of a weak acid. In method A, phenolphthalein was used to detect the end point, whereas in method B, the glass electrode was used as the detection device. Which set of data is more precise?

	Method A	Method B
	122.4 g	122.8 g
	122.0	122.2
	122.6	122.6
	121.8	122.4
		122.5
Average	122.2 g/equiv	122.5 g/equiv

Using Equation (4–4) the variance for the data obtained by method A is 2×10^{-1}, whereas the variance for the data obtained by method B is 5×10^{-2}. Applying the F test now:

$$F = \frac{s_1^2}{s_2^2} = \frac{2 \times 10^{-1}}{5 \times 10^{-2}} = 4$$

From Table 4–1, where v_1 now is 3 and v_2 is 4, we find that the value of F is 6.59 at the 95% confidence level. Since the calculated value of F is smaller than this, we can conclude that the data obtained using phenolphthalein are just as precise as those obtained with the glass electrode.

The t Test

In 1908 Gosset[3] devised what he called *Student's t* to take into account the smallness of the usual number of measurements encountered in practice and variations in the number of pieces of data used to calculate the average. He defined t as:

$$\pm t = (m - \mu) \frac{n^{\frac{1}{2}}}{s} \tag{4–8}$$

where m is the average of the set of data, μ can be considered as the "true" value, n is the number of pieces in the set of data, and s is the standard deviation for the set. Rearranging Equation (4–8) gives:

$$\mu = m \pm \frac{ts}{n^{\frac{1}{2}}} \tag{4–9}$$

From Equation (4–9) we can see that the true value will fall within a distance of $\pm ts/n^{\frac{1}{2}}$ (the confidence interval) from the average. How large this confidence interval is will depend upon the number of measurements taken, their standard deviation, and the confidence level desired. If in practice the true value (known from some other source) falls outside this interval, we can conclude that there is a systematic error in the data in addition to the random errors. When this occurs, attempts should be made to scrutinize the analytical method to locate and eliminate the systematic error. Values of t are tabulated in most texts on statistics, and a partial listing is given in Table 4–2.

Table 4–2. VALUES OF t FOR DIFFERENT CONFIDENCE LEVELS

Degrees of Freedom, v	90%	95%	99%
1	6.31	12.71	63.66
2	2.92	4.30	9.93
3	2.35	3.18	5.84
4	2.13	2.78	4.60
5	2.02	2.57	4.03
6	1.94	2.45	3.71
7	1.90	2.37	3.50
8	1.86	2.31	3.46
9	1.83	2.26	3.25
10	1.81	2.23	3.17

If μ is considered to be the known value for the percentage of a constituent in a sample (this true value must be obtained from some other source than the method being tested) the t test can be used to evaluate the quality of an analytical method, the performance of an experimenter, or the effect of changing parameters within the method. If μ is considered to be the average of one set of data and m the average of a second set of data pertaining to the same determination, one can use the t test to determine variations in the performance of personnel, equipment, and the method.

The t test consists of calculating the value of t by means of Equation (4–8) and comparing it with the statistically obtained value of t in tables. This is done at a particular confidence level decided upon by the judge of the data. When the calculated t exceeds the statistical value of t, there is a real difference (a systematic error) between the mean and the true value. When the calculated t is less than the tabulated t, the difference between the mean and the true value is acceptable statistically (due only to random errors) and considered negligible (that is, the two values are "identical").

As an illustration let us apply the "t test" to the weighing data in set B on p. 75.

$$t = (9.2482 \text{ g} - 9.2474 \text{ g}) \frac{(5)^{\frac{1}{2}}}{0.0002 \text{ g}} = 4(2.24) = 8.96$$

From Table 4–2 we find that the value of t for 4 degrees of freedom is 2.78 at the 95% confidence level and 4.60 at the 99% confidence level. Since our calculated value of t is much greater than either of these, there is a real error (systematic) in the data and a search should be made for it since the values are not acceptable.

Example. In a gravimetric determination of nickel with dimethylglyoxime, a student turns in the values 3.681, 3.635, 3.621, 3.593%. The National Bureau of Standards value is 3.557%. Does the average of these values, 3.632% of Ni, have a difference from the true value that is real, or is it statistically possible to obtain such a difference?

The calculated value for the standard deviation of the experimental results, s, is 0.037%. There are four pieces of data in the set. Thus, using Equation (4–8) the student can calculate a value of t for the data:

$$t = \frac{(3.632 - 3.557)(4)^{\frac{1}{2}}}{0.037} = 4.02$$

From Table 4–2, for three degrees of freedom and at 95% confidence level, the value of t is 3.18. Since his calculated t is greater than 3.18, the difference between the student's mean and the true value is a real one and not merely due to statistical fluctuations of indeterminate errors.

Note: For 99% confidence level the tabulated value of t is 5.84. The student's calculated value is less than this, so that he should suspect a real difference (since the 95% t is exceeded) but have to conclude that it is statistically possible to have this large a discrepancy.

The comparison of results obtained by two different experimenters or from two different methods or under two different sets of conditions is a common, valuable, and necessary operation in analytical chemistry. One must be certain, however, that the criteria used in making judgements have a sound statistical basis and are not just whimsical. The t test provides an excellent basis for the comparison of the average values of two sets of data.

The procedure for comparing means using the t test is more complicated than that for comparing an average with the true value. Each of the two sets of data may have a different number of pieces; each probably will have a different standard deviation so Equation (4–8) is no longer applicable. A modification of it that compensates for these differences must be used; see Equation (4–10):

$$t = \left(\frac{m_1 - m_2}{s_{12}}\right)\left(\frac{n_1 n_2}{n_1 + n_2}\right)^{\frac{1}{2}} \tag{4–10}$$

where m_1 is the average of the data in set 1 of n_1 pieces, and m_2 is the average of the data in set 2 of n_2 pieces. s_{12} is the standard deviation of any value in either set based on the data in both sets. It is computed according to Equation (4–11).

$$s_{12} = \left(\frac{\sum_{i_1}(X_{i_1} - m_1)^2 + \sum_{i_2}(X_{i_2} - m_2)^2}{(n_1 - 1) + (n_2 - 1)}\right)^{\frac{1}{2}} \tag{4–11}$$

In effect, Equation (4–11) represents a combination of the equations for the standard deviations of each set of data. The form of Equation (4–11) is completely analogous to that of Equation (4–3) for computing the standard deviation of a single set of data.

In order to make a valid and meaningful comparison of two sets of data, the precision of each set must be roughly comparable. So, before running the t test, an F test must be run to compare the precisions of the two sets of data.

To illustrate the comparison of means using the t test the following example is given.

Example.   Student A determines the percentage of copper in a sample by using a partition chromatographic separation of the copper from its interferences followed by an EDTA titration to determine the number of milligrams of copper present. Student B determined the percentage of copper in the same unknown by extraction of copper 8-hydroxyquinolinate. A spectrophotometric measurement on the extract was used to determine the amount of copper. The results that each obtained are.

	Student A	Student B
	37.35 mg Cu	37.49 mg Cu
	37.58	37.63
	37.17	37.87
	37.03	
Average	37.28 mg Cu	37.66 mg Cu

The true value is not known. The question is—is there a real difference between the two averages obtained, or is this difference statistically acceptable, considering the two different methods used?

In order to be able to compare two averages, the precision of the data in each set must be roughly comparable, that is, the F test must be passed.

The variance for the data obtained by student A is 565×10^{-4} whereas the variance for student B's data is 370×10^{-4}

$$F = \frac{565 \times 10^{-4}}{370 \times 10^{-4}} = 1.53$$

From Table 4–1, F is 19.16. Since our calculated F is less than that, the precision of the two data sets is comparable.

From Equation (4–11) the standard deviation for the combined data sets can be calculated.

$$s_{AB} = \left(\frac{1695 \times 10^{-4} + 739 \times 10^{-4}}{3 + 2} \right)^{\frac{1}{2}} = 0.22 \text{ mg}$$

This can now be substituted into Equation (4–10) along with the other pertinent information:

$$t = \frac{(37.66 - 37.28)}{0.22} \left(\frac{3 \times 4}{3 + 4} \right)^{\frac{1}{2}} = \frac{0.38}{0.22} \left(\frac{12}{7} \right)^{\frac{1}{2}}$$
$$= 2.26$$

Using Table 4–2 again, for five degrees of freedom (three in student A's data and two in student B's data), we find that the tabulated value of t at the 95% confidence level is 2.57, and at the 99% confidence level it is 4.03. Since the value of t calculated above for these data is less than either tabulated value of t, we are forced to conclude that the difference between the results obtained by these different methods is not meaningful and can be attributed solely to chance. Hence, we conclude that both methods will give us the same value for the amount of copper in the sample.

Rejection of Data

Occasionally in a series of measurements or calculated results, one value will have a deviation that is considerably larger than that of any of the other pieces of data. Naturally this concerns the experimenter, so the question arises as to whether or not this is a valid piece of data, and also whether or not it should be kept and included in the results of the experiment. Once a piece of data has been obtained, it cannot be discarded except for valid reasons, and the fact that it does not agree with the rest of the data is not sufficient cause for rejection *per se*. Not liking the result is not a valid reason for rejecting it.

Frequently, especially with beginning analysts, a piece of data may be widely divergent from the rest of the set because an error was made in the analysis. Thus, whenever such a large deviation crops up, first check the arithmetic of the calculations, then check your memory of what you did with that sample as contrasted to what you did with the others. Was there an observable difference in behavior at some stage? If you know that a mistake was made (for example, spilled solution, air bubble in the burette tip), then obviously the data will be erroneous and should not be included. If you suspected that something may have been awry during the analysis (uncertainty about standardization of the pH meter, channeling in the chromatographic column, flow rate of the gas chromatograph) but were not certain, and then the result for that sample is different from the others, your suspicions are probably correct and it can be discarded honestly. During a series of successive operations (for example, titrations, colorimeter readings, duplicate gas chromatograph analysis), the first one of the series is the least reliable. Unfamiliarity with the techniques involved (burette reading, indicator color change, meter reading, sample injection technique) can cause poor performance. Thus when the first (and only the first) result obtained differs from the rest, it can be rejected with a clear conscience. This cannot be done where the operations are done simultaneously on all samples (for example, in gravimetric analyses, paper chromatography, TLC) for there is no "first" to the series. Thus, when we talk of the rejection of data we are considering only the case where there is no question about the validity of the data in the mind of the experimenter. He has no suspicions that he did anything incorrectly, yet the result is widely divergent. What should be done with it?

Consideration of the normal error curve shows that deviations of large magnitude, either positive or negative, do indeed occur naturally, although infrequently. Thus to be safe, one should include all data at all times. With beginning analysts, divergent data occurs more than is statistically normal and so the use of statistical methods to judge the propriety of discarding an unwanted result must be considered. Many tests, such as the t test for the comparison of averages with the true value cannot be applied, since the true value is unknown. Other statistical methods are based on infinitely large populations, and hence are inapplicable when only three or four replicate analyses have been carried out on the sample.

In 1951, Dean and Dixon[2] published an article dealing with statistics for small sets of data, such as are normally encountered in the analytical laboratory. Included in this paper is the Q test for the rejection of data. This test has a sound statistical basis, and was designed for use with only three to ten replicate analyses. The Q test is applicable when one, and only one, result deviates from the rest of the set; it will not work if there are two results that are a considerable distance from the average. Nor is the Q test applicable when all but one of the pieces of data in the set are identical. It will always reject data under these conditions—for example, given 3.413, 3.413, 3.414 mequiv/g as the experimentally obtained values for the capacity of an ion-exchange resin, the Q test would permit rejection of the last value, 3.414 mequiv/g. Common sense tells us that 3.414 mequiv/g is a valid result, not divergent from the other two, and that it should not be rejected. The Q test states: When the value of Q calculated from the experimental data is equal to or greater than the value of $Q_{0.90}$ tabulated for that number of observations, the suspected observation may be rejected, at the 90% confidence level. The value of Q is calculated from the data by taking the distance of the suspect value from its nearest neighbor in magnitude, and dividing this by the range of the data, including the suspect value. That is:

$$Q = \frac{(X_2 - X_1)}{\omega} \qquad (4\text{--}12)$$

$Q_{0.90}$ is a statistical term computed at a 90% confidence level. The use of it as a comparison in the Q test implies that one is correct 90% of the time in discarding a result that has a calculated Q greater than $Q_{0.90}$. Or to phrase it differently, there is only a ten percent chance that a result would be so divergent normally. Table 4–3 presents the values of $Q_{0.90}$ for three to ten pieces of data.

Table 4–3. VALUES OF $Q_{0.90}$ FOR THREE TO TEN OBSERVA-
TIONS

Number of Observations	Rejection Quotient, $Q_{0.90}$
3	0.94
4	0.76
5	0.64
6	0.56
7	0.51
8	0.47
9	0.44
10	0.41

Example. A student obtained the following results for the gravimetric determination of nickel by precipitation with dimethylglyoxime—7.414%, 7.410%, 7.435% nickel. The last value is noticeably higher than the other two, so the question arises concerning its validity and whether it must be included in the final average. The standard deviation and average value would be much lower, if it could be discarded. The student is unaware of any experimental reason for not including the value. Calculate the value of Q for the data:

$$Q = \frac{7.435 - 7.414}{7.435 - 7.410} = \frac{0.021}{0.025} = 0.84$$

In Table 4–3 we find that the value of $Q_{0.90}$ for three observations is 0.94. Since the suspect value gives a value of Q that is less than this, it is statistically possible to obtain it purely by chance, and thus it must be retained. Thus the average calculated percentage of nickel of 7.420% with a standard deviation of 0.013% nickel and a relative standard deviation of 1.8 p.p.t.

Example.   For the standardization of sodium hydroxide against primary standard potassium acid phthalate, the following values were obtained by a student for the normality of the solution: 0.1014, 0.1012, 0.1015, 0.1021, 0.1012 N. All but 0.1021 N seem to cluster around a common value, so that 0.1021 M becomes suspect. Calculate the value of Q for the data:

$$Q = \frac{0.1021 - 0.1015}{0.1021 - 0.1012} = \frac{0.0006}{0.0009} = 0.67$$

From Table 4–3, $Q_{0.90}$ for five observations is found to be 0.64. Since the calculated Q is larger than that, the value of 0.1021 should be discarded. Doing this, the average normality is 0.1013 N with a standard deviation of 0.0001 N and a relative standard deviation of 1 p.p.t. (Note that by discarding the value of 0.1021 N, the average has dropped from the 0.1015 N that it would have been including the suspect value, the standard deviation is considerably better, down from 0.0004, with the relative standard deviation decreased from 4 p.p.t.)

As a general practice, when the calculated value of Q is below, but quite close to the tabulated value of $Q_{0.90}$, return to the laboratory and perform one or two more replicate analyses. When these agree with the bulk of the data, not only is the confidence in the correctness of these data strengthened, the numerical value of $Q_{0.90}$ has decreased, so that the suspect value probably may be discarded now.

The Method of Least Squares

The preparation of a calibration curve is done in many chemical analyses. Ideally, most of these calibrations are linear. Thus, given a set of data that are presumed to obey a linear relation, the problem involved is to plot them and draw the best straight line through the points. This can be, and frequently is, done by inspection and intuitive placement of the transparent straight-edge on the points on the graph paper. Statistics provide a much sounder basis for drawing the straight line through the data points.

Let us assume that the data fit the equation:

$$y = mx + b$$

where x is the concentration of the standard solution, and y is the measured property of it. m is the slope of the straight line, and b its intercept on the y (ordinate) axis. When the values of m and b have been determined, the proper straight line has been established, and it can then be drawn through the points. It can be shown statistically that the best straight line through the series of experimental points is that line for which the sum of the squares of the deviations of the points from the value on the line (S) is a minimum. This is known as the *method of least squares*. If x_e and

y_e are the experimental data (coordinates), and y_c is the value of y on the straight line for the parameter x_e, then the expression for the method of least squares can be written:

$$S = \sum_e (y_e - y_c)^2 = \sum_e [y_e - (mx_e + b)^2]$$ (4-13)

and the best straight line occurs when S is a minimum. By applying differential calculus to this, it can be shown that S is a minimum when:

$$m = \frac{\sum\limits_n (x_e - \bar{x})(y_e - \bar{y})}{\sum\limits_n (x_e - \bar{x})^2}$$ (4-14)

$$b = \bar{y} - m\bar{x}$$ (4-15)

where n is the number of points, $\bar{x}$ is the average of all the values of x_e and $\bar{y}$ is the average of all of the values of y_e.

To illustrate, let us consider plotting the following data obtained[4] in the determination of a metal by atomic absorption.

Concentration of Metal (x_e), μg/ml	Absorbance (y_e)	$(x_e - \bar{x})(y_e - \bar{y})$	$(x_e - \bar{x})^2$
0.000	0.000	0.580	1.030
0.390	0.228	0.214	0.390
0.780	0.476	0.022	0.055
1.560	0.888	0.173	0.298
2.340	1.267	0.922	1.759
Average 1.014	Average 0.572	Sum 1.911	Sum 3.532

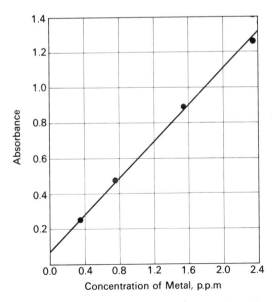

Fig. 4-2. Least squares plot for the atomic absorption of a metal.

The average, $\bar{x}$, of the values of x_e (concentration of metal) is 1.014 $\mu g/ml$ and the average, $\bar{y}$, of the values of y_e (absorbance) is 0.572. The preceding table also includes the square of the deviations of x_e and their sum, and the product of the deviations of x_e times the deviations of y_e and their sum. Thus, from Equation (4–14):

$$m = \frac{1.911}{3.532} = 0.543$$

and from Equation (4–15):

$$b = 0.572 - (0.543)(1.014) = 0.022$$

Giving for the equation of the line through these data points:

$$y = 0.543\ x + 0.002$$

Fig. 4–2 shows the plot of the data and the line drawn through them according to the above equation.

SIGNIFICANT FIGURES

A number used to express the results of a physical measurement or of a calculation should contain sufficient digits to express the accuracy of the measurement or calculation. The general rule used in chemistry states that the last digit of a number, and only the last digit of the number, has any uncertainty in it. All of the other digits in the number contain no uncertainty. To illustrate, a sample is weighed on an analytical balance that has an accuracy of $\pm$ 0.1 mg. To report its weight as 1.40638 g, is incorrect since the last decimal place is meaningless, because the balance is only capable of giving accurate information to the fourth decimal place. The weight properly should be written as 1.4064 g. Using this number of significant figures, the last digit, the 4, is uncertain by $\pm$ 1 and this accurately represents the capability of the balance. It is equally incorrect to express the sample weight as 1.406 g, for in weighing the sample, there is no uncertainty about the number of milligrams taken. Writing the weight with only three decimal places implies that there is. Full advantage of the accuracy and sensitivity of a measuring instrument should be taken and the results obtained with it should reflect this accuracy.

When trying to determine the correct number of significant figures to use in a number, the presence of zeroes may cause confusion. Consider the number, 0.4060 g. How many significant figures does it have? Four. The zero to the left of the decimal point is merely to indicate the order of magnitude, to show that the weight is less than one gram. In no way is it a part of the number. The other two zeroes are significant figures. As a general rule for numbers smaller than 1, zeroes preceding the first nonzero digit are not significant, but merely indicate the order of magnitude of the number. Use of the exponential form for writing numbers eliminates confusion. Thus 0.004103 contains four significant figures, the three zeroes preceding the 4 are not significant. This can be seen more clearly when the number is written as 4.103×10^{-3}.

When writing numbers larger than one, the use of the exponential form is essential for clarity. Zeroes to the right of the last nonzero digit of a number larger than one, can be either significant or not; there is no way for the person reading the number to decide. Consider the number written as 4,510,000. How many significant figures does it contain? Three? Four? Seven? When the number is written like this there is no way to judge. Some, perhaps all, of the zeroes to the right of the 1 may be merely to locate the decimal point. Some, maybe all, may be significant figures. In order to eliminate this confusion, the number should be written as, say 4.510×10^6, which states clearly that there are four significant figures and still locates the decimal point.

It is customary at all intermediate stages of calculations to carry along one more significant figure than is proper. The calculation is rounded off to the correct number of significant figures only at the very end. This practice causes the error in the final result to be an accurate reflection of the errors in the components. Only the final digit will contain a minimum of uncertainty.

In performing calculations, one must be constantly alert so that the numerical result does not reflect an accuracy that is greater or less than the least accurate number used in the calculation. When using computers, desk calculators, or even with hand calculations, it is very easy to obtain long strings of digits. It is deceptive to believe these really reflect accuracy. In performing calculations we must be sure we eliminate all meaningless, deceptive, excess digits from the result. The operational rules used for addition and substraction are different from those used for multiplication and division. In addition and subtraction, the number of decimal places limits the number of significant figures, whereas in multiplication and division the number of decimal places is irrelevant. The result is restricted by the relative accuracy of the numbers involved in the calculation. The precision and accuracy of an experiment can never be increased by the computational process. Under certain conditions they can be decreased.

In addition and subtraction, the number of significant figures in the sum or difference can change from the number of significant figures of the components. Only the last digit of the sum or difference may contain any uncertainty. A sum or difference may contain no more decimal places than that component number having the fewest decimal places. Consider each of the following additions:

	1	2	3
	43.1	0.0025	10.414
	4.31	4.1167	0.0037
	0.431	5.9071	9.02
Sum	47.8	10.0263	19.43

In the first sum, all three numbers have identical significant figures, namely three, but 43.1 has the fewest decimal places and hence limits the number of significant figures in the answer. Only one decimal place can be used, so that 47.8 is the correct sum. In the second sum, all three numbers have the same number of decimal places, even though the first one has the fewest significant figures. The result can be expressed to four decimal places. Note that in this case the sum has one more significant figure than any member. In the third sum, all three numbers have different numbers of significant figures, the sum is limited to two decimal places by 9.02. The number 0.0037 cannot be included in this sum because it lies beyond the limits of the accuracy of the least accurate of the numbers. Nothing can be added beyond the second decimal place.

The same general considerations apply to subtractions.

	1	2	3
	44.341	19.4197	4.96
	−4.4432	−19.4153	−0.00321
Difference	39.898	0.0044	4.96

The first difference is limited to three decimal places by 44.341. Note that in the second subtraction, the difference has only two significant figures, whereas each of the two components has six—a tremendous decrease in significant figures and, hence, in relative accuracy of the difference. In the third set a subtraction cannot be made because the limit is at the second decimal place.

The relative accuracy, in parts per thousand, of a number determines the significant figures in multiplications and divisions. The answer cannot be any more accurate, in relative terms, than the least accurate number involved in the calculation. Consider the following multiplication: 16.4×0.3196. For both numbers it is assumed that only the last digit contains any uncertainty, and that this uncertainty is ± 1. Thus, the relative error in 16.4 is one part in 164 or 6.1 parts per thousand. The relative error in 0.3196 is one part in 3196 or 0.3 p.p.t. 3196 is the more accurate number. The product of this multiplication can therefore be no more accurate than 6.1 parts per thousand, since 16.4 is the least accurate number. Multiplication produces the digits 5.24144, which obviously is an incorrect increase in the number of significant figures. Strictly speaking this number should be rounded off to 5.2. The number 5.24 has a relative accuracy of 1.9 p.p.t. which is better than the 6.1 p.p.t. limit. In practice, however, most chemists would leave the product at 5.24, for the three significant figures gives a closer indication of the true accuracy than does 5.2, which has an error of 19 p.p.t.

For the division $63.21 \div 0.012$, the number of significant figures in the result is limited by the relative accuracy of 0.012, which is 83.5 p.p.t. The answer, expressed as 5×10^3, has an error of 200 p.p.t., whereas when expressed as 5.2×10^3 only has an error of 19.2 p.p.t. Again the tendency would be to use 5.2×10^3 as being more representative of the accuracy of the divisor.

The *logarithm* or *antilogarithm* of a number, when used as the answer of a calculation or when directly involved in a calculation (as in pH, pM, Nernst equation) must also have the correct number of significant figures. As in multiplication and division, the logarithm can be no more accurate than the initial number, relatively in p.p.t. In general this means that the *mantissa* of the logarithm should contain the same number of significant figures as the original number. Similarly, in taking an antilogarithm, the number should have no more digits than the mantissa of the logarithm. The *characteristic* of a logarithm is used to indicate the order of magnitude of the number. Like zeroes before decimal points, the characteristic in no way contributes to the relative accuracy of the number or the number of significant figures. For example, when the hydrogen ion concentration of a solution is 4.4×10^{-3} M, the pH of the solution is 2.35. The 2 gives the order of magnitude; only the .35 is representative of the accuracy of the concentration. In the concentration this is 1 part in 44, or 22.7 p.p.t. Thus the mantissa, 0.35, with a relative accuracy of 28.6 p.p.t. adequately reflects the accuracy of the concentration. pK_a for acetic acid at 0°C is 4.7807. The K_a at this temperature is thus 1.657×10^{-5}.

When, however, a logarithm is used as a number in a calculation (as in Nernst equation calculations) it is treated as any other number. The error in the logarithm under these conditions is determined either by the number of decimal places (addition and subtraction) or the total number of digits used in the logarithm (multiplication and division). The relative error in the logarithm, 4.63, when used in a calculation is 1 part in 463 or 2.2 p.p.t.

The accuracy of any analytical procedure can only be as good as the least accurate of the steps comprising the procedure. To illustrate this, consider the partition chromatographic separation of a mixture of metals. Assume we start with a 0.5 g solid sample. The single-pan balance can be read to ± 0.1 mg but two readings are necessary so that the error in the weight of the sample is ± 0.4 p.p.t. The sample is dissolved and made up to volume in a 250.0-ml volumetric flask. The uncertainty here is ± 0.1 ml, or 0.4 p.p.t. A 5.0-ml aliquot is taken with a pipette, which has a tolerance of 0.01 ml. The error in this step is 2.0 p.p.t. After separation has been effected, the metal ion is titrated with EDTA consuming about 40.0 ml of solution. The titration error is 0.5 p.p.t. Thus, in this procedure, the least accurate step is the measurement of the aliquot, so that the results will not be more accurate than 2 p.p.t.

PROBLEMS

1. What is the relative accuracy in parts per thousand of each of the following measurements?
   (a) 70 mg of dimethlglyoxime weighed to the nearest ± 0.2 mg?
   (b) A 20 ft chromatographic column measured to the nearest 1/8 in?
   (c) 2.00 ml of standard sodium hydroxide measured from a burette that is read to ± 0.02 ml?
   (d) An absorbance of 0.500 read to ± 0.005?
   (e) A pH of about 3 read on the meter to ± 0.01 pH unit?

2. Determine the relative accuracy in parts per thousand of each of the following results:
   (a) found: 3.87%   true: 4.36%
   (b) found: 1.192 mg   taken: 1.180 mg
   (c) found: 1.35 p.p.m. calculated: 1.24 p.p.m.
   (d) found: 99.9%   purity: 100.01%

3. How accurately must each of the following measurements be made in order to obtain the relative accuracy specified?
   (a) A balance scale read, in order to have a 1.0 p.p.t. error when weighing (two readings are necessary) out 0.100 g of zinc metal?

(b)   The meter needle of a spectrophotometer read, in order to have a 10 p.p.t. error when reading absorbances of around 0.90?

(c)   A burette read, to measure out 40 ml of solution with a 1.0 p.p.t. error?

(d)   A ruler read, when measuring a distance of about 60 cm that a solvent front has traveled, so as to be accurate within 5 p.p.t. ?

4.   For each of the following sets of data calculate: (a) the range, (b) the standard deviation, (c) the variance, (d) the relative standard deviation, and (e) the 95% confidence interval.

i	ii	iii
37.63 mg	0.00987 M	2.51%
37.31	0.00983	2.49
37.99	0.00993	2.42
	0.00990	2.50
		2.50

5.   (a)   During a colorimetric determination of iron with 1,10-phenanthroline, a student obtained the values 6.31 mg, 6.27 mg, and 6.28 mg. The true value (taken from the National Bureau of Standards analysis sheet) is 6.19 mg. Is the difference between the student's average for the amount of iron and the true amount of iron present meaningful or is it merely caused by chance?

(b)   Student 1 obtained 0.1111 N, 0.1109 N, 0.1113 N, 0.1112 N for the value of the normality of a solution of NaOH. Student 2, for the same solution, obtained the values 0.1107 N, 0.1103 N, 0.1105 N, 0.1106 N. Is there a real difference between the results of the two students?

(c)   What is the maximum standard deviation permitted at the 95% confidence level when the value of the percentage of copper in an alloy is to be determined in triplicate to within 0.02% of the correct value?

6.   Calculate the average value and the relative standard deviation for each of the following sets of data. Apply the Q test to the data where appropriate.

(a) K_a = 4.63 × 10^{-4}, 4.18 × 10^{-4}, 4.27 × 10^{-4}

(b) $pH_{\frac{1}{2}}$ = 6.41, 6.41, 6.47, 6.25

(c) R_f = 0.873, 0.861, 0.885, 0.858, 0.849

(d) M = 0.1003, 0.1004, 0.1003, 0.1008

(e) A = 0.4061, 0.4065, 0.4066, 0.4068, 0.4067, 0.4065, 0.4066

7.   (a)   The following data were obtained for the colorimetric determination of methylene blue. Calculate the values of m and b for the best straight line through these points.

Concentration, mg/ml	Absorbance
0.00125	0.076
0.00200	0.130
0.00500	0.300
0.01000	0.615

(b)   C. C. Templeton, *J. Chem. Eng. Data*, **5,** 514 (1960) gives solubility data for the solubility product of $BaSO_4$ in solutions of NaCl at 25°C. The following have been calculated from his data.

$\sqrt{\mu}$	log K_{sp}	$\sqrt{\mu}$	log K_{sp}
0.22	−9.04	0.63	−8.35
0.32	−8.81	0.78	−8.22
0.45	−8.57	0.89	−8.05

Plot these data and using the method of least squares draw the best straight line through the data points. What is the value for the solubility product constant of $BaSO_4$ at zero ionic strength?

8.   How many significant figures are there in each of the following numbers?
   (a)   4.7
   (b) 4.7×10^{-3}
   (c) 4.7×10^2
   (d)   6.506
   (e)   6.560
   (f)   0.0656
   (g)   56,600
   (h)   560.0605
   (i) 0.165×10^{-4}

9.   Perform the following arithmetical manipulation, expressing the result to the proper number of significant figures.

   (a)   6.731   (b)   0.00648   (c)   46.6312 g
         0.6731   0.00593   − 46.5899
      + 5.0   0.00028   ‾‾‾‾‾‾‾‾
      ‾‾‾‾‾‾‾   + 0.10649
                                  ‾‾‾‾‾‾‾‾

   (d) $17.463 - 6.71 \times 10^{-5} =$ (e) $2.13 \times 6.078 \times 5.89 =$
   (f) $1.2 \times 478.631 =$ (g) $\dfrac{6.4361}{0.284} =$
   (h) $\dfrac{0.687}{27.56} =$ (i) $[H^+] = 1.2 \times 10^{-8}$, pH $=$
   (j)   pM $= 11.3$, $[M^{n+}] =$

10.   Solve each of the following expressions, expressing the results to the correct number of significant figures.

   (a) $\dfrac{(0.4378 + 69.21)\,(4.21)}{173.68}$

   (b) $3.0 \times 10^{-5} = \dfrac{(3.79 \times 10^{-4})^2}{(4.783 \times 10^{-2} - x)}$

   (c) $x = \dfrac{-1.43 \times 10^{-2} + \sqrt{(1.43 \times 10^{-2})^2 + 4 \times 8.23 \times 10^{-6}}}{2}$

   (d) $E = +1.697 + \dfrac{0.0591}{2}\log\left[\dfrac{(6.3 \times 10^{-2})^2(1.43 \times 10^{-1})}{(2.523 \times 10^{-1})}\right]$

   (e)   capacity $= \dfrac{1.63 \text{ ml} \times 0.1068 \, N}{1.0473 \text{ g}}$

   (f) $\alpha_0 =$
   $$\dfrac{(4.683 \times 10^{-2})(1.2 \times 10^{-5})}{(3.15 \times 10^{-4})^2 + (4.683 \times 10^{-2})(3.15 \times 10^{-4}) + (4.683 \times 10^{-2})(1.2 \times 10^{-5})}$$

REFERENCES

1. Advisory Board of *Analytical Chemistry*, "Guide for Measures of Precision and Accuracy", *Anal. Chem.*, **44,** 2420 (1972).
2. Dean, R. B. and Dixon, W. J., *Anal. Chem.*, **23,** 637 (1951).
3. Gosset, W. S., *Biometrika*, **6,** 1 (1908).
4. Marshall, J. C., *Atomic Absorption Newsletter*, **8,** 85 (1969).

CHAPTER 5

CHEMICAL EQUILIBRIUM

EQUILIBRIUM CONSTANTS

For any chemical reaction that involves an equilibrium

$$nN + mM \rightleftharpoons pP + qQ \tag{5-1}$$

the following expression defines the equilibrium constant:

$$K_{eq} = \frac{a_P^p \times a_Q^q}{a_N^n \times a_M^m} \tag{5-2}$$

Equation (5–2) is an exact, thermodynamically meaningful expression that is valid under all conditions of temperature and pressure for all solutions, dilute or concentrated, ideal or regular, ionic or molecular. a is the *activity* of that species indicated by the subscript, where the activity of a species is a measure of its willingness to become involved in chemical reactions. For solutions, the activity of the solvent is defined as the ratio of the vapor pressure of the solvent in the solution under the experimental conditions to the vapor pressure of the pure solvent at one atmosphere pressure and the temperature of the solution; so that $a = p/p_0$. The activity of the solute is defined so that as the mole fraction of the solute in the solution approaches zero, the activity of the solute will approach the value of the mole fraction. In other words, the activity of a solute is the mole fraction of the solute in an infinitely dilute solution. Activity can be considered as a comparison between the behavior of the solute in a real solution and the behavior that the solute would exhibit in an ideal solution of the same composition of one molar concentration and at one atmosphere pressure. This is not very helpful for there is no such thing in reality as an ideal one molar solution.

For most purposes, the activity of a substance can be considered to be its reactive concentration. It is not the overall molar concentration of the species in solution, but rather the number of moles per liter of the species that appear to take part in a particular reaction. Activity differs from molar concentration because some ions or molecules in a solution are shielded by the other components,

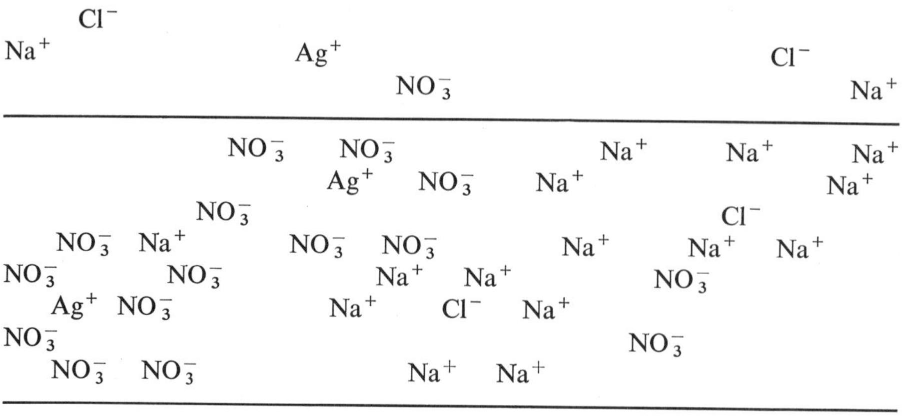

Cl^-

Na^+ Ag^+ Cl^-
                                    NO_3^- Na^+

                    NO_3^- NO_3^- Na^+ Na^+ Na^+
                    Ag^+ NO_3^- Na^+ Na^+
              NO_3^-
        NO_3^- Na^+ NO_3^- NO_3^- Na^+ Na^+ Na^+
NO_3^- NO_3^- Na^+ Na^+ NO_3^-
    Ag^+ NO_3^- Na^+ Cl^- Na^+
NO_3^- NO_3^-
    NO_3^- NO_3^- Na^+ Na^+

Fig. 5–1. Schematic representation of the reaction between $AgNO_3$ and NaCl: *Upper;* in very dilute solution; *Lower;* in a moderately concentrated solution.

and hence "don't know" they should be reacting. Electrostatic attractions between oppositely charged ions or dipoles cause a sphere or atmosphere of oppositely charged particles to grow and exist around every solute particle. Safely encapsulated in this protective shield of particles, the solute particle is unaware of events taking place in the rest of the solution. Even when a particle does try to become involved, the ionic crowd holds it back, so that its behavior is restricted and not what it would be if left alone. Figure 5–1 is a drawing of this condition for the reaction between NaCl and $AgNO_3$ to precipitate AgCl. In the upper portion of the drawing, for an extremely dilute solution, there is nothing to hinder the silver ions from finding a chloride ion and precipitating as silver chloride. The sodium and nitrate ions are very scarce. So, in dilute solutions the activity of the solute is identical to the molar concentration of the ions. In the lower drawing, for a moderately concentrated solution, conditions are more crowded. Here, each silver ion has a group of negatively charged ions surrounding it and each chloride ion has a cloud of positively charged ions around it. And there are many, many more ions in the solution. After all, 1 ml of 0.1 M Na^+Cl^- contains 1.2×10^{20} ions. Thus it is quite probable that some of the silver and some of the chloride ions will escape reaction; they will be unaware a reaction is going on because of their protection by the ions around them.

The activity of a solute in a given medium can be measured by freezing point depressions, solubilities, electrode potentials, and other means. These measurements are not easy to make and in most cases require extra time and equipment. Unless you are interested in studying an equilibrium from a physical chemist's approach, activity measurements distract from the main purpose of the experiment. Consequently, it would be convenient to be able to calculate activities from molar concentrations. At first this would appear to be a simple matter, for the following relationship between activity and concentration is well-known:

$$a = fC \qquad (5\text{–}3)$$

where f is called the *activity coefficient* of the species. Unfortunately, the activity coefficient is literally defined as the number by which the molar concentration must be multiplied in order to obtain the activity. Thus, in effect the problem is not solved, merely transferred to the activity coefficient.

Nevertheless, for each species in Equation (5–2) we can substitute the relationship between activity and molar concentration given by Equation (5–3).

$$K_{eq} = \frac{f_P^p \times f_Q^q}{f_N^n \times f_M^m} \times \frac{[P]^p \times [Q]^q}{[N]^n \times [M]^m} \tag{5-4}$$

Equation (5–4) is also a rigorous thermodynamic expression holding under all conditions.

Activity Coefficients

The difference between the activity of an ion and its molar concentration is caused by electrostatic interactions. The magnitude of this difference can be deduced from the number of electric charges in the solution and the strength of their interactions. In 1923, P. Debye and E. Hückel created the *ion atmosphere* concept of solutions, which is depicted in Fig. 5–1. Using this model, they estimated the energy of an ion at the center of the crowd and the long range interactions among ions in solution. They developed a mathematical relationship between activity coefficients and the numbers of charges present in a solution,

$$\log f_i = \frac{-Z_i^2 A \sqrt{\mu}}{1 + B a^\circ \sqrt{\mu}} \tag{5-5}$$

where Z_i is the charge on the ion, μ is the ionic strength of the solution, and f_i is the activity coefficient of the ion under consideration. A is a constant that includes Avogadro's number, the charge on the electron, the Boltzmann distribution constant, the dielectric constant of the solvent, and the temperature. For aqueous solutions at 25°C, A is 0.511. B is also a constant that includes all of the above factors, but in a different arrangement. For aqueous solutions at 25°C, $B = 3.29 \times 10^7$. a° is the distance of closest approach, in Ångstroms, of the ions—one measure of the diameter of an ion.

The ionic strength is a measure of the concentrations of electric charges in a solution.

$$\mu = \tfrac{1}{2} \sum_i [i] \, Z_i^2 \tag{5-6}$$

In Equation (5–6), i stands for any ion in the solution and the summation is over all of the cations and anions present.

Equation (5–5) enables the calculation of the activity coefficient of any one type of ion. The activity coefficient for a single ion cannot be measured experimentally for it is impossible to obtain a solution containing ions of only one charge. Only the mean activity coefficient for a pair of oppositely charged ions can be measured. This is called just that: the *mean ionic activity coefficient* for a salt and given the symbol $f_\pm$. It is defined as:

$$f_\pm^{(x+y)} = f_+^x \cdot f_-^y \tag{5-7}$$

where x and y are the number of ions of each charge in the salt. Thus for Na^+Cl^-, $f_\pm^2 = f_{Na^+} \cdot f_{Cl^-}$; whereas for $Al_2(SO_4)_3, f_\pm^5 = f_{Al^{3+}}^2 \cdot f_{SO_4^{2-}}^3$. Rewriting the Debye-Hückel equation of Equation (5–5) for calculating the mean ionic activity coefficient:

$$\log f_\pm = -\frac{|Z_+ Z_-| A \sqrt{\mu}}{1 + Ba^\circ \sqrt{u}} \tag{5-8}$$

In deriving Equations (5–5) and (5–8) Debye and Hückel assumed: (1) all ions in the solution have the same average diameter; (2) the bulk dielectric constant can be applied anywhere throughout the solution; (3) the cloud of counter-ions surrounding an ion is spherical; and (4) only long range electrostatic interactions occur between the ions. Consequently, Equations (5–5) and (5–8) can only be used under conditions where these assumptions are true. For extremely dilute solutions, calculated and experimentally measured mean ionic activity coefficients agree very well. For most of the solutions used in analytical chemistry the assumptions are no longer valid. In practice, it is found that even at $\mu = 0.001$ M Equation (5–8) gives values that differ from the measured $f_\pm$ values. Table 5–1 compares the measured and calculated values of the mean ionic acitivity coefficient for Na^+Cl^- at 25°C.

The problem of explaining and calculating activity coefficients for solutions more concentrated than 0.001 M has challenged physical chemists for many years and several different relationships have been derived to solve the problem. Most of them are limited to restricted circumstances. Perhaps the most useful equation is merely a modification of the Debye-Hückel equation that was proposed in 1938 by C. W. Davies:

$$\log f_\pm = -\frac{|Z_+ Z_-| A \sqrt{\mu}}{1 + \sqrt{\mu}} + 0.15 |Z_+ Z_-| \mu \tag{5-9}$$

By using 1 as the coefficient of the square root of the ionic strength in the denominator of Equation (5–9), that is $Ba^\circ = 1.00$, Davies assigned a distance of closest approach of 3.04 Å for all ions in all solutions. Equation (5–9) is applicable for

Table 5–1. OBSERVED AND CALCULATED ACTIVITY COEFFICIENTS FOR NaCl
AT 25°C

| | | Mean Ionic Activity Coefficient | |
| | | Calculated | Calculated |
Molality	Measured	by Debye-Hückel Equation	by Davies Equation
0.001	0.9650	0.9645	0.9649
0.005	0.9275	0.9251	0.9268
0.010	0.9022	0.8985	0.9016
0.05	0.8205	0.8067	0.8207
0.10	0.7813	0.7539	0.7804

SOURCE: Ref. 20.

Table 5–2. ACTIVITY COEFFICIENTS AND ACTIVITIES AT 25°C

Substance	Molality	Mean Ionic Molal Activity Coefficient	Activity
HCl	0.001	0.966	0.000966
	0.010	0.905	0.00905
	0.100	0.796	0.0796
	1.00	0.809	0.809
	5.00	2.38	11.90
H_2SO_4	0.001	0.830	0.000830
	0.010	0.544	0.00544
	0.100	0.266	0.0266
	1.00	0.132	0.132
	5.00	0.208	1.04
$LaCl_3$	0.001	0.790	0.000790
	0.010	0.560	0.00560
	0.100	0.314	0.0314
	1.00	0.342	0.342
	2.00	0.825	1.650
$Th(NO_3)_4$	0.10	0.279	0.0279
	1.00	0.207	0.207
	5.00	0.791	3.96

calculating the mean ionic activity coefficients for all electrolytes up to an ionic strength of 0.2 M. It can also be used for calculating individual activity coefficients for ions, although in this case there is no way to check its accuracy. This modification by Davies gives much better values for $f_\pm$ than does the Debye-Hückel equation, as Table 5–1 shows for Na^+Cl^-

Table 5–2 lists some values of measured activity coefficients and activities for selected electrolytes at several concentrations. Fig. 5–2 shows graphically the variation of the mean ionic activity coefficient for typical 1:1, 1:2, 1:3, and 1:4 electrolytes with ionic strength. Notice that for all these electrolytes the value of the activity coefficient at 0.001 M already is less than one, that is the activity of the ions is less than the molar concentration of them. The activity coefficient decreases as the concentration of a salt increases. The extent of this decrease depends upon the identity of the electrolyte. Fig. 5–2 shows that at equal molar concentrations the decrease follows the order 1:1 < 1:2 < 1:3 < 1:4. It is important to realize that the difference between activity and molarity of a salt can be enormous, especially when dealing with moderately concentrated solutions of highly charged electrolytes. $f_\pm$ for $Cu^{2+}SO_4^{2-}$ is only 0.150 in a 0.10 M solution! Or, to put it more forcefully, the activity of 0.10 M $Cu^{2+}SO_4^{2-}$ is only 0.015 M! The value of the activity coefficient decreases to a minimum, after which, as the concentration increases further, the activity coefficient begins to increase. In concentrated solutions (>5 M) the activity coefficient often becomes greater than one because the solvent activity no longer can be assumed to be one. Notice in Table 5–1 that for 5 M HCl $f_\pm$ is 2.38.

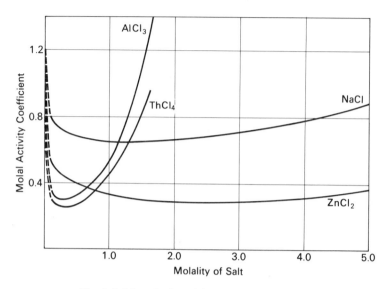

Fig. 5–2. Mean ionic activity coefficients at 25°C.

The interpretation of these changes in activity coefficients with increasing ion concentration, and the cause of the differences in behavior of activity coefficients for different salts of the same charge type (for example, 1:1) are crucial to any theory of strong electrolyte solutions. Activity and activity coefficients still are not explained too satisfactorily for concentrated solutions.

Example.   Using the Davies modification of the Debye-Hückel equation, calculate the mean ionic activity coefficient for $AlCl_3$ in $0.100\ M\ AlCl_3$.

First the ionic strength of the solution must be calculated.

$$\mu = \tfrac{1}{2}\{[Al^{3+}](3)^2\} + \tfrac{1}{2}\{[Cl^-](1)^2\}$$

$$= \tfrac{1}{2}\{(0.10)(9)\} + \tfrac{1}{2}\{(0.30)(1)\} = \tfrac{1}{2}(1.20) = 0.60\ M$$

Then this and the other values can be substituted into the Davies Equation, recalling that for aqueous solutions at 25°C, A is 0.511.

$$\log f_\pm = -\frac{0.511(3)(1)\sqrt{0.60}}{1 + \sqrt{0.60}} + 0.15(3)(1)(0.060)$$

$$= -\frac{1.19}{1.78} + 0.27 = -0.40$$

Taking the antilogarithm of this gives $f_\pm = 0.40$. From this coefficient and the molarity of the $AlCl_3$ the activity is found to be:

$$a_{AlCl_3} = 0.40 \times 0.10\ M = 0.040\ M$$

It is interesting to note that the measured value[20] of $f_\pm$ for $AlCl_3$ is 0.34 in a 0.10 M solution.

It is customary, when performing chemical equlibrium calculations to try to simplify the arithmetic involved. Ion activities or activity coefficients are not readily available for a broad enough spectrum of solutions to be used routinely in place of molar concentrations in equilibrium calculations. Thus attempts to use Equations (5–2) and (5–4) can be very frustrating. When the measured activities are not available, approximations of the activities may be calculated by means of Equations (5–3) and (5–9). These calculations are very tedious and complicate the simplicity of the equilibrium calculations. It is, therefore, very tempting to ignore the first term in Equation (5–4) containing the activity coefficients. This amounts to assuming that this quotient is unity. If one succumbs to this temptation, the equilibrium constant can be expressed in terms of molar concentrations. The numerical difference between the equilibrium constant of Equation (5–4) with and without inclusion of the activity coefficient quotient is readily calculated. The constant as expressed by Equation (5–2) is called the *thermodynamic equilibrium constant* and given the symbol, **K**. The constant expressed by Equation (5–4) with the activity coefficient quotient unity is called the *molar concentration equilibrium* constant and is given the symbol k. For accurate equilibrium calculations, the thermodynamic equilibrium constant should be used. Because activities are difficult to translate into molar concentrations (which are the concentration terms the laboratory chemist normally employs), the molar concentration constant usually replaces the thermodynamic one in routine calculations. The numerical error involved in using k for **K** invariably leads to incorrect answers for real solutions.

From the chemical reaction, the ionic strength of the solution, and Equations (5–4) and (5–9), the correct value of the molar concentration equilibrium constant to be used at the specified ionic strength can be calculated. This will eliminate the error discussed in the preceding paragraph. To illustrate the method of doing this, let us consider the dissociation of phosphoric acid into three protons and the phosphate ion:

$$H_3PO_4 \rightleftharpoons 3H^+ + PO_4^{3-}$$

The thermodynamic equilibrium constant expression for this ionization is:

$$\mathbf{K}_a = \frac{a_{H^+}^3 \cdot a_{PO_4^{3-}}}{a_{H_3PO_4}} = \frac{f_{H^+}^3 \cdot f_{PO_4^{3-}}}{f_{H_3PO_4}} \times \frac{[H^+]^3 \, [PO_4{}^{3-}]}{[H_3PO_4]}$$

whereas the molar concentration equilibrium constant is:

$$k_a = \frac{[H^+]^3 \, [PO_4{}^{3-}]}{[H_3PO_4]}$$

Substituting the value for the molar concentration constant into the expression for the activity constant gives:

$$\mathbf{K}_a = k_a \frac{f_{H^+}^3 \cdot f_{PO_4^{3-}}}{f_{H_3PO_4}}$$

Rearranging this expression and taking the logarithm of both sides of it

$$\log k_a = \log K_a + \log f_{H_3PO_4} - 3\log f_{H+} - \log f_{PO_4^{3-}}$$

To go one step further and express this difference in terms of the ionic strength, the Davies equation is substituted for each of the activity coefficients terms. In general, molecular species are not affected by long range electrostatic forces from charged particles. Thus for uncharged solutes, $f = 1$ or $\log f = 0$. Thus in the above expression, $\log f_{H_3PO_4} = 0$. For the other activity coefficients:

$$\log f_{H+} = -\frac{0.511\,(1)^2\,\sqrt{\mu}}{1 + \sqrt{\mu}} + 0.15\,(1)^2\,\mu$$

$$= -\frac{0.511\,\sqrt{\mu}}{1 + \sqrt{\mu}} + 0.15\,\mu$$

$$\log f_{PO_4^{3-}} = -\frac{0.511\,(3)^2\,\sqrt{\mu}}{1 + \sqrt{\mu}} + 0.15\,(3)^2\,\mu$$

$$= -\frac{4.60\,\sqrt{\mu}}{1 + \sqrt{\mu}} + 1.35\,\mu$$

Substituting all of these activity coefficient relationships into the equation for k_a:

$$\log k_a = \log K_a + 0 - 3\left(-\frac{0.511\,\sqrt{\mu}}{1 + \sqrt{\mu}} + 0.15\,\mu\right) - \left(-\frac{4.60\,\sqrt{\mu}}{1 + \sqrt{\mu}} + 1.35\,\mu\right)$$

$$= \log K_a + \frac{6.13\,\sqrt{\mu}}{1 + \sqrt{\mu}} - 1.80\,\mu$$

Thus, when the ionic strength of a solution of phosphoric acid is known, the concentration equilibrium constant applicable to that solution can be calculated from the thermodynamic equilibrium constant that is usually tabulated in books. Let us assume that we have a phosphoric acid solution with an ionic strength of 0.100 M. From Appendix 1, $K_a = 1.81 \times 10^{-22}$. Thus for our solution

$$\log k_a = -21.743 + \frac{6.13\,(1.00 \times 10^{-1})^{\frac{1}{2}}}{1 + (1.00 \times 10^{-1})^{\frac{1}{2}}} - 1.80\,(1.00 \times 10^{-1})$$

$$= -21.743 + 1.470 - 0.180 = -20.453$$

$$k_a = 3.53 \times 10^{-21}$$

which is roughly twenty times larger than K.

The relationship can be worked out between the molar concentration equilibrium constant and the activity equilibrium constant for any equilibrium in terms of ionic strength.

The application of ionic strength corrections is the correct and rigorous method to take into account the differences between activities and molar concentrations. The only error involved lies in the use of the Davies equation. The technique is cumbersome and for many beginning students hopelessly confusing. It serves as a serious distraction from an understanding of the application of equilibrium principles. So, in order to avoid this complication, and yet realizing that we do know how to adjust the numerical values of the constants for the ionic strength of the solutions, let us proceed to neglect the correction factor. It is convenient to do this, and the results obtained by the incorrect calculations are adequate for most routine purposes. Naturally, the lower the ionic strength of the solutions, the more accurate the results will be. Neglecting the activity coefficient will certainly not be an accurate procedure for solutions more concentrated than about $0.01M$. Nevertheless, incorrect as it may be, let us for all future work in this book, assume that the solutions are sufficiently dilute that the activity coefficient quotient in Equation (5–4) is unity. Then we will rewrite and use Equation (5–4) in its approximate form:

$$\mathbf{K}_{eq} \cong k_{eq} = \frac{[P]^p \, [Q]^q}{[N]^n \, [M]^m} \tag{5–10}$$

The assumption that the activity coefficient quotient is one holds best when the long range electrostatic forces are at a minimum. This means that the electrical charges in the solution should be at a minimum. Equation (5–10) will give the most accurate numerical results when:

1. The solutions are dilute. Notice from Table 5–2 and Fig. 5–2 that the activity coefficients tend toward one as the molar concentrations decrease.
2. The ions present in solution are univalent. Note from Table 5–2 and Fig. 5–2 that the value of the activity coefficient, at any concentration, decreases in the sequence: monavalent > divalent > trivalent ions.
3. The ionization is simple. Thus Equation (5–10) will apply more rigorously for a weak acid such as acetic acid that can only ionize into two ions, than it will for ethylenediaminetetraacetic acid which ionizes into five ions, one of which is tetravalent.

Temperature Effects

Equilibrium constants are temperature dependent. An increase in the temperature of the system will displace the position of the equilibrium in the system toward that direction which absorbs heat. In other words, when the reaction is endothermic, the equilibrium constant increases with increasing temperature; and when it is, exothermic, the equilibrium constant decreases with increasing temperature. The magnitude of the change will depend upon the heat of the reaction for the particular system. Without knowing the heat of reaction, one cannot predict whether an equilibrium constant will increase or decrease with temperature. It is safe to say that errors will be introduced unless the constant appropriate for that temperature is used. Table 5–3 gives the values for selected equilibrium constants at different temperatures.

Pressure Effects

The external pressure will also change the equilibrium position in a system and hence the numerical value of the equilibrium constant. For ionic equilibria in

Table 5–3. EFFECT OF TEMPERATURE ON EQUILIBRIUM CONSTANTS

Species	Type of Equilibrium Constant	T, °C	Value of K
H_2O	K_w	0	1.11×10^{-15}
		25	1.00×10^{-14}
		50	5.46×10^{-14}
		100	5.51×10^{-13}
CH_3COOH	K_a	0	1.657×10^{-5}
		25	1.754×10^{-5}
		50	1.633×10^{-5}
NH_3	K_b	0	1.20×10^{-4}
		25	1.76×10^{-5}
		50	3.46×10^{-6}
$AgCl$	K_{sp}	5	2.6×10^{-11}
		25	1.8×10^{-10}
		55	2.1×10^{-9}
$Ag(NH_3)_2^+$	K_{st}	0	$5.9 \times 10^{+7}$
		25	$1.1 \times 10^{+7}$
		52	$1.4 \times 10^{+6}$

SOURCE: Ref. 21.

solution, the change in the solution volume with increasing pressure is negligibly small, and the slight changes in atmospheric pressure normally encountered in the laboratory will not cause a noticeable change in the numerical value of an equilibrium constant. When working at very high pressures or at very low pressures, changes in the equilibrium constant from the value at one atmosphere should be investigated.

The expression for the activity equilibrium constant is rigorous and can be applied to all solution equilibria. The approximation of this, as given by Equation (5–10) must be used judiciously. The technique of applying these expressions is the same, however, regardless of the nature of the equilibrium reaction being studied. All equilibrium reactions involve the same concepts, and the numerical solution of problems involving the equilibrium constant usually contains the same kinds of assumptions and mathematical manipulations. Once the general technique has been mastered, all applications of the equilibrium constant follow smoothly and readily. There are certain techniques and principles that have been found to be very useful in solving equilibrium constant problems, so now let us look at the general procedure for solving problems involving equilibria to see what the method, the principles, the assumptions, and the mathematics, as well as the precautions, are.

GENERAL PROCEDURE FOR SOLVING EQUILIBRIUM PROBLEMS

There are two concepts that have proven to be very useful and fruitful when discussing equilibrium in ionizing solutions. While at first it may seem that the use of these two concepts is complex, making easy problems difficult, once they are mastered complicated problems become much simpler and more understandable. The best way to learn these concepts is to apply them to conditions that are known and easy to comprehend, even though there are intuitive ways to obtain the same relationships in simple solutions.

The Electroneutrality Principle

The first of the two concepts is a very simple one to grasp, namely the fact that the net electrical charge in all solutions of electrolytes must always be zero. This is dignified by the ostentatious title of *the electroneutrality principle*. All that this says is that the sum of all the positive charges in a solution must be equal to the sum of all the negative charges in the solution. Let us express this in terms of moles of electrical charges—the sum of the molar concentrations of all the positive charges in the solution must be equal to the sum of the molar concentrations of all the negative charges in a solution. As you know, electrical charges exist in solutions on the ions present. So, in order to count charges, you have to count ions. The best way to organize the bookkeeping of charges in any solution is in terms of the molar concentration of each of the ions bearing the charges. This sounds simple enough, and in general, it is. The important thing to remember is that it is electrical charges that are being accounted for and that the molar concentrations of the ions are merely the counting units used. Thus, a Na^+ ion has only one charge so that counting one ion gives the correct number of charges. But a Ba^{2+} ion, or a SO_4^{2-} ion has two charges so that in order to obtain the correct number of electric charges by counting ions, the number of ions must be multiplied by the charge on each ion. Thus a 0.10 M $MgSO_4$ solution is 0.2 M in positive charges and also 0.2 M in negative charges. Remember that in this bookkeeping system, neutral, uncharged species are not counted.

In formulating the electroneutrality principle expression for any solution, all that is done is to count the number of positive charges (in molar concentration) and equate this to the number of negative charges (also in molar concentration). The concentration of charges is the number of moles of any ion present multiplied by the charge on that ion. Thus the electroneutrality principle formulation for 0.02 M Na_2SO_4 is:

$$[Na^+] = 2]SO_4^{2-}]$$

where the SO_4^{2-} concentration is multiplied by two because there are two charges on each ion and it is the charges that are being counted. In this example, the correctness of this expression can be perceived intuitively, since each mole of salt that dissolves yields two Na^+ but only one SO_4^{2-}. To check the validity of the expression written, insert the concentrations, when known, and prove the equality. The molar concentration of sodium ions in this solution is 0.04 M, since each molecule of Na_2SO_4 ionizes into two Na^+ ions. The molar concentration of sulfate ions is the same as the molar concentration of dissolved salt, 0.02 M. Thus the numerical expression of the electroneutrality principle becomes:

$$0.04 = 2(0.02 \; M)$$

which, of course, is a valid statement.

Example. State the electroneutrality principle for a solution containing 0.1 M $HClO_4$, 0.10 M HCl, and 0.2 M $Mg(ClO_4)_2$.

This can be written as:

$$[H^+] + 2[Mg^{2+}] = [Cl^-] + [ClO_4^-]$$

Each concentration term represents the total concentration of that ion in the solution. Substitute the numerical values of the concentrations to check whether the above expression is correct. The hydrogen ion concentration in the solution is 0.2 M; 0.1 M of it coming from the perchloric acid and 0.10 M of it from the HCl. The magnesium ion concentration is 0.2 M, all from the magnesium perchlorate. The chloride ion concentration is 0.10 M, from the HCl only. The perchlorate ion concentration is 0.50 M; 0.10 M coming from the perchloric acid and 0.4 M coming from the magnesium perchlorate. Substituting the numbers into the above equation:

$$0.20 \; M + 2(0.20 \; M) = 0.10 \; M + (0.50 \; M)$$

or

$$0.60 \; M = 0.60 \; M$$

This appears to be simple, and in practice it is.

Example. Write the electroneutrality principle for a solution that is 0.10 M in acetic acid and 0.10 M in potassium acetate.

This can be written:

$$[H^+] + [K^+] = [OAc^-]$$

The acetic acid molecules are not counted since they contain no charges. You cannot substitute the concentrations into this expression to validate it because the concentrations are not known yet. The concentration of hydrogen ions in the solution is unknown because the extent of dissociation of acetic acid has not been found yet. For the same reason, the concentration of the acetate ions is unknown. All that is known, since potassium acetate, a strong electrolyte, dissociates completely, is that the concentration of potassium ions is 0.10 M. Substituting this into the electroneutrality principle expression gives:

$$[H^+] + 0.10 \; M = [OAc^-]$$

which turns out to be a very useful relationship when solving equilibrium constant equations.

The Material Balance

The second useful concept in solving equilibrium problems is called the *material balance*. The material balance is an extremely necessary process to carry out on any system that involves a chemical reaction. In fact, most chemists perform this operation, consciously or unconsciously, when discussing the quantitative aspects of chemical reactions. All that the material balance involves is accounting for the chemical in the solution; the amount of chemical added must be equal to the amount of it that has not reacted plus the amount of it that has undergone reaction. One thing that bothers most students when first attempting to use the material balance is deciding what chemical to carry out a material balance on. The solution to this question is simple—whatever you want to do it on. You choose. Of course, it is more fruitful to carry out an accounting of materials for a substance that is involved in the reactions being discussed, but it is not wrong to do it on anything else. Let's clarify the use of the material balance by means of an example.

Example.   Write the material balance expression for a 0.10 M acetate acid solution.

First of all, it should be realized that what this means is—account for all of the acetate in the solution. Of course, it could also mean—account for all the protons in the solution. Use the symbol C to represent the analytical or total concentration of a substance in a solution without regard to the actual forms that it manifests itself in the solution. When we do that, $C_{acetate} = 0.1\ M$. In the solution, however, some of the acetic acid molecules will ionize. All of the acetate in this solution exists either in the form of acetic acid molecules or in the form of acetate ions. This is a verbal statement of the material balance expression; written in terms of molar concentration:

$$C_{acetate} = [\text{acetic acid molecules}] + [\text{acetate ions}]$$

The material balance for the protons of acetic acid would lead to a similar expression, for the protons are either bound in acetic acid molecules or they are ionized. This gives us:

$$C_{protons} = [\text{acetic acid molecules}] + [H^+]$$

Why do we bother doing this? Not only does it help in understanding what is actually present in the solution, it provides another equation containing unknown molar concentrations of species. Quite frequently, when dealing with complex equilibrium problems, one needs many equations.

Example. Write the material balance expression for a 0.10 M CuSO$_4$ solution that is also 0.8 M in NH$_3$ and has a pH of 4.0.

First, we have to decide what chemical to perform a material balance on. Nothing in the problem gives us any ideas, so let's do it on several things, just to show that it is possible. Often, it is also necessary. In order to carry out the material balance you must know what is going on in the solution. What is the chemistry taking place in this solution? Ammonia molecules react with the protons to form ammonium ions

$$NH_3 + H^+ \rightleftharpoons NH_4^+$$

Ammonia molecules also react with the copper ions to form the copper tetraammine complex ion

$$Cu(H_2O)_4^{2+} + 4NH_3 \rightleftharpoons Cu(NH_3)_4^{2+} + 4H_2O$$

Now that we know the chemistry we can perform a material balance. Let us account for the copper first, just because it is simpler. The total amount of copper in the solution, C_{Cu}, is 0.10 M. From the above reaction we can see that the copper exists either as the aquo complex or as the tetraammine complex. So the material balance is:

$$C_{Cu} = [Cu(H_2O)_4^{2+}] + [Cu(NH_3)_4^{2+}] = 0.10 \ M$$

Let us account for the ammonia. In the solution, $C_{NH_3} = 0.8 \ M$. According to the two reactions above, the ammonia exists as the free molecules or as the ammonium ion or in the copper tetraammine complex.

$$C_{NH_3} = [NH_3] + [NH_4^+] + 4[Cu(NH_3)_2^{2+}]$$

The concentration of the copper complex is multiplied by four since we are attempting to account for the ammonia. There are four times as many moles of ammonia tied up in the complex as there are moles of complex.

Most of the time the material balance expression cannot be checked by introducing numerical values. One or several of the concentrations included in the material balance are also included in the equilibrium expressions that we are trying to solve, so the molar concentration of these species is unknown initially. However, upon completion of the problem, the numerical values for all the concentrations are known. At this time it is possible and a good practice, to substitute the concentrations into all material balance expressions to validate them.

Outline of Technique for Solving Equilibrium Problems

To attack an equilibrium problem blindly is frustrating. To consider each and every equilibrium problem as a new and different challenge is exhausting. There is a successful, sensible approach that can be used to solve any equilibrium problem, no matter how complex the problem may be, and no matter what kind of equilibrium is involved. Naturally, this approach contains very general steps involving the use of general principles. The approach is:

1. Write balanced chemical reactions for all equilibria involved in the problem.

    This is absolutely essential, for it ensures that you know what chemistry is going on in the problem. The major reason that students make mistakes in solving equilibrium problems is that they do not understand the chemistry involved in the problem—the technique of solving the equations, the algebra required, are usually relatively simple and present no problems. Since students usually do not have an encyclopedic knowledge of chemical reactions, the best way to find out the chemistry required is to look it up or ask someone who does know.

2. Write the equilibrium constant expressions for all of the equilibrium reactions involved in the problem and written out in step (1).

3. Decide which of the terms the equilibrium constant expression(s) must be solved for, in order to obtain the answer requested in the problem.

    Frequently a problem asks for a percentage, a weight of a solid, a volume of solution, or a pH; quantities not contained explicitly in the equilibrium constant expression(s). When this is the case, selection of the correct term to solve for is more difficult. Do not select your unknown at random. Use logic. Select as the unknown, that term which will lead simply and directly to the desired information. Pick the term that will contain the information required. If the problem asks for the pH of a solution, don't solve the equilibrium constant for chloride ion concentration! A little thought in this step will save a lot of time, effort, and frustration later on.

4. Find numerical values and/or concentration interrelationships for all other terms in the equilibrium constant expression(s).

    Having decided in the previous step what the unknown will be, nothing else can be unknown. Here is where the electroneutrality principle and the material balance have proven invaluable. When you substitute numbers and relationships into the equilibrium constant equations there should be only one unknown—the one decided on in step (3).

5. Make simplifying assumptions.

    Quite frequently at this point the resultant expression is very complicated. The mathematics are almost always soluble, but not conveniently. Unless there are compelling reasons for solving equilibrium constant expressions rigorously, simplify things by making some assumptions. The errors about activities involved in going from Equation (5–4) to Equation (5–10) often are larger than errors created by making assumptions to obtain a simplified mathematical solution to a complex equilibrium expression. The particular assumptions used will depend largely upon the chemistry of the problem and the magnitude of the numbers. General types of assumptions most frequently used are:

    (a) One of the reactions involved really doesn't go sufficiently far to completion to be worth worrying about (or *vice versa*; the reaction goes so far to completion that it isn't worth worrying about the amount not reacted).

    (b) One of the concentrations, in relation to another concentration in the the solution, is negligibly small. It may not be small in the absolute sense, but when compared to the concentration from which it is to be subtracted, it can be neglected. Use a little chemical intuition, common sense, and experience in deciding upon assumptions. After these assumptions have been made, higher-order algebraic equations become simple expressions that can be solved quickly.

6. Solve the equations for the unknown.

7. Check all of the assumptions that were made in step (5) to see if they were valid.

    Now that the numbers are available, it is easy enough to determine whether the reaction really does take place to any appreciable extent and whether that concentration really is negligibly small. When the assumptions are not valid, go back and resolve the equations excluding the poor assumptions, but retaining those that are valid. In the long run it is easier, faster and more efficient to solve the approximate expressions involving assumptions and then go back and resolve more exactly. Most assumptions, if made intelligently, are valid most of the time.

8. Continue working with the number obtained in step (7) to get the answer asked for by the problem.

Let us illustrate this procedure with an example.

Example. What weight of solid NaOH must be added to 375 ml of 0.0825 M propionic acid to obtain a solution having a pH of 5.00?

1. The sodium hydroxide added to the solution is neutralizing some, but not all of the propionic acid, thus decreasing the hydrogen ion concentration. The chemical reaction for this neutralization is:

$$Na^+OH^- + CH_3CH_2COOH \rightleftharpoons CH_3CH_2COO^-Na^+ + H_2O \tag{1}$$

Propionic acid is a weak acid, so that some of the unneutralized acid remaining will dissociate according to the reaction:

$$CH_3CH_2COOH + H_2O \rightleftharpoons CH_3CH_2COO^- + H_3O^+ \tag{2}$$

For convenience, let us symbolize propionic acid, HPr, and the propionate anion, Pr$^-$.

2. The major equilibrium present in the solution is the acid dissociation of propionic acid according to reaction (2). (While water will dissociate also into H$^+$ and OH$^-$, the extent is so slight in this solution that it can be neglected.) The equilibrium constant expression for reaction (2) is:

$$K_a = \frac{[H_3O^+][Pr^-]}{[HPr]} = 1.336 \times 10^{-5}$$

3. None of the terms in the equilibrium constant expression is what was asked for in the problem. The problem wants a weight of sodium hydroxide. Referring back to reaction (1), it can be seen that for every mole of NaOH that reacts, a mole of propionic acid is consumed and a mole of propionate anion is produced. Thus, except for the slight amount of propionate also produced from the dissociation reaction (2), the concentration of propionate in the solution represents the amount of NaOH added. Solve the equilibrium constant expression for [Pr$^-$]. [H$_3$O$^+$] is given so there is no sense in solving for it. Solving for [HPr] becomes much too complicated and indirect to be of practical value.

4. Write the electroneutrality principle expression for the solution at equilibrium. Refer to reactions (1) and (2) in order to do this.

$$[Na^+]+[H_3O^+]=[CH_3CH_2COO^-]+[OH^-]$$

From the statement of the problem, it is known that [H$_3$O$^+$] $= 1.00 \times 10^{-5}$ M. Since the solution has a pH of 5.00, the [OH$^-$] $= 1.00 \times 10^{-9}$ M, which is small enough to neglect in our calculation. [Na$^+$] will depend upon how much NaOH is added, and it really is the answer to the problem. Thus:

$$[Na^+]=[CH_3CH_2COO^-]-1.00 \times 10^{-5}$$

Write the material balance for all the propionate in the solution.

$$C_{Pr}=[HPr]+[Pr^-]=0.0825 \ M$$

While we know that the initial amount of propionic acid was 0.0825 M, at equilibrium we do not know how many moles of it have been neturalized and how much of the rest is ionized.

Rearranging the material balance:

$$[HPr] = 0.0825 - [Pr^-]$$

Now we have expressions or numbers for all of the terms in the equilibrium constant expression, except our unknown, the propionate ion concentration. Substituting them in:

$$1.336 \times 10^{-5} = \frac{(1.00 \times 10^{-5})([Pr^-])}{(0.0825M - [Pr^-])}$$

5. There is no reason to make any assumptions. The expression is simple and readily solved.

6. $$1.10 \times 10^{-8} - 1.336 \times 10^{-5}[Pr^-] = 1.00 \times 10^{-5}[Pr^-]$$

$$[Pr^-] = \frac{1.10 \times 10^{-8}}{2.336 \times 10^{-5}} = 4.72 \times 10^{-2}M$$

7. A comparison of the concentration of propionate ion in the solution at equilibrium with the initial amount of propionic acid, C_{Pr}, shows that we were wise not to have made any assumptions. $[Pr^-]$ is more than half of C_{Pr}. Insertion of the value for the propionate ion concentration along with the hydrogen ion concentration into the electroneutrality expression proves that the original assumption—the extent of dissociation of propionic acid at equilibrium is negligible—was a valid one. $[Na^+] = 4.72 \times 10^{-2} M - 1.00 \times 10^{-5} = 4.72 \times 10^{-2} M$.

8. Neither the propionate ion concentration nor the sodium ion concentration is the answer to the problem. Since the only source of sodium ions in the solution is from the added sodium hydroxide, this concentration can be used to determine how much base was added.

weight of NaOH added $= [Na^+]$ (solution volume) (mol wt NaOH)
$$= 4.72 \times 10^{-2} M \times 0.375\ 1 \times 40.0\ g/mol$$
$$= 0.708\ g$$

This is the answer that the problem requested.

This series of steps will be used throughout the rest of this book to solve equilibrium problems. Adjustments will be necessary occasionally in some problems.

The general concepts of chemical equilibrium and the details of solving equilibrium problems are applicable to all equilibria, regardless of the type of chemical reaction involved. To illustrate the generality of application of techniques and principles, the similarities among different kinds of equilibria, and the differences necessary in some cases, let us now look at four different cases of solution equilibria—acid-base, solubility, complex ion formation, and distribution.

ACID-BASE EQUILIBRIA

General Acid-Base Theory

When any weak acid, H_nA, is dissolved in any ionizing solvent, SH, whose dielectric constant is high enough to separate the charged species, the following equilibria are established:

$$H_nA + SH \rightleftharpoons SH_2^+ + H_{n-1}A^-$$

$$H_{n-1}A^- + SH \rightleftharpoons SH_2^+ + H_{n-2}A^{2-} \qquad (5\text{--}11)$$

$$H_{n-2}A^{2-} + SH \rightleftharpoons SH_2^+ + H_{n-3}A^{3-}$$

and continuing until all the protons are removed from H_nA.

$$HA^{(n-1)-} + SH \rightleftharpoons SH_2^+ + A^{n-}$$

For each of these equilibria we can write the molar concentration equilibrium constant, as given by Equation (5–10).

$$K_{a_1}'' = \frac{[SH_2^+][H_{n-1}A^-]}{[SH][H_nA]}, \quad K_{a_2}'' = \frac{[SH_2^+][H_{n-2}A^{2-}]}{[SH][H_{n-1}A^-]}, \quad K_{a_3}'' = \frac{[SH_2^+][H_{n-3}A^{3-}]}{[SH][H_{n-2}A^{2-}]}$$

The symbol K has the subscript a to indicate that the reaction to which it pertains is that of the compound behaving as an acid (that is, donating a proton to the solvent), while the numerical subscript on the a indicates which proton has been donated (for example, 1 for the loss of the first proton, 2 for the loss of the second proton).

By thermodynamic convention, the activity of any pure substance is unity. The substitution of molar concentrations for activities is most accurate for dilute solutions. Under these conditions the solvent is only slightly polluted by the addition of very small amounts of solute; in other words, the activity of the solvent SH in 0.001 M acid or less is essentially the same as the activity of the pure solvent. Since the activity of the solvent is assumed to be one it does not appear in the denominator of Equation (5–2) nor in Equation (5–4). And consequently, the molar concentration of the solvent does not show up in Equation (5–10). The above equilibrium constants are simplified by this elimination and correctly written as:

$$K_{a_1} = \frac{[SH_2^+][H_{n-1}A^-]}{[HA]}, \quad K_{a_2} = \frac{[SH_2^+][H_{n-2}A^{2-}]}{[H_{n-1}A^-]}, \quad K_{a_3} = \frac{[SH_2^+][H_{n-3}A^{3-}]}{[H_{n-2}A^{2-}]}$$

These constants are applicable to any solution of a weak acid in any ionizing solvent, regardless of the charge type of the acid, that is, for acids such as H_5Y^+ (EDTA in strongly acidic solution), HCN, or HCO_3^-.

The analogous equilibria pertain, the corresponding equilibrium constants can be written, and the same assumptions are valid when treating a weak base, B, dissolved in any ionizing solvent, SH.

$$B + SH \rightleftharpoons BH^+ + S^- \qquad (5\text{--}12)$$

with the equilibrium constant (assuming a solvent activity of one):

$$K_b = \frac{[BH^+][S^-]}{[B]}$$

where the subscript b on the K indicates that it is for the reaction in which the solute behaves as a base, that is, takes on a proton. If the base can take on more than one proton, then the b will have a subscript to designate which proton is being considered in the equilibrium reaction (for example, 1 for the gain of the first proton, 2 for the gain of the second proton). Again these constants can be applied to any solution of a weak base in any ionizing solvent, regardless of the charge type of the base, for example, for bases such as NH_2—CH_2—CH_2—NH_3^+, NH_3, or OH^-.

This theory of acids and bases was developed independently in 1923 by both J. N. Brönsted in Denmark and T. M. Lowry in England.

It should be emphasized at the outset, that the Brönsted–Lowry theory is not limited to a single solvent. Just because water is the most readily available solvent, the one most commonly used for acid–base reactions, does not mean that the Brönsted–Lowry theory is limited to water. It is not. The theory is applicable in any ionizing solvent, SH.

Any acid or base is classified as strong or weak on the basis of the equilibrium position of reactions (5–11) or (5–12). When the equilibrium position lies one hundred percent to the right, or immeasurably close to it, essentially no H_nA or B species exist in the solution. For the strong acid reaction, $H_nA + SH \rightleftharpoons H_{n-1}A^- + SH_2^+$ there is no real competition between the SH molecule and $H_{n-1}A^-$ for the proton. SH is much more powerful in attracting and holding protons as it removes completely the first proton from H_nA to form essentially all $H_{n-1}A^-$. For the strong base reaction

$$B + SH \rightleftharpoons BH^+ + S^-$$

again there is no real competition between SH and B for the protons. In this case however, B is much more powerful in attracting and holding protons, so it removes protons from SH to convert essentially all of B into BH^+. When this occurs, H_nA and B are considered to be strong acids and strong bases *in that solvent*, SH. Thus HCl and NaOH are called strong acid and strong base, respectively, in water.

When the ionization reactions of Equations (5–11) and (5–12) do not occur completely, the solutions will contain molecular H_nA as well as the SH_2^+ and $H_{n-1}A^-$, and B as well as BH^+ and S^-. There is real competition between the solvent molecules and the bases present in the solution ($H_{n-1}A^-$, $H_{n-2}A^{2-}$, or B) for the proton, so that neither the solvent molecules nor the base triumphs in binding all the protons. H_nA is called a weak acid and B is called a weak base *in that solvent*. Thus acetic acid and ammonia are called weak acid and weak base, respectively, in water.

How weak a given acid or base is will depend upon the exact position of the equilibrium; the further to the right that it lies, the stronger the acid or base. There will be a high concentration of the ionized species in the solution, causing the numerical value of the equilibrium constant to be large. Thus we find that a solution of thiocyanic acid (HSCN) in water, which has an acid dissociation constant of 0.14, acts as a stronger acid than hydrocyanic acid (HCN) in water, which has the very small dissociation constant of 6.04×10^{-10}. A solution of perchloric acid, $HClO_4$, in pure (glacial) acetic acid has an overall acid dissociation constant of 1.3×10^{-5}. In glacial acetic acid, $HClO_4$ is a stronger acid than is HCl which has an overall acid dissociation constant of only 2.8×10^{-9}. Ammonia dissolved in water ($K_b = 1.7 \times 10^{-5}$) is a stronger base than aniline dissolved in water ($K_b = 4.2 \times 10^{-10}$). Pyridine dissolved in glacial acetic acid (overall base dissociation constant of 8.0×10^{-7}) is a stronger base than ammonia in glacial acetic acid (overall base dissociation constant of 4.0×10^{-7}).

The Brönsted-Lowry acid–base theory, as outlined above applies to any conjugate acid–base pair, for example, NH_3 and NH_4^+, or HCN^- and CN^-. For the acid–base reaction

$$HA + SH \rightleftharpoons SH_2^+ + A^- \qquad (5\text{–}13)$$

the dissociation constant for the acid, HA, is

$$K_a = \frac{[SH_2^+][A^-]}{[HA]}$$

The acid–base reaction of the conjugate base, A^-, is:

$$A^- + SH \rightleftharpoons HA + S^-$$

and the base dissociation constant for A^- is:

$$K_b = \frac{[S^-][HA]}{[A^-]}$$

Multiplying together the equilibrium constants for the acid and its conjugate base

$$K_a \times K_b = [SH_2^+][S^-] \qquad (5\text{–}14)$$

The right-hand side of Equation (5–14) is also the autoprotolysis constant expression for the solvent ($SH + SH \rightleftharpoons SH_2^+ + S^-$). Combining Equations (5–14) and (5–17) shows that the relationship between the strength of an acid and the strength of its conjugate base or between the strength of a base and the strength of its conjugate acid is given by:

$$K_a \times K_b = K_s \quad \text{or} \quad pK_a + pK_b = pK_s \qquad (5\text{–}15)$$

So that if we know the strength of an acid or base, the strength of its conjugate base or acid can be obtained from Equation (5–15). Acid dissociation constants are the only ones tabulated in most books, but by using Equation (5–15) the base dissociation constants can be calculated.

It should not be surprising to find the relative strengths of an acid and its conjugate base interrelated through the autoprotolysis constant of the solvent. Equation (5–13) shows that the acid–base reaction establishing the strength of the conjugates involves the transfer of a proton from the acid to the solvent and from the solvent to the base. The facility with which a solvent molecule donates or accepts a proton is an integral part of the exchange.

The strongest acid that can exist in any solvent is the solvated proton, SH_2^+. Any chemical that would act as a stronger acid, will give its proton up completely to the solvent, and thus exist in solution as its conjugate base. This is merely another way of stating that the equilibrium position of Equation (5–13) for a strong acid lies exclusively to the right. The strongest base that can exist in any solvent is the solvent anion, S^-, because any stronger base will remove the proton from the solvent molecule and exist completely as its conjugate acid. In other words, the equilibrium position of the base dissociation reaction for a strong base [Equation (5–12)] lies completely to the right.

The acid–base dissociation reaction for the pure solvent, SH, can be written as:

$$SH + SH \rightleftharpoons SH_2{}^+ + S^- \qquad (5\text{--}16)$$

which has the equilibrium constant:

$$K_s = [SH_2{}^+][S^-] \qquad (5\text{--}17)$$

Since the solvent is pure, its activity will be one and not appear in the denominator of Equation (5–17). Writing out some specific illustrations of these, for water:

$$H_2O + H_2O \rightleftharpoons H_3O^+ + OH^-$$
$$K_s = [H_3O^+][OH^-] = 1.00 \times 10^{-14}$$

for methanol:

$$CH_3OH + CH_3OH \rightleftharpoons CH_3OH_2^+ + CH_3O^-$$
$$K_s = [CH_3OH_2^+][CH_3O^-] = 2.0 \times 10^{-17}$$

for glacial acetic acid:

$$CH_3COOH + CH_3COOH \rightleftharpoons CH_3COOH_2^+ + CH_3COO^-$$
$$K_s = [CH_3COOH_2^+][CH_3COO^-] = 3.6 \times 10^{-15}$$

for liquid ammonia:

$$NH_3 + NH_3 \rightleftharpoons NH_4^+ + NH_2^-$$
$$K_s = [NH_4^+][NH_2^-] = 10^{-27}$$

Equations (5–11) and (5–12) show clearly that the apparent strength of any acid or base depends upon the solvent in which it is dissolved. You might expect that in any particular solvent, different acids would exhibit different strengths. This is not always true! When acids are so strong that their equilibrium positions lie completely to the right, no differences in relative strength can be measured. Such a series of acids is said to be *leveled* by the solvent. The solvent in which acid strengths appear equal is called a *leveling solvent* for that group of acids. Water is a leveling solvent for the acids, $HClO_4$, H_2SO_4, HCl, and HNO_3. In glacial acetic acid these acids have the overall dissociation constants: $HClO_4$—1.3×10^{-3}; H_2SO_4—5.8×10^{-8}; HCl—2.8×10^{-9}. Conductance studies have been unable to detect the presence of any ions in solutions of nitric acid in glacial acetic acid, which means that it is the weakest of these four acids. Similar examples can be cited for bases in water and in more acidic solvents, such as glacial acetic acid.

Equations (5–11) and (5–12) describe the overall reactions for acids and bases, but they do not indicate any detailed mechanism. When the solvent molecule removes a proton from an acid, it occurs in several steps. The bond between the hydrogen and the rest of the molecule ruptures so as to leave both of the electrons in the residue. This forms two species: the proton, and the rest of the original acid.

The two ions formed will remain in contact with one another, held by the electrostatic attraction between their opposite charges. When the dielectric constant of the solvent is greater than 13, the two ions will separate from each other and exist independently in solution. Both will be surrounded by the cloud of solvent molecules. The first of these two steps, the bond breaking one, is called *ionization* and produces an ion pair, H^+A^-, in solution. The second of these steps, the physical separation of the two ions into independent entities, is called *dissociation*.

Kolthoff and Bruckenstein[2,11] have studied acid–base behavior in glacial acetic acid and derived quantitative relationships for the equilibria present in this solvent. The dielectric constant of glacial acetic acid is so low (only 6.13) that almost all ions are paired with one of opposite charge and exist in solution as ion pairs. Consequently, the equilibria as given by Equations (5–11) and (5–12) have to be subdivided into the following two-step sequence:

$$HA + HOAc \underset{\text{ionization}}{\rightleftharpoons} H_2OAc^+A^- \underset{\text{dissociation}}{\rightleftharpoons} H_2OAc^+ + A^- \qquad (5\text{--}18)$$

$$B + HOAc \underset{\text{ionization}}{\rightleftharpoons} BH^+OAc^- \underset{\text{dissociation}}{\rightleftharpoons} BH^+ + OAc^- \qquad (5\text{--}19)$$

The equilibrium constants for each of these steps are written as ionization constants, K_i, and dissociation constants, K_d. Thus for a weak acid:

$$K_i = \frac{[H_2OAc^+A^-]}{[HA]} \qquad (5\text{--}20)$$

$$K_d = \frac{[H_2OAc^+][A^-]}{[H_2OAc^+A^-]} \qquad (5\text{--}21)$$

The usual assumptions about the solvent activity and the activity quotient were made. The hydrogen ion concentration of a solution refers to the concentration of the protons existing free, solvated of course, but not tied up in ion pairs. In glacial acetic acid, the hydrogen ions that are not free exist either as molecules of HA or in the ion pairs, $H_2OAc^+A^-$. The overall dissociation constant, K_A, represents the equilibrium between the free and the combined hydrogen ions as expressed in Equation (5–18):

$$K_{HA} = \frac{[H_2OAc^+][A^-]}{[HA] + [H_2OAc^+A^-]} \qquad (5\text{--}22)$$

Substitution of the expressions for the ionization and dissociation constants (Equations (5–20) and (5–21)) gives:

$$K_{HA} = \frac{K_iK_d}{1 + K_i} \qquad (5\text{--}23)$$

Similarly, for a weak base in glacial acetic acid:

$$K_i = \frac{[BH^+OAc^-]}{[B]}, \quad K_d = \frac{[BH^+][OAc^-]}{[BH^+OAc^-]}, \quad K_B = \frac{[BH^+][OAc^-]}{[B] + [BH^+OAc^-]}$$

$$K_B = \frac{K_iK_d}{1 + K_i} \qquad (5\text{--}24)$$

Table 5–4 gives measured overall ionization constants, K_{HA} and K_B, for some acids and bases in glacial acetic acid.

Table 5–4. SELECTED VALUES FOR OVERALL DISSOCIATION CONSTANTS FOR ACIDS AND BASES IN GLACIAL ACETIC ACID

Acid	K_{HA}	Base	K_B
$HClO_4$	1.3×10^{-5}	Pyridine	8.0×10^{-7}
H_2SO_4	5.8×10^{-8}	Ammonia	4.0×10^{-7}
HCl	2.8×10^{-9}	Urea	5.8×10^{-11}
		Water	2.9×10^{-13}

SOURCE: Refs. 2 and 11.

Kolthoff, Bruckenstein, and Chantooni[12] have studied acid–base equilibria in acetonitrile (CH_3CN) extensively. Acetonitrile is an aprotic solvent with a dielectric constant of 36, which is sufficiently large to dissociate any ion pairs, and indeed there is little evidence for their existence in acetonitrile. In acetonitrile, perchloric acid is completely dissociated, whereas most other acids exist almost entirely in the molecular form, HA. Acetonitrile is a poor solvating solvent; that is, it does not form hydrogen bonds with anions so as to stabilize them in solution. As a consequence, in acetonitrile, the anions tend to stabilize themselves by association with the undissociated acid molecule, HA. This tendency for an acid, either HA or BH^+, to form a hydrogen-bonded complex with its conjugate base, either A^- or B, has been called *homoconjugation*. Homoconjugation is found extensively in acetonitrile solutions, so that in addition to the regular acid ionization equilibrium

$$HA + SH \rightleftharpoons SH_2^+ + A^- \qquad K_{HA} = \frac{[SH_2^+][A^-]}{[HA]} \qquad (5\text{–}25)$$

there also is present the homoconjugation equilibrium:

$$HA + A^- \rightleftharpoons AHA^- \qquad K_{AHA} = \frac{[AHA^-]}{[HA][A^-]} \qquad (5\text{–}26)$$

The behavior of picric acid $[(NO_3)_3C_6H_2OH]$ in acetonitrile was studied extensively because its acid form and its conjugate base have different absorption spectra. Thus, it is possible to distinguish clearly between the two forms in solution and to measure each concentration accurately. Solutions of picric acid in acetonitrile more dilute than 0.1 M can be described adequately by the simple ionization equilibrium of Equation (5–25). At concentrations larger than 0.1 M, however, the picrate ion reacts with two molecules of the undissociated acid according to the reaction:

$$3HPic \rightleftharpoons H^+ + Pic(HPic)_2^- \qquad (5\text{–}27)$$

for which the equilibrium constant below can be written:

$$K_{3HPic} = \frac{[H^+][Pic(HPic)_2^-]}{[HPic]^3} \qquad (5\text{-}28)$$

assuming the activity coefficient quotient to be one.

Combining Equations (5–25) and (5–26) gives:

$$2HA \rightleftharpoons H^+ + AHA^- \qquad \text{For example, } 2H_2SO_4 \rightleftharpoons H^+ + HSO_4^- \cdot H_2SO_4 \qquad (5\text{-}29)$$

which has the equilibrium constant

$$K_{2HA} = K_{HA} \times K_{AHA} = \frac{[H^+][AHA^-]}{[HA]^2} \qquad (5\text{-}30)$$

Kolthoff, Bruckenstein, and Chantooni[12,13] determined the numerical values for the constants of Equations (5–25), (5–26), (5–28), and (5–30). Values of these for the more common acids are given in Table 5–5. Water behaves as a fairly strong base in acetonitrile.

Bruckenstein and Mukherjee[3] investigated ethylenediamine as a solvent for acids and bases. Ethylenediamine is a strongly basic liquid with a dielectric constant of 12.9. Acids that have an aqueous acid dissociation constant of 10^{-5} or greater are all leveled by ethylenediamine. Since the dielectric constant is less than 13, ion pair formation is considerable, and the equilibria expressed in Equations (5–18) and (5–19) are present in acid–base reactions. The equilibrium constants determined in this solvent are the overall acid dissociation constants as defined by Equations (5–22) and (5–24) and some of these are given in Table 5–6.

Kolthoff and Reddy[14] studied dimethyl sulfoxide $[(CH_3)_2SO]$ as a solvent for acid–base reactions. This solvent has a dielectric constant of 46.7, so the formation of ion pairs is not prevalent. Perchloric acid, hydrochloric acid, and the first proton from sulfuric acid are ionized completely. The second acid dissociation constant for sulfuric acid is much smaller in dimethyl sulfoxide than it is in water. Dimethyl sulfoxide forms a 1:1 adduct with nitric acid. Carboxylic acids behave as very weak acids. Water behaves as a very weak base. The acid–base equilibria in dimethyl sulfoxide are essentially those present in aqueous solutions as given by Equations (5–11) and (5–12). Some acid dissociation constants measured in dimethyl sulfoxide are given in Table 5–7.

Table 5–5. EQUILIBRIUM CONSTANTS FOR ACIDS IN ACETONITRILE

Acid	K_{HA}	K_{AHA}^-	K_{2HA}	K_{3HA}
HCl	1.1×10^{-9}	1.7×10^2	2.0×10^{-7}	—
HBr	3.1×10^{-6}	2.7×10^2	8.3×10^{-4}	—
HNO₃	1.3×10^{-9}	2.0×10^2	2.5×10^{-7}	—
H₂SO₄(1)	1.6×10^{-8}	4×10^3	5.5×10^{-5}	—
(2)	1.0×10^{-26}	1×10^{30}		—
Picric	1.3×10^{-9}	1.6×10^2		8×10^{-7}

SOURCE: Refs. 12 and 13.

Alcohols, acetone, chloroform, benzene, glacial acetic acid, alkanes, and many other nonaqueous liquids are widely used as solvents in separation methods. A knowledge of the acid–base behavior of compounds in such solvents, as well as the knowledge of the differences between acid–base behavior in nonaqueous solvents and in water is vital to effective use of separation techniques. In water, ion-pair formation and homoconjugation are not extensive, so they can be neglected. As was shown above, in many organic solvents these are the major factors in determining acid strengths. Water is still the most commonly used solvent in analytical chemistry, so the illustrations of equilibrium calculations will be performed for aqueous solutions. Once the techniques of calculating acid–base equilibria in water have been mastered, it is not difficult to extend them to nonaqueous systems.

An outstanding example of the utilization of acid–base properties to effect separations is a series of tests developed by Dr. Vincent Dole at Rockefeller University[8] as a part of the methadone treatment program for heroin addicts. During the course of the methadone treatment, patients are tested routinely to

Table 5–6. OVERALL ACID DIS-
SOCIATION CONSTANTS IN
ETHYLENEDIAMINE

Acid	K_{HA}
HCl	9.8×10^{-5}
HBr	2.3×10^{-4}
HI	1.1×10^{-3}
$HClO_4$	8.0×10^{-4}
HNO_3	6.3×10^{-4}
CH_3COOH	6.5×10^{-6}

SOURCE: Ref. 16.

Table 5–7. ACID DISSOCIATION
CONSTANTS IN DIMETHYL
SULFOXIDE

Acid	K_a
HSO_4^-	8×10^{-10}
CH_3COOH	5×10^{-11}
C_6H_5COOH	1×10^{-10}
Picric	80

SOURCE: Ref. 16.

ascertain whether they are still taking narcotics, tranquilizers, amphetamines, or barbiturates. The urine tests developed by Dr. Dole are simple, easy, and rapid to perform. The separation of the drugs is based upon differences in their base strengths. All of these drugs are bases of varying strengths. In urine (normal pH 5–6.5) they will be protonated and exist as their conjugate acids. These acids are cations which can be adsorbed onto cation-exchange paper. To remove the drugs selectively from the paper, the acids are neutralized to form the uncharged base. This uncharged species is not attracted to the negatively charged exchange sites on the ion exchange paper. The bases, being neutral, can be extracted into chloroform, where they can be detected. The procedure for the separation is as follows.

A piece of cation-exchange paper is soaked in a sample of the patient's urine. All of the drugs present are adsorbed from the urine onto the paper. The rest of the test consists of removing the drugs selectively from the paper with buffers of different pH values.

To detect barbiturates, the cation-exchange paper is soaked in a pH 2.2 citric acid buffer. At pH 2.2, all of the bases will be fully protonated and cationic. The barbiturates, however are acids (veronal—$pK_a = 7.98$; phenobarbital—$pK_a = 7.45$). The fully protonated species are neutral and will be eluted easily from the resin paper. This aqueous solution of barbiturates is then extracted with chloroform. The organic phase is spotted onto a silica gel thin-layer chromatographic plate, which, after development and treatment with silver acetate, will exhibit brown spots if barbiturates were present in the urine.

A pH 9.3 borate buffer is used next to extract morphine or methadone from the ion-exchange paper. Morphine ($pK_b = 6.13$), cocaine ($pK_b = 5.59$), and quinine ($pK_b = 6.0$), moderately strong bases, will remain protonated until the pH of the solution approaches 9. In the pH 9.3 borate buffer used, they exist as the uncharged base, which is readily removed from the cation-exchange resin. The aueqous solution of bases is then extracted with chloroform. The chloroform extract is spotted onto a thin-layer chromatographic plate and developed. Interestingly enough, the first thin-layer chromatographic test is for quinine, which is used in some areas to cut the typical bag of heroin. Iodoplatinate, which is then sprayed onto the TLC plate, produces different colored spots for morphine, methadone, cocaine, hydromorphone, and chlorpromazine.

To detect amphetamines, the ion-exchange paper is treated with a pH 11.0 carbonate buffer. Benzedrine, the most common amphetamine, is a strong base and will remain protonated up to moderately high pH values. Not until pH 11.0 does enough free base exist to be removed from the cation-exchange paper. The aqueous solution is extracted with chloroform, and the extract separated by means of thin-layer chromatography. After development of the chromatogram, the presence of amphetamines is detected by spraying the plate with ninhydrin. Benzedrine will show up as a characteristic red spot.

This separation illustrates the necessity of being able to think about acid–base equilibria in terms of the actual species present in the solution at various pH values Dr. Dole has taken advantage of changes in the relative concentrations of the conjugates as a function of pH, and used buffers to maintain constant pH values Quantitative applications of acid–base equilibrium are ubiquitous in analytical chemistry.

Acid-Base Calculations

Calculations involving acid–base dissociation constants can be used to facilitate an understanding of acid–base equilibria. In order to perform mathematical operations correctly, it is essential to have a thorough knowledge of the chemistry in the solution. The results of the calculations provide necessary information about the concentrations of conjugate acids and bases at equilibrium under a wide variety of experimental conditions. Acid–base equilibrium calculations are very fruitful in teaching the algebraic manipulations involved in all other types of equilibrium problems, and in deciding upon the assumptions that must be made in order to simplify the arithmetic.

Determination of the Numerical Value of Acid Dissociation Constants

One very common experimental method for the determination of dissociation constants of weak acids or of weak bases is to dissolve a very accurately weighed amount of an acid or base to an exact volume, and then to measure the pH of the resultant solution. From these data it is possible to calculate the equilibrium constant for the dissociation reaction. An illustration will best serve to show the technique.

Example.   1.221 g of solid benzoic acid (C_6H_5-COOH), mol wt 122.1, is weighed on the analytical balance, dissolved in a 500.0-ml volumetric flask, and made up to the mark with deionized water at 25°C. After thorough mixing, a 50.0-ml aliquot of the solution is taken and its pH measured as 2.961. Calculate the K_a and pK_a for benzoic acid, and the K_b and pK_b for the conjugate base, benzoate ion.

The equilibrium reaction taking place in the volumetric flask is merely the ionization and dissociation of benzoic acid, according to:

$$C_6H_5\text{—COOH} + H_2O \rightleftharpoons C_6H_5\text{—COO}^- + H_3O^+$$

The equilibrium constant expression (K_a) that pertains to this reaction is:

$$K_a = \frac{[H_3O^+][C_6H_5\text{–COO}^-]}{[C_6H_5COOH]}$$

The problem requests that the numerical value of K_a be obtained. In order to do that, numerical values for the three concentrations, $[H_3O^+]$, $[C_6H_5COO^-]$, and $[C_6H_5COOH]$ must be found. These can be obtained quite readily through application of the electroneutrality principle and the material balance relationship for benzoic acid.

Since all of the ions present in the solution come only from the dissociation of the benzoic acid molecules, the electroneutrality principle expression for this solution is:

$$[C_6H_5\text{–COO}^-] = [H_3O^+]$$

The benzoic acid molecules are either ionized in solution or they are not ionized, and thus the material balance is:

$$C_{HBz} = [C_6H_5COOH] + [C_6H_5COO^-]$$

Substituting for [C₆H₅COO⁻] from the electroneutrality principle into the material balance expression gives:

$$C_{HBz} = [C_6H_5COOH] + [H_3O^+]$$

or upon rearrangement:

$$[C_6H_5COOH] = C_{HBz} - [H_3O^+]$$

Now we have relationships for the two forms of benzoic acid in the solution in terms of numerical data available, so it is merely a matter of inserting the numbers into them.

From the statement of the problem it is possible to calculate the total concentration of benzoic acid in all forms, C_{HBz}, in the solution.

$$C_{HBz} = \frac{1.221 \text{ gram}}{122.1 \text{ gram/mole}} \times \frac{1000 \text{ milliliter/liter}}{500 \text{ milliliter}}$$

$$= 0.02000 \ M$$

All solution equilibrium constants are evaluated for molar concentrations, so that to use them, all concentrations must be expressed in moles per liter of solution. From the measured pH of the solution the hydrogen ion concentration is:

$$\text{pH} = -\log [H_3O^+] = 2.961$$

$$[H_3O^+] = 1.09 \times 10^{-3} \ M$$

Inserting the hydrogen ion concentration into the electroneutrality principle gives us:

$$[C_6H_5COO^-] = [H_3O^+] = 1.09 \times 10^{-3} \ M$$

while inserting the hydrogen ion concentration and the total concentration of benzoic acid into the material balance expression yields:

$$[C_6H_5COOH] = 2.000 \times 10^{-2} - 1.09 \times 10^{-3} \ M$$

$$= 1.891 \times 10^{-2} \ M$$

Substituting these three numerical values into the equilibrium constant expression:

$$K_a = \frac{(1.09 \times 10^{-3})(1.09 \times 10^{-3})}{(1.891 \times 10^{-2})}$$

$$= \frac{1.20 \times 10^{-6}}{1.891 \times 10^{-2}} = 6.32 \times 10^{-5}$$

Since there were no assumptions made in solving this problem, there are none to check at this point. The number calculated from the equilibrium constant expression is one of those asked for in the problem.

The problem also asked for the pK_a for the weak acid.

$$pK_a = -\log K_a = -\log (6.32 \times 10^{-5})$$

$$= 4.199$$

The K_b and pK_b for the conjugate base, benzoate ion, are calculated by means of Equation (5–15):

$$K_b = \frac{K_w}{K_a} \quad \text{or} \quad pK_b = pK_w - pK_a$$

pK_b for the benzoate ion is $14.000 - 4.199 = 9.801$ from which the K_b is found to be:

$$pK_b = -\log K_b = 9.801$$

$$K_b = 1.58 \times 10^{-10}$$

This problem illustrates the straightforward application of the electro-neutrality principle and the material balance to a simple solution. It also provides practice in the algebraic manipulations involved in solving equilibrium constant problems. At the same time, it provides an insight into one way in which those mysterious numbers, tabulated in books as acid dissociation constants, are obtained in the laboratory. Let us look at another type of calculation involving equilibrium constants, which is nothing more than a variation on the above problem.

Calculations Involving Solutions of the Acid or the Base Alone

Once the numerical value of an acid or base dissociation constant has been determined, it can be applied to other solutions of the same acid or base at the same temperature. The simplest application involves an aqueous acid or base solution that contains no species able to interact with either the acid or its conjugate base. There will be ionic strength effects, of course. The solution contains no other source of the acid or its conjugate base or of a base and the conjugate acid of a base. Consequently, the sole source of the ions of the acid or base in solution is the acid or base dissociation reaction. There is nothing in the solution that will react with the acid, base or their conjugates; that is, nothing will precipitate, complex or extract them, or in any way whatsoever affect their concentrations. From the point of view of chemical separations, this is a highly restricted situation, but it is worth-while going through a sample calculation to show the techniques involved. The assumptions made and equations derived for these solutions are *not* generally applicable to other solutions involving acid–base equilibria; they are strictly valid in "pure" solutions of the acid or the base.

Example. Calculate the pH of 375 ml of 1.26×10^{-3} M benzoic acid.

The acid dissociation reaction is the same as in the preceding example. The equilibrium constant expression is also identical to the one above. The example asks for the pH of the solution. In order to obtain that, the hydrogen ion concentration must be calculated. This can be achieved by solving the equilibrium constant expression, but in order to do this, the concentration of the undissociated benzoic acid molecules and the concentration of the benzoate anions present in the solution must be known.

The volume of the solution is extraneous to this problem. pH is an intrinsic property and independent of the volume of the solution present; that is, 5.00 ml of this solution of benzoic acid will have the same pH as the 375 ml does.

The electroneutrality principle for the solution is the same as in the previous example:

$$[H_3O^+] = [C_6H_5COO^-]$$

since there are no other cations or anions present in the solution.

Similarly, the material balance for benzoic acid is the same as in the previous example. The benzoic acid exists in this solution in two forms; as un-ionized molecules of the acid, or dissociated into protons and benzoate ions.

$$C_{HBz} = [C_6H_5COOH] + [C_6H_5COO^-] = 1.26 \times 10^{-3} \ M$$

Substituting for the benzoate concentration from the electroneutrality principle, and rearranging the material balance expression gives:

$$[C_6H_5COOH] = 1.26 \times 10^{-3} - [H_3O^+]$$

Both the benzoate species concentrations are known now in terms of the hydrogen ion concentration. $[H_3O^+]$ is the only unknown permitted in the final expression. Substituting these relationships into the equilibrium constant expression gives:

$$\frac{[H_3O^+][H_3O^+]}{(1.26 \times 10^{-3} - [H_3O^+])} = 6.32 \times 10^{-5}$$

This equation can now be solved for the molar concentration of the hydronium ion. In the process of doing this, the quadratic equation

$$[H_3O^+]^2 + 6.320 \times 10^{-5}[H_3O^+] - 7.96 \ 10^{-8} = 0$$

is generated. In order to obtain a rigorous solution of this problem, the equation must be solved. For most purposes, however, such a solution is not necessary, and a close approximation will suffice. By making a simple assumption, the quadratic equation can be avoided, and the mathematics of the problem can be simplified considerably, saving time, effort, and minimizing computational errors. This assumption is—the benzoic acid molecules do not dissociate very much, so that the concentration of the ionized benzoate ion, $C_6H_5COO^-$, is negligibly small in comparison to the total concentration of benzoic acid present, C_{HBz}. Using this assumption, $[C_6H_5COOH] = C_{HBz} = 1.26 \times 10^{-3} \ M$.

One of the biggest problems for beginning students when solving equilibrium problems is in deciding whether or not to make this assumption at this point. The safe way would be never to make it and always solve the quadratic equation. This is also the difficult and time-consuming solution. Another alternative is to make the assumption in all cases. This is the easy and time-saving solution. Unfortunately, this latter way also gives the wrong, and occasionally, an absurd answer in many cases. Some in-between course of action is needed.

For moderately strong acids or bases, those having K_a or K_b values greater than 10^{-4}, ionization will be appreciable. When working with constants $\geq 10^{-4}$ it is advisable to solve the quadratic equation. For very dilute solutions ($10^{-3} \ M$ or less) of relatively weak acids (K_a around 10^{-5}) the extent of the ionization also will be fairly large, so that the quadratic equation should be solved. For very weak acids and bases, $K_a = 10^{-6}$ or smaller, it is almost always safe to neglect the amount of dissociation and avoid solving the quadratic equation. In general, it is desirable to be reasonable and rational about this, but also to try to get away with the simplest method. The criteria for deciding what is negligible and what is not depends upon the purpose for which the problem is being solved. If the work is approximate, perhaps 10–20% dissociation can be overlooked. For very accurate physicochemical measurements, even 0.5% dissociation must be accounted for. For the purposes of this book, 5% dissociation will be taken arbitrarily as the upper limit. Any dissociation greater than 5% will invalidate the assumption and make it necessary to solve the quadratic equation.

Returning to the problem after this aside, let us assume that the ionization of benzoic acid is negligible, then:

$$[H_3O^+]^2 = 7.96 \times 10^{-8}$$

$$[H_3O^+] = 2.82 \times 10^{-4} \ M$$

Be sure to check whether or not the assumption about the negligibility of the dissociation of benzoic acid is correct. 5% of C_{HBz} is $6.30 \times 10^{-5} \ M$. From the calculated hydronium ion concentration above and the electroneutrality principle, the concentration of benzoate ions in the solution is $2.82 \times 10^{-4} \ M$. This concentration is greater than 5% of the total acid, so that the assumption was not a valid one. Note that it is not in keeping with the general guidelines stated above, so it probably shouldn't have been made in the first place. The quadratic equation must be solved; this yields:

$$[H_3O^+] = 2.53 \times 10^{-4} \ M$$

Even though this is the concentration obtained by solving the equilibrium constant expression, it is not the answer to the problem; the pH of the solution must be found.

$$pH = -\log [H_3O^+] = -\log (2.53 \times 10^{-4} \ M) = 3.60$$

Techniques similar to those in the preceding example are used in solving problems involving weak bases. To illustrate this type of calculation:

Example. Calculate the pH of an 0.00875 M ethylamine ($C_2H_5NH_2$) solution.

The chemical reaction involved in this example is:

$$C_2H_5NH_2 + H_2O \rightleftharpoons C_2H_5NH_3^+ + OH^-$$

which has the equilibrium constant expression:

$$K_b = \frac{[OH^-][C_2H_5NH_3^+]}{[C_2H_5NH_2]} = 4.7 \times 10^{-4}$$

The problem asks for the pH of the solution. In order to obtain it, the hydrogen ion concentration must be found. But ethylamine is a base and upon dissociation will produce hydroxide ions. When we know the concentration of the hydroxide ions produced, the hydrogen ion concentration can be calculated from the autoprotolysis expression for water. To solve the equilibrium constant expression for the hydroxide ion concentration, both the concentration of the free base, ethylamine, and its conjugate acid, ethylammonium ion, must be known.

The electroneutrality principle for the solution is:

$$[C_2H_5NH_3^+] = [OH^-]$$

since there are no other cations or anions present in the solution.

The material balance for the ethylamine in the solution is:

$$C_{EtNH_2} = [C_2H_5NH_2] + [C_2H_5NH_2^+] = 8.75 \times 10^{-3} \ M$$

since the base exists as either the ethylamine or the ethylammonium ion; nothing else happens to it in this solution. Substituting the electroneutrality expression into the material balance and solving the resultant expression for the concentration of the free base:

$$[C_2H_5NH_2] = 8.75 \times 10^{-3} - [OH^-]$$

so that we now have the concentration for the two forms of the amine in terms of the only allowed unknown, the hydroxide ion concentration. Substituting them into the equilibrium constant expression, gives:

$$K_b = \frac{[OH^-][OH^-]}{(8.75 \times 10^{-3} - [OH^-])} = 4.7 \times 10^{-4}$$

Since ethylamine is a moderately strong base and since the solution is relatively dilute, the chances are that any simplifying assumptions about the extent of dissociation of the base will be invalid. So, we will not bother to make them, but just solve the quadratic equation initially. Rearrangement of the equilibrium constant expression gives:

$$[OH^-]^2 + 4.7 \times 10^{-4} [OH^-] - 4.11 \times 10^{-6} = 0$$

Which when solved gives for the hydroxide ion concentration:

$$[OH^-] = 1.8 \times 10^{-3} \ M$$

A quick comparison of the hydroxide ion concentration with the total concentration of ethylamine in the solution shows that about 21% of it is ionized, so it was a shrewd maneuver not to bother making the assumption about negligible dissociation.

The number obtained from the solution of the equilibrium constant expression is not the answer to the problem. So,

$$pOH = -\log [OH^-] = -\log (1.8 \times 10^{-3} \ M) = 2.74$$

From the autoprotolysis expression for water:

$$pH + pOH = 14.00$$

$$pH = 14.00 - pOH = 14.00 - 2.74 = 11.26$$

And this is the answer asked for in the statement of the problem.

The calculation of the pH of a solution containing only the conjugate base of a weak acid or the conjugate acid of a weak base frequently is treated as difficult and quite different from the above problems. This is nonsense! The Brönsted–Lowry theory does not distinguish among kinds of weak bases or weak acids, and the equilibrium constant expression applies to all of them. Calculations of the pH of a solution of ammonium chloride or of ethylammonium chloride are identical to the calculation of the pH of the solution of benzoic acid shown above. The calculation of the pH of a solution of sodium carbonate, potassium acetate, or any base is identical to that for the solution of ethylamine just completed. To illustrate this point, let us compare the calculation of the pH of a solution of sodium benzoate with that previously done for ethylamine.

Example.   Calculate the pH of 500 ml of a 0.00200 M sodium benzoate solution.

The chemical reaction involved in this is:

$$C_6H_5COO^- + H_2O \rightleftharpoons C_6H_5COOH + OH^-$$

with the equilibrium constant:

$$K_b = \frac{[OH^-][C_6H_5COOH]}{[C_6H_5COO^-]} = 1.582 \times 10^{-10}$$

(*Note:* Except for the differences in the chemical identity of the base involved, the reaction and the equilibrium constant expression for ethylamine and benzoate ion are identical.)

The problem asks for the pH of the solution, but the equilibrium constant contains only hydroxide ion concentration. So, again this must be solved for; after which the hydrogen ion concentration is obtained using the autoprotolysis expression for water.
The electroneutrality principle expression for the solutions is:

$$[Na^+] = [C_6H_5COO^-] + [OH^-]$$

Charge type differences between the two bases account for the difference in the electroneutrality principle expression from that of the previous example. The sodium ion is not involved in any reaction so that its concentration remains constant at 2.00×10^{-3} M.

$$[C_6H_5COO^-] = 2.00 \times 10^{-3} - [OH^-]$$

The material balance for the benzoate in the solution is:

$$C_{Bz} = [C_6H_5COO^-] + [C_6H_5COOH] = 2.00 \times 10^{-3} \ M$$

since the benzoate exists only as the base or its conjugate acid in the solution. Substituting for the benzoate ion concentration from the electroneutrality principle expression:

$$2.00 \times 10^{-3} = 2.00 \times 10^{-3} - [OH^-] + [C_6H_5COOH]$$

which simplifies to:

$$[C_6H_5COOH] = [OH^-]$$

Substituting the values for the concentrations of the two forms of the benzoate into the equilibrium constant expression produces an equation that contains only the one unknown, the hydroxide ion concentration.

$$K_b = \frac{[OH^-][OH^-]}{(2.00 \times 10^{-3} - [OH^-])} = 1.582 \times 10^{-10}$$

Since the K_b for the weak base, benzoate ion, is very small, the base will not react to any appreciable extent. Any hydroxide ion formed during the reaction will be negligibly small compared to the original concentration of sodium benzoate. Neglecting the hydroxide ion concentration in the denominator of the expression gives:

$$[OH^-]^2 = 3.164 \times 10^{-13}$$

$$[OH^-] = 5.62 \times 10^{-7} \ M$$

(*Note*: Autoprotolysis of water contributes hydroxide ions to the solution which may not be negligibly small when considering dilute solutions of weak bases. This additional source of hydroxide ion has been neglected above, probably incorrectly.) To check the assumption that was made: $5.62 \times 10^{-7} \ M$ is 0.028% of 2.00×10^{-3} M, which certainly is much smaller than 5%. Our assumption was valid.

The number obtained by solving the equilibrium constant expression is not the answer that the example requests; the pH must be found.

$$pOH = -\log [OH^-] = -\log (5.62 \times 10^{-7} \ M) = 6.25$$

Using the autoprotolysis expression for water:

$$pH = 14.00 - pOH = 14.00 - 6.25 = 7.75$$

This is the answer. Since the pH obtained is greater than seven, the solution will be a basic one, which is logical. It should be apparent that these last two examples are indeed identical and are solved in an identical fashion.

In analytical separations the solutions of acids or of bases usually are not free from common ions or chemicals that interact with the acids or bases. The remaining examples will involve solutions that are more complex than the simple ones illustrated above. The most frequently encountered solution is one that contains both the weak acid and its conjugate base, so let us see what to do when we have a problem dealing with such a solution.

Calculations in Mixtures of Conjugate Acid–Base Systems

During acid–base titrations the conjugate form of the titrate is produced throughout the titration, so the calculation of the pH for an acid–base titration curve (other than for the initial solution) up to the equivalence point involves mixtures of a conjugate acid–base pair. One of the most commonly encountered acid–base systems is the buffer. A *buffer* contains a mixture of an acid and its conjugate base, or a base and its conjugate acid. Since mixtures of conjugate acids and bases are encountered so routinely, we should learn how to calculate the pH of such mixtures. In certain respects these problems are more straightforward than the previous examples.

Example. What is the pH of 750 ml of a solution that contains 0.00250 moles of benzoic acid and 0.00125 moles of sodium benzoate?

The chemical reaction present in this solution is the dissociation we have encountered earlier of benzoic acid into its conjugate base, benzoate ion:

$$C_6H_5COOH + H_2O \rightleftharpoons C_6H_5COO^- + H_3O^+$$

which has the same equilibrium constant expression:

$$K_a = \frac{[H_3O^+][C_6H_5COO^-]}{[C_6H_5COOH]} = 6.32 \times 10^{-5}$$

The problem asks for the pH of the solution, which means that the equilibrium constant expression should be solved for the hydrogen ion concentration. To do this, numerical values or relationships involving only the hydrogen ion concentration must be found for the two other concentrations. These can be found, as before, from the material balance and the electroneutrality principle relationships.

The electroneutrality principle for this solution is:

$$[Na^+] + [H_3O^+] = [C_6H_5COO^-]$$

The concentration of sodium ions is obtained from the amount of sodium benzoate present in the solution.

$$\text{molar concentration of sodium benzoate added} = \frac{0.00125 \text{ mole}}{0.750 \text{ liter}}$$
$$= 0.00167 \ M$$

Since the sodium ions undergo no reaction in this solution, $[Na^+] = 0.00167 \ M$, which makes the electroneutrality principle;

$$[C_6H_5COO^-] = 1.67 \times 10^{-3} \ M + [H_3O^+]$$

The material balance for the benzoate present in the solution is:

$$C_{Bz} = [C_6H_5COOH] + [C_6H_5COO^-]$$

Some of the total benzoate is from the original benzoic acid taken. Of this, some has ionized to form benzoate ions and some remains as undissociated molecules. Some of the total benzoate is from the sodium benzoate added. Some of this benzoate has reacted to form the conjugate acid, benzoic acid, and some of it has remained as benzoate ions. As a result of these equilibrium reactions between the acid and its conjugate base, the equilibrium concentrations of benzoic acid and of benzoate ion will not be identical to the amounts put into the solution. All that we do know, is that the total concentration of the conjugate base and the acid is constant and equal to the total amount of the acid plus base present originally. The relative distribution of benzoate between the acidic form and the basic form is not known.

The concentration of benzoic acid taken initially can be calculated:

$$\text{initial concentration of benzoic acid} = \frac{0.00250 \text{ mole}}{0.750 \text{ liter}} = 0.00333 \ M$$

Adding together the initial concentration of benzoic acid and the initial concentration of the sodium benzoate gives 0.00500 M for C_{Bz}. Now the material balance reads:

$$C_{Bz} = [C_6H_5COOH] + [C_6H_5COO^-] = 5.00 \times 10^{-3} \ M$$

Substituting the benzoate ion concentration obtained from the electroneutrality expression gives:

$$[C_6H_5COOH] + 1.67 \times 10^{-3} \ M + [H_3O^+] = 5.00 \times 10^{-3} \ M$$

which upon rearrangement:

$$[C_6H_5COOH] = 3.33 \times 10^{-3} \ M - [H_3O^+]$$

Now that we have expressions for the two benzoic acid-form concentrations, they can be substituted into the acid dissociation constant expression.

$$6.320 \times 10^{-5} = \frac{[H_3O^+](1.67 \times 10^{-3} + [H_3O^+])}{3.33 \times 10^{-3} - [H_3O^+]}$$

Solution of this equation will lead to a quadratic expression. So, let's try to avoid having to solve this by making some assumptions. In both the numerator and the denominator there are additive terms involving the hydrogen ion concentration. If they could be eliminated, the arithmetic would be simpler. Consider each of these terms individually. For convenience only, let us assume: (1) the concentration of hydrogen ion present in the solution at equilibrium is negligible as compared to the initial concentration of sodium benzoate taken (this simplifies the numerator); and (2) the concentration of hydrogen ion present in the solution at equilibrium is negligibly small compared to the concentration of benzoic acid taken initially (this simplifies the denominator).

Making these assumptions, the preceding equilibrium constant expression reduces to:

$$6.320 \times 10^{-5} = \frac{[H_3O^+](1.67 \times 10^{-3})}{3.33 \times 10^{-3}}$$

which can be readily solved to yield:

$$[H_3O^+] = 1.26 \times 10^{-4} \ M$$

The next step is to check the validity of the assumptions: (1) The calculated value 1.26×10^{-4} M is 7.5% of the original concentration of sodium benzoate taken, 1.67×10^{-3} M. Thus the first assumption was incorrect. The expression must be reformulated, not making this assumption and the resultant quadratic equation solved. (2) The value 1.26×10^{-4} M is 3.8% of the original benzoic acid concentration, 3.33×10^{-3} M. Thus, this assumption is valid and can be kept.

Rewriting the equilibrium constant expression:

$$6.320 \times 10^{-5} = \frac{[H_3O^+](1.67 \times 10^{-3} + [H_3O^+])}{3.33 \times 10^{-3}}$$

which when solved gives:

$$[H_3O^+] = 1.20 \times 10^{-4} \ M$$

But this is not the requested answer to the problem, so we must take the pH.

$$pH = -\log (1.20 \times 10^{-4}) = 3.92$$

In the preceding example, the acid is much stronger than its conjugate base, so the resultant pH of the solution is acidic. This need not be the case for all conjugate acid–base pairs. When the acid is sufficiently weak, the base strength of the conjugate base predominates in establishing the final pH of a solution containing both. Thus the pH of an equimolar mixture of boric acid and its conjugate base, sodium borate, is 9.2; and for hydrocyanic acid and its conjugate base, sodium cyanide, the pH of an equimolar mixture is also 9.2. Likewise, with weak bases and their conjugate acids, when the conjugate acid is stronger than the base, the pH of the solution will be acidic. A solution of equal concentration of pyridine and pyridinium chloride has a pH of 5.2.

Distributions of Species in Solutions of Weak Acids and Bases

A very useful, and often necessary, piece of information is the fraction in a solution of the total concentration of a weak acid or a weak base that exists in the ionized form. The hydrogen ion concentration is not equal to the concentration of dissociated acid in the solutions under discussion, because the pH is adjusted by adding additional acid or base. When an acid can exist as more than one ion, the fraction of the total acid present in each one of the forms gives a very clear description of the equilibrium. The fraction ionized is a very useful concept in solving complex equilibrium problems. Therefore, let us define a term, α, as the fraction of the total analytical concentration of a substance that exists in a specified form in solution. In the case of acids and bases, the subscript on alpha will designate the number of protons present in the desired species. Thus, α_{0_H} represents the fraction of the total acid present that contains no ionizable protons, α_{1_H} represents the fraction of the total acid present that contains one ionizable proton, and so on. This can be illustrated for a solution of benzoic acid.

$$\alpha_{0_H} = \frac{[C_6H_5COO^-]}{C_{HBz}} \qquad \alpha_{1_H} = \frac{[C_6H_5COOH]}{C_{HBz}} \qquad (5\text{-}31)$$

where, of course, the sum of all the fractions must equal one, or in this case,

$$\alpha_{0_H} + \alpha_{1_H} = 1$$

Naturally, the fraction of a weak acid that exists as the unprotonated form depends upon both the value of the acid dissociation constant of the acid as well as the pH of the solution. The higher the pH, the more of the acid that will be unprotonated. Similarly, for different acids at the same pH, the larger the value of K_a, the more of the acid that will be ionized. Let us develop a quantitative expression for the alphas in terms of K_a and $[H_3O^+]$.

In a solution of a weak acid, HA, the material balance for the acid is:

$$C_{HA} = [HA] + [A^-]$$

The fraction ionized of the total acid present is given by α_{0_H}.

$$\alpha_{0_H} = \frac{[A^-]}{C_{HA}}$$

Substituting the material balance for C_{HA}

$$\alpha_{0_H} = \frac{[A^-]}{[HA] + [A^-]}$$

Solving the equilibrium constant expression for the dissociation of the weak acid in order to obtain the concentration of the undissociated molecules at equilibrium:

$$[HA] = \frac{[H_3O^+][A^-]}{K_a}$$

which upon substitution into the expression for α_{0_H} given above:

$$\alpha_{0_H} = \frac{[A^-]}{\dfrac{[H_3O^+][A^-]}{K_a} + [A^-]}$$

which simplifies to:

$$\alpha_{0_H} = \frac{1}{\dfrac{[H_3O^+]}{K_a} + 1} = \frac{K_a}{[H_3O^+] + K_a} \tag{5-32}$$

Notice that Equation (5–32) does not contain any concentration terms for either the weak acid or its conjugate base, so that it is applicable to any solution of a monobasic acid at a known pH. By means of Equation (5–32) the fraction of any weak monoprotic acid dissociated at any pH can be calculated. Then knowing the fraction dissociated, the actual molar concentrations can be obtained from the total concentration of the acid in the solution.

Example.   Calculate the fraction of benzoic acid that exists as the conjugate base, benzoate ion, at a pH of 6.00.

Solution of this problem merely involves substitution of the hydronium ion concentration and the K_a for benzoic acid into Equation (5–32). At a pH of 6.00, $[H_3O^+] = 1.00 \times 10^{-6}$ M. $K_a = 6.32 \times 10^{-5}$

$$\alpha_{0_H} = \frac{6.320 \times 10^{-5}}{1.00 \times 10^{-6} + 6.320 \times 10^{-5}}$$

$$= 0.985$$

Which tells us that at a pH of 6.00, 98.5% of the benzoic acid in a solution exists as the benzoate ion. The molar concentration of the benzoate ion can be determined from the total acid concentration and the definition of alpha.

Let us assume that we have a 2.50×10^{-2} M solution of benzoic acid. Then, from Equation (5–31) the molar concentration of benzoate ion in this solution at a pH of 6.00 will be:

$$[C_6H_5COO^-] = \alpha_{0_H}C_{HBz}$$

$$= (0.985)(2.50 \times 10^{-2} \ M) = 2.44 \times 10^{-2} \ M$$

(*Note:* As stated earlier $[H_3O^+] \neq [Bz^-]$ since NaOH must have been added.)

A graph of log α_{0_H} as a function of pH for benzoic acid is shown in Fig. 5–3. Notice from Equation (5–32) that when $[H_3O^+] = K_a$, α_0 is $\frac{1}{2}$. Or to rephrase this, when one half of the acid exists in the ionized form, the pH of the solution is equal to the pK_a for the acid. This is a very useful relationship.

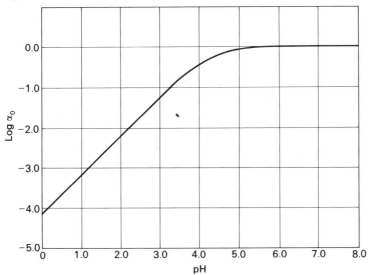

Fig. 5–3. Log α_{0_H} as a function of pH for benzoic acid.

Polyprotic Acids and Polyfunctional Bases

Some of the most useful reagents in effecting separations are acids or bases that contain more than one acidic proton or more than one basic nitrogen or oxygen. Tartaric acid (HOOC—CHOH—CHOH—COOH), citric acid (HOOC—CH$_2$—C(OH)(COOH)—CH$_2$—COOH), ethylenediaminetetraacetic acid (see p. 206), nitrilotriacetic acid (N(CH$_2$COOH)$_3$), to name a few, are polybasic acids that also are extremely useful complexing agents. Ethylenediamine (H$_2$N—CH$_2$—CH$_2$—NH$_2$), triethylenetetraamine (H$_2$N—CH$_2$—CH$_2$—NH—CH$_2$—CH$_2$—NH—CH$_2$—CH$_2$—NH$_2$), hexamethylenetetramine (urotropine, (CH$_2$)$_6$N$_4$) are all polyfunctional bases that serve as complexing agents or as buffers. pH calculations in solutions of these acids and bases are more complex than those discussed previously because of the presence of more than one acidic hydrogen or more than one basic nitrogen in the molecule. To illustrate the techniques involved, let us investigate the calculations for a solution of carbonic acid (carbon dioxide dissolved in water).

Example. Calculate the concentration of H_3O^+, HCO$_3^-$, and CO$_3^{2-}$ present in a 0.00100 M solution of carbonic acid. (For the purposes of this problem, let us erroneously assume that there is an entity called the H_2CO_3 molecule that exists in this solution.)

The chemical equilibria possible in the solution are:

$$H_2CO_3 + H_2O \rightleftharpoons H_3O^+ + HCO_3^-$$

and

$$HCO_3^- + H_2O \rightleftharpoons H_3O^+ + CO_3^{2-}$$

so there are two equilibrium constant expressions:

$$K_{a_1} = \frac{[H_3O^+][HCO_3^-]}{[H_2CO_3]} = 4.45 \times 10^{-7}$$

$$K_{a_2} = \frac{[H_3O^+][CO_3^{2-}]}{[HCO_3^-]} = 4.96 \times 10^{-11}$$

The problem asks for three different concentrations. The choice of which to solve for first is arbitrary. Since more often it is the pH of such solutions that is of interest, let's select $[H_3O^+]$ solely because it will serve to illustrate the technique for other problems. Having decided upon our unknown, we must find numbers or inter-relationships for all the remaining terms in the equilibrium constant expressions. The hydrogen ion concentration that is obtained as the answer must satisfy both K_{a_1} and K_{a_2} since in a homogeneous solution, there can be only one concentration of hydrogen ions.

The electroneutrality principle for the solution is:

$$[H_3O^+] = [HCO_3^-] + 2[CO_3^{2-}]$$

A material balance on the carbonic acid gives:

$$C_{CO_3} = [H_2CO_3] + [HCO_3^-] + [CO_3^{2-}] = 1.00 \times 10^{-3} \ M$$

since these are the only possible forms in which the carbonic acid can exist in this solution.

We have managed to write four equations that contain only four unknown concentration terms—two acid dissociation constant expressions, the electroneutrality principle, and the material balance. It is now possible to solve these equations for any one of the terms desired. The practical problem is how to solve the equations most efficiently. The one shown, is but an example of different ways to obtain an answer.

Substitute into the material balance expression the bicarbonate ion and carbonic acid concentrations given by the K_{a_1} and K_{a_2} expressions:

From K_{a_2}

$$[HCO_3^-] = \frac{[H_3O^+][CO_3^{2-}]}{K_{a_2}}$$

From K_{a_1}

$$[H_2CO_3] = \frac{[H_3O^+][HCO_3^-]}{K_{a_1}}$$

but this last equation still contains the bicarbonate ion concentration, that we are trying to eliminate; so substitute the relationship for it, into the expression, giving now:

$$[H_2CO_3] = \frac{[H_3O^+]^2[CO_3^{2-}]}{K_{a_1}K_{a_2}}$$

which now can be substituted into the material balance.

$$C_{CO_3} = \frac{[H_3O^+]^2[CO_3^{2-}]}{K_{a_1}K_{a_2}} + \frac{[H_3O^+][CO_3^{2-}]}{K_{a_2}} + [CO_3^{2-}]$$

In the expression, we still have a term whose value we do not know, the carbonate ion concentration. Thus we must eliminate it from this equation. This can be done by inserting into the electroneutrality principle expression the value for the bicarbonate ion concentration obtained from K_{a_2}:

$$[H_3O^+] = \frac{[H_3O^+][CO_3^{2-}]}{K_{a_2}} + 2[CO_3^{2-}]$$

which when rearranged and solved for the carbonate ion concentration gives

$$[CO_3^{2-}] = \frac{[H_3O^+]K_{a_2}}{[H_3O^+] + 2K_{a_2}}$$

This concentration expression now can be substituted into the material balance relationship.

$$C_{CO_3} = \frac{[H_3O^+]K_{a_2}}{[H_3O^+] + 2K_{a_2}} \left(\frac{[H_3O^+]^2}{K_{a_1}K_{a_2}} + \frac{[H_3O^+]}{K_{a_2}} + 1 \right)$$

which upon simplification gives:

$$C_{CO_3} = \frac{[H_3O^+]^3 + K_{a_1}[H_3O^+]^2 + K_{a_1}K_{a_2}[H_3O^+]}{K_{a_1}[H_3O^+] + 2K_{a_1}K_{a_2}} \tag{5-33}$$

$$= 1.00 \times 10^{-3} \ M$$

Since the numerical values for K_{a_1} and K_{a_2} are known, Equation (5-33) can be solved for $[H_3O^+]$. In order to do this, however, the cubic equation must be solved, which is more difficult mathematically than solving a quadratic equation. We tried to avoid solving quadratic equations, so let us see if we can make some simplifying assumptions that will enable us to simplify the expression above. Careful inspection of the relative acidity of the two protons on carbonic acid, as indicated by the values of K_{a_1} and K_{a_2}, allows an estimate of the concentrations of the various species present. When we have a good guess about these, then certain assumptions will be made that will simplify things considerably.

In the case of many weak acids and bases, the dissociations after the loss of the first proton are sufficiently weak that, for all practical purposes, they can be neglected. In the case of carbonic acid, the difference between the numerical values of the two acid dissociations shows that the first proton is much more acidic than the second. The first proton will ionize first and almost exclusively. Since K_{a_1} is quite small, the extent of this dissociation will be slight, and hence the extent of the second dissociation will be even slighter.

As a general rule of thumb, when $K_{a_2}/K_{a_1} \leq 10^{-4}$, the second ionization occurs to only a negligibly small extent. In the case of carbonic acid, that we are considering here, $K_{a_2}/K_{a_1} = 1.05 \times 10^{-4}$, so the assumption can be made in this solution.

Thus, in beginning the solution of the problem, we ignore at first the second dissociation of carbonic acid, and solve only the first equilibrium constant for the hydronium ion concentration. This reduces the problem to one of calculation of the concentration of hydronium ion for a weak, monoprotic acid, analogous to our previous problem for benzoic acid. The K_{a_1} expression, using the amended electro-neutrality principle and the amended material balance becomes:

$$K_{a_1} = \frac{[H_3O^+][H_3O^+]}{(1.00 \times 10^{-3} - [H_3O^+])} = 4.45 \times 10^{-7}$$

Since the numerical value of K_{a_1} is so small, the concentration of the hydrogen ion in the denominator will be negligibly small in comparison to the original concentration of carbonic acid, and it can be forgotten about. Thus:

$$[H_3O^+]^2 = (4.45 \times 10^{-7})(1.00 \times 10^{-3})$$

$$[H_3O^+] = 2.11 \times 10^{-5} \ M$$

Checking the assumption we made to solve K_{a_1}, 2.11×10^{-5} is 2.11% of 1.00×10^{-3}, which is within our definition of being negligible.

To continue on with the problem. The hydrogen ion concentration calculated now satisfies all equations in which it appears. Since we have assumed that the carbonate ion concentration is negligible, the electroneutrality principle reduces to $[H_3O^+] = [HCO_3^-] = 2.11 \times 10^{-5} \ M$. Which gives us the second concentration asked for by the problem.

In order to calculate the carbonate ion concentration, K_{a_2} must be solved since we have assumed that the carbonate ion concentration is negligibly small in the electroneutrality principle and the material balance. We know the bicarbonate ion and the hydronium ion concentrations already, so this presents no problem.

$$K_{a_2} = \frac{[H_3O^+][CO_3^{2-}]}{[HCO_3^-]} = \frac{(2.11 \times 10^{-5})[CO_3^{2-}]}{(2.11 \times 10^{-5})} = 4.69 \times 10^{-11}$$

$$[CO_3^{2-}] = 4.69 \times 10^{-11} \ M$$

Because of the initial assumption that the extent of dissociation of bicarbonate ion into carbonate is negligibly small, $[CO_3^{2-}] = K_{a_2}$. This is a general condition which follows directly from the first assumption. Because of this remarkable conclusion, it becomes extraordinarily easy to calculate the concentration of the unprotonated anion to check the validity of the first assumption before actually making it. In this problem, $[CO_3^{2-}]$ is only 0.0002% of $[HCO_3^-]$ so that the initial assumption concerning its negligibility is certainly a valid one.

As a general practice, for dibasic acids, when $K_{a_1} \geq K_{a_2} \times 10^4$, just solve K_{a_1} to obtain the pH of the solution. The concentration of the binegative anion will be equal to K_{a_2}. When K_{a_1} is less than $10^4 K_{a_2}$, then the cubic equation Equation (5–33) must be solved.

When solving pH problems involving tribasic or higher acids, the same assumption is made. When $K_{a_1} > 10^4 K_{a_2}$ then the second and all successive acid dissociations are neglected. When this is not possible, you're in for a lot of trouble and hard work with the complicated mathematics that result.

This whole treatment, however, only is valid in solutions of pure polybasic acids. When the pH of the solution is adjusted through addition of a strong acid or a strong base, different assumptions must be made. When the conjugate bases are added from external sources the treatment must also be altered.

In analytical chemistry, the completely unprotonated anion of a polybasic acid often is a precipitant (such as dimethylglyoximate), a complexing agent (such as citrate), or is adsorbed onto an anion-exchange resin (such as tartrate). Because of this, we are interested in the concentration of the reagent species and how the concentration changes with the pH of the solution. The calculation, under the conditions of known hydrogen ion concentration, is much simpler than the one in the preceding example. This simplicity is brought about by extending the concept of the fraction of the acid dissociated, α, to dibasic acids.

For the general case of the dibasic acid, H_2A, the values of the alphas are by definition:

$$\alpha_{0_H} = \frac{[A^{2-}]}{C_{H_2A}} \qquad \alpha_{1_H} = \frac{[HA^-]}{C_{H_2A}} \qquad \alpha_{2_H} = \frac{[H_2A]}{C_{H_2A}}$$

Initially, let us concern ourselves with α_{0_H}, since this is the alpha most frequently used. We would like to derive a relationship for it in terms of the acid dissociation constants and the hydrogen ion concentration of the solution.

The material balance for the solution will be:

$$C_{H_2A} = [H_2A] + [HA^-] + [A^{2-}]$$

which when substituted into the definition for α_{0_H} gives:

$$\alpha_{0_H} = \frac{[A^{2-}]}{[H_2A] + [HA^-] + [A^{2-}]}$$

If the concentration terms in the denominator of the above expression could be expressed solely in terms of $[A^{2-}]$ and $[H_3O^+]$, it would be possible to obtain a simple, and usable expression for α_{0_H}. This can be accomplished by solving the appropriate equilibrium constant expressions in terms of these concentrations only, and substituting the values obtained for $[H_2A]$ and $[HA^-]$ into the above equation.

$$\alpha_{0_H} = \frac{[A^{2-}]}{\dfrac{[H_3O^+]^2[A^{2-}]}{K_{a_1}K_{a_2}} + \dfrac{[H_3O^+][A^{2-}]}{K_{a_2}} + [A^{2-}]}$$

which when simplified gives:

$$\alpha_{0_H} = \frac{K_{a_1}K_{a_2}}{[H_3O^+]^2 + [H_3O^+]K_{a_1} + K_{a_1}K_{a_2}} \qquad (5\text{--}34)$$

By using Equation (5–34), the concentration of the unprotonated anion can be calculated readily when the pH and the analytical concentration of the acid in the solution are known.

Example. Calculate the concentration of free carbonate ion in 1.25×10^{-3} M carbonic acid at a pH of 8.00.

This problem consists of nothing more than mere substitution of numbers into Equation (5–34) and the use of the definition for α_{0_H} to calculate the desired concentration.

At a pH of 8.00:

$$\alpha_{0_H} = \frac{(4.45 \times 10^{-7})(4.69 \times 10^{-11})}{(1.00 \times 10^{-8})^2 + (1.00 \times 10^{-8})(4.45 \times 10^{-7}) + (4.45 \times 10^{-7})(4.69 \times 10^{-11})}$$

$$= \frac{2.08 \times 10^{-17}}{(1.00 \times 10^{-16}) + (4.45 \times 10^{-15}) + (2.08 \times 10^{-17})}$$

$$= \frac{2.08 \times 10^{-17}}{4.57 \times 10^{-15}} = 4.56 \times 10^{-3}$$

Therefore from the definition of alpha and the total concentration of the carbonic acid present in all forms in the solution:

$$[CO_3^{2-}] = \alpha_{0_H} C_{CO_3} = (4.56 \times 10^{-3})(1.25 \times 10^{-3} \ M) = 5.61 \times 10^{-6} \ M$$

Expressions for α_{1_H} and α_{2_H} can be derived in a similar fashion from the definitions of these terms and the material balance for the solution. Also, it can be shown that the relationships between α_{0_H} and α_{1_H}, and between α_{0_H} and α_{2_H} are:

$$\alpha_{1_H} = \frac{[H_3O^+]}{K_{a2}} \alpha_{0_H} \tag{5–35}$$

$$\alpha_{2_H} = \frac{[H_3O^+]^2}{K_{a_1} K_{a2}} \alpha_{0_H} \tag{5–36}$$

For diacidic bases, such as ethylenediamine, the use of alphas is analogous. For ethylenediamine, the following equilibria occur:

$$H_2N-CH_2-CH_2-NH_2 + H_2O \rightleftharpoons H_2N-CH_2-CH_2-NH_3^+ + OH^-$$

$$H_2N-CH_2-CH_2-NH_3^+ + H_2O \rightleftharpoons {}^+H_3N-CH_2-CH_2-NH_3^+ + OH^-$$

Let us follow the prevalent practice and abbreviate ethylenediamine as en. Using this notation in writing the base dissociation constant expressions:

$$K_{b_1} = \frac{[enH^+][OH^-]}{[en]} = 9.1 \times 10^{-5}$$

$$K_{b_2} = \frac{[enH_2^{2+}][OH^-]}{[enH^+]} = 1.5 \times 10^{-7}$$

It is much simpler and more convenient to consider the ethylenediamine system or any polyamine equilibria in terms of the conjugate acids, rather than as the bases. When this is done the same reasoning and the same equations that have been derived for alphas and the pH dependence of alphas will be applicable to the polyamine systems. As an illustration, consider the equilibria in the ethylenediamine system in terms of the conjugate acids:

$$^+H_3N—CH_2—CH_2—NH_3^+ + H_2O \rightleftharpoons H_2N—CH_2—CH_2—NH_3^+ + H_3O^+$$

$$K_{a_1} = \frac{[enH^+][H_3O^+]}{[enH_2^{2+}]}$$

$$H_2N—CH_2—CH_2—NH_3^+ + H_2O \rightleftharpoons H_2N—CH_2—CH_2—NH_2 + H_3O^+$$

$$K_{a_2} = \frac{[en][H_3O^+]}{[enH^+]}$$

Examination of these four equilibria, the two base dissociations and the dissociations of the two conjugate acids, reveals the interrelations of the acid and base dissociation constants. K_{b_1} and K_{a_2} contain the same ethylenediamine species and the solvent, so that $K_{b_1} \cdot K_{a_2} = K_w$, in accordance with the relative strengths of conjugates as given Equation (5–15). K_{b_2} and K_{a_1} contain the same ethylenediamine species, so that $K_{b_2} \cdot K_{a_1} = K_w$. When tables of the dissociation constants for the conjugate acids of polyacidic amines are not available, the values can be calculated readily from the tabulated base dissociation constants by means of these relationships. Equations (5–34), (5–35), and (5–36) can then be applied to determine the extent of the dissociation in any solution of stated pH.

Polyprotic acids containing more than two ionizable protons are handled in a manner analogous to the one illustrated for a dibasic acid. Problems involving solutions of phosphoric acid (H_3PO_4), nitrilotriacetic acid (H_3X), ethylenediaminetetraacetic acid (H_4Y), and diethylenetriaminepentaacetic acid (H_5L) appear more complex only because of the more complicated equations. The techniques used to establish the equations and the mathematics of solving them have already been shown. The assumptions involved are the same ones made for any acid solution. Usually the concentration of the unprotonated anion is the species of interest and this is calculated easily by using the α_{0_H} for the acid in question. For tribasic acids, such as phosphoric or nitrilotriacetic, the relationship between α_{0_H} and the hydronium ion concentration is:

$$\alpha_{0_H} = \frac{K_{a_1}K_{a_2}K_{a_3}}{[H_3O^+]^3 + K_{a_1}[H_3O^+]^2 + K_{a_1}K_{a_2}[H_3O^+] + K_{a_1}K_{a_2}K_{a_3}} \tag{5-37}$$

Values of α_{0_H} for EDTA as a function of pH are tabulated in Appendix 2. The discussion of EDTA and the equations for the calculation of its alphas, as well as their interrelationships, will be deferred until the section on complex ion equilibrium. Ringbom's[19] book has tabulated values of α_{0_H} for other important ligands. Appendix 3 lists values of α_{0_H} for NH_3 as a function of pH.

The successive ionization of the protons of polyprotic acids enables the formation of intermediate species which, in addition to being the conjugate base of a weak acid, still contain protons which can exhibit acidic properties. For example, phosphoric acid, H_3PO_4, ionizes to form $H_2PO_4^-$ which is the conjugate base of phosphoric acid but still contains two acidic protons; HPO_4^- which is the conjugate base of the dihydrogen phosphate still has a single proton that imparts acidic properties to it; and PO_4^{3-} which is the conjugate base of the monohydrogen phosphate and has no protons nor any acidic properties—it is a strong base. When these intermediate species are placed in aqueous solution, part of their behavior is as a weak acid and part of their behavior is as a weak base. The calculation of the pH of a solution of such intermediates must be based on reactions describing both the acid and the base behavior. To illustrate this type of calculation and to derive the equations applicable to any intermediate species, let us use the carbonic acid system and work with solutions of $NaHCO_3$.

In a sodium bicarbonate solution, the chemical equilibria present are:

$$HCO_3^- + H_2O \rightleftharpoons H_3O^+ + CO_3^{2-}$$

$$HCO_3^- + H_2O \rightleftharpoons H_2CO_3 + OH^-$$

Having the equilibrium constants:

$$K_{a_2} = \frac{[H_3O^+][CO_3^{2-}]}{[HCO_3^-]} = 4.69 \times 10^{-11}$$

$$K_{b_2} = \frac{[OH^-][H_2CO_3]}{[HCO_3^-]} = 2.25 \times 10^{-8}$$

The problem posed is to derive a relationship between the hydrogen ion concentration and the total bicarbonate concentration involving no other terms than equilibrium constants. To do this, let us start with the electroneutrality principle and the material balance for the bicarbonate in the solution. The electroneutrality principle expression for a bicarbonate solution can be written as:

$$[Na^+] + [H_3O^+] = 2[CO_3^{2-}] + [HCO_3^-] + [OH^-]$$

The sodium ion is not involved in any reactions, so its concentration is the known initial amount.

The material balance on the carbonate in the system:

$$C_{CO_3} = [H_2CO_3] + [HCO_3^-] + [CO_3^{2-}]$$

Including the autoprotolysis expression for water, there are now five equations available with five unknowns in them, so that the problem can be solved. From the stoichiometry of $NaHCO_3$, we know that in the solution, $[Na^+] = C_{CO_3}$. Therefore, let us substitute the material balance expression into the electroneutrality principle in place of $[Na^+]$, rearrange the result slightly, and solve this for $[H_3O^+]$.

$$[H_3O^+] = 2[CO_3^{2-}] + [HCO_3^-] + \frac{K_w}{[H_3O^+]} - [H_2CO_3] - [HCO_3^-] - [CO_3^{2-}]$$

which simplifies to:

$$[H_3O^+] = [CO_3^{2-}] + \frac{K_w}{[H_3O^+]} - [H_2CO_3]$$

Now we must eliminate both the concentrations of the carbonic acid and of the carbonate ion present in the solution. In order to do this, solve the K_{a_1} and K_{a_2} expressions for carbonic acid in terms of the $[HCO_3^-]$ and then substitute the resultant expressions into the above equation.

$$[H_3O^+] = \frac{K_{a_2}[HCO_3^-]}{[H_3O^+]} + \frac{K_w}{[H_3O^+]} - \frac{[H_3O^+][HCO_3^-]}{K_{a_1}}$$

or

$$[H_3O^+]^2 = K_{a_2}[HCO_3^-] + K_w - \frac{[H_3O^+]^2[HCO_3^-]}{K_{a_1}}$$

$$[H_3O^+]^2 = \frac{K_w + K_{a_2}[HCO_3^-]}{1 + \dfrac{[HCO_3^-]}{K_{a_1}}} \tag{5-38}$$

In order to solve Equation (5–38) it is necessary to know the equilibrium concentration of bicarbonate ion $[HCO_3^-]$, in the solution. The two reactions have decreased the concentration from the initial one. It is customary, at this point, instead of proceeding further to relate C_{CO_3} in terms of $[HCO_3^-]$ only, to assume that the extent of the acid–base interactions between the bicarbonate ion and water are very slight, do not proceed to any appreciable extent, and consequently, $C_{CO_3} = [HCO_3^-]$. For almost all intermediate species of polyprotic acids this assumption is valid. Making the substitution produces:

$$[H_3O^+] = \left(\frac{K_w + K_{a_2}C_{CO_3}}{1 + \dfrac{C_{CO_3}}{K_{a_1}}} \right)^{\frac{1}{2}} \tag{5-39}$$

This equation should be used to calculate the pH of intermediate species of weak acids. Even though it is not a complicated expression to solve and all the terms are readily available, Equation (5–39) has not caught on and is very seldom used. A simplified version, which is often incorrect, is preferred. For not-too-dilute solutions of an acid with a moderately large K_{a_2}, the numerator of Equation (5–39) can be simplified; that is, for $K_{a_2}C_{CO_3} \gg K_w$, K_w may be neglected. Note, however, that for acids where K_{a_2} is small (10^{-10} or less) when C_{CO_3} is low (10^{-3} M or less) this assumption is *not* valid.

For many solutions, $C_{CO_3}/K_{a_1} \gg 1$, so that the one in the denominator of Equation (5–39) can be neglected. This is only a valid assumption when C_{CO_3}/K_{a_1} is fifty or greater. Note that it is not valid for $NaHSO_4$.

When these two assumptions are applied to Equation (5–39) it reduces to the extremely simple form:

$$[H_3O^+] = (K_{a_1} \cdot K_{a_2})^{\frac{1}{2}} \tag{5-40}$$

or

$$pH = \tfrac{1}{2}(pK_{a_1} + pK_{a_2})$$

Let us now illustrate the application of these equations by calculating the pH of a couple of solutions of intermediate species.

Example.   Calculate the pH of 70 ml of 0.0667 M NaHCO$_3$.

The problem involves the substitution of numbers into either Equation (5–39) or (5–40), with the most difficult part of the problem, deciding which equation to use. $K_{a_2} C_{CO_3} = (4.69 \times 10^{-11})(6.67 \times 10^{-2}) = 3.13 \times 10^{-12}$. This is sufficiently large compared to K_w to neglect K_w in the numerator of Equation (5–39). C_{CO_3}/K_{a_1} is obviously much greater than 50, so that Equation (5–40) can be safely used.

$$ \text{pH} = \tfrac{1}{2}(pK_{a_1} + pK_{a_2}) = \tfrac{1}{2}(6.35 + 10.33) = 8.34 $$

Example.   Calculate the pH of a 0.00100 M solution of sodium hydrogen iminodiacetate.

$$ \text{HN} \diagup^{\displaystyle CH_2-COOH}_{\displaystyle \diagdown CH_2-COO^-Na^+} \qquad K_{a_1} = 1.05 \times 10^{-3} \qquad K_{a_2} = 1.3 \times 10^{-10} $$

As in the preceding problem, the only difficult portion of the solution lies in determining which equation to use. Since $K_{a_2} C_{HA^-} = 1.3 \times 10^{-13}$ this is not sufficiently greater than K_w to permit K_w to be neglected. $C_{HA^-}/K_{a_1} = 0.95$, so that this certainly is not greater than 1, and the denominator cannot be simplified either. Equation (5–39) must be used.

$$ H_3O^+ = \left(\frac{1.00 \times 10^{-14} + (1.3 \times 10^{-10})(1.00 \times 10^{-3})}{1 + \dfrac{1.00 \times 10^{-3}}{1.05 \times 10^{-3}}} \right)^{\frac{1}{2}} $$

$$ = \left(\frac{1.4 \times 10^{-13}}{1.95} \right)^{\frac{1}{2}} = 2.7 \times 10^{-7} \ M $$

$$ \text{pH} = 6.57 $$

(*Note*: Had Equation (5–40) been used, $[H_3O^+] = 3.7 \times 10^{-7} \ M$, pH $= 6.43$ would have been calculated, an error of 37% in the hydrogen ion concentration.)

Buffer Solutions

A *buffer solution* is a solution that is capable of resisting changes in pH when reasonably large quantities of acid or of base are added to it, or when it is diluted. Naturally, there will be slight changes in the pH of the solution, but these are not equivalent to the amount of acid or base that are added. Buffer solutions are used when it is necessary to carry out a chemical reaction that consumes or produces hydrogen ions, but the reaction must be carried out at a constant pH. Buffers are used in EDTA titrations to maintain a constant pH in the titrate solution. EDTA chelates (see below) decrease in stability with decreasing pH, yet the titration reaction is:

$$ M^{n+} + HY^{3-} \rightleftharpoons MY^{(n-4)+} + H^+ $$

The proton released must be consumed, for if it is allowed to increase the acidity of the solution, the equilibrium position will shift to the left, and the titration reaction will not go to completion. Buffer solutions are widely used in separation procedures to ensure that the species in the solution that are being separated have the desired number of protons or electric charges. This was essential for the success of the drug separation discussed earlier.

A buffer is a solution that contains approximately equimolar concentrations of a weak acid and its conjugate base. The solution equilibrium is:

$$HA + H_2O \rightleftharpoons A^- + H_3O^+$$

When an acid is added to such a solution, the concentration of the protons on the right-hand side of the reaction is increased, causing the equilibrium to shift toward the left and consume some of the excess protons (Le Châtelier's principle). When a base is added to a buffer solution, the concentration of protons on the right-hand side of the equation is decreased, shifting the equilibrium to the right. The conjugate acid dissociates in an attempt to restore the equilibrium state.

The equilibrium constant expression for the equilibrium of a buffer is:

$$K_a = \frac{[H_3O^+][A^-]}{[HA]}$$

which can be rearranged to the form:

$$[H_3O^+] = K_a \frac{[HA]}{[A^-]}$$

From this form of the constant we can see that addition of a base to a buffer solution decreases the numerator of the right-hand side and increases the denominator, thus decreasing the ratio slightly. If, however, the concentrations of the buffer acid and its conjugate base are large compared to the amount of base added, the change in the ratio will be relatively slight, and will produce only a relatively slight decrease in the hydronium ion concentration. When an acid is added to a buffer solution, the denominator of the above equation will decrease and the numerator will increase. But again, if the added amount of acid is small compared to the concentration of the conjugate acid–base pair, the increase in the ratio is relatively slight and the resultant increase in the hydrogen ion concentration is small.

It should be apparent that the change in the ratio of acid to conjugate base, upon addition of additional strong acid or base, will be least when the initial ratio is one. This tells us that a buffer solution is most effective when it consists of equimolar concentrations of the two conjugate forms. From the above equation we can conclude also that when the ratio of acid to conjugate base is ten or greater the buffer loses its ability to resist changes in pH when additional acid is added. Similarly, when the ratio of the base to the conjugate acid is ten or greater the buffer loses its effectiveness to resist changes in pH when additional base is added. This gives us limits for the useful operation of a buffer solution: from $[HA]/[A^-] = 10/1$ to $[HA]/[A^-] = 1/10$. Inserting these limits into the equilibrium constant expression above gives us the following limiting hydrogen ion concentration range for effectiveness: $[H_3O^+] = K_a (10/1)$ to $K_a (1/10)$. Or taking the negative logarithm of both sides, the *effective buffer range* is pH $= pK_a \pm 1$.

The *level* of a buffer is its pH value when $[HA] = [A^-]$, that is, the value of the

pK_a of the conjugate acid of the buffer system. The range of a buffer is the pH region over which it will resist effectively changes in pH upon addition of acids and bases. Some examples of buffer solutions and their levels of effectiveness are given in Table 5–8.

Table 5–8. TYPICAL BUFFER SYSTEMS

Buffer System	pK_a	Buffer Level
$H_3PO_4-H_2PO_4^-$	2.17	1.17–3.17
Citric acid–H_2citrate$^-$	3.13	2.13–4.13
Phthalic acid–Hphthalate$^-$	3.14	2.14–4.14
HF–F$^-$	3.17	2.17–4.17
$CH_3COOH-CH_3COO^-$	4.76	3.76–5.76
Pyridinium ion–pyridine	5.18	4.18–6.18
Hphthalate$^-$–phthalate^{2-}	5.40	4.40–6.40
$H_2CO_3-HCO_3^-$	6.35	5.35–7.35
$H_2PO_4^--HPO_4^{2-}$	7.21	6.21–8.21
$NH_4^+-NH_3$	9.24	8.24–10.24
$HCO_3^--CO_3^{2-}$	10.33	9.33–11.33
$CH_3NH_3^+-CH_3NH_2$	10.67	9.67–11.67
$HPO_4^{2-}-PO_4^{3-}$	12.36	11.36–13.36

Buffer solutions are not able to receive enormous amounts of acid or base without becoming destroyed. The amount of acid or base that can be consumed by a buffer solution will be determined by the concentrations of the conjugate acid–base pair. The amount of acid or base that a buffer can consume is called its *capacity*. The capacity of a buffer solution is defined as the number of equivalents of an acid or base that must be added to one liter of the buffer to cause a change in the pH of the solution by one unit. Mathematically the capacity is measured by the *buffer index*:

$$\beta = \frac{dC_b}{d\text{pH}} = -\frac{dC_a}{d\text{pH}}$$

Or as we have stated above, it is the change in the concentration of acid (C_a) or of base (C_b) per pH unit.

To simplify the discussion, let us discuss the buffer capacity solely in terms of adding acid to the conjugate acid–base pair, which will affect the concentration of base in the system. Under this restriction, the equation describing the buffer index can be given by:

$$\beta = \frac{dC_b}{d\text{pH}} = 2.303\left(\frac{K_w}{[H_3O^+]} + [H_3O^+] + \frac{CK_a[H_3O^+]}{(K_a + [H_3O^+])^2}\right) \quad (5-41)$$

where $C = [HA] + [A^-]$ in the case of an acid and its conjugate, and $C = [BH^+] + [B]$ when the buffer is composed of a base and its conjugate. C represents the total concentration of both acid and conjugate base in the buffer system. The first two terms of Equation (5–41) are there because of the buffering effect of water. The third term is due to the buffering effect of the conjugate acid-base pair. Let us see how this equation assists us in evaluating buffer systems.

Example. Calculate the buffer index of a $0.100\ M\ NH_3$ –$0.100\ M\ NH_4Cl$, pH = 9.24 buffer.

At pH = 9.24, $[H_3O^+]$ = $5.8 \times 10^{-10}\ M$. For NH_4^+, K_a = 5.8×10^{-10}.

$$C = [NH_3] + [NH_4^+] = 0.100\ M + 0.100\ M = 0.200\ M$$

Substituting all of these values into Equation (5–41):

$$\beta = 2.303\left(\frac{1.00 \times 10^{-14}}{5.8 \times 10^{-10}} + 5.8 \times 10^{-10} + \frac{(0.200)(5.8 \times 10^{-10})(5.8 \times 10^{-10})}{(5.8 \times 10^{-10} + 5.8 \times 10^{-10})^2}\right)$$

$$\beta = 0.115\ M$$

This tells us that a change in the concentration of ammonia in this buffer by $0.115\ M$ is required to change the pH of the buffer solution by one pH unit. To illustrate the use of the buffer index, let us add 1.00 ml of $0.50\ M$ HCl to 500 ml of this NH_3–NH_4Cl buffer, and calculate the change in the pH that will be produced.

First we must find the change in the number of equivalents of acid that occurs. This is merely the number of equivalents of protons added to the buffer solution

$$\text{no. of mmol of } H_3O^+ \text{ added} = 1.00\ \text{ml} \times 0.50\ M = 0.50\ \text{mmol}$$

The change in the concentration of protons in the buffer solution is:

$$\frac{0.50\ \text{mmol}}{500\ \text{ml}} = 1.00 \times 10^{-3}\ M$$

We know that the buffer index of this solution is $0.115\ M$. From the definition of the buffer index:

$$\beta = 0.115\ M = -\frac{dC_a}{d\text{pH}}$$

which upon rearrangement gives:

$$d\text{pH} = -\frac{dC_a}{\beta}$$

Substituting the known values into this equation:

$$d\text{pH} = -\frac{1.00 \times 10^{-3}\ M}{0.115\ M} = -0.0087$$

where the negative sign tells us that the pH decreases upon addition of acid. Thus the final pH can be calculated as: pH = 9.24 − 0.01 = 9.23.

The use of Equation (5–41) to calculate the buffer index assumes that there is no appreciable change in the volume of the solution upon addition of the strong acid or base. Since the expression for the buffer index includes concentration terms, the value of β will decrease when there is appreciable dilution.

pH Titrations

One excellent way to characterize an unknown substance that is either acidic or basic is in terms of its acid or base dissociation constant. A second property useful for identification of unknown compounds is the equivalent weight. Both of these characteristic properties can be determined readily by titration of the substance with a solution of standard base or acid. The pH of the solution is measured at selected intervals. This measured pH is graphed as a function of the number of milliequivalents of the standard acid or base added. From the resulting graph, both the equivalent weight and the acid dissociation constant of the unknown material can be determined. In order to have a better understanding of pH titrations, let us see how the pH of a solution of a weak acid changes during its titration with a strong base.

The acid dissociation reaction of the weak acid, HA, in solution will be:

$$HA + H_2O \rightleftharpoons H_3O^+ + A^-$$

with its concentration equilibrium constant:

$$K_a = \frac{[H_3O^+][A^-]}{[HA]}$$

Before the actual titration is started, the solution of the weak acid of volume V will have a pH that can be calculated from the concentration of the acid, if this is known. The technique is identical to that illustrated above for the calculation of the pH of a solution of benzoic acid.

Upon addition of standard base, say NaOH, the acid–base reaction

$$NaOH + HA \rightleftharpoons Na^+A^- + H_2O$$

takes place, decreasing the amount of free acid and increasing the amount of the conjugate base, A^-, present in the solution. Allowing for the dilution caused by the addition of v ml of the standard base, the pH of the solution can now be calculated at any point. The solution during the titration is a mixture of a weak acid and its conjugate base, so its pH is calculated in the manner illustrated for the mixture of benzoic acid and sodium benzoate before.

At that point where the number of milliequivalents of standard base added is exactly one-half of the total amount of weak acid present, half of this acid will have been neutralized producing its conjugate base, and the other half of the acid will remain unreacted. Thus, an excellent buffer is produced. But equally important is the fact that at this point, regardless of the volume of the solution, the concentrations of the conjugate acid and the conjugate base will be identical.

$$[H_3O^+] = K_a \frac{[HA]}{[A^-]}$$

Since half-way to the equivalence point of the titration, $[HA] = [A^-]$, at this point $[H_3O^+] = K_a$ or $pH = pK_a$.

At the point where an exactly equivalent amount of strong base has been added to the weak acid solution (the equivalence point), none of the weak acid will remain in the solution. There will not be any excess of the strong base. Here the solution will contain only the conjugate base of the weak acid, and its pH can be calculated from the base dissociation constant for the reaction:

$$A^- + H_2O \rightleftharpoons HA + OH^-$$

$$K_b = \frac{[HA][OH^-]}{[A^-]}$$

(Be sure to remember the dilution of the solution by the addition of the strong base.) The calculation at the equivalence point of a pH titration was illustrated by the calculation of the pH of a solution of sodium benzoate earlier.

After all of the weak acid has reacted, continued addition of the strong base is the same as merely diluting the base, since there is nothing in the solution with which it can react. Hence, to calculate the pH of the solution past the equivalence point, use dilution effects only.

To illustrate all of these calculations, let us calculate the pH of the titrate solution during the titration of 125 ml of 0.0425 M benzoic acid with standard 0.105 N NaOH.

$$C_6H_5COOH + OH^- \rightleftharpoons C_6H_5COO^- + H_2O$$

In the initial solution before we begin the titration we have:

$$125 \text{ ml} \times 0.0425 \ M = 5.32 \text{ millimoles of benzoic acid}$$

Before any NaOH is added, the pH of the solution is calculated as that of a pure benzoic acid solution. The electroneutrality principle is $[H_3O^+] = [Bz^-]$, while the material balance on benzoate is: $C_{HBz} = [HBz] + [Bz^-] = 0.0425 \ M$. Assuming that the extent of the ionization of benzoic acid is negligible,

$$[H_3O^+] = \sqrt{K_a C_{HBz}} = \sqrt{(6.320 \times 10^{-5})(4.25 \times 10^{-2})}$$

$$= 1.64 \times 10^{-3} \ M$$

$$pH = 2.78$$

Comparison of $[H_3O^+]$ with C_{HBz} shows that the assumption about the extent of the dissociation was correct.

After the addition of 5.00 ml of the base:

$$5.00 \text{ ml} \times 0.105 \ N = 0.525 \text{ milliequivalents of base added}$$

The base will react with the benzoic acid to reduce its amount by 0.525 milli-equivalents and, in so doing, produce 0.525 milliequivalents of sodium benzoate. The volume of the solution will be increased by 5.00 ml, to 130 ml. Thus, at equilibrium:

$$C_{HBz} = \frac{5.32 \text{ mequiv} - 0.525 \text{ mequiv}}{130 \text{ ml}} = 3.69 \times 10^{-2} \ M = [HBz] + [H_3O^+]$$

$[HBz] = C_{HBz} - [H_3O^+]$; assuming $[H_3O^+]$ is negligibly small, $C_{HBz} = [HBz]$

$$[Bz^-] = \frac{0.525 \text{ mequiv}}{130 \text{ ml}} + [H_3O^+] = 4.03 \times 10^{-3} \ M + [H_3O^+]$$

which when substituted into the equilibrium constant expression:

$$[H_3O^+] = (6.320 \times 10^{-5}) \frac{3.69 \times 10^{-2}}{4.03 \times 10^{-3} + [H_3O^+]}$$

$$= 5.10 \times 10^{-4} \ M$$

$$pH = 3.29$$

(*Note*: In performing this calculation it was assumed that $[H_3O^+] < C_{HBz}$, but not that $[H_3O^+] < [Bz^-]$ since the amount of benzoate ion formed by the titration reaction at this stage is very small. Comparison of the calculated $[H_3O^+]$ with each of the two benzoate forms confirms the correctness of this procedure.)
After 25.4 ml of NaOH have been added:

$$25.4 \text{ ml} \times 0.105 \ M = 2.66 \text{ mequiv of NaOH added}$$

This added base will react to reduce the amount of benzoic acid to $5.32 - 2.66$ mequiv = 2.66 mequiv. In reacting it will produce 2.66 mequiv of benzoate ion. The volume of the solution will be increased to 150.4 ml. At this new equilibrium:

$$[HBz] = \frac{2.66 \text{ mequiv}}{150.4 \text{ ml}} = 1.77 \times 10^{-2} \ M$$

$$[Bz^-] = \frac{2.66 \text{ mequiv}}{150.4 \text{ ml}} = 1.77 \times 10^{-2} \ M$$

which when substituted into the acid dissociation constant expression:

$$[H_3O^+] = (6.320 \times 10^{-5}) \frac{1.77 \times 10^{-2}}{1.77 \times 10^{-2}} = 6.320 \times 10^{-5} \ M$$

$$pH = 4.20$$

(*Note*: This is the half-neutralized point of the titration, where pH $= pK_a$.)
When 50.7 ml, an exactly equivalent amount of NaOH, has been added:

$$50.7 \text{ ml} \times 0.105 \ M = 5.32 \text{ mequiv of NaOH added}$$

All of the benzoic acid will have reacted producing 5.32 mequiv of sodium benzoate. The volume of the solution will now be 175.7 ml. The benzoate ion concentration:

$$C_{Bz} = \frac{5.32 \text{ mequiv}}{175.7 \text{ ml}} = 3.03 \times 10^{-2} \ M$$

The electroneutrality principle statement for this solution now is: $[Na^+] = [Bz^-] +$

[OH$^-$], and the material balance for benzoate is: $C_{Bz} = $ [HBz] + [Bz$^-$] = 3.03 × 10^{-2} M. Combining these two expressions gives: [OH$^-$] = [HBz], which when substituted into the K_b expression for the benzoate ion:

$$[OH^-] = \sqrt{K_b C_{Bz}} = \sqrt{(1.58 \times 10^{-10})(3.03 \times 10^{-2})}$$

$$= 2.19 \times 10^{-6} \ M$$

$$pOH = 5.66 \quad pH = 8.34$$

This calculation was made assuming that [OH$^-$] < [Bz$^-$] which is verified by the results obtained.

After 60.0 ml of NaOH have been added:

There is now an excess of the base in the solution. 50.7 ml of the NaOH were consumed in reacting with the benzoic acid, leaving 9.3 ml of NaOH in excess, unreacted in the solution. This excess will be sufficient to suppress any base dissociation of the benzoate ion, so that this need not be considered in the calculations. The total volume of the solution is 185.0 ml. Thus the excess NaOH has been diluted to:

$$[OH^-] = 0.105 \ M \ \frac{9.3 \ ml}{185.0 \ ml}$$

$$= 5.28 \times 10^{-3} \ M$$

$$pOH = 2.28 \quad pH = 11.72$$

These data, along with some other points calculated for this titration, have been plotted as Fig. 5–4, the titration curve for benzoic acid with sodium hydroxide.

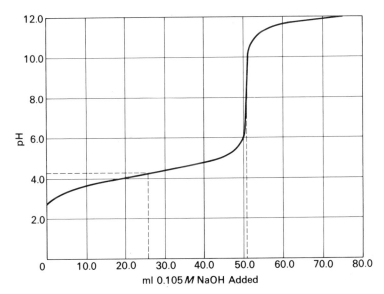

Fig. 5–4. Titration of 125 ml of 0.0425 M benzoic acid with 0.105 M NaOH.

Notice the buffer region of the curve, $pK_a \pm 1$. This region extends from 5.0 ml of NaOH added to 45.0 ml of NaOH added; an extremely large amount of base added for such a small change in pH. The region near the equivalence point is exceptionally steep: a change in pH of 4.2 during the addition of only 1.5 ml of NaOH. This makes location of the equivalence point very easy and minimizes any errors involved.

Now let us suppose that the curve of Fig. 5–4 is obtained experimentally after dissolving 0.6497 g of an unknown weak acid in 125 ml of water. This resulting solution is titrated with the 0.105 M NaOH. By using a pH meter and a glass electrode, the pH of the titrate solution can be measured after each successive addition of the standard NaOH. These data are then plotted to give the titration curve. From the midpoint of the steep rise in the curve at the equivalence point, around 50 ml of NaOH added, it is determined that 50.7 ml of the base are required to titrate all of the unknown acid. Thus, 50.7 ml $\times$ 0.105 N = 5.32 mequiv of base are required. From the stoichiometry of the titration reaction, we know we have 5.32 mequiv of the weak acid present. The *equivalent weight* of an acid is the number of grams in an equivalent of the acid, or milligrams in a milliequivalent. Thus the equivalent weight of the acid can be calculated:

$$\text{equiv weight acid} = \frac{649.7 \text{ mg}}{5.32 \text{ mequiv}} = 122 \text{ mg/mequiv}$$

The value for the K_a for the acid can be obtained from the point when half of the acid present has been titrated. (*Remember?* pH = pK_a at this point.) Since 50.7 ml of base are required to titrate all of the acid, 25.35 ml would be needed to titrate only half of the acid. From Fig. 5–4, it can be seen that the pH of the solution when 25.35 ml of NaOH have been added is 4.20. Thus, at this point, $[H_3O^+]$ = 6.32 $\times$ 10^{-5} M. Since at this point, K_a = $[H_3O^+]$, the K_a for the unknown acid is 6.32 $\times$ 10^{-5}. With a little effort and time spent looking through tables of acid dissociation constants and molecular weights, it can be concluded that the unknown acid must be benzoic acid.

EXPERIMENT 5–I
Preparation and Standardization of Approximately 0.1 M NaOH

Of the strong bases suitable for use as titrants in acid–base titrations, NaOH is the base most commonly encountered. Both KOH and LiOH are more expensive and more difficult to purify. Of the alkaline earth hydroxides, only barium hydroxide is sufficiently soluble even to consider for use as a titrant. A saturated solution of $Ba(OH)_2$ is approximately 0.1 M. It is used occasionally, but complications arising from the insolubility of barium salts formed during the titration (such as $BaSO_4$) and from the insolubility of $BaCO_3$ formed in the $Ba(OH)_2$ titrant upon absorption of atmospheric carbon dioxide, make $Ba(OH)_2$ less desirable as a titrant than NaOH.

Ordinary reagent grade sodium hydroxide is about 97% pure and contains about 1% sodium carbonate. It is rapidly hygroscopic. Included among the impurities are about 0.02% potassium, 0.02% heavy metals, with smaller amounts of chloride, sulfate, phosphate, and nitrate. Pure sodium hydroxide is not readily purchased, so a standard solution of NaOH cannot be made directly by weighing out the exact amounts of the solid and dissolving them to volume in a volumetric flask. Instead, a solution of approximate concentration is prepared first, after which the exact concentration is determined by titration of a substance of very high and exactly known purity (a *primary standard*).

Both solid sodium hydroxide and solutions of sodium hydroxide absorb carbon dioxide from the air quite readily, giving rise to the reaction:

$$CO_2 + 2OH^- \rightleftharpoons CO_3^{2-} + H_2O$$

Unless it is removed, the presence of the weaker base, carbonate ion, in the solution of the strong base will cause indistinct end points when titrating weak acids and can cause premature end points when using visual indicators. In reacting with each mole of the carbon dioxide, two hydroxide ions are consumed. For the carbonate now present in the solution to react completely as the equivalent of NaOH, it must do so according to the reaction:

$$CO_3^{2-} + 2H^+ \rightleftharpoons CO_2 + H_2O$$

Calculation of α_{0H}, α_{1H}, and α_{2H} for carbonate at a pH of 9.0 (the value of pH at which the phenolphthalein color change is observed) reveals that about 96% of the carbonate in the solution exists as HCO_3^-, 4% exists as CO_3^{2-}, and only 0.2% remains as H_2CO_3. This confirms that the carbonate formed in the NaOH solution does not react to an extent equivalent to the NaOH consumed in dissolving the carbon dioxide. Thus, one problem during the preparation of standard NaOH solutions is the removal of carbonate. Once standardized, the solution must be protected from additional absorption of carbon dioxide.

Two methods are commonly used for the removal of sodium carbonate from the sodium hydroxide solution. In one, a small amount of a barium salt, for example, $Ba(OH)_2$, is added to the sodium hydroxide–sodium carbonate solution. The barium carbonate which is formed is insoluble, so it precipitates. The precipitate can be filtered off or the supernatant liquid decanted. This method has its drawbacks. The NaOH solution has been freed from carbonate, but it is now contaminated with barium ions. The same difficulties are encountered as when using $Ba(OH)_2$ as a titrant—namely, the possible precipitation of salts during titration and the formation of insoluble $BaCO_3$ in the bottles and burettes as the solution absorbs carbon dioxide from the air.

The second and more frequently used technique requires the preparation of a 50% aqueous solution of NaOH. When equal weights of NaOH and water are mixed, a very viscous solution is produced in which Na_2CO_3 is insoluble. Unfortunately, the solution is so viscous that the precipitate remains suspended in it and must either be filtered off or the solution centrifuged for long periods of time to settle the solid so the supernatant liquid can be decanted off. When filtering the 50% NaOH to remove the Na_2CO_3 precipitate paper, glass filter crucibles, or porous porcelain filter crucibles cannot be used since such concentrated NaOH readily attacks and disintegrates them. An asbestos filter mat in a Gooch crucible must be used for this filtration. The clear, concentrated NaOH is then diluted with carbon dioxide-free water to obtain the approximately 0.1 N NaOH solution. Solutions of 50% sodium hydroxide (w/w) are commercially available at a cost approximately equal to solid pellets of NaOH. If commercial 50% NaOH is not used, make the concentrated solution as follows.

Preparation of the 0.1 N NaOH.   Prepare an asbestos mat in a Gooch crucible. Wash the mat thoroughly with deionized water to remove loose shreds of asbestos, but do not dry it. Empty the suction flask and suspend a clean, dry test tube beneath the funnel.

Rapidly weigh on the rough laboratory scales (on a watch glass) about 11 g of reagent grade NaOH pellets. Using a piece of paper, immediately wipe up any pellets which may have been spilled and flush the solid NaOH down the sink with copious amounts of water.

Place 10 ml of deionized water in a 50-ml beaker or Erlenmeyer flask (a plastic beaker or flask would be excellent) and, while stirring continuously, pour the pellets into the water. *Caution*: The extreme amounts of heat evolved during the dissolution causes splattering. Stir cautiously until all of the solid NaOH has dissolved. Keep the beaker covered with a watch glass as much as possible to minimize absorption of carbon dioxide. Cool the 50% NaOH solution to room temperature. Using suction, filter the viscous solution through the Gooch crucible. Be sure that the end of the funnel does not protrude so far into the test tube that it will be immersed in the filtered NaOH solution. Stop the suction as soon as most of the liquid has been forced through the Gooch filter mat. Remove the test tube from the suction flask, and immediately stopper the tube with a cork (a rubber stopper will react with the concentrated NaOH). The filtrate must be clear; if it is not, refilter it. Add 6 ml of this solution to one liter of carbon dioxide-free deionized water.

In a 1500 ml beaker or Erlenmeyer flask, boil one liter of deionized water for a few minutes to remove all dissolved carbon dioxide. Cool the water to room temperature. To this cooled, carbon dioxide-free water, add 4 ml of the commercial 50% NaOH solution and stir until the solution is homogeneous. Transfer the dilute NaOH solution to a clean, 1-liter polyethylene bottle, close the bottle with a screw cap, and swirl gently to mix the solution. A soft-glass bottle should not be used because the NaOH will slowly attack the glass, contaminating the standard solution and decreasing the concentration of the NaOH. Bottles with ground glass stoppers should never be used because the attack of the NaOH on the ground glass joint is rapid and will cause the stopper to freeze in the joint.

Potassium acid phthalate is the intermediate species formed when one of the ionizable protons of o-phthalic acid is neutralized.

o – phthalic acid   biphthalate   phthalate
                                      (acid phthalate)

$$K_{a_1} = 7.2 \times 10^{-4} \qquad K_{a_2} = 4.0 \times 10^{-6}$$

Potassium acid phthalate is both acidic and basic. It is used as a primary standard base in glacial acetic acid to standardize perchloric acid solutions. It behaves as a weak acid in aqueous solution ($K_{b_2} = 1.4 \times 10^{-11}$ which is negligibly weak as a base), so that it is used as a primary standard acid to standardize sodium hydroxide solutions.

Potassium acid phthalate, molecular weight 204.23, is a white solid. It is not hygroscopic. It dissolves slowly in water up to a solubility limit of 100 gram/liter at 25°C. It is readily available commercially in a high grade of purity ($> 99.95\%$ for the primary standard grade) at a reasonable cost.

The chemical reaction occurring during the standardization of NaOH is

The pH at the equivalence point of this titration is around 9, so that phenolphthalein ($pK_{In} = 9.76$) is an excellent indicator for the detection of the end point.

The chemical indicator phenolphthalein is a dibasic acid which undergoes the following structural changes as it is neutralized.

colorles$^-$ pink

$$pK_{In} = 9.76$$

effective pH range of use: 8.3–10

The consumption of the first hydroxide does not cause a change in the color. The second hydroxide removes a proton from the phenolphthalein, the proton having a pK_a of 9.7. This increases the electron mobility in the molecule and causes the absorption maximum to shift to the visible region. Consequently, the unprotonated phenolphthalein anion appears pink. This transition from colorless to pink usually becomes visible around a pH of 9, but depends upon solution conditions.

Standardization of the NaOH. Dry 4–5 g of primary standard potassium acid phthalate in a weighing bottle, in a drying oven at 120°C for two hours, but not overnight. See Fig. 3–1 for the correct arrangement of the weighing bottle for drying samples in the oven. Cool the dried standard to room temperature in a desiccator.

Using an analytical balance, accurately weigh out 0.8 to 0.9-g portions of the dried potassium acid phthalate into each of four 250-ml Erlenmeyer flasks. Dissolve each of the samples in 50 to 75 ml of cooled, carbon dioxide-free, deionized water. This salt dissolves slowly, so make sure that each sample has dissolved completely before beginning to titrate it.

Add 2–3 drops of 0.1% alcoholic phenolphthalein indicator solution to each sample solution, and titrate the solution with the carbon dioxide-free dilute NaOH solution. The end point is the appearance of the palest possible pink color that remains in the solution for at least thirty seconds. The solution will turn pink and then fade as the end point is approached due to inhomogeneity and hence local excesses during mixing. After the end point, the pink color will deepen as more and more of the excess NaOH is used to transform the indicator from its colorless to its pink species. At the correct end point, the pink remains for a satisfactory length of time, and yet is just discernible. Upon standing the color of the solution will fade because the carbon dioxide absorbed from the air reacts with the excess sodium hydroxide present to form $NaHCO_3$. Since the pH of a solution of $NaHCO_3$ is less than 9, the phenolphthalein reverts to its colorless form.

It is good practice, after the first titration, to compute a rough normality for the sodium hydroxide. From this normality and the approximate weight of successive potassium acid phthalate samples, the volume of titrant expected to be used can be calculated. When an approximate value of the volume of NaOH to be consumed is known, the successive samples can be titrated rapidly right up to within a milliliter of the equivalence point, at which time the titrant is added more slowly for the careful detection of the end point.

From the weight of each potassium acid phthalate sample, the equivalent weight of this primary standard, and the volume of the NaOH solution used to reach the end point of the titration, the molarity of the NaOH can be calculated. The equation for the titration reaction shows that the equivalent weight of the potassium acid phthalate is the same as its molecular weight, since only one hydrogen ion is removed during the titration.

$$\frac{\text{g KH phthalate in sample}}{\text{mol wt of KH phthalate}} = \text{no. moles KH phthalate titrated}$$

$$\frac{\text{vol NaOH}}{\text{to reach end point}} \times \text{molarity NaOH} = \frac{\text{no. moles NaOH needed}}{\text{to titrate KH phthalate}}$$

Since the titration reaction consumes one mole of NaOH for each mole of potassium acid phthalate, at the equivalence point the numer of moles of each that have reacted must be identical. This enables us to equate the two expressions above and, upon rearrangement:

$$M\ \text{NaOH} = \frac{\text{wt KH phthalate sample}}{204.23\text{g/mol} \times \text{vol NaOH used}}$$

using the appropriate units of weight and volume (grams and liters or milligrams and milliliters).

From the four values for the molarity of the NaOH solution, calculate the average molarity, the standard deviation for the standardization, and the relative standard deviation for the determination. The value of the relative standard deviation should be less than two parts per thousand for this standardization.

Do not consume too much of the standard sodium hydroxide during its standardization for the solution will be required for two or three later experiments; for example, the determination of the capacity of the ion-exchange resin and the determination of the K_a and equivalent weight of the unknown weak acid. While the purpose of this particular experiment is to determine accurately the concentration of the NaOH solution (standardize it), the purpose of preparing the NaOH is to be able to use it in subsequent acid–base titrations.

EXPERIMENT 5-2
Determination of the Capacity of a Cation-Exchange Resin

The purpose of this experiment is to determine the number of milliequivalents of exchange sites on a known amount of an ion-exchange resin. (See Chapter 12 for the structure of ion-exchange resins.) If the resin initially contains exchangeable hydrogen ions, replacement of them with sodium ions will form an acid in the eluate. The exchange reaction may be written as:

$$2R\text{—}SO_3^-H^+ + 2\,Na^+ + SO_4^{2-} \rightleftharpoons 2\,R\text{—}SO_3^-Na^+ + 2H^+ + SO_4^{2-}$$

The sulfuric acid formed through this exchange will be eluted from the bottom of the ion-exchange column and can be titrated with standard sodium hydroxide. From the titration, the amount of hydrogen ion eluted from the resin can be calculated and hence the equivalents of exchangeable ions per unit weight (capacity) can be obtained. The ion-exchange reaction is an equilibrium reaction, but it is forced to completion by the large excess of the sodium sulfate passed through the column.

Procedure.   Place a small plug of glass wool at the bottom of a 25-ml burette or a small (1 × 29 cm) chromatographic column. Fill the column about half-full with deionized water. Be sure there are no air bubbles in the column after this process. Weigh out accurately into a 50-ml beaker 1.1–1.2 g of an air-dried cation-exchange resin in the H-form. Since the usual capacity values are obtained for the resin in equilibrium with the atmosphere, do not dry the resin in the oven or store it in a desiccator. The calculated capacity will vary considerably with the water content of the ion-exchange resin.

With the aid of a stream of deionized water or a small camel-hair brush, transfer the resin quantitatively through a small funnel into the column. Make sure that no grains of resin are left either in the beaker or in the funnel. If necessary, add additional distilled water to the column so that the resin is completely sub-merged. Dislodge any air bubbles adhering to the resin beads by applying inter-mittent pressure to a piece of rubber tubing attached to the tip of the column, thereby causing the level of the liquid in the ion-exchange column to rise and fall slightly, moving the air bubbles to the surface. Any air attached to or enclosing a particle of the resin will prevent the sodium sulfate solution from coming in contact with that particle and hence no exchange of ions will occur. Adjust the level of the water in the column so that it is about 1 cm above the top of the resin beads. Hereafter, never let the liquid level fall below this limit, or air will enter the bed of resin.

See Fig. 3–8, p. 61 for the arrangement of the apparatus for column operation. Prepare 300 ml of 0.50 M Na_2SO_4. Fill the 125-ml separatory funnel with the Na_2SO_4 solution, and place the tip of the funnel in the neck of the ion-exchange column. Adjust the stopcocks of the separatory funnel and of the ion-exchange column so that the rates of flow of solution into the top of the column and of eluate from the bottom of the column are both about 2 ml per minute. Collect the effluent in a 500-ml Erlenmeyer flask.

When all of the sodium sulfate solution has been passed through the ion-exchange resin, rinse out any acid remaining in the column by passing 50 ml of deionized water through the column. Collect this rinse in the same flask containing the column eluate.

Add 2–3 drops of 0.1% alcoholic phenolphthalein to the 350 ml of acid solution. Titrate very cautiously with standard 0.1 N NaOH. Remember that there is but a single sample of acid eluate available to titrate, so that if the end point is overshot, the entire experiment must be repeated.

From the volume of NaOH required to reach the phenolphthalein end point, and the weight of the cation-exchange resin weighed out initially, calculate the capacity of the air-dry resin in milliequivalents per gram.

$$\text{no. mequiv of NaOH used} = \text{vol NaOH in ml} \times N \text{ NaOH}$$

From the stoichiometry of the titration reaction, each equivalent of base titrates one equivalent of acid. Thus the number of milliequivalents of base used is also the number of milliequivalents of hydrogen ion present in the ion-exchange resin.

$$\text{capacity of resin} = \frac{\text{no. mequiv of exchangeable hydrogen}}{\text{wt of resin sample}}$$

$$= \frac{\text{ml of NaOH} \times N \text{ NaOH}}{\text{wt in grams of resin}}$$

EXPERIMENT 5–3
Determination of the pK_a and Equivalent Weight of a Weak Acid by Potentiometric pH Titration

The purpose of this experiment is to determine the equivalent weight and the acid dissociation constant of a weak acid. This is achieved by measuring the change in the pH of the titrate solution during the course of an acid–base titration with a glass-calomel electrode system. The resultant titration data are graphed and from the curve, as described earlier (see p. 154), the K_a and equivalent weight are calculated.

A general description of the pH meter (Fig. 2–10), the glass electrode (Fig. 2–11), and the calomel electrode (Fig. 2–12) was presented in Chapter 2. The operation of the particular pH meter used will be explained by the laboratory instructor. pH meters are relatively expensive ($330 and up) so they should be treated with respect. Glass and calomel electrodes, which are extremely fragile (as well as expensive), should be handled with great care. Equipment used properly will give good results and have longer lifetimes. Be absolutely certain that you understand the correct procedure for using the pH meter, before beginning the laboratory work.

The number of pH meters available is limited. Students will probably have to perform this experiment in pairs using a single unknown acid. Cooperation in this partnership is essential to produce a more efficient performance of the experiment. One partner can weigh out the samples of the unknown while the other arranges the burette, stirrer, pH meter, and other equipment. During the titration, one student should read the pH meter (± 0.01 pH unit) while the other reads the burette (± 0.01 ml). Each pair of partners will be limited to 1.5 hours use of the pH meter. This should be ample time if the experiment is thoroughly understood and the assignments well-planned in advance of the laboratory period, and the partners cooperate.

Titration of the unknown acid. The unknown is a solid weak acid. It is not necessary to dry the solid either in the drying oven or in a desiccator. Using a weighing bottle, weigh out by difference into 250-ml beakers two samples of the size specified by the instructor. Each sample should consume 30–40 ml of the standard base in reaching its equivalence point. Dissolve each sample in 100 ml of deionized water. To the last sample add 2–3 drops of 0.1% alcoholic phenolphthalein solution just to see the pH at which the palest pink is visible.

Insert the magnetic stirring bar and the electrodes into the solution. Make absolutely certain that the electrodes are situated sufficiently high above the stirring bar that they will not be hit by it. It is worth the effort to make sure that the initial burette reading is 0.00 ml. Read the initial pH of the solution. The stirring motor should not disturb the pH meter reading if everything is thoroughly grounded and the resistance across the electrode system is not too high. If fluctuations in the meter readings are noted which disappear when the stirring motor is turned off, fix the ground on the pH meter.

Add standard base to the unknown acid solution, and record the amount added (± 0.01 ml) and the resulting pH (± 0.01 pH unit). Tabulate the readings in your laboratory notebook—one column headed *ml of NaOH added* and the other *pH of titrate*. Try to record pH changes of 0.2–0.3 pH units or volume increments of 5.0 ml, which ever occurs first. During the initial portions of the titration, take readings every 5 ml of NaOH added (see Fig. 5-4) but as the curve begins to rise steeply near the equivalence point, read every 0.2 pH units. After the equivalence point, when the curve begins to level off again, the volume change will become the limiting factor again. Since pH changes upon dilution, as well as through reaction, no water may be added during the course of the titration. Therefore, *Do not* wash the drop off the tip of the burette; remove the drop by touching the burette tip to the surface of the solution in the beaker. *Do not* wash down the sides of the beaker. Continue the titration past the equivalence point until the curve levels off again. (About 10 ml past the equivalence point should be a sufficient excess of NaOH to add.) Note the pH of the phenolphthalein color change for the one sample containing it.

Plot on a piece of graph paper *ml NaOH added (abscissa) vs pH (ordinate)*. Draw a smooth line through the points. Do not play connect the dots! The equivalence point is the midpoint of the steeply rising portion of the titration curve. This can be determined by extending the nearly horizontal portions of the curve before and after the equivalence point in toward the center of the graph. Near what appears to the eye to be the midpoint of the vertical rise in the curve, draw a vertical line between the two extensions. Determine the midpoint of this vertical line accurately. Mark this pH on the steep rise of the titration curve. The pH at the equivalence point will not be 7.00. (*Why?* See Fig. 5–4.) From the abscissa at this pH determine the volume of NaOH needed to reach the equivalence point. Determine one-half the equivalence point volume of NaOH ($V_{eq}/2$). Label this volume on the abscissa of the graph. Read the pH of the solution at this volume. At this halfway point the solution is, as you realize by now, an outstanding buffer composed of equal concentrations of A^- and HA. The pH of the buffer solution equals the pK_a of the weak unknown acid. From the volume of standard NaOH required to reach the equivalence point, and the known weight of the sample of the unknown weak acid, calculate the equivalent weight for each sample (see p. 154). Calculate the average equivalent weight and its range.

From the pH at the point halfway to the equivalence point, calculate the K_a for each sample of the acid. Average the two. Although the value for pK_a should be reproducible within 0.1 pH units, it may be quite different from the pK_a value found in tables. As has been discussed earlier, this latter value is the thermodynamic pK_a and pertains to zero ionic strength. The difference between the experimentally determined value and the tabulated value is due to activity effects and measurement errors.

Turn in all graphs with the unknown report form, making certain that the graphs are labeled clearly and correctly. When the graphs are returned to you, they should be pasted on the proper left-hand pages of your laboratory notebook.

EXPERIMENT 5–4
Standardization of 0.1 M Perchloric Acid in Glacial Acetic Acid

Perchloric acid dissolved in glacial acetic acid is about 75% dissociated so that it can be considered a strong acid in the solvent. In fact, as Table 5–4 shows, it is the strongest inorganic acid in this solvent. Because of this extensive dissociation, perchloric acid is the common standard titrant for the titration of bases dissolved in glacial acetic acid.

As mentioned in the previous experiment, potassium acid phthalate donates the carboxylic acid proton, thus functioning as a weak acid in water; however, in glacial acetic acid, the carboxylate ion accepts a proton, functioning as a fairly strong base. The reaction

in glacial HOAC

serves as the basis for the standardization of perchloric acid against primary standard potassium acid phthalate in glacial acetic acid.

The dye crystal violet behaves as an acid–base indicator in glacial acetic acid.

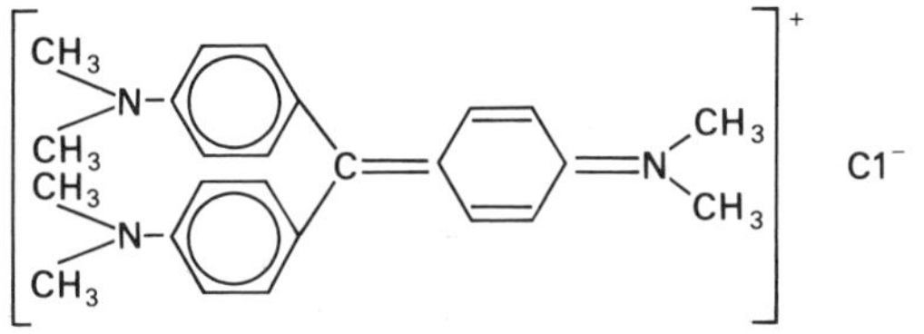

The unprotonated cation shown above is violet, the monoprotonated form is pure blue, and the doubly-protonated form is yellow. The K_b values and hence the color transitions for this dye lie so close together that the appropriate end-point color should be checked to be certain that it occurs at the steepest rise of the titration curve. During the titration the solution will turn from purple to blue-purple to blue to blue-green to green and finally to yellow. Pure blue is the desired end-point color, but the correct hue is determined best empirically by means of a potentiometric titration.

A potential is developed between the glass electrode and the saturated calomel electrode in glacial acetic acid. The magnitude of the potential is determined by the concentration of hydrogen ions in the solution. Since activity coefficients and liquid junction potentials are not known in glacial acetic acid, the meter potential readings cannot be translated into aqueous pH values. The potential readings are not very reproducible either. Thus, meter readings are accepted as being what they are, without any attempt at correlation to aqueous pH values.

The glass electrode will respond rapidly in glacial acetic acid when the electrode has been soaked in water so that the membrane remains hydrated. The water content of the glass membrane of the electrode decreases over time so the electrode should not remain in the glacial acetic acid solvent too long or inconsistent readings (that is, the potential varies not only because of changes in the hydrogen ion concentration but also because of changes in the water content of the membrane) will result. To keep the water content fairly constant, the electrodes should be submerged in distilled water between titrations.

Determination of the indicator color transition at equivalence point. Dry approximately 1 gram of primary standard potassium acid phthalate in the oven at 105°C for at least two hours, and then cool in the desiccator for at least one hour. Weigh three samples of approximately 0.16 g of the dried KHP into 125-ml Erlenmeyer flasks. Weigh one sample of approximately 0.16 g into a 150-ml glass or plastic beaker (Note 1).

To the sample in the plastic beaker, add 50 ml of glacial acetic acid (Note 2) and 2 drops of 0.2% crystal violet indicator solution (Note 3). Warm the beaker gently, if necessary, to dissolve the sample. Cool to room temperature. Dry the glass and calomel electrodes with absorbant tissue thoroughly and immerse them into this solution. Carefully place the magnetic stirring bar into the beaker.

Fill the 10-ml microburette with the approximately 0.1 M perchloric acid in glacial acetic acid solution that is to be standardized (Note 4). Since microburettes are notoriously difficult to fill, and since glacial acetic acid is extremely hazardous both to clothing and skin, do not attempt to fill the burette by pouring the solution through the top of the burette. Rather, immerse the tip of the burette in a small beaker filled with solution, and with a rubber suction bulb on the top of the burette, suck the solution up to above the zero marking. Zero and read the burette. Record this initial reading. It is most convenient to tabulate the experimental data as indicated in the previous experiment, with the addition of a third column which notes the color of the solution at each burette reading.

Set the pH meter to the $-mV$ scale; adjust the rate of magnetic stirring so as to avoid cavitation. Titrate the potassium acid phthalate with the perchloric acid solution, taking burette and meter readings frequently, about every 0.5 ml on the flat portion of the curve and every drop on the rising portion of the curve.

Graph the meter readings in millivolts as a function of the volume of perchloric acid in glacial acetic acid added, placing the indicator color transitions at the potential values where each occurs. Determine the midpoint of the steep rise in the potential (this inflection point is the equivalence point). The color transition nearest the equivalence point in the titration curve is used as the end point in all subsequent titrations.

Standardization procedure. To the first of the standard potassium acid phthalate samples in the Erlenmeyer flasks add 40 ml of glacial acetic acid. Warm to dissolve the solid if necessary. Cool the solution to room temperature. Add 2 drops of 0.2% crystal violet and titrate using a microburette with the solution of perchloric acid in glacial acetic acid until the correct end-point color transition is observed.

Repeat the standardization using the microburette on the second and third samples of the potassium acid phthalate.

From the weight of each sample taken and the molecular weight of potassium acid phthalate, calculate the number of millimoles of standard base in each sample:

$$\frac{\text{wt KHP sample in mg}}{204.2 \text{ mg/mmol}} = \text{no. mmol KHP taken}$$

This amount of base is equal to the number of millimoles of standard acid required to titrate it:

$$\text{no. mmol KHP} = \text{no. mmol HClO}_4$$

From the volume and number of millimoles of perchloric acid required to reach the equivalence point, calculate the molarity of the perchloric acid in glacial acetic acid solution.

$$\text{no. mmol HClO}_4 = \text{vol HClO}_4 \times \text{molarity of HClO}_4$$

Average the three molarities, and then calculate the standard deviation and relative standard deviation. The relative standard deviation should be less than 5 p.p.t.

NOTES

1. While glassware can be used, it is attacked slowly by the acid, so that if plastic beakers are available, they are preferable.
2. The presence of water in the solutions will cause erratic results. Therefore, all glassware should be dried before using.

3. This solution is prepared by dissolving 0.2 g of solid crystal violet in 100 ml of anhydrous acetic acid.
4. Stock solutions of 0.1 M perchloric acid in glacial acetic acid are available commercially from several laboratory supply houses. The solution may be prepared, however, by dissolving 8.5 ml of reagent grade 72% perchloric acid in 900 ml of reagent grade glacial acetic acid. Add about 10 ml of reagent grade acetic anhydride to react with the water, and dilute the solution to one liter with glacial acetic acid. Mix thoroughly. The solution is stable.

EXPERIMENT 5-5
Extraction and Nonaqueous Titration of Total Alkaloids in Tobacco *

A number of alkaloids have been found in tobaccos, but the principal ones are nicotine and nornicotine.

nicotine   nornicotine

$pK_{a_1} = 6.15$, $pK_{a_2} = 10.85$

The purpose of this experiment is to determine the total alkaloid content, expressed in terms of percent nicotine, present in a sample of tobacco. Since the alkaloids occur in the protonated form in tobacco, it is first necessary to remove the protons with a strong base to form the neutral species. Either concentrated sodium hydroxide or barium hydroxide can be used successfully. Then these uncharged molecules can be extracted from the other components present in the tobacco into a nonpolar solvent. Chloroform is the most efficient solvent for this extraction and benzene is the next most efficient extractant. In order to keep the specific gravity of the extractant below one so that the two phases will separate more easily, a mixture of 90% benzene–10% chloroform is used. This mixture has a 99–100% extraction efficiency for the alkaloids.

The extract is titrated with perchloric acid in glacial acetic acid. Both alkaloids behave as diacidic bases in this solvent so the titration reaction can be written as:

* Based on material presented by R. H. Cundiff and P. C. Markunas, *Anal. Chem.*, **27**, 1650 (1955).

Procedure. Using the single-pan analytical balance, weigh 2.5–3.5 g of a tobacco sample (cigarette, pipe, snuff, or cigar) into a 250-ml Erlenmeyer flask. To this add 1 g of solid barium hydroxide followed by 15 ml of saturated aqueous barium hydroxide solution. Swirl the flask to wet the tobacco thoroughly, adding more of the barium hydroxide solution if necessary. Using a pipetting bulb, carefully pipette 100.0 ml of the 90% benzene–10% chloroform extraction solvent into the flask. Stopper the flask with a cork, and shake vigorously for 20 minutes, stopping to vent the flask every few minutes, especially at first.

To the solution in the flask add about 2 g of Celite, swirl the flask gently to disperse this, and allow the two liquid phases to separate. Carefully filter the organic phase into a 125-ml Erlenmeyer flask through phase separating paper, making sure that as little as possible of the aqueous phase gets into the funnel. Stopper the flask to prevent evaporation of the highly volatile extract.

Using a pipetting bulb, carefully pipette a 25.00-ml aliquot of the extract into another 125-ml Erlenmeyer flask (Note 1). Pass a stream of air (use the aspirator at the desk) over the solution for about five minutes in order to remove any ammonia which might be present (Note 2).

Add four drops of 0.2% crystal violet indicator solution. Titrate with the standard 0.1 M perchloric acid in glacial acetic acid, using the same color transition for the end point that was used for the standardization process. Again a 10-ml microburette should be sufficiently large to contain the amount of titrant needed. Repeat the titration on a second and third aliquot of the extract.

From the volume of the standard perchloric acid required to reach the end point and the molarity of the standard acid, calculate the number of millimoles of perchloric acid required to titrate each aliquot:

$$\text{no. mmol } HClO_4 \text{ required} = \text{ml } HClO_4 \times \text{molarity } HClO_4$$

From the stoichiometry of the titration reaction, calculate the number of millimoles of total alkaloid titrated in each aliquot:

$$\text{no. mmol nicotine} = \tfrac{1}{2} \text{ no. mmol } HClO_4$$

From the volume of the aliquot titrated and the total volume of the extracting solvent, calculate the total number of millimoles of alkaloids present in the sample:

$$\text{total no. mmol nicotine} = \frac{100 \text{ ml solvent}}{25 \text{ ml aliquot}} \times \text{no. mmol in each aliquot}$$

Using the molecular weight of nicotine, calculate the total weight of alkaloids as nicotine, present in the sample:

$$\text{wt nicotine in sample} = \text{no. mmol nicotine} \times \text{mmol wt nicotine}$$

Now the percentage of nicotine can be calculated using the weight of the sample of tobacco:

$$\% \text{ nicotine} = \frac{\text{wt nicotine}}{\text{wt sample}} \times 100$$

Or combining all of the preceding equations:

$$\% \text{ nicotine} = \frac{4 \times \text{vol HClO}_4 \times M_{\text{HClO}_4} \times \frac{1}{2} \times 0.1622 \text{ mg/mmol}}{\text{wt tobacco sample}} \times 100$$

Average the percentages found for each of the three aliquots, after which calculate the standard deviation and relative standard deviation. The relative standard deviation should be between 2 and 3 p.p.t. (Note 3).

NOTES

1. If the first titration requires less than 5 ml of the titrant, take a 50-ml aliquot of the extract for the second titration. Alternatively, the titrant can be diluted quantitatively.
2. The presence of ammonia in the extract leads to erroneously high results since it also titrates with perchloric acid. Between 1 and 2% of the ammonia present extracts into the benzene–chloroform solvent, but this is removed completely by aspiration. None of the alkaloids arevolatized during this process.
3. The accuracy of this determination is between 1.5 and 2.0 p.p.t.

SOLUBILITY EQUILIBRIA

One of the oldest, most widely used, and the most accurate of the separation techniques is *precipitation*. A reagent is added to a solution containing a mixture of ions and, under the appropriate conditions, only one of the ions forms an insoluble salt with the reagent. After all of the ion has been precipitated, the solid is filtered off, washed, dried, and weighed. By means of the stoichiometry of the precipitation reaction, the percent of the component present in the initial sample is calculated from the measured weights of the sample and of the precipitate. In order for separation by precipitation to be successful, the equilibria present in the system must be known and controlled accurately. Under these conditions, precipitation provides a powerful means of obtaining extremely accurate results.

For any solid in equilibrium with its ions dissolved in any solvent, the following equilibrium will exist:

$$A_m B_n(s) \rightleftharpoons m \ A(aq)^{n+} + n \ B(aq)^{m-}$$

For which the thermodynamic equilibrium constant can be written:

$$K_{sp} = \frac{a_A^m \times a_B^n}{a_{A_m B_n}}$$

By definition, the activity of a pure phase is unity, so that the solid in equilibrium with the solution will have an activity of one. Thus, the denominator of the preceding equilibrium expression is unity and is never explicitly written in solubility constant expressions. When expressed in terms of activities, the solubility product constant is applicable to any ionic substance, regardless of the extent of its solubility. In practice, solubility product constants are used only for slightly soluble substances because soluble salts produce solutions having high ionic strengths. For example, sodium chloride has a molar solubility of 6.13 M at 0°C. The activity effects in solutions of such high ionic strengths would be great and highly dependent upon the ions present in the solution. Under these conditions the use of the solubility product constant would be highly complex and probably lead to inaccurate results. The use of the molar concentration equilibrium constant would be of little practical value. Moreover, it is highly unlikely that sodium ion would be precipitated from aqueous solution as its chloride salt, and thus provide a method for separating it from any other ions. The practical errors involved in such a procedure would be prohibitively high.

As a result of these considerations, solubility product equilibrium constants are applied only to slightly soluble ionic substances, for that is where they can be applied simply and are of the most value. When using molar concentration solubility product constants, the assumptions made in going from activities to molar concentrations must be fulfilled in order to obtain valid results. Under these limitations, the solubility product equilibrium constant expression can be written as:

$$K_{sp} = [A^{n+}]^m [B^{m-}]^n \qquad (5\text{--}42)$$

When discussing solubility equilibria, confusion frequently arises because of the misuse of two terms. The first of these is brought about through a failure to understand the difference between the molar solubility of a salt, s, and the molar concentration of its ions when dissolved in the solution, [ ]. For example, the molar solubility of lead iodide, PbI_2, is 1.3×10^{-3} M. This means that 1.3×10^{-3} moles of the solid salt will dissolve in each liter of solution. When the salt has dissolved, there will be 1.3×10^{-3} moles of lead ions in each liter of solution but there will be 2.6×10^{-3} moles of iodide ions in each liter. Thus the molar concentration of iodide ions in the solution is not equal to the molar solubility of the solid but is twice its value. This is perfectly logical, since each molecule of lead iodide dissolves to form two iodide ions. To cite another example, the molar solubility of $Ce(IO_3)_3$ in water is only one-third the molar concentration of the iodate ions present in the resultant solution.

The second confusion arises from a tendency to estimate relative solubilities of salts from the numerical value of the solubility product constant. It is not correct to state that silver phosphate, Ag_3PO_4, is less soluble than silver chloride, $AgCl$, because its solubility product constant is 1.4×10^{-16} whereas that for silver chloride is 1.78×10^{-10}. Calculation of the molar solubilities of these two salts shows that silver phosphate, in actuality, is slightly more soluble than silver chloride for its molar solubility is 4.8×10^{-5} M whereas that of silver chloride is 1.3×10^{-5} M.

Solubility product constants as measures of the relative solubilities of salts can be compared only when the form of the solubility product constant expression is identical in both cases. This is true for both $BaSO_4$ and $AgCl$ so the comparison is indeed a valid one. It is not true for $AgCl$ and Ag_3PO_4 so that any comparison in this case is erroneous. It is helpful to remember that equilibrium constants have units, even though almost everyone neglects to use them. Only when the units (for examples, $mol^2/liter^2$ or $mol^3/liter^3$) of two solubility product constants are identical can meaningful comparisons be made of the solubilities of the salts on the basis of the numerical values of the two constants.

Solubility Calculations

In order to be able to understand precipitation separations and to be able to manipulate the equilibria involved, let us now look at the methods of working with problems involving the solubility product constant.

Determination of the Numerical Value of the Solubility Product Constant

Solubility product constants frequently are determined by allowing the solid to come to equilibrium with a supernatant liquid over a period of several days. When equilibrium is established, an aliquot of the liquid is taken and the concentration of the dissolved solid determined. From this concentration and the formula of the compound, the K_{sp} can be evaluated.

Example. Solid $La_2(C_2O_4)_3$ (mol wt = 542.0 g/mol) is shaken with water until equilibrium is established. It is found that 6.13×10^{-5} g of the solid was dissolved in 100 ml of solution. Calculate the numerical value for the solubility product constant for $La_2(C_2O_4)_3$.

The solubility equilibrium involved in this problem is:

$$La_2(C_2O_4)_3(s) \rightleftharpoons 2La^{3+}(aq) + 3C_2O_4{}^{2-}(aq)$$

For which the equilibrium constant can be written:

$$K_{sp} = [La^{+3}]^2 [C_2O_4^{2-}]^3$$

The problem asks for the numerical value of the solubility product constant, so that numerical values must be obtained for the concentration of each of the ions. These concentrations can be obtained readily from the molar solubility of the salt and the material balance for the precipitate. The molar solubility of the salt can be calculated from the weight of it that has dissolved:

$$\text{molar solubility, } s = \frac{6.13 \times 10^{-5} \text{ g}}{542.0 \text{ g/mol}} \times \frac{1000 \text{ ml/liter}}{100 \text{ ml}}$$

$$= 1.13 \times 10^{-6} \text{ } M$$

For each molecule of the precipitate that dissolves, two lanthanum(III) ions and three oxalate ions will be produced. Thus, in solution, the molar concentrations of these ions will be:

$$[La^{+3}] = 2s = 2.26 \times 10^{-6} \text{ } M$$

$$[C_2O_4^{2-}] = 3s = 3.39 \times 10^{-6} \text{ } M$$

Substituting these concentrations into the solubility product expression:

$$K_{sp} = (2.26 \times 10^{-6})^2 (3.39 \times 10^{-6})^3 = 2.00 \times 10^{-28}$$

This is the answer requested by the problem, arrived at by making no assumptions.

Determination of Ion Concentrations or Molar Solubilities in "Pure" Solutions

Once the numerical value of the solubility product constant has been evaluated, it can be used to solve other problems involving solubility equilibrium. Among the easiest problems are those inolving dissolution of a solid in a "pure" solution. As was the case for acid–base equilibrium, *"pure" solution* means a solution that does not contain anything that will interact with the ions of the precipitate in any way, other than through ionic strength effects. In other words, there are no ions in common with the precipitate present, nor any species that will react chemically with any of the ions of the precipitate. For example, the determination of the molar solubility of AgCl in 0.0001 M $NaNO_3$ or in water would fall in this category. This type of problem is extremely simple to solve because it is the previous problem in reverse.

Example.   Calculate the molar solubility of $La_2(C_2O_4)_3$ in 500 ml of water.

The solubility equilibrium is identical to that given above, as is the expression for the solubility product constant. The numerical value for this constant is still 2.00×10^{-28}. The electroneutrality principle is the same:

$$3[La^{3+}] = 2[C_2O_4^{2-}]$$

The material balance of the dissolved precipitate gives:

$$s = \tfrac{1}{2}[La^{3+}] = \tfrac{1}{3}[C_2O_4^{2-}]$$

Which upon rearrangement gives:

$$[La^{+3}] = 2s \quad \text{and} \quad [C_2O_4^{2-}] = 3s$$

Substituting these relationships into the solubility product constant expression gives:

$$(2s)^2(3s)^3 = 2.00 \times 10^{-28} = 108\ s^5$$

Solving this expression for s:

$$s = 1.13 \times 10^{-6}\ M$$

This is the answer the problem requested and it was obtained without making any assumptions.

Determination of the Molar Solubility or Ion Concentrations in Solutions Containing an Ion Common with one of the Ions of the Precipitate

This condition is encountered much more frequently than the case solved above. In performing separations or gravimetric analyses, a reagent is added to a solution of an ion until all of the substance has precipitated. Then, to make sure precipitation is complete, a little bit more reagent is added. At this juncture, we have a precipitate in equilibrium with a solution containing an excess amount of one of its ions. Solution of problems of this kind involves substituting the excess concentration into the solubility product constant expression and solving for the concentration of the other ion.

Example. Calculate the molar solubility of $La_2(C_2O_4)_3$ in 670 ml of 0.00100 M $La(NO_3)_3$.

The solubility equilibrium and the equilibrium constant expression for $La_2(C_2O_4)_3$ are still the same ones used previously. The volume of the solution is extraneous to the problem. The problem asks for the molar solubility, s. In selecting an ion concentration term in the solubility product constant as the unknown in the problem, choose that concentration which will make the problem the simplest to solve. For this type of solubility equilibrium it is generally easiest to solve the expression for the molar concentration of the ion of the precipitate that is not involved in any side reactions, nor has any way of getting into the solution other than through dissolution of the precipitate. In this particular problem, this concentration is that of the oxalate ion, for the lanthanum(III) comes from two sources, the added $La(NO_3)_3$ as well as through the dissolution of the precipitate. Thus, $[C_2O_4^{2-}]$ is the term of the equilibrium constant to solve for.

The electroneutrality condition for this solution is:

$$3[La^{3+}] = 2[C_2O_4^{2-}] + [NO_3^-]$$

The material balance on the lanthanum ions in the solution must account for those from the solubility of the precipitate and for those added in the form of the $La(NO_3)_3$.

$$C_{La} = [La^{3+}]_{added} + [La^{3+}]_{dissolved}$$

From the formula of the precipitate we can see that $[La^{3+}]_{dissolved} = 2s$, which when substituted into the material balance expression gives:

$$C_{La} = [La^{3+}]_{added} + 2s$$

To simplify the algebra of this problem, let us assume that the amount of precipitate that dissolves is very slight compared to the concentration of the lanthanum nitrate added. If we can assume this, the lanthanum(III) ion concentration arising from the precipitate's solubility can be neglected. The material balance simplifies to:

$$C_{La} = [La^{3+}]_{added} = 1.00 \times 10^{-3} \ M$$

Substituting this value into the solubility product expression and solving for the oxalate concentration gives:

$$[C_2O_4^{2-}] = \left(\frac{K_{sp}}{[La^{3+}]^2}\right)^{\frac{1}{3}} = \left(\frac{2.00 \times 10^{-28}}{(1.00 \times 10^{-3})^2}\right)^{\frac{1}{3}} = (2.00 \times 10^{-22})^{\frac{1}{3}}$$

$$[C_2O_4^{2-}] = 5.84 \times 10^{-8} \ M$$

This is not the answer that the problem asks for; that is the molar solubility, s. From the formula of the precipitate.

$$[C_2O_4^{2-}] = 3s$$

Therefore:

$$s = 1/3 \ (5.84 \times 10^{-8} \ M) = 1.95 \times 10^{-8} \ M$$

which is the requested answer to the problem.

To check the validity of the assumption about the contribution of the dissolved lanthanum(III) ions to the total concentration of lanthanum(III) ions in solution, let us calculate this former concentration:

$$[La^{3+}]_{dissolved} = 2s = 3.90 \times 10^{-8} \ M$$

This indeed is negligibly small when compared to $1.00 \times 10^{-3} \ M$ so that our assumption was valid, and the algebra of the problem could be kept simple.

Determination of Whether or Not Precipitation Will Occur

In order to effect a separation it is necessary to know the concentration of the precipitant in solution required to start the formation of the desired precipitate when the concentration of the constituent is known. The concentration of the reagent can be calculated quite simply by means of the solubility product constant expression. In order to solve problems of this type, it is assumed that when precipitation is just beginning the concentrations of the ions of the precipitate in solution just satisfy the solubility product constant expression.

Example.   At what concentration of oxalate ion will $La_2(C_2O_4)_3$ just begin to precipitate from a $1.00 \times 10^{-5} \ M \ La(NO_3)_3$ solution?

The solubility equilibrium is the same one used before, and so is the expression for the solubility product constant. The problem asks for the oxalate concentration, so that it is necessary to have a value for the lanthanum ion concentration in order to solve the solubility product constant expression. This concentration is stated in the problem. At the point when precipitation just begins, no lanthanum has been removed from the solution by precipitate formation. Thus, $[La^{3+}] = 1.00 \times 10^{-5} \ M$. Substituting into the solubility constant expression gives:

$$[C_2O_4^{2-}] = \left(\frac{K_{sp}}{[La^{3+}]^2}\right)^{\frac{1}{3}} = \left(\frac{2.00 \times 10^{-28}}{(1.00 \times 10^{-5})^2}\right)^{\frac{1}{3}}$$

$$= (2.00 \times 10^{-18})^{\frac{1}{3}} = 1.26 \times 10^{-6} \ M$$

Which is the answer requested by the problem and no assumptions have been made in obtaining it.

In order to begin to precipitate lanthanum oxalate, a dilute solution of oxalate ions is added dropwise, with thorough mixing. When the concentration of $1.26 \times 10^{-6} \ M$ oxalate ions is exceeded, the solution will show a faint cloudiness, which indicates the beginning of the formation of the lanthanum oxalate precipitate.

The Effect of pH on Solubility Equilibria

When one of the ions of a precipitate is either acidic or basic, the pH of the solution will affect the equilibrium solubility of the precipitate or the amount of precipitant that must be added to a solution to cause such a precipitate to begin to form. The presence of this concomitant equilibrium means there are two simultaneous equilibrium conditions to be fulfilled. The concentrations of all substances involved in either of the two equilibrium processes must satisfy the combined equilibrium constant for both processes. Neither of the two equilibria can be neglected, for the presence of one affects the equilibrium position and hence the concentrations of the other. A very important point to keep in mind at all times is that any homogeneous solution can have only a single concentration of any one ion. When an ion is involved in more than one equilibrium process, the same equilibrium concentration of the ion must satisfy all equilibrium constant expressions in which that ion concentration appears.

When an ion of a precipitate is either a strong acid or a strong base (H^+ or OH^-), the only additional equilibrium to be considered is the autoprotolysis of the solvent. The insoluble acids that exist can be dissolved by adding bases (a common example is the dissolution of ethylenediaminetetraacetic acid in dilute sodium hydroxide). More prevalent examples involve metal hydroxides. Problems involving the solubility of metal hydroxides in water are solved no differently from those of any other precipitates. The unique feature is that one of the ions is the solvent anion.

Example. Calculate the pH of 125 ml of a saturated solution of cadmium hydroxide.

The solubility equilibrium is:

$$Cd(OH)_2 \rightleftharpoons Cd^{2+} + 2OH^-$$

with the solubility product constant:

$$K_{sp} = [Cd^{2+}][OH^-]^2 = 5.9 \times 10^{-15}$$

The problem asks for the pH of the solution. The volume of the solution is extraneous to the solution. In order to obtain the pH, the [OH^-] in the solution must be calculated from the K_{sp}. Since the cadmium ion concentration is not known, it must be expressed in terms of the hydroxide ion concentration. This can be done by using the electroneutrality principle.

The electroneutrality principle condition for the solution is:

$$2[Cd^{2+}] = [OH^-]$$

which is also the material balance for the precipitate. From the electroneutrality principle:

$$[Cd^{2+}] = \tfrac{1}{2}[OH^-]$$

Substituting this relationship into the K_{sp} and solving for [OH^-]:

$$(\tfrac{1}{2}[OH^-])([OH^-])^2 = 5.9 \times 10^{-15}$$

$$[OH^-] = 2.3 \times 10^{-5} \ M$$

This is not the answer that the problem requested. The pOH of the solution is 4.64. From the pK_w relationship:

$$pH = 14.00 - pOH = 14.00 - 4.64$$

$$= 9.36$$

An unstated assumption in solving this problem is: the concentration of hydroxide produced by the autoprotolysis of water is negligibly small compared to the concentration of hydroxide ion produced through dissolution of $Cd(OH)_2$. Comparison of the two values, 1.00×10^{-7} and 2.3×10^{-5} M, shows that this is a valid assumption in this case. For very insoluble metal hydroxides, such as $Pb(OH)_2$ this assumption cannot be made.

Alteration of the pH of the solution is the usual way to cause precipitation of metal hydroxides. This process is no different from merely adding any precipitant to a solution (say adding Cl^- to precipitate $AgCl$), and problems treating this are solved by exactly the same procedure used for the earlier problem on the amount of oxalate needed to cause $La_2(C_2O_4)_3$ to precipitate. The wording may appear different, but the problem is the same.

Example. At what pH will $Fe(OH)_3$ just begin to precipitate from a 1.00×10^{-3} M $Fe(NO_3)_3$ solution?

The equilibrium and solubility product constant expression are:

$$Fe(OH)_3(s) \rightleftharpoons Fe^{3+}(aq) + 3OH^-$$

$$K_{sp} = [Fe^{3+}][OH^-]^3 = 3.7 \times 10^{-40}$$

The problem asks for the pH. In order to calculate that, determine the hydroxide ion concentration at which $Fe(OH)_3$ just begins to form. This concentration can be found from the K_{sp} provided the iron(III) concentration is known. The iron(III) concentration is given by the statement of the problem as 1.00×10^{-3} M. Substituting this value into the solubility product constant expression gives:

$$[OH^-] = \left(\frac{K_{sp}}{[Fe^{3+}]}\right)^{\frac{1}{3}} = \left(\frac{3.7 \times 10^{-40}}{1.00 \times 10^{-3}}\right)^{\frac{1}{3}}$$

$$= (3.7 \times 10^{-37})^{\frac{1}{3}} = 7.2 \times 10^{-13} \, M$$

This is not the answer that the problem requests. The pOH of the solution is 12.14.

$$pH = 14.00 - pOH = 14.00 - 12.14$$

$$pH = 1.86$$

The pH of the solution at which ferric hydroxide begins to precipitate is 1.86. An extremely acidic solution! Yet the hydroxide does precipitate.

When strong bases, such as NaOH or $Ba(OH)_2$, are used to adjust the pH of the metal ion solution, the equilibria present are those shown above. The use of strong bases as precipitants is undesirable since very high local concentrations of hydroxide ion are developed, causing hydroxy complexes to form as well as producing gelatinous, polymeric, impure precipitates. To avoid these hazards when precipitating metal hydroxides, a weak base such as ammonia, is the more frequent source of hydroxide ions. The use of ammonia as a precipitant adds the weak base equilibrium of ammonia to the metal hydroxide solubility equilibrium. To illustrate the method of solving problems involving two equilibria, let us consider the precipitation of a metal hydroxide with ammonia.

Example. At what molar concentration of ammonia will $La(OH)_3$ just begin to precipitate from 900 ml of 0.00123 M $La(NO_3)_3$?

The equilibria involved can be diagrammed as:

$$La(OH)_3(s) \overset{K_{sp}}{\rightleftharpoons} La^{3+} + 3OH^-$$
$$+$$
$$3NH_4^+$$
$$\updownarrow K_b$$
$$3NH_3 + H_2O$$

with the equilibrium constant expressions:

$$K_{sp} = [La^{3+}][OH^-]^3 = 1.7 \times 10^{-19}$$

$$K_b = \frac{[NH_4^+][OH^-]}{[NH_3]} = 1.7 \times 10^{-5}$$

The problem asks for the equilibrium concentration of ammonia. In order to solve for that, the ammonium and hydroxide ion concentrations in the K_b expression, must be known. The hydroxide ion concentration can be found from the K_{sp} expression, provided that the lanthanum(III) concentration in the solution is known. It is. Since the hydroxide ion concentration appears in both equilibrium constant expressions, its single value must satisfy both of them. The general mode of attack on the problem then, is to solve the K_{sp} expression for the hydroxide ion concentration; then this and the ammonium ion concentration are inserted into the base dissociation constant expression and the latter solved for the ammonia concentration. In this problem the ammonium ion concentration is not given, so it must be related to some other ion concentration in the solution. In order to develop this relationship, we will use the inevitable electroneutrality principle.

The electroneutrality principle expression for the solution gives us:

$$3[La^{3+}] + [NH_4^+] = [NO_3^-] + [OH^-]$$

From the statement of the problem we know that:

$$[La^{3+}] = 1.23 \times 10^{-3} \ M \quad \text{and} \quad [NO_3^-] = 3.69 \times 10^{-3} \ M$$

Substituting these values into the electroneutrality principle gives:

$$3(1.23 \times 10^{-3}) + [NH_4^+] = 3.69 \times 10^{-3} + [OH^-]$$

$$[NH_4^+] = [OH^-]$$

This same conclusion could have been arrived at by recognizing that for every molecule of ammonia that reacts with the solvent, one hydroxide ion and one ammonium ion are produced. Since we have not yet removed any of the hydroxide ions by precipitation as lanthanum hydroxide, the hydroxide ion concentration in the solution must be identical to that of the ammonium ions.

Substituting the lanthanum ion concentration into the K_{sp} expression, and solving it for the hydroxide ion concentration gives:

$$[OH^-] = \left(\frac{K_{sp}}{[La^{3+}]}\right)^{\frac{1}{3}} = \left(\frac{1.7 \times 10^{-19}}{1.23 \times 10^{-3}}\right)^{\frac{1}{3}}$$

$$= (1.38 \times 10^{-16})^{\frac{1}{3}} = 5.2 \times 10^{-6}\ M = [NH_4^+]$$

Substituting these values into the K_b expression, and solving for the free ammonia concentration:

$$[NH_3] = \frac{[OH^-][NH_4^+]}{K_b}$$

$$[NH_3] = \frac{(5.2 \times 10^{-6})(5.2 \times 10^{-6})}{1.7 \times 10^{-5}}$$

$$= 1.7 \times 10^{-6}\ M$$

This is not very much ammonia.

It is very convenient to have enough ammonia present in the solution to provide hydroxide ions enough to precipitate all of the metal ion, yet still maintain the hydroxide ion concentration in the solution at a low level. The concentration of hydroxide ion present in an ammonia solution can be controlled by means of the *common ion effect*; that is, by adding ammonium ions to the solution. This procedure permits us to have a high ammonia concentration and a low hydroxide ion concentration at the same time. Let us see how problems involving this practice can be solved.

Example. What must be the concentration of ammonium nitrate present in a solution that is 0.100 M in ammonia and 0.00123 M in $La(NO_3)_3$ in order to just prevent the precipitation of $La(OH)_3$?

The diagram of the equilibria involved and the expressions for the equilibrium constants are the same as in the preceding problem. From the answer to the previous problem it should be apparent that unless some ammonium ion is present to suppress the base dissociation of so much ammonia, enough hydroxide will be produced to precipitate lanthanum hydroxide. When solving problems the point at which a precipitate just begins to form is considered identical to the point at which it just does not form. Both conditions just satisfy the equilibrium constant statements.

The problem asks for the ammonium ion concentration. The attack on the problem is identical to that in the previous example: solve the K_{sp} expression for the hydroxide concentration; substitute that and the ammonia concentrations into the base dissociation constant expression; then solve K_b for the ammonium ion concentration.

Applying the electroneutrality principle to the solution:

$$3[La^{3+}] + [NH_4^+] = [NO_3^-] + [OH^-]$$

The problem states that $[La^{3+}] = 1.23 \times 10^{-3}\ M$. Nitrate ion can come from two sources in this problem, from the lanthanum nitrate and from the ammonium nitrate to be added, so its concentration is unknown initially. The material balance on ammonium ions in the solution is:

$$C_{NH_4^+} = [NH_4^+]_{NH_4NO_3} + [NH_4^+]_{NH_3}$$

The total concentration of ammonium ions, $C_{NH_4^+}$, is also unknown; however, it is *not* equal to the concentration of hydroxide ion formed from the base dissociation of ammonia.

Solving the K_{sp} for the hydroxide ion concentration, as in the previous problem, will give the same answer as before, namely 5.2×10^{-6} M, since the lanthanum ion concentration is the same. Substituting [OH$^-$] and [NH$_3$] into the K_b expression and solving for the ammonium ion concentration:

$$[NH_4^+] = \frac{(1.7 \times 10^{-5})(1.00 \times 10^{-1})}{5.2 \times 10^{-6}} = 0.33 \ M$$

Thus, if a 0.100 M NH$_3$ solution is made 0.33 M in ammonium ions, the hydroxide ion concentration will be reduced to such a low level that La(OH)$_3$ will not precipitate when the solution is next made 0.00123 M in lanthanum nitrate.

When the ions of a precipitate are weak acids or bases, they will interact with the solvent by means of acid or base reactions. Some of the ion of the precipitate is converted to its conjugate base or conjugate acid, and removed from the direct equilibrium with the solid. In accordance with Le Châtelier's principle, more of the solid will then dissolve to try to restore the equilibrium concentration. Hence the presence of acidic or basic ions in a solid enhances its solubility. Precipitates containing $Fe(H_2O)_6^{3+}$, $Cr(H_2O)_6^{3+}$, $Al(H_2O)_6^{3+}$, $Tl(H_2O)_6^{3+}$, and $Th(H_2O)_x^{4+}$ are affected by the acidity of the cation, while those containing F^-, CN^-, $C_2O_4^{2-}$, PO_4^{3-}, CrO_4^{2-} are affected by the basicity of the anion. When solving solubility problems involving such precipitates, both the dissolution equilibrium and the acid–base dissociation equilibrium must be taken into consideration in order to obtain realistic results. Let us illustrate.

Example. Calculate the molar solubility of AgCN in water. Also calculate the concentration of all species present in the solution at equilibrium.

The pertinent equilibria can be diagrammed as:

$$AgCN(s) \overset{K_{sp}}{\rightleftharpoons} Ag^+ + CN^-$$
$$+$$
$$H_2O$$
$$K_b \updownarrow$$
$$HCN + OH^-$$

Which have the following equilibrium constant expressions:

$$K_{sp} = [Ag^+][CN^-] = 2.3 \times 10^{-16}$$
$$K_b = \frac{[HCN][OH^-]}{[CN^-]} = 1.7 \times 10^{-5}$$

The problem asks for the molar solubility of the precipitate. $s = [Ag^+] = C_{CN}$. Since the cyanide ion undergoes a side reaction, while the silver ion does not participate in any other equilibria, it is reasonable, and most convenient, to solve the solubility product expression for the silver ion concentration in order to obtain the molar solubility of AgCN. Since no concentrations are given for any of the species in the solution, all of the concentration terms in both the K_{sp} and the K_b must be expressed as functions of the silver ion concentration. This is the only unknown term permitted. With the electroneutrality principle and the material balance, we have four equations containing only four unknowns, so that the problem can be solved.

The electroneutrality principle for the solution is:

$$[Ag^+] = [CN^-] + [OH^-]$$

The material balance on the precipitate that has dissolved is:

$$[Ag^+] = [CN^-] + [HCN] = C_{CN}$$

The two cyanide terms must be expressed in terms of the silver ion concentration, since that is the only unknown allowed. The cyanide ion concentration can be related to the silver ion concentration through the solubility product expression, giving:

$$[CN^-] = \frac{K_{sp}}{[Ag^+]}$$

The hydrogen cyanide concentration can be found from the K_b:

$$[HCN] = \frac{K_b[CN^-]}{[OH^-]}$$

Equating the electroneutrality principle with the material balance,

$$[CN^-] + [OH^-] = [CN^-] + [HCN]$$

$$[OH^-] = [HCN]$$

which is apparent from the stoichiometry of the reaction. Substituting into the K_b relationship gives:

$$[HCN] = \frac{K_b[CN^-]}{[HCN]}$$

$$[HCN] = \sqrt{K_b[CN^-]}$$

We already have the relationship between the cyanide ion concentration and the silver ion concentration in the K_{sp}. Substituting that into the previous expression for [HCN] gives:

$$[HCN] = \left(\frac{K_{sp}K_b}{[Ag^+]}\right)^{\frac{1}{2}} = [OH^-]$$

Now we have relationships for [OH$^-$], [HCN], and [CN$^-$] in terms of [Ag$^+$]. Substitution of the [HCN] and [CN$^-$] expressions into the material balance relationship gives:

$$[Ag^+] = \frac{K_{sp}}{[Ag^+]} + \left(\frac{K_{sp}K_b}{[Ag^+]}\right)^{\frac{1}{2}}$$

In order to obtain an exact solution to the problem this relationship must be solved. It can be transformed into a cubic equation and solved, although this is tedious to do. Let us see if we can make some assumptions that will simplify things.

Since the K_b for the cyanide ion, 1.7×10^{-5}, is moderately large, let us try assuming that most of the cyanide ion in the solution will exist as the conjugate acid, HCN, so that the concentration of the cyanide ion will be negligible compared to that of the hydrogen cyanide. If this is so, then the cyanide ion concentration term can be neglected in the material balance expression, producing the much simpler equation:

$$[Ag^+] = [HCN] = \left(\frac{K_{sp}K_b}{[Ag^+]}\right)^{\frac{1}{2}}$$

$$[Ag^+]^3 = K_{sp}K_b$$

Substituting the numerical values of these equilibrium constants into this equation:

$$[Ag^+] = \{(2.3 \times 10^{-16})(1.7 \times 10^{-5})\}^{\frac{1}{3}}$$

$$= 1.6 \times 10^{-7} \ M$$

In order to check the assumption we made, let us calculate the cyanide ion concentration from the solubility product constant expression:

$$[CN^-] = \frac{K_{sp}}{[Ag^+]} = \frac{2.3 \times 10^{-16}}{1.6 \times 10^{-7}} = 1.4 \times 10^{-9} \ M$$

This is indeed negligibly small compared to the silver ion concentration, less than 1% of $[Ag^+]$ in fact. The assumption is valid and we saved a lot of time and effort by making it.

Since the problem asks for the molar solubility, s, of silver cyanide, by calculating the silver ion concentration we have answered the first part of the problem. Now let us calculate the concentration of all the other species in the solution. We have already calculated the silver ion concentration and the cyanide ion concentration, so that all that remains to be found is [HCN] and [OH $^-$].

Using the previous expression for the hydrogen cyanide concentration:

$$[HCN] = \left(\frac{K_{sp}K_b}{[Ag^+]}\right)^{\frac{1}{2}} = \left(\frac{(2.3 \times 10^{-16})(1.7 \times 10^{-5})}{1.6 \times 10^{-7}}\right)^{\frac{1}{2}}$$
$$= 1.6 \times 10^{-7} \ M$$

(*Note*: the cyanide concentration is 1% of the HCN concentration, again validating the assumption that essentially all of the cyanide undergoes the base reaction.) Since we found that $[OH^-] = [HCN]$, the $[OH^-]$ is also $1.6 \times 10^{-7} \ M$. The pH of the saturated solution of AgCN is 7.20.

Another type of calculation of interest in separation methods is the solubility in a solution having a stated pH of a precipitate whose anion is a weak base. By proper adjustment of the pH of the solution, all of the anion can be protonated, and hence the precipitate does not form.

Example.   Calculate the molar solubility of AgCN in a solution having a final pH of 8.00.

The equilibria and equilibrium constant expressions involved are the same as in the previous problem. The material balance on the dissolved precipitate is still valid. Since we do not know how this solution reached a final pH of 8.00 (buffered ? NaOH ?), the electroneutrality principle expression must be unknown, so it should be ignored. Other than this, the attack on the problem is essentially the same as in the previous case. The molar solubility is asked for. More information is given in this problem (namely the pH), so that it is simpler to solve than the preceding one.

Again, since the dissolved cyanide ion undergoes base dissociation, the molar solubility is represented by the silver ion concentration. The cyanide and hydrogen cyanide concentrations must be found in terms of the silver ion concentration. The hydroxide ion concentration is obtained from the statement of the problem. There are various ways to attack this problem, one of them follows.

To reiterate the material balance on the dissolved precipitate:

$$[Ag^+] = [CN^-] + [HCN] = C_{CN}$$

[HCN] can be calculated from the base dissociation constant expression and substituted into the material balance:

$$[Ag^+] = [CN^-] + \frac{K_b[CN^-]}{[OH^-]}$$

At a pH of 8.00 $[H_3O^+] = 1.00 \times 10^{-8}$ M, and $[OH^-] = 1.00 \times 10^{-6}$ M. Substituting this into the second term on the right-hand side of the material balance:

$$[Ag^+] = [CN^-] + \frac{(1.7 \times 10^{-5})[CN^-]}{1.0 \times 10^{-6}}$$

$$= [CN^-] + 1.7 \times 10^1 [CN^-]$$

$$[CN^-] = 0.056[Ag^+]$$

which upon substitution into the solubility product expression gives:

$$[Ag^+](5.6 \times 10^{-2}[Ag^+]) = 2.3 \times 10^{-16}$$

$$[Ag^+] = 6.4 \times 10^{-8} \ M = s$$

which is the answer to the problem, that was arrived at in this case without making any assumptions. Comparison of the molar solubilities calculated in this and in the preceding problem shows that as the pH of the solution decreases the protonation of the cyanide ion is more extensive so that the solubility of the precipitate increases.

The Effect of Complex Ion Formation on Solubility

When one of the ions of a precipitate forms a complex ion with some substance present in the solution, the concentration of the uncomplexed ion in equilibrium with the solid will decrease. In accordance with Le Châtelier's principle, more of the solid will then dissolve in an attempt to increase the equilibrium concentrations. This means, of course, that a precipitate will be more soluble in a solution of a complexing agent than it will be in pure water. Either the anion or the cation of the precipitate can undergo complexation reactions as is shown below.

$$AgCl(s) \rightleftharpoons Ag^+ + Cl^-$$
$$+$$
$$2NH_3$$
$$\updownarrow$$
$$Ag(NH_3)_2^+$$

$$CaF_2(s) \rightleftharpoons Ca^{2+} + 2F^-$$
$$+$$
$$Fe^{3+}$$
$$\updownarrow$$
$$FeF_6^{3-}$$

This increase in solubility through complexation is used very widely in effecting separation of ions by precipitation. A complexing agent is added to the solution containing the ions to be separated. The complexing agent is selected because it forms a very stable complex with one of the ions, but does not react or forms only a very weak complex with the other ions. The result is: when the precipitant is added only the uncomplexed ion will precipitate.

Further discussion of this topic and mathematical treatment of the equilibria involved will be deferred until after a treatment of complex ion equilibria (see p. 215).

Separation of a Mixture of Ions by Precipitation

When a solution contains two or more ions that are precipitated by the same reagent, if the solubilities of the precipitates are sufficiently different it may be possible to separate the ions by precipitating essentially all of the less soluble one, without precipitating any of the more soluble one. The criteria for complete removal or separation depend upon the purpose of the separation. When the concentration of any substance has been reduced to one-thousandth of its initial value, the contamination error caused by the remaining material will be only 1 p.p.t. When a substance reacts so as to consume only one-thousandth of its total concentration present, the error due to its interference will be only 1 p.p.t. Thus, during a separation an error of 1 p.p.t. is caused by the incomplete reaction of the desired substance, while a second 1 p.p.t. error is caused by the interfering reaction of another substance. These errors of 1 p.p.t. are usually small enough to be negligible for most separations. Therefore, both the relative solubilities and the relative concentrations of the two ions to be separated become important in effecting separations. In this book, we shall consider an ion to be removed completely when its concentration in solution has decreased either to 10^{-6} M or to one one-thousandth of its initial value.

The first step in determining whether or not a separation by precipitation is feasible is to find out which ion will precipitate and which ion stays in solution. Because of differences in the form of the K_{sp} expression for different precipitates and of concentration differences, this *cannot* be established by merely comparing K_{sp} values. It is accomplished by substituting the known ion concentrations into the respective K_{sp} expressions and solving to find the concentration of reagent needed just to cause precipitation to start. That ion which requires the smallest reagent concentration to precipitate will precipitate first and will continue to be precipitated in a pure form until the reagent concentration in solution reaches the value necessary to begin precipitation of the second ion. After that, the two ions will precipitate together. When there is a sufficient difference in the solubilities, all

(>99.9%) of the first will have precipitated before the second precipitation begins. This condition, which is needed for a successful separation, must be verified initially.

The second step is to find out how much of the ion precipitated first will remain in solution unreacted when the second ion begins to precipitate. Since we know the concentration of the precipitating agent in solution at the point when the second ion starts to precipitate, we can calculate the amount of the first ion in solution at this point. Substitute this reagent concentration into the solubility product constant expression for the first precipitate. If the resulting ion concentration is only one-thousandth of the initial concentration of the first ion or if it is less than 10^{-6} M, then a separation can be effected by precipitation with a common reagent. Let us attempt to clarify this technique with an example.

Example.   100 ml of solution containing 0.00225 M $AgNO_3$ and 0.00515 M $TlNO_3$ is treated with 0.0100 M KI. Can the two cations be separated by precipitation as their iodide salts?

The equilibria involved and their solubility products are:

$$AgI(s) \rightleftharpoons Ag^+(aq) + I^-(aq) \qquad K_{sp} = [Ag^+][I^-] = 8.30 \times 10^{-17}$$

$$TlI(s) \rightleftharpoons Tl^+(aq) + I^-(aq) \qquad K_{sp} = [Tl^+][I^-] = 6.5 \times 10^{-8}$$

To find out whether AgI or TlI will precipitate first, solve each of the two solubility product expressions for the iodide ion concentration needed to begin precipitation. The concentration of iodide required to start precipitation of AgI is:

$$[I^-] = \frac{K_{sp}}{[Ag^+]} = \frac{8.30 \times 10^{-17}}{2.25 \times 10^{-3} \ M} = 3.7 \times 10^{-14} \ M$$

The concentration of iodide required to start precipitation of TlI is:

$$[I^-] = \frac{K_{sp}}{[Tl^+]} = \frac{6.5 \times 10^{-8}}{5.15 \times 10^{-3} \ M} = 1.3 \times 10^{-5} \ M$$

From these results it is quite apparent that a much higher concentration of iodide ion in solution is needed to start forming TlI than is needed to start forming AgI. As the dilute KI solution is added to the solution containing both $AgNO_3$ and $TlNO_3$, the concentration of iodide ion at which AgI starts to precipitate will be reached first. As additional KI is added, AgI will precipitate and continue to precipitate. At the same time the concentration of iodide ion in the solution will increase slowly. Eventually that concentration of iodide will be reached at which thallous iodide begins to precipitate. So TlI will precipitate. If all of the silver has finished precipitating, then the TlI will precipitate uncontaminated by AgI. If, however, not all of the AgI has been precipitated, a mixed precipitate of AgI and TlI will be formed, and no separation of the two cations is feasible.

To see what the situation is in this problem, let us find the concentration of silver ions remaining unprecipitated at the iodide concentration necessary to start precipitation of thallous iodide. To do this, substitute this iodide concentration into the silver iodide solubility product expression.

$$[Ag^+] = \frac{K_{sp}}{[I^-]} = \frac{8.30 \times 10^{-17}}{1.3 \times 10^{-5} \ M} = 6.4 \times 10^{-12} \ M$$

By the criterion of lowering the concentration to one-thousandth of its initial concentration, silver will have been completely removed at this point. By the criterion of lowering the concentration to less than 10^{-6} M, silver will be absent from the solution insofar as interfering with the thallous iodide precipitation is concerned. Thus a separation of silver from thallium is feasible by precipitation as their iodides.

Fig. 5–5 depicts the problem graphically. Note the increase in $[I^-]$ (decrease in pI) is gradual so long as AgI is precipitating. When AgI is almost completely precipitated, the rise in $[I^-]$ is extremely rapid going from 10^{-2} M to 10^{-5} M in less than 0.5 ml. When pI = 8.0, $[Ag^+] = [I^-]$. From that point until TlI starts to precipitate, only 0.2 ml of KI is consumed; so care is essential in the laboratory. Since TlI is relatively soluble, the increase in $[I^-]$ when it is completely precipitated is much less drastic than for AgI. At pI = 3.59, $[Tl^+] = [I^-]$. To reduce the thallous ion concentration to one-thousandth of its initial value requires pI to be 1.89; whereas to lower $[Tl^+]$ to 1×10^{-6} M, pI must be 1.19. Both values are impossible to attain with these solutions.

pH plays a very important role in precipitation separations, for as was pointed out earlier, the ions of a great number of precipitates are either acidic or basic. By altering the pH of the solution, the concentration of the free ion in solution can be altered, which in turn will alter the reagent concentration necessary to precipitate the ion. The most common example of the manipulation of pH to effect separations of ions is the sulfide precipitation–qualitative analysis scheme. At low pH values, sulfide ion becomes protonated; it exists as H_2S and is not available to precipitate

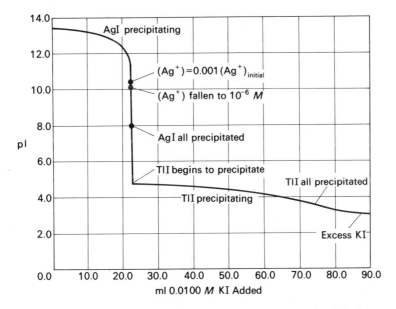

Fig. 5–5. Separation of silver from thallium by precipitation of their iodides.

metal ions. At high pH values most of the sulfide exists as S^{2-} which will react with the metal ions to form insoluble sulfide precipitates. The Group II cations (copper, lead, bismuth, cadmium, mercury, arsenic, antimony, and tin) have sulfides that are so insoluble that the protonation of the sulfide ion in 0.3 M acid solution still leaves enough free sulfide ion to cause a precipitate to form. The sulfides of certain Group III cations (iron, zinc, cobalt, nickel, and manganese), however, are sufficiently soluble not to precipitate from acid solution. These two groups of ions are separated by adjusting the acidity of the sample solution to 0.3 M, and saturating the solution with hydrogen sulfide. When all of the Group II ions have been precipitated and removed, the sulfide ion concentration is increased by raising the pH to an alkaline value which ionizes the hydrogen sulfide. At high pH values the insoluble sulfides of the Group III ions will precipitate.

When one is trying to separate a mixture by precipitation with a basic anion, it is necessary to find out if there is a pH range over which such a separation can be effected. Below some minimum pH, the least soluble ion cannot be precipitated quantitatively. Above some maximum pH, the more soluble ion will precipitate. When the difference between the minimum and maximum pH values is positive and sufficiently large (about one pH unit), a separation of the ions by precipitation is feasible. When the maximum pH value is smaller than the minimum pH value, the more soluble ion will start to precipitate before all of the less soluble ion has been precipitated, so that a separation of the two ions is not possible. In effect, what is being determined is the pH range over which the most insoluble substance will precipitate quantitatively in high purity. This range is shown graphically below.

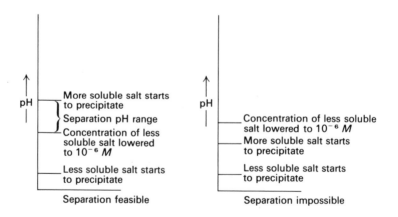

To clarify and illustrate this type of consideration, let us use an example.

Example. A solution is 0.0423 M in $NiSO_4$ and 0.00651 M in $MnSO_4$. Over what pH range can these two ions be separated by precipitation as their sulfides?

The equilibria involved and their equilibrium constants are:

$$MnS(s) \rightleftharpoons Mn^{2+}(aq) + S^{2-}(aq) \quad K_{sp} = [Mn^{2+}][S^{2-}] = 2.3 \times 10^{-13}$$

$$NiS(s) \rightleftharpoons Ni^{2+}(aq) + S^{2-}(aq) \quad K_{sp} = [Ni^{2+}][S^{2-}] = 2.0 \times 10^{-21}$$

$$H_2S + H_2O \rightleftharpoons H_3O^+ + HS^- \qquad K_{a_1} = \frac{[H_3O^+][HS^-]}{[H_2S]} = 1.0 \times 10^{-7}$$

$$HS^- + H_2O \rightleftharpoons H_3O^+ + S^{2-} \qquad K_{a_2} = \frac{[H_3O^+][S^{2-}]}{[HS^-]} = 1.3 \times 10^{-13}$$

The general technique used to solve these problems is to substitute the concentrations of each ion into the appropriate solubility product constant expression so as to calculate the concentration of sulfide ion in solution necessary just to begin the precipitation of each ion. Then we know which ion will precipitate first. The more insoluble ion can be considered precipitated quantitatively when its concentration has been reduced to 10^{-6} M. Next calculate the sulfide ion concentration when the metal ion concentration of 10^{-6} M has been reached. Using this sulfide ion concentration, the concentration of H_2S in a saturated solution, and the acid dissociation constants of H_2S, calculate the pH needed to produce this sulfide concentration. This is the minimum pH; below this pH the concentration of unprecipitated metal ion will be greater than 10^{-6} M. Using the initially calculated sulfide ion concentration at which the more soluble ion starts to precipitate, calculate the pH needed to produce this concentration of sulfide ions. This is the maximum pH, above which the second ion precipitates. The range between these two pH values is the pH region over which a separation can be effected.

The sulfide ion concentration at which precipitation of each ion will begin is: for manganese

$$[S^{2-}] = \frac{K_{sp}}{[Mn^{2+}]} = \frac{2.3 \times 10^{-13}}{6.51 \times 10^{-3}} = 3.5 \times 10^{-11} \ M$$

for nickel

$$[S^{2-}] = \frac{K_{sp}}{[Ni^{2+}]} = \frac{2.0 \times 10^{-21}}{4.23 \times 10^{-2}} = 4.7 \times 10^{-20} \ M$$

Since it requires less sulfide ion, the nickel sulfide will precipitate first. When enough of the nickel has precipitated to reduce the nickel concentration to 1.00×10^{-6} M, the sulfide ion concentration in the solution will have risen to:

$$[S^{2-}] = \frac{K_{sp}}{[Ni^{2+}]} = \frac{2.0 \times 10^{-21}}{1.00 \times 10^{-6}} = 2.0 \times 10^{-15} \ M$$

This is the sulfide ion concentration in the solution when essentially all of the nickel ion has precipitated. We already have found the sulfide ion concentration at which the manganese ion will begin to precipitate. Now let us find the hydrogen ion concentration required in a saturated solution of H_2S to reduce the sulfide ion concentration to each of these values. The concentration of dissolved H_2S gas in a saturated solution is 0.10 M. Combining the two acid dissociation constant expressions for hydrogen sulfide and rearranging to solve for the hydrogen ion concentration:

$$[H_3O^+]^2 = \frac{K_{a_1} K_{a_2} [H_2S]}{[S^{2-}]} = \frac{(1.0 \times 10^{-7})(1.3 \times 10^{-13})(1.0 \times 10^{-1})}{[S^{2-}]}$$

$$[H_3O^+] = \left(\frac{1.3 \times 10^{-21}}{[S^{2-}]} \right)^{\frac{1}{2}}$$

This expression is used to calculate the hydrogen ion concentrations requested. When the nickel ion concentration has been decreased to $1.0 \times 10^{-6}\ M$, the hydrogen ion concentration will be:

$$[H_3O^+] = \left(\frac{1.3 \times 10^{-21}}{2.0 \times 10^{-15}}\right)^{\frac{1}{2}} = (6.5 \times 10^{-7})^{\frac{1}{2}} = 8.1 \times 10^{-4}\ M$$
$$pH = 3.09$$

When the manganese sulfide just begins to precipitate, the hydrogen ion concentration will be:

$$[H_3O^+] = \left(\frac{1.3 \times 10^{-21}}{3.5 \times 10^{-11}}\right)^{\frac{1}{2}} = (3.7 \times 10^{-11})^{\frac{1}{2}} = 6.1 \times 10^{-6}\ M$$
$$pH = 5.21$$

Thus the separation of these two ions can be affected between a pH of 3.09 and 5.21. Below pH = 3.09 not all of the nickel will have precipitated. Above a pH of 5.21 manganese will precipitate. In the laboratory, a solution containing nickel and manganese sulfates would have its pH buffered at, say, 4, then saturated with H_2S. All of the nickel will then precipitate as NiS, leaving the manganese ion in solution. The NiS can be filtered off. If desired, the pH of the solution can be raised to about 8, and the MnS precipitated quantitatively.

EXPERIMENT 5-6
Separation and Gravimetric Determination of Nickel as its Dimethyl-glyoximate

In 1905 it was discovered that the organic reagent dimethylglyoxime,

$$CH_3{-}C{-}C{-}CH_3,$$
$$\parallel \quad \parallel$$
$$HON \quad NOH$$

formed a strawberry red precipitate with nickel ions. Further study in 1907 revealed that this precipitate formation was quantitative enough to be applied to the gravimetric determination of nickel. In ammoniacal solutions above pH = 7, only nickel forms a precipitate with dimethylglyoxime, although dimethylglyoxime complexes with cadmium, cobalt, iron, lanthanum, lead, palladium, and zinc. In dilute mineral acid solution only palladium will precipitate, although gold will interfere. The palladium precipitate forms at a pH of about 3, but then dissolves in ammoniacal solution. The reaction for the precipitation of nickel can be written as:

$$Ni(NH_3)_4^{2+} + 2HDMG \rightleftharpoons Ni(DMG)_2(s) + 2NH_4^+ + 2NH_3$$

where DMG^- represents the dimethylglyoximate anion.

The red nickel precipitate has the nickel atom bound to four nitrogen atoms in square planar symmetry. The N—Ni—N bond angle is 80° and the Ni—N—O bond angle is 120°. The oxygen-oxygen bond distance is 2.40 Å and consists of hydrogen bonds.

In the solid phase the planes are stacked on one another in layers having a Ni—Ni bond distance of 3.245 Å.[4]

The insolubility of the nickel chelate is attributed to its inability to coordinate water along the z axis because of the square planar symmetry. Thus it cannot form a hydroxo complex, even in alkaline solutions. Both copper and palladium form soluble complexes with dimethylglyoxime that contain hydroxyl groups, $Cu(DMG)_2OH^-$ and $Pd(DMG)_2OH^-$. This type of complex has not been found containing nickel.

The solubility of nickel dimethylglyoximate is 3.4×10^{-5} g/100 ml in water at a pH of 7; 1.9×10^{-4} g/100 ml in 1:1 water:ethanol; 1.4×10^{-4} g/100 ml in pure ethanol; 2×10^{-4} g/100 ml in 4% (w/v) ammonium tartrate at a pH of 7.5; and 3.7×10^{-2} g/100 ml in 1:1 NH_3:water.[15] It is often stated that during the precipitation of nickel dimethylglyoximate the solution should not contain more than 50% ethanol. Above this percentage the precipitate is said to dissolve. Examination of the solubility data above shows that the difference in solubility of the precipitate between 50% ethanol and pure ethanol is relatively slight, and the direction of the difference belies the increase in solubility. The real increase in solubility (0.16 mg/100 ml) occurs between pure water and 50% ethanol. Since a large excess of the reagent is undesirable anyway, there is no justification for more than 10% ethanol in the solution. Up to 33% ethanol has been found to give minimum solubility losses. It should be pointed out that dimethylglyoxime is insoluble in water and is dissolved in pure ethanol; consequently, addition of the precipitant must of necessity add some alcohol to the solution. The solubility of nickel dimethylglyoximate in 1:1 NH_3:H_2O is higher than in any other medium cited above. Thus too high an ammonia concentration during precipitation can cause very appreciable solubility losses. Fortunately these losses can be recovered by boiling the solution to remove the excess ammonia.

The purpose of this experiment is to separate the nickel present from any of the other ions in an ore or alloy. The amount of nickel can be determined by precipitation with dimethylglyoxime from a slightly ammoniacal solution, filtering, and weighing the dried precipitate.

Procedure.   Using the analytical balance, weigh by difference three samples of a nickel ore or steel (Note 1) into 600-ml beakers. To each sample add 20 ml concentrated HNO_3, cover the beaker with an appropriately sized watch glass, place in the hood, and warm gently until reddish fumes are evolved. When all of the sample has dissolved (this can be established by the absence of black particles in the bottom of the beaker. The dissolution can take one or two hours, depending upon the nature of the sample) heat carefully until the volume of solution is reduced to about 5 ml (Note 2). Dilute the acid solution to about 250 ml with deionized water.

Add 5 g of solid tartaric acid to each of the sample solutions, stirring well until all of it has dissolved. Keeping the beakers covered as much of the time as is practical, slowly add 6 M NH_3 to each, stirring well, until each solution is just alkaline (pH $\sim$ 8) to pHydrion paper. If any of the solutions is not clear at this point, add more tartaric acid until it becomes perfectly clear (Notes 3 and 4).

To this clear solution, add just enough 1 M HCl to make the solution slightly acidic (pH $\sim$ 5). Heat the solution to 70–80°C, and stir in 20 ml of 1% alcoholic dimethylglyoxime solution. Then slowly add 3 M NH_3, drop by drop, with constant, rapid stirring until the solution is again slightly alkaline (pH $=$ 8–9) and smells faintly of ammonia. The bulky red precipitate will form during this addition (Note 5). Digest the precipitate on a hot plate or steam bath for one hour (Note 6). Test for complete precipitation (Note 7), then allow the solutions to cool to room temperature.

Filter each precipitate (see Fig. 3–3, p. 48) through a clean, porous porcelain filter crucible (see Fig. 2–5, p. 23) that has been brought to constant weight by drying in the oven at 105–115°C for one hour, cooling in a desiccator, and weighing (p. 50). During filtration keep the top quarter inch of the crucible surface dry since the precipitate has a tendency to creep over wet surfaces. If the rim of the crucible is wet, the precipitate might creep over and out the top of the crucible and be lost. Test the cool filtrate with dimethylglyoxime for complete precipitation. Wash the precipitate with cold water until the washings are free from chloride ion (How do you test for this?).

Dry the precipitates at 105–115°C for one hour (Note 8), cool in the desiccator, and weigh. Repeat this drying process until constant weight is obtained. From the weight of the sample, the weight of the precipitate, and the gravimetric factor of 0.20319 for nickel in nickel dimethylglyoximate, calculate the percent of nickel present in each sample of the alloy or ore.

$$\text{weight of nickel in the precipitate} = \text{wt } Ni(DMG)_2 \times 0.20319 \frac{\text{g Ni}}{\text{g } Ni(DMG)_2}$$

$$\% \text{ nickel in sample} = \frac{\text{wt nickel in precipitate} \times 100}{\text{wt sample}}$$

Calculate the average of these percentages, the standard deviation, and the relative standard deviation for the analyses.

NOTES

1. Excessive amounts of precipitate are bulky, hard to wash, and difficult to transfer quantitatively. If pure $NiSO_4 \cdot 6 H_2O$ is used as an unknown, 0.16–0.17 g samples will give about 0.15 g of the nickel dimethylglyoximate. When $Ni(NH_4)_2(SO_4)_2 \cdot 6H_2O$ is used, only 0.10–0.12 g samples are needed for 0.15 g of precipitate.
2. At this point all of the iron should be in the iron(III) state. If a steel sample is dissolved in concentrated HCl, after dissolution HNO_3 must be added and the solution boiled gently to oxidize any iron (II) remaining.

3. Iron(III), chromium(III), aluminum(III), and bismuth(III) will precipitate as their hydroxides if insufficient tartaric acid to complex them has been added. Cobalt(II), manganese(II), copper(II), and zinc(II) will form ammine complexes, and thus be soluble in ammoniacal solution. Tungsten and silicon will remain insoluble and interfere if present in any appreciable extent.

4. Any insoluble residue at this point should be filtered off, washed with dilute aqueous ammonia, and the washing added to the sample solution.

5. The alcoholic dimethylglyoxime is added to the acidic solution, which is then made ammoniacal in order to obtain a precipitate that is more convenient to transfer and that can be washed more easily and thoroughly. Direct addition of the dimethylglyoxime to the ammoniacal solution is undesirable for these reasons.

6. Boiling the solution causes volatilization of the alcohol. The excess dimethylglyoxime will precipitate from aqueous solution, causing high results.

7. Since dimethylglyoxime is only slightly soluble in water (0.06 g/100 ml at 20°C) large excesses of the precipitant should be avoided in order to prevent precipitating the reagent.

8. Thermogravimetric studies show that the precipitate is stable and does not lose any weight until 200°C. Above this temperature rapid decomposition takes place.

EXPERIMENT 5–7
Homogeneous Precipitation of the Nickel as Its Dimethylglyoximate

The technique of homogenous precipitation involves the thermal decomposition of a compound to form the precipitating agent, molecule by molecule, throughout the solution. A variant technique is to mix the ion and the precipitating reagent at a pH too low to cause a reaction to occur. The pH of the solution is then slowly, and homogeneously, raised by the thermal decomposition of urea.

$$NH_2-\overset{\overset{\displaystyle O}{\|}}{C}-NH_2 + H_2O \rightleftharpoons 2NH_3 + CO_2$$

Nickel and dimethylglyoxime will not react in acid solution. If urea is added to an acid solution containing these two substances, and then the solution heated to decompose the urea, forming ammonia, the pH of the solution slowly will be raised. Eventually a pH of 7 is exceeded, so the precipitate of nickel dimethylglyoximate forms.

The advantages of homogeneous precipitation are that crystalline precipitates are formed since the reagent is added slowly (literally molecule by molecule). Large local excesses of precipitant are absent, so that impurities are not entrapped in the crystal lattice. The result is a precipitate that is purer and easier to handle.

Procedure. Follow the procedure given in the preceding experiment for the dissolution of the sample, addition of tartaric acid, and adjustment of the pH to about 5. To each pH 5 solution of the nickel sample add 20 g of urea, and place the solutions on the hot plate at 80–85°C. Carefully add 50 ml of warm 1% dimethylglyoxime in 1-propanol to each solution. Cover each beaker with its watch glass and heat at 80–85°C for one hour. At this time, check the solution with pHydrion paper to determine whether the pH is 8 or greater. If it is not, continue heating the solutions until the pH has risen to about a pH of 8.

Cool the solutions to room temperature in covered beakers. If a white precipitate occurs during the cooling, it is probably excess dimethylglyoxime. Dissolve this white precipitate by adding 20 ml of 1-propanol and heating the solution back up to 80°C. Then recool to room temperature.

Filter, wash, test, and dry the precipitate as instructed in the previous experiment. Calculate the percentage of nickel present in the initial sample and the average, standard deviation, and relative standard deviation for the analyses.

The regular procedure for the nickel determination should take about four hours of laboratory time, whereas the homogeneous precipitation procedure will probably require at least six hours.

COMPLEX ION EQUILIBRIA

Complex ions play extremely important and useful roles in effecting chemical separations. By taking advantage of differences in the properties of the complex ions formed between various metal ions and the same ligand, mixtures can be separated. Ions are complexed to enhance or enable separations by other separation techniques, for example precipitation, ion exchange, or extraction. Ions are converted to complex ions to prevent them from undergoing certain chemical reactions and interfering in the reaction with the desired reagent, that is, *masking*. An understanding of the equilibria among complex species and their components is necessary in order to understand the bases of an extremely large number of chemical separations. The ability to use complex ion formation as an adjunct tool is necessary in attempting to develop successful separation procedures.

For the reaction describing the formation of a complex ion, $M_aL_b^{(an-bm)+}$

$$a\, M^{n+} + b\, L^{m-} \rightleftharpoons M_aL_b^{(an-bm)+}$$

the thermodynamic equilibrium constant expression can be written in terms of the activities of the species involved in the formation reaction:

$$K = \frac{a_{M_aL_b}^{(an-bm)+}}{a_{M^{n+}}^a \cdot a_{L^{m-}}^b}$$

This constant represents a measure of the extent to which the reaction for the formation of the complex species will occur. For dilute solutions of the components, of low ionic strength, the same assumptions that were made for acid–base and for solubility equilibria can be made, that is, the activity coefficients of all ions can be assumed to be equal to one so that the equilibrium constant can be written in terms of the molar concentrations of the reactants and products. The constant written in the fashion shown in Equation (5–43) is called the formation constant, K_f, or the stability constant, K_{st}, of the complex ion.

$$K_{st} = \frac{[M_aL_b^{(an-bm)+}]}{[M^{n+}]^a[L^{m-}]^b} \tag{5–43}$$

When the reaction involving the complex and its components is written in a fashion backward to that given above (from right to left), the equilibrium constant expression for that reaction is the inverse of the one in Equation (5–43). This constant is a measure of the breakdown or instability of the complex and is called the instability constant, K_{inst}. As can be deduced from what has been said, the numerical value of the instability constant is the reciprocal of the numerical value of the stability constant. All three expressions and symbols are in common usage so that in reading chemical literature or using tabulated data, be sure to ascertain the direction of the reaction that the constant describes. Formation or stability constants usually are larger than one and are written with positive exponents in the power of ten, for example, 1×10^7, whereas instability constants are generally less than one and are written with negative exponents in the power of ten, for example, 1×10^{-7}. In tabulating constants it is convenient to use $\log K_{st}$ for stability constants since this gives a small, positive number, whereas pK_{inst} is used for instability constants to obtain a convenient number.

To illustrate the reactions involving the formation of complex ions and the application of stability constants, let us consider the reaction between copper ions and ammonia to form the cupric tetraammine complex ion.

$$Cu^{2+} + 4NH_3 \rightleftharpoons Cu(NH_3)_4^{2+}$$

Since the reaction describes the formation of a complex ion, the overall stability constant for the cupric tetraammine complex ion is the equilibrium constant for the reaction:

$$K_{st} = \frac{[Cu(NH_3)_4^{2+}]}{[Cu^{2+}][NH_3]^4} = 1.13 \times 10^{13} \qquad (5\text{--}44)$$

$$\log K_{st} = 13.05$$

The larger the numerical value of the stability constant of a complex ion, the more stable the complex is.

Caution must be used when comparing complex ion stabilities by the numerical values of their stability constants. Just as the relative solubility of two salts could not be obtained from a comparison of the two K_{sp} values unless these expressions were of the same form, so the relative stability of two complexes cannot be estimated from a comparison of their K_{st} values unless the form of the two K_{st} expressions is identical. Thus $Cu(NH_3)_4^{2+}$ with a K_{st} of 1.1×10^{13} actually is more stable than $Zn(NH_3)_4^{2+}$ with its K_{st} of 4.2×10^8. The comparison of the numerical values of these two stability constants is a valid one, because the form of the expression for the constant is identical in both cases. A comparison of the stabilities of $Cu(NH_3)_4^{2+}$ and $Ni(NH_3)_6^{2+}$ cannot be made by comparison of the numerical values of their stability constants, since the form of the equilibrium constants is not the same in the two cases. The term for the molar concentration of ammonia is raised to the sixth power in the case of the nickel complex, but only to the fourth power in the case of the copper complex. Again it is important to emphasize that stability constants actually do have units, although almost everyone neglects to use them. When the units of the two stability constants are identical, then the constants can be compared, but when the units are different, any comparison will lead to false conclusions.

A complex ion usually contains several coordinate covalent bonds. There is no reason to assume that all of these bonds between the metal ion and the ligand are formed simultaneously and instantly. In fact, it has been found that, indeed, the bonds are formed sequentially, in a stepwise fashion. Thus, for the cupric ammine complex, each of the ammonia molecules adds on, one by one, giving rise to a series of copper ammine complexes. The formation of each of these lower complexes can be described by a chemical reaction representing the addition of one molecule of ammonia to the next lower copper ammine complex. The equilibrium constants for each reaction in this series are called the stepwise formation constants and are given the symbol, k, with a subscript designating the number of ammonia molecules in the complex formed in the reaction. The series of stepwise reactions involved in the formation of the cupric tetraammine complex ion is:

$$Cu^{2+} + NH_3 \rightleftharpoons Cu(NH_3)^{2+}$$

$$k_1 = \frac{[Cu(NH_3)^{2+}]}{[Cu^{2+}][NH_3]} = 1.86 \times 10^4 \tag{5-45}$$

$$\log k_1 = 4.27$$

$$Cu(NH_3)^{2+} + NH_3 \rightleftharpoons Cu(NH_3)_2^{2+}$$

$$k_2 = \frac{[Cu(NH_3)_2^{2+}]}{[Cu(NH_3)^{2+}][NH_3]} = 3.89 \times 10^3 \tag{5-46}$$

$$\log k_2 = 3.59$$

$$Cu(NH_3)_2 + NH_3 \rightleftharpoons Cu(NH_3)_3^{2+}$$

$$k_3 = \frac{[Cu(NH_3)_3^{2+}]}{[Cu(NH_3)_2^{2+}][NH_3]} = 1.00 \times 10^3 \tag{5-47}$$

$$\log k_3 = 3.00$$

$$Cu(NH_3)_3^{2+} + NH_3 \rightleftharpoons Cu(NH_3)_4^{2+}$$

$$k_4 = \frac{[Cu(NH_3)_4^{2+}]}{[Cu(NH_3)_3^{2+}][NH_3]} = 1.55 \times 10^2 \tag{5-48}$$

$$\log k_4 = 2.19$$

It can be shown algebraically that $K_{st} = k_1 k_2 k_3 k_4$.

For each of the lower copper ammine complexes a reaction can be written describing its formation from the metal ion and the ligand, that is copper and ammonia. Each of these formation reactions can be described by means of an equilibrium constant. These equilibrium constants are called merely the formation or stability constants of the particular complex. The symbol for these constants is β, in order to avoid confusion with the upper and lower case k's used to describe the overall and stepwise formation constants. The subscript on the β indicates the number of ligands involved in the complex formed. Thus, again, using the copper ammine complexes, a second series of reactions and constants can be written:

$$Cu^{2+} + NH_3 \rightleftharpoons Cu(NH_3)^{2+} \qquad \beta_1 = \frac{[Cu(NH_3)^{2+}]}{[Cu^{2+}][NH_3]} = 1.86 \times 10^4 \tag{5-49}$$

$$\log \beta_1 = 4.27$$

Note: since this reaction is the same as the first one of the stepwise reactions, $k_1 = \beta_1$.

$$Cu^{2+} + 2NH_3 \rightleftharpoons Cu(NH_3)_2^{2+} \qquad \beta_2 = \frac{[Cu(NH_3)_2^{2+}]}{[Cu^{2+}][NH_3]^2} = 7.25 \times 10^7 \qquad (5\text{-}50)$$

$$\log \beta_2 = 7.86$$

This reaction is the sum of the first two stepwise reactions, so $\beta_2 = k_1 k_2$.

$$Cu^{2+} + 3NH_3 \rightleftharpoons Cu(NH_3)_3^{2+} \qquad \beta_3 = \frac{[Cu(NH_3)_3^{2+}]}{[Cu^{2+}][NH_3]^3} = 7.25 \times 10^{10} \qquad (5\text{-}51)$$

$$\log \beta_3 = 10.86$$

This reaction is the sum of the first three stepwise reactions, so $\beta_3 = k_1 k_2 k_3$.

$$Cu^{2+} + 4NH_3 \rightleftharpoons Cu(NH_3)_4^{2+} \qquad \beta_4 = \frac{[Cu(NH_3)_4^{2+}]}{[Cu^{2+}][NH_3]^4} = 1.13 \times 10^{13} \qquad (5\text{-}52)$$

$$\log \beta_4 = 13.05$$

Now, this reaction is the same as the reaction written initially for the formation of the cupric tetraammine complex. This reaction is also the sum of the above stepwise reactions so that $\beta_4 = K_{st} = k_1 k_2 k_3 k_4$.

When an excess of ammonia is added to a copper solution, the highest ammine complex, for example, $Cu(NH_3)_4^{2+}$, will be formed almost exclusively. Under these conditions only the reaction for its formation and the equilibrium constant describing this, for example, K_{st} or β_4, need to be considered in describing and working problems in the system. For almost all practical applications of complex ions to separation processes this is what is encountered. As long as the excess ligand concentration is sufficiently great, any slight variation in solution conditions will not alter the amount of metal ion complexed. The complexes present in solutions containing mixtures of lower complexes vary considerably with changes in solution conditions.

When the amount of ammonia in the copper solution is equal to or less than the amount of copper in the solution, then all of the copper–ammine complexes will be formed, not just the tetraammine. Under these conditions, a material balance on the copper in the solution will be:

$$C_{Cu} = [Cu^{2+}] + [Cu(NH_3)^{2+}] + [Cu(NH_3)_2^{2+}] + [Cu(NH_3)_3^{2+}]$$
$$+ [Cu(NH_3)_4^{2+}] \quad (5\text{-}53)$$

The amount of each of these complexes present in any solution will really be determined by the formation constant of each complex and the total amount of ammonia present in the system. Thus, an equation expressing the distribution of the various lower complexes in these terms would be a more useful one. Such an equation can be obtained quite simply by solving each of the stability constant expressions above (the β expressions) for the concentration of its ammine complex and then substituting each of these into Equation (5–53). This gives:

$$C_{Cu} = [Cu^{2+}](1 + \beta_1[NH_3] + \beta_2[NH_3]^2 + \beta_3[NH_3]^3 + \beta_4[NH_3]^4) \qquad (5\text{-}54)$$

A convenient way to express the amount of any one of these ammine complexes present in a solution is in terms of its fraction of the total amount of copper present. This concept has been used previously in discussing the ionization of polyprotic acids (see p. 135). Applying the same kind of reasoning, if α is defined as the fraction of the total concentration of copper present that exists as any one particular species, and the subscript on the alpha denotes the number of ammonia molecules in that species, then:

$$\alpha_{0_{NH_3}} = \frac{[Cu^{2+}]}{C_{Cu}} = \frac{1}{1 + \beta_1[NH_3] + \beta_2[NH_3]^2 + \beta_3[NH_3]^3 + \beta_4[NH_3]^4} \qquad (5\text{-}55)$$

$$\alpha_{1_{NH_3}} = \frac{[Cu(NH_3)^{2+}]}{C_{Cu}} = \beta_1[NH_3]\alpha_{0_{NH_3}} \qquad (5\text{-}56)$$

$$\alpha_{2_{NH_3}} = \frac{[Cu(NH_3)_2^{2+}]}{C_{Cu}} = \beta_2[NH_3]^2\alpha_{0_{NH_3}} \qquad (5\text{-}57)$$

$$\alpha_{3_{NH_3}} = \frac{[Cu(NH_3)_3^{2+}]}{C_{Cu}} = \beta_3[NH_3]^3\alpha_{0_{NH_3}} \qquad (5\text{-}58)$$

$$\alpha_{4_{NH_3}} = \frac{[Cu(NH_3)_4^{2+}]}{C_{Cu}} = \beta_4[NH_3]^4\alpha_{0_{NH_3}} \qquad (5\text{-}59)$$

Equations (5–55) through (5–59) can be derived using Equations (5–49) through (5–54). The fraction of the total copper that is present in the system in the form of each complex is independent of the total amount of copper in the system, but is dependent upon the equilibrium concentration of ammonia [see Equations (5–55) through (5–59)]. Fig. 5–6 shows how the relative amount of each of the copper–ammine complexes changes as the amount of ammonia in the system at equilibrium is increased. Note that because of the overlapping of the curves, the complexes $Cu(NH_3)^{2+}$, $Cu(NH_3)_2^{2+}$, and $Cu(NH_3)_3^{2+}$ never comprise more than about 50% of the mixture.

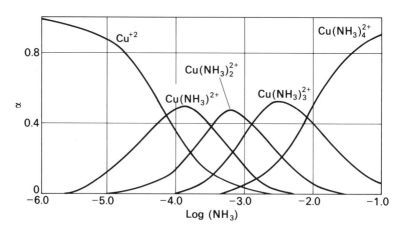

Fig. 5–6. Distribution of species in copper–ammonia systems.

At very low ammonia concentrations, that is, 10^{-5} M, only the monoammine complex is formed and at very high concentrations of ammonia, that is, 1.0 M, only the tetraammine complex is formed. But within these limits, a solution of copper and ammonia will contain a mixture of the ammine complexes. Fig. 5–6 shows that at 10^{-3} M NH_3, all five possible copper species are present. We see that 1.0% of, the copper is uncomplexed by ammonia, 15% of the copper exists as $Cu(NH_3)^{2+}$, 46% as the $Cu(NH_3)_2^{2+}$, 34% as the $Cu(NH_3)_3^{2+}$, and only 4% as the $Cu(NH_3)_4^{2+}$. At an equilibrium concentration of 0.0100 M ammonia, there is no Cu^{2+} or $Cu(NH_3)^{2+}$, and very little of the diammine complex $\sim 6\%$. 41% of the copper is in the form of $Cu(NH_3)_3^{2+}$, and 53% of the copper exists as $Cu(NH_3)_4^{2+}$. This reaffirms the earlier statements that the lower complexes exist predominantly when there are low concentrations of ammonia.

In order to describe the net amount of complexing present in a solution that contains many species composed of the same metal and ligand, Bjerrum in 1915 introduced the concept of the average ligand number, $\bar{n}$. This term is defined as the average number of ligands bound to each metal ion in a solution. It is obtained by dividing the concentration of the bound (complexed) ligand by the total concentration of metal ion in the solution:

$$\bar{n} = \frac{C_L - [L]}{C_M} \tag{5-60}$$

For example, in the copper system that we are using as our illustration, $\bar{n}$ would be:

$$\bar{n} = \frac{C_{NH_3} - [NH_3]}{C_{Cu}}$$

The material balance expression for all of the ammonia in the system, C_{NH_3}, is:

$$C_{NH_3} = [NH_3] + [Cu(NH_3)^{2+}] + 2[Cu(NH_3)_2^{2+}] + 3[Cu(NH_3)_3^{2+}]$$
$$+ 4[Cu(NH_3)_4^{2+}] \tag{5-61}$$

Substituting Equation (5–61) and the material balance for copper given by Equation (5–53) into Equation (5–60) gives:

$$\bar{n} = \frac{[Cu(NH_3)^{2+}] + 2[Cu(NH_3)_2^{2+}] + 3[Cu(NH_3)_3^{2+}] + 4[Cu(NH_3)_4^{2+}]}{[Cu^{2+}] + [Cu(NH_3)^{2+}] + [Cu(NH_3)_2^{2+}] + [Cu(NH_3)_3^{2+}] + [Cu(NH_3^3)_4^{2+}]} \tag{5-62}$$

Not only is this expression formidable in appearance, it is unusable experimentally for usually it is impossible to measure the concentrations of all of the complex species. However, Equation (5–62) can be broken down to an expression which is the sum of four fractions; one for each of the terms in the numerator. By comparison with Equations (5–56) through (5–59) it can be seen clearly that each of these terms is one of the alpha expressions. Substituting each of these alphas into Equation (5–62) gives:

$$\bar{n} = \alpha_{1NH_3} + 2\alpha_{2NH_3} + 3\alpha_{3NH_3} + 4\alpha_{4NH_3} \tag{5-63}$$

Thus, if one can measure the equilibrium concentration of free ligand in the solution, the fraction of each of the complexes in the solution by Equations (5–55) through (5–59) can be calculated. From these alpha values the average ligand number can be computed by Equation (5–63). To familiarize you with this technique, let us solve a problem of this nature.

Example.   A solution which is 0.0100 M in $CuSO_4$ is made 0.0010 M in free ammonia. Calculate the molar concentration of all the copper species present in the solution at equilibrium and the average ligand number of the copper ammine complexes in this solution.

The equilibria present and the stability constants for each of the copper ammine complexes are given by Equations (5–49) through (5–52). The expressions for the fractions of the total amount of copper in the solution existing in the form of each of the complexes are given by Equations (5–55) through (5–59).

Substituting the equilibrium ammonia concentration and the values for the stability constants into the expression for α_{0NH_3}

$$\alpha_{0NH_3} = 1/[1 + (1.86 \times 10^4)(1.00 \times 10^{-3}) + (7.25 \times 10^7)(1.00 \times 10^{-3})^2$$
$$+ (7.25 \times 10^{10})(1.00 \times 10^{-3})^3 + (1.13 \times 10^{13})(1.00 \times 10^{-3})^4]$$

$$\alpha_{0NH_3} = 1/(1 + 1.86 \times 10^{+1} + 7.25 \times 10^{+1} + 7.25 \times 10^{+1} + 1.13 \times 10^{+1})$$

$$\alpha_{0NH_3} = 1/175.9 = 0.00568$$

By substituting into the definition of α_{0NH_3}, as given in Equation (5–55):

$$[Cu^{2+}] = \alpha_{0NH_3}C_{Cu} = (5.68 \times 10^{-3})(1.00 \times 10^{-2}\ M)$$
$$= 5.68 \times 10^{-5}\ M$$

α_{1NH_3} can be calculated by substituting the value for α_{0NH_3} just calculated along with the value for the formation constant for $Cu(NH_3)^{2+}$ into Equation (5–56):

$$\alpha_{1NH3} = \beta_1[NH_3]\alpha_{0NH_3} = (1.86 \times 10^4)(1.00 \times 10^{-3})(5.68 \times 10^{-3})$$
$$= 0.106$$

And using this value in the definition of α_{1NH_3} as given in Equation (5–56):

$$[Cu(NH_3)^{2+}] = \alpha_{1NH_3}C_{Cu} = (0.106)(1.00 \times 10^{-2}\ M)$$
$$= 1.06 \times 10^{-3}\ M$$

α_{2NH_3} is calculated in the same fashion from Equation (5-57):

$$\alpha_{2NH_3} = \beta_2[NH_3]^2\alpha_{0NH_3} = (7.25 \times 10^7)(1.00 \times 10^{-3})^2(5.68 \times 10^{-3})$$
$$\alpha_{2NH_3} = 0.412$$

and substituting this value into the definition of α_{2NH_3} as given in Equation (5–57):

$$[Cu(NH_3)_2^{2+}] = \alpha_{2NH_3}C_{Cu} = (0.412)(1.00 \times 10^{-2}\ M)$$
$$= 4.12 \times 10^{-3}\ M$$

Continuing in the identical manner to calculate α_{3NH_3} from Equation (5–58):

$$\alpha_{3NH_3} = \beta_3[NH_3]^3\alpha_{0NH_3} = (7.25 \times 10^{10})(1.00 \times 10^{-3})^3(5.68 \times 10^{-3})$$

$$= 0.412$$

and substituting this value into the definition of α_{3NH_3} in Equation (5–58):

$$[Cu(NH_3)_3^{2+}] = \alpha_{3NH_3}C_{Cu} = (0.412)(1.00 \times 10^{-2}\ M)$$

$$= 4.12 \times 10^{-3}\ M$$

And finally for the calculation of α_{4NH_3} from Equation (5–59):

$$\alpha_{4NH_3} = \beta_4[NH_3]^4\alpha_{0NH_3} = (1.13 \times 10^{13})(1.00 \times 10^{-3})^4(5.68 \times 10^{-3})$$

$$= 0.0642$$

and substituting this value into the definition of α_{4NH_3} from Equation (5–59):

$$[Cu(NH_3)_4^{2+}] = \alpha_{4NH_3}C_{Cu} = (0.0642)(1.00 \times 10^{-2}\ M)$$

$$= 6.42 \times 10^{-4}\ M$$

Now, having the fraction of the copper present in the solution that is contained in each of the four ammine complexes, the average ligand number, n, can be calculated readily by substituting all of the fractions, α's, into Equation (5–63).

$$\bar{n} = (0.106) + 2(0.412) + 3(0.412) + 4(0.0642)$$

$$= 2.423$$

Thus, for the copper solution in this problem the average number of ammonia molecules that are complexed to a copper ion is 2.4.

As was stated earlier, when the concentration of the complexing agent in the solution is relatively high, compared to the copper concentration, only the most fully coordinated complex ion will exist to any extent in the solution. This is illustrated in the case of the copper–ammonia system by the increase in the value of the average ligand number, $\bar{n}$, as the concentration of ammonia increases. $\bar{n}$ increases from 3.56 when the equilibrium ammonia concentration is 0.010 M to 3.94 at 0.100 M ammonia and when the ammonia concentration is 1.00 M, $\bar{n}$ is 3.99. The practical consequence of this increase in $\bar{n}$ is a simplification of equilibrium concentrations when the concentration of the ligand in solution is high, because lower complexes are not formed. Since these now can be neglected in solving complex ion equilibrium constant expressions, only the stability constant expression for the highest complex formed need be used. This simplifies things considerably.

Complex Ion Calculations

Determination of the Numerical Value of Stability Constants

The experimental methods for evaluating stability constants usually are different from the methods used to evaluate acid–base dissociation constants and solubility product constants. Often there is considerable difficulty in determining the amount of free metal ion in the presence of large amounts of complexed metal ion, or conversely. The laboratory techniques frequently used are colorimetric or involve potentiometric titrations of the metal ion in the presence and in the absence of the complexing agent. Without going into the methods, let us assume that the desired concentrations can be measured, and see how to calculate the stability constants.

Example.   A solution is prepared by mixing 0.0100 moles of $CdSO_4$ with 1.00 mole of NH_3 followed by dilution to 1.00 liter in a volumetric flask. The concentration of uncomplexed cadmium ion is found to be 6.50×10^{-10} M. Calculate the overall stability constant for the cadmium tetraammine complex.

The formation reaction is:

$$Cd^{2+} + 4NH_3 \rightleftharpoons Cd(NH_3)_4^{2+}$$

and the overall stability constant for the complex ion is:

$$K_{st} = \frac{[Cd(NH_3)_4^{2+}]}{[Cd^{2+}][NH_3]^4}$$

This expression is to be solved for the K_{st}, so numerical values must be obtained for each of the three molar concentrations. These can be found by using the electro-neutrality principle and the material balance expressions:
The electroneutrality condition for the final solution is:

$$2[Cd^{2+}] + 2[Cd(NH_3)_4^{2+}] = 2[SO_4^{2-}]$$

The material balances on cadmium in the solution and on ammonia are:
for cadmium

$$C_{Cd} = [Cd^{2+}] + [Cd(NH_3)_4^{2+}] = 1.00 \times 10^{-2} \ M$$

for ammonia

$$C_{NH_3} = [NH_3] + 4[Cd(NH_3)_4^{2+}] = 1.00 \ M$$

The problem states that $[Cd^{2+}] = 6.50 \times 10^{-10}$ M. Since this concentration of uncomplexed cadmium ions is so small, mathematically it is "impossible" to subtract it from the total concentration of 1.00×10^{-2} M. Thus:

$$[Cd(NH_3)_4^{2+}] = C_{Cd} = 1.00 \times 10^{-2} \ M$$

Inserting this value into the material balance equation for ammonia, and solving for the uncomplexed ammonia concentration gives:

$$[NH_3] = 1.00 \ M - 4(1.00 \times 10^{-2} \ M) = 0.96 \ M$$

Now numerical values for all three of the concentrations included in the stability constant expression have been obtained. Substitution of them into the K_{st} expression gives:

$$K_{st} = \frac{1.00 \times 10^{-2}}{(6.50 \times 10^{-10})(0.96)^4} = 1.82 \times 10^7$$

The experimental methods used to determine stability constants are discussed in M. M. Jones's book on coordination chemistry.[6] A comprehensive listing of stability constants has been published by the Chemical Society of London.[21] Appendices 5, 7, 8, and 9 list some of these constants.

Once the numerical value for a stability constant has been determined, it is possible to use this value to determine the concentration of any one of the substances involved in the complex formation equation. Only two examples will be given of typical applications of the stability constants. Both are frequently encountered in separation procedures, for the information obtained from them is needed for successful separations. The first example is the calculation of the concentration of the metal ion remaining uncomplexed at equilibrium when a ligand has been added to a solution of the metal ion. The second is the calculation of the concentration of ligand that must be added to a metal ion solution to reduce the concentration of uncomplexed metal ion to some very small, specified value.

Example.   Calculate the concentration of cadmium remaining uncomplexed when 50.0 ml of 0.200 M NH_3 is added to 50.0 ml of 0.0200 M $CdSO_4$.

The complex forming reaction and the stability constant expression are the same as those involved in the previous problem. The problem asks that the stability constant expression be solved for $[Cd^{2+}]$. To do this, numerical values must be obtained for the other two molar concentrations. These can be found from the material balance expressions for ammonia and the cadmium in the solution.

The material balance expression for cadmium is:

$$C_{Cd} = [Cd^{2+}] + [Cd(NH_3)_4^{2+}]$$

$$= \frac{50.0 \text{ ml} \times 0.0200 \ M}{100.0 \text{ ml}} = 0.0100 \ M$$

The material balance expression for ammonia is:

$$C_{NH_3} = [NH_3] + 4[Cd(NH_3)_4^{2+}]$$

$$= \frac{50.0 \text{ ml} \times 0.200 \ M}{100.0 \text{ ml}} = 0.100 \ M$$

Solving the cadmium material balance equation for the concentration of the cadmium tetraammine complex gives:

$$[Cd(NH_3)_4^{2+}] = 1.00 \times 10^{-2} \ M - [Cd^{2+}]$$

Solving the ammonia material balance expression for the concentration of the uncomplexed ammonia gives:

$$[NH_3] = 0.100 \ M - 4[Cd(NH_3)_4^{2+}]$$

Substituting into this, the expression for the concentration of the cadmium tetraammine complex found from its material balance:

$$[NH_3] = 0.100 \ M - 4(1.00 \times 10^{-2} \ M - [Cd^{2+}])$$

$$= 6.0 \times 10^{-2} \ M + 4[Cd^{2+}]$$

Thus we have now obtained the required relationships. Inserting both into the stability constant expression:

$$K_{st} = \frac{1.00 \times 10^{-2} - [Cd^{2+}]}{[Cd^{2+}](6.0 \times 10^{-2} + 4[Cd^{2+}])^4} = 1.82 \times 10^7$$

In order to obtain an exact and rigorous solution to the problem this equation must be solved. The mathematics can be simplified, however, if some assumptions can be made. Since the concentration of ammonia is relatively high in the solution, let us assume that the concentration of cadmium remaining uncomplexed at equilibrium will be extremely low (compare, $[Cu^{2+}]$ in a 0.10 M NH_3 solution as shown in Fig. 5–6). When this assumption is made it is possible to neglect the concentration of free cadmium in the numerator in comparison to the concentration of the tetraammine complex. In the denominator, let us assume that the concentration of uncomplexed cadmium ion also will be negligibly small when compared to the free ammonia concentration.

Making these assumptions:

$$1.82 \times 10^7 = \frac{1.00 \times 10^{-2}}{[Cd^{2+}](6.0 \times 10^{-2})^4}$$

Rearranging this expression:

$$[Cd^{2+}] = \frac{1.00 \times 10^{-2}}{2.36 \times 10^2} = 4.2 \times 10^{-5} \ M$$

Which is the answer that the problem asked for. Checking on the assumptions: the concentration of uncomplexed cadmium ion is less than one percent of both the concentration of complexed cadmium and of the free ammonia. This is indeed negligible so that the assumptions were correct in both cases.

The second type of problem is encountered when attempting to *mask* a metal ion so that it will not be present in its free form at a concentration sufficiently high to cause any interference with another reaction. The value of the low concentration to which the uncomplexed ion is to be reduced is determined by the system and the manipulations that are to be performed with it.

Example.   How many moles of ammonia must be added to 50.0 ml of 0.0100 M $CdSO_4$ to reduce the concentration of free cadmium ions to $1.00 \times 10^{-6}\ M$?

The chemical reaction forming the complex ion and the stability constant expression pertaining to the reaction are the same as the ones in the two previous problems.

In order to arrive at the answer to this problem, the equilibrium constant expression must be solved for the concentration of free ammonia at equilibrium. This concentration, however, is only part of the necessary amount of ammonia that must be added to the solution, for there will also be some ammonia complexed with the cadmium. The total concentration of ammonia in the system, C_{NH_3}, is the answer to the problem. This amount can be obtained from the material balance for ammonia, once the numerical values of the two terms that comprise it have been determined.

The material balance for the cadmium in the system at equilibrium is:

$$C_{Cd} = [Cd^{2+}] + [Cd(NH_3)_4^{2+}] = 1.00 \times 10^{-2} \ M$$

The statement of the problem gives the desired concentration of free cadmium ions, so that the concentration of the complexed cadmium is readily obtained from the material balance.

$$[Cd(NH_3)_4^{2+}] = 1.00 \times 10^{-2} \ M - 1.00 \times 10^{-6} \ M$$

$$= 1.00 \times 10^{-2} \ M$$

Inserting the concentrations of the two forms of cadmium into the stability constant expression gives:

$$K_{st} = \frac{1.00 \times 10^{-2}}{(1.00 \times 10^{-6})([NH_3])^4} = 1.82 \times 10^7$$

Rearranging this:

$$[NH_3]^4 = \frac{1.00 \times 10^{-2}}{1.82 \times 10^1} = 5.50 \times 10^{-4}$$

$$[NH_3] = 0.153 \ M$$

This is not the answer to the problem, however. The problem asks how much ammonia must be added. Reverting to the material balance for ammonia:

$$C_{NH_3} = [NH_3] + 4[Cd(NH_3)_4^{2+}] = 0.153 \ M + 4(1.00 \times 10^{-2})$$

$$= 0.193 \ M$$

Assuming that this can be added with no change in the solution volume:

$$\text{no. mmol } NH_3 \text{ added} = 50.0 \ \text{ml} \times 0.193 \ M$$

$$= 9.6 \ \text{mmol}$$

Thus, in order to reduce the concentration of free cadmium ions down to a level sufficiently low to be noninterfering (to mask it) 9.6 millimoles of ammonia must be added to this solution.

The Effect of pH on Complexation

The fact that *ammonia is a base* has been neglected in solving all of the previous problems. In reality, its basicity cannot be neglected, for in any aqueous solution the base dissociation will occur concurrently. Hence, only a fraction of the total ammonia present in the system exists as NH_3 molecules and is available for complexation. In the cadmium–ammonia system cited earlier, the diagram of the equilibria is:

$$Cd^{2+} + 4NH_3 \overset{K_{st}}{\rightleftharpoons} Cd(NH_3)_4^{2+}$$
$$+$$
$$H_2O$$
$$K_b \ \big\Updownarrow$$
$$NH_4^+ + OH^-$$

This diagram shows clearly that the hydroxide ion concentration (that is, the pH) determines to what extent the side reaction competes successfully with the cadmium ions for the ammonia molecules. At low concentrations of hydroxide ions (low pH), the predominant reaction will be the formation of ammonium ion; whereas at high concentrations of hydroxide ion (high pH), the predominant reaction will be the formation of the cadmium tetraammine complex ion.

Use of the degree of ionization (α) provides an easy and convenient way to solve complex ion equilibrium problems involving competing acid–base equilibria. As was discussed under solubility equilibria, when a chemical is involved simultaneously in two competing equilibrium reactions, its molar concentration in the solution must satisfy both equilibrium constant expressions. In the case of the cadmium–ammonia system used before, the concentration of ammonia molecules calculated from the base equilibrium constant must also satisfy the complex ion equilibrium constant expression. But, to obtain the concentration of free ammonia molecules from the base equilibrium constant, one must take into account that some of the ammonia present in the system exists as the cadmium complex. Thus, in the presence of competing equilibria, α_{0_H} is defined as the fraction of the net concentration of uncomplexed ligand that exists as the unprotonated species. In the cadmium ammonia case:

$$\alpha_{0_H} = \frac{[NH_3]}{C_{NH_3} - 4[Cd(NH_3)_4^{2+}]} = \frac{[NH_3]}{C'_{NH_3}} = \frac{[NH_3]}{[NH_3] + [NH_4^+]} \qquad (5\text{--}64)$$

Solving the K_b expression for ammonia to obtain the ammonium ion concentration, and then substituting this into Equation (5–64) gives:

$$\alpha_{0_H} = \frac{[NH_3]}{[NH_3] + \dfrac{K_b[NH_3]}{[OH^-]}} = \frac{1}{1 + \dfrac{K_b}{[OH^-]}}$$

Substituting into this expression the value for the hydrogen ion concentration obtained from the autoprotolysis constant expression for the solvent, water:

$$\alpha_{0_H} = \frac{1}{1 + \dfrac{K_b[H_3O^+]}{K_w}} = \frac{1}{1 + \dfrac{[H_3O^+]}{K_a}} = \frac{K_a}{K_a + [H_3O^+]} \qquad (5\text{--}65)$$

Equation (5–65) is identical to the expression that was derived earlier for weak acids [Equation (5–32)], because, of course, what is being calculated here is the fraction of the weak acid, ammonium ion, that exists in solution as its unprotonated form, the ammonia molecule. Equation (5–65) shows us clearly that for a ligand, only the uncomplexed free acid and its uncomplexed, free conjugate base are involved in the expression for acid–base ionization; any of the ligand that is complexed with a metal ion must be excluded from consideration.

Numerical values of α_{0_H} for ammonia as a function of pH are given in Appendix 3.

Example. Calculate the molar concentration of cadmium that is complexed in a solution that is 0.0100 M in cadmium ion, 0.100 M in ammonia, and has a pH of 7.00.

The reaction scheme is the same as diagrammed earlier. The relative equilibrium constant expressions are:

$$K_{st} = \frac{[Cd(NH_3)_4^{2+}]}{[Cd^{2+}][NH_3]^4} = 1.82 \times 10^7$$

$$K_b = \frac{[NH_4^+][OH^-]}{[NH_3]} = 1.7 \times 10^{-5}$$

The problem asks that the stability constant expression be solved for the concentration of the complex ion. In order to do this, values for the cadmium ion and the ammonia concentrations are needed. One could obtain the value of the ammonia concentration from the K_b expression by using the pH, the material balance for ammonia, and the total ammonia concentration. It is much simpler to use the value of α_{OH} for ammonia at the specified pH as obtained from Appendix 3.

From Appendix 3, at a pH of 7.00, $\alpha_{OH} = 5.55 \times 10^{-3}$ Since the value of α_{OH} is small, very few free NH_3 molecules exist in the solution, so it is logical to assume that only a very small amount of the complex ion is formed. The material balance for ammonia in the solution is:

$$C_{NH_3} = [NH_3] + [NH_4^+] + 4[CdNH_3)_4^{2+}] = 0.100 \ M$$

Because of the slight formation of the complex, the cadmium complex concentration can be neglected in the material balance in relation to the magnitude of the other two terms, giving:

$$C'_{NH_3} = [NH_3] + [NH_4^+] = 0.100 \ M$$

From the definition of α_{OH} in a system containing a complex ion:

$$[NH_3] = \alpha_{O_H} C'_{NH_3} = (5.55 \times 10^{-3})(1.00 \times 10^{-1} \ M)$$

$$= 5.55 \times 10^{-4} \ M$$

The value for the cadmium ion concentration can be obtained from the material balance expression for cadmium:

$$C_{Cd} = [Cd^{2+}] + [Cd(NH_3)_4^{2+}] = 0.0100 \ M$$

$$[Cd^{2+}] = 0.0100 \ M - [Cd(NH_3)_4^{2+}]$$

Now we have values for both of the other concentrations and they can be substituted into the stability constant expression.

$$1.82 \times 10^7 = \frac{[Cd(NH_3)_4^{2+}]}{(1.00 \times 10^{-2} - [Cd(NH_3)_4^{2+}])(5.55 \times 10^{-4})^4}$$

$$= \frac{[Cd(NH_3)_4^{2+}]}{9.49 \times 10^{-16} - 9.49 \times 10^{-14}[Cd(NH_3)_4^{2+}]}$$

which when solved for the complex ion concentration gives:

$$[Cd(NH_3)_4^{2+}] = 1.73 \times 10^{-8} \ M$$

This is indeed a very small amount of complex, so that the assumption that was made concerning the relative concentration of the complex with regard to consuming a negligible amount of ammonia in its formation is a valid one.

Note that when this assumption cannot be made:

$$C'_{NH_3} = [NH_3] + [NH_4^+] = C_{NH_3} - 4[Cd(NH_3)_4^{2+}]$$

and

$$[NH_3] = \alpha_{0_H}(C_{NH_3} - 4[Cd(NH_3)_4^{2+}])$$

This is then raised to the fourth power in the stability constant expression. Not a very simple task to solve then!

The most useful complexing agents for separations are the conjugate bases of weak acids—for example, cyanide, oxalate, citrate, tartrate, nitrilotriacetate, and ethylenediaminetetraacetate. Their utility in effecting separations involves their basicity, so that their effectiveness in complexing a particular metal ion will be dependent, naturally, upon the pH of the solution. Very little complex will be formed in acid solutions where the ligand is protonated in preference to forming a metal complex. In basic solutions, the complex ions will be formed predominantly because the concentration of hydronium ions in the solutions is exceedingly low.

A problem identical to the one above using ammonia can be formulated involving the formation of a complex between a metal and any one of the basic ligands mentioned before.

Example. Calculate the concentration of uncomplexed silver ion in a solution which contains 0.500 M HCN and 0.0100 M AgNO$_3$ and has a pH of 8.00.

The equilibria involved are:

$$Ag^+ + 2CN^- \overset{K_{st}}{\rightleftharpoons} Ag(CN)_2^-$$
$$+$$
$$H_3O^+$$
$$K_a \updownarrow$$
$$HCN + H_2O$$

The equilibrium constant expressions are:

$$K_a = \frac{[H_3O^+][CN^-]}{[HCN]} = 6.04 \times 10^{-10}$$

$$K_{st} = \frac{[Ag(CN)_2^-]}{[Ag^+][CN^-]^2} = 7.1 \times 10^{19}$$

The problem asks for the concentration of free silver ion in the solution, so the stability constant expression must be solved for the silver ion concentration. In order to do this, the concentrations of the cyanide ion and of the silver–cyano complex must be found. These concentrations are obtained from the electroneutrality principle expression and the material balances in the solution.

The electroneutrality condition for the solution is:

$$[H_3O^+] + [Ag^+] = [CN^-] + [Ag(CN)_2^-] + [NO_3^-]$$

The material balance for the cyanide in the solution is:

$$C_{CN} = [HCN] + [CN^-] + 2[Ag(CN)_2^-] = 0.500 \ M$$

The material balance for the silver in the solution is:

$$C_{Ag} = [Ag^+] + [Ag(CN)_2^-] = 0.0100 \ M$$

From the pH of the solution it is relatively straightforward to calculate the value of α_{0H} for cyanide:

$$\alpha_{0H} = \frac{K_a}{K_a + [H_3O^+]} = \frac{6.04 \times 10^{-10}}{6.04 \times 10^{-10} + 1.00 \times 10^{-8}}$$

$$= \frac{6.04 \times 10^{-10}}{1.06 \times 10^{-8}} = 6.0 \times 10^{-2}$$

Since the K_{st} for the silver–cyano complex is high and the value of α_{0H} is not too low, let us assume that most of the silver in the solution will exist as the silver–cyano complex. Thus the material balance for cyanide becomes:

$$C_{CN} = [HCN] + [CN^-] + 2(1.00 \times 10^{-2}) = 0.500 \ M$$

which gives us:

$$C'_{CN} = [HCN] + [CN^-] = 0.480 \ M$$

From the definition of α_{0H} in the presence of a complex ion:

$$[CN^-] = \alpha_{0H} C'_{CN} = (0.060)(0.480) = 0.029 \ M$$

Rearrangement of the material balance for silver gives:

$$[Ag(CN)_2^-] = 1.00 \times 10^{-2} - [Ag^+]$$

With this we have obtained values for the two concentration terms that we were seeking. Substituting them into the stability constant expression:

$$7.1 \times 10^{19} = \frac{1.00 \times 10^{-2} - [Ag^+]}{[Ag^+](2.9 \times 10^{-2})^2}$$

$$5.9 \times 10^{14}[Ag^+] = 1.00 \times 10^{-2} - [Ag^+]$$

Let us notice that the last term on the right-hand side of the equation is too small, relatively, to be added to the expression for the silver ion concentration on the left-hand side of the equation, so it must be neglected. Doing this:

$$[Ag^+] = \frac{1.00 \times 10^{-2}}{5.9 \times 10^{14}} = 1.7 \times 10^{-17} \ M$$

From the numerical value of the free silver ion concentration it is obvious that most of the silver ions in the solution will be complexed by the cyanide at this pH value. The assumption made initially that the concentration of uncomplexed silver is negligibly small compared to the concentration of complexed silver is certainly valid since $[Ag(CN)^-] = 1.00 \times 10^{-2}$ M, and $[Ag^+] = 1.7 \times 10^{-17}$ M. The second assumption that the concentration of uncomplexed silver ions was so small that it could not be added to 5.9×10^{14} $[Ag^+]$ is also valid.

EDTA and Its Equilibria

Aminopolycarboxylic acids have become extremely useful as chelating agents in separation processes. Because of the presence and geometric positioning of the electron pair donors, nitrogen and oxygen atoms, aminopolycarboxylic acids form very stable chelates with a great many metal ions. One of the most widely used and most important of these chelating agents is ethylenediaminetetraacetic acid, H_4Y, or EDTA.

$$^-OOC-CH_2 \diagdown \qquad \diagup CH_2-COO^-$$
$$N-CH_2-CH_2-N$$
$$HOOC-CH_2 \diagup \underset{H^+}{|} \qquad \underset{H^+}{|} \diagdown CH_2-COOH$$

EDTA forms very stable chelates with over 56 metal ions, usually one metal ion reacting with a single ligand molecule. EDTA is a white, crystalline solid that has a very low solubility in water (~ 0.02 g/100 ml). It is insoluble in acids and many organic solvents. This solid is nonhygroscopic and contains no waters of crystallization. The compound is stable to drying at elevated temperatures and melts at 241.5°C. Because of the low water solubility of the free acid, the disodium salt is the usual form used to prepare solutions. The disodium salt is quite soluble in water, giving solutions with a pH around 4.8. The disodium salt is readily available commercially as its dihydrate, $Na_2H_2Y \cdot 2H_2O$, in very high purity.

As is shown in the structural formula given above, EDTA is a tetrabasic acid. A solution of the acid will contains the species H_4Y, H_3Y^-, H_2Y^{2-}, HY^{3-}, and Y^{4-}. The exact fraction of each form present in a particular solution will depend upon the pH of the solution. The acid–base equilibria involved are:

$$H_4Y + H_2O \rightleftharpoons H_3O^+ + H_3Y^- \qquad K_{a_1} = \frac{[H_3O^+][H_3Y^-]}{[H_4Y]} = 1.02 \times 10^{-2}$$

$$pK_{a_1} = 1.99$$

$$H_3Y^- + H_2O \rightleftharpoons H_3O^+ + H_2Y^{2-} \qquad K_{a_2} = \frac{[H_3O^+][H_2Y^{2-}]}{[H_3Y^-]} = 2.14 \times 10^{-3}$$

$$pK_{a_2} = 2.67$$

$$H_2Y^{2-} + H_2O \rightleftharpoons H_3O^+ + HY^{3-} \qquad K_{a_3} = \frac{[H_3O^+][HY^{3-}]}{[H_2Y^{2-}]} = 6.92 \times 10^{-7}$$

$$pK_{a_3} = 6.16$$

$$HY^{3-} + H_2O \rightleftharpoons H_3O^+ + Y^{4-} \qquad K_{a_4} = \frac{[H_3O^+][Y^{4-}]}{[HY^{3-}]} = 5.50 \times 10^{-11}$$

$$pK_{a_4} = 10.26$$

In any solution of EDTA the material balance must include all five forms.

$$C_{EDTA} = [H_4Y] + [H_3Y^-] + [H_2Y^{2-}] + [HY^{3-}] + [Y^{4-}]$$

As a rule, only the completely unprotonated anion, Y^{4-}, chelates with metal ions, so that its concentration in any EDTA solution is the one of interest. The concentration of Y^{4-} can be found quite readily by using the concept of the degree of ionization.

$$\alpha_{0_H} = \frac{[Y^{4-}]}{C_{EDTA}}$$

To obtain the expression for α_{0_H} as a function of $[H_3O^+]$, solve each of the stepwise acid–base equilibrium constants to obtain an expression containing only the proton concentration and the concentration of the unprotonated anion, Y^{4-}. Substitute each of these terms into the appropriate portion of the material balance expression for EDTA given earlier. Then substitute the material balance expression into the definition of α_{0_H} as stated before to arrive at:

$$\alpha_{0_H} = \frac{1}{1 + \dfrac{[H_3O^+]}{K_4} + \dfrac{[H_3O^+]^2}{K_3K_4} + \dfrac{[H_3O^+]^3}{K_2K_3K_4} + \dfrac{[H_3O^+]^4}{K_1K_2K_3K_4}} \qquad (5\text{--}66)$$

The fraction of the completely unprotonated anion is the one of greatest interest, but the fractions of the other forms must also be known for certain applications. These fractions can be calculated from the α_{0_H} expression according to the relationships:

$$\alpha_{1_H} = \frac{[H_3O^+]}{K_4} \alpha_{0_H} \qquad (5\text{--}67)$$

$$\alpha_{2_H} = \frac{[H_3O^+]^2}{K_3K_4} \alpha_{0_H} \qquad (5\text{--}68)$$

$$\alpha_{3_H} = \frac{[H_3O^+]^3}{K_2K_3K_4} \alpha_{0_H} \qquad (5\text{--}69)$$

$$\alpha_{4_H} = \frac{[H_3O^+]^4}{K_1K_2K_3K_4} \alpha_{0_H} \qquad (5\text{--}70)$$

Fig. 5–7 shows the distribution of the various forms of EDTA as a function of the pH of the solution. Appendix 2 lists the tabulated values of α_{0_H} for EDTA.

All of the chelation reactions of EDTA are pH sensitive. The higher the pH of the medium, the greater the amount of unprotonated anion, Y^{4-} present in the solution (see Fig. 5–7), and the greater the extent of the chelation reaction. The lower the pH of the solution, the higher the concentration of the various protonated

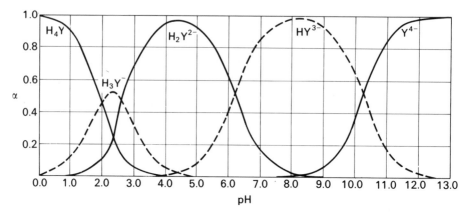

Fig. 5–7.   Distribution of EDTA species as a function of pH.

forms of EDTA, and the less metal chelate formed. The competition of the complexation equilibrium with the acid–base equilibria can be diagrammed as follows:

$$M^{n+} + Y^{4-} \overset{K_{st}}{\rightleftharpoons} MY^{(n-4)+}$$
$$+$$
$$H_3O^+$$
$$\updownarrow K_{a_4}$$
$$HY^{3+}, \text{ etc.}$$

Where the expression for the stability constant for the EDTA chelate is:

$$K_{st} = \frac{[MY^{(n-4)+}]}{[M^{n+}][Y^{4-}]}$$

Fortunately, EDTA forms very stable chelates with almost all metal ions,
which means that the stability constants are very large, for example, K_{st} for
$NiY^{2-} = 4.2 \times 10^{18}$. Even when the concentration of the chelating anion,
Y^{4-}, is very low, the reaction will proceed to completion. Since EDTA forms only
one complex with metal ions, the complications due to the formation of lower
complexes at lower concentrations of the ligand do not exist with EDTA. EDTA is
most frequently used in basic solutions so as to have a large fraction of the EDTA
in solution as the Y^{4-} anion.

The commercially available diprotonated anion, H_2Y^{2-}, is commonly used to
prepare EDTA solutions. The actual species reacting in any solution will be dependent upon the pH of that solution, but below a pH of 13 there will be some protonated forms present. Consequently, reactions of EDTA with metal ions liberate
protons, and the presence of a buffer is required to maintain the pH of the solution

constant. A commonly used buffer is made of NH_3—NH_4Cl at a pH of 10. Fig. 5–7 shows that at this pH, an EDTA solution contains about 65% HY^{3-} and 35% Y^{4-}. Thus at a pH of 10, the reaction of EDTA with a metal ion should be written:

$$M^{n+} + HY^{3-} \rightleftharpoons MY^{(n-4)+} + H^+$$

Numerical problems involving EDTA are usually simpler than those involving monodentate ligands since only 1:1 chelates need to be considered. Let us illustrate with an example.

Example. Calculate the amount of lead that remains uncomplexed when a solution of 0.0525 M $Pb(NO_3)_2$ is made 0.0650 M in Na_2H_2Y and buffered at a pH of 10.00.

The equilibria present in this solution can be diagrammed as follows:

$$Pb^{2+} + Y^{4-} \overset{K_{st}}{\rightleftharpoons} PbY^{2-}$$

$$+$$
$$H_3O^+ \qquad K_{st} = \frac{[PbY^{2-}]}{[Pb^{2+}][Y^{4-}]} = 1.1 \times 10^{18}$$
$$\Updownarrow K_{a4}$$
$$HY^{3-}$$

The problem asks that the stability constant expression be solved for the concentration of the uncomplexed lead ion. To do this, molar concentrations of the lead–EDTA chelate and of the unprotonated EDTA anion must be known. The former can be obtained readily from the material balance for lead in the solution:

$$C_{Pb} = [Pb^{2+}] + [PbY^{2-}] = 0.0525 \ M$$

Which upon rearrangement:

$$[PbY^{2-}] = 0.0525 \ M - [Pb^{2+}]$$

Since the pH of the solution is relatively high, the competing side-reaction protonating the Y^{4-} anion will probably not occur to any appreciable extent. Therefore, let us assume that the concentration of the lead ions that are not complexed is negligibly small compared to 0.0525 M. This gives us $[PbY^{2-}] = 0.0525 \ M$.

The concentration of the unprotonated EDTA can be obtained from the value of α_{0_H}

$$[Y^{4-}] = \alpha_{0_H} C'_{EDTA}$$

where $C'_{EDTA} = C_{EDTA} - [PbY^{2-}] = 0.0650 \ M - 0.0525 \ M = 0.0125 \ M$. C'_{EDTA} is used here instead of C_{EDTA} because the EDTA that is chelated to the lead is not available to act as a base and accept a proton. From Appendix 2, α_{0_H} for EDTA at a pH of 10.00 is 0.355. Therefore:

$$[Y^{4-}] = (0.355)(0.0125 \ M) = 0.00444 \ M$$

Now that we have the numerical values for the two concentrations that are needed, $[PbY^{2-}]$ and $[Y^{4-}]$, let us substitute them into the stability constant expression:

$$1.1 \times 10^{18} = \frac{5.25 \times 10^{-2}}{[Pb^{2+}](4.44 \times 10^{-3})}$$

$$[Pb^{2+}] = \frac{5.25 \times 10^{-2}}{4.88 \times 10^{15}} = 1.1 \times 10^{-17} \ M$$

This low concentration shows that for all practical purposes, all of the lead present in the solution is chelated. The assumption made about the relative concentrations between the chelated and the unchelated lead was obviously justified and valid.

One of the most widespread applications of EDTA is as a *masking agent*; to chelate a particular metal ion so that effectively it is unable to undergo another chemical reaction, such as precipitation or extraction. As has been shown, both the amount of EDTA present in the solution and the pH of the solution will determine the effectiveness of EDTA as a masking agent. This change in effectiveness with pH is very useful in separations of metal ions. Let us consider a problem that illustrates how we can establish the pH that must be used to mask one ion in a mixture of ions.

Example.   A solution is 0.0225 M in $MgSO_4$ and 0.0122 M in $ZnSO_4$. Over what pH region will 0.0250 M EDTA be effective in masking the zinc so that the magnesium can be reacted with another reagent without any interference from the zinc?

The reactions involved in the problem are:

$$Mg^{2+} + H_3Y^- \rightleftharpoons MgY^{2-} + 3H^+$$

$$Zn^{2+} + H_3Y^- \rightleftharpoons ZnY^{2-} + 3H^+$$

which have the stability constants:

$$K_{st} = \frac{[MgY^{2-}]}{[Mg^{2+}][Y^{4-}]} = 4.9 \times 10^8; \; K_{st} = \frac{[ZnY^{2-}]}{[Zn^{2+}][Y^{4-}]} = 3.2 \times 10^{16}$$

The problem requests that the chelation reaction of zinc should be allowed to take place, but that Mg^{2+} must not be allowed to react with EDTA. This can be achieved by lowering the pH of the solution to such a value that the protonating side reaction becomes the predominant one for Mg^{2+} but not for Zn^{2+}. In order to find the pH values that the problem asks for, one must find the α_{0H} values for EDTA when all the zinc has chelated and when the magnesium just begins to chelate. Then, from these α_{0H} values, the pH that will produce them can be looked up in Appendix 2. The α_{0H} values are obtained by solving the stability constant expressions for the concentration of the unprotonated Y^{4-} anion. In the case of magnesium, the stability constant expression is solved at the point when the metal will just begin to complex appreciably and, in the case of zinc, when all of the metal ion has been chelated.
    Let us assume that the statement, "when magnesium just begins to form an EDTA chelate" means the point at which the concentration of MgY^{2-} will be 0.1% of the total concentration of the magnesium in the solution. (Other assumptions about this can be made, such as $[MgY^{2-}] = 1\% \, C_{Mg}$ or that $[MgY^{2-}] = 1.0 \times 10^{-6}$ M. The assumption that actually is used will determine the usable upper pH limit.)
    At this point:

$$[MgY^{2-}] = 0.10\% \, C_{Mg} = (0.00100)(2.25 \times 10^{-2} \, M)$$

$$= 2.25 \times 10^{-5} \, M$$

The material balance for magnesium in the solution is:

$$C_{Mg} = [Mg^{2+}] + [MgY^{2-}] = 2.25 \times 10^{-2} \, M$$

Since $[MgY^{2-}]$ is now known:

$$[Mg^{2+}] = 2.25 \times 10^{-2} - 2.25 \times 10^{-5} \, M$$
$$= 2.25 \times 10^{-2} \, M$$

Substituting these two magnesium concentrations into the stability constant expression for the Mg–EDTA chelate and solving for the molar concentration of the Y^{4-} anion gives:

$$[Y^{4-}] = \frac{2.25 \times 10^{-5}}{(2.25 \times 10^{-2})(4.9 \times 10^{8})} = 2.04 \times 10^{-12} \, M$$

The material balance for EDTA in the solution, according to the restrictions established in the statement of the problem, is:

$$C'_{EDTA} = [Y^{4-}] + [HY^{3-}] + [H_2Y^{2-}] + [H_3Y^-] + [ZnY^{2-}]$$

C'_{EDTA} is the concentration of all species containing EDTA that are not chelated to a metal ion:

$$C'_{EDTA} = C_{EDTA} - [ZnY^{2-}]$$
$$= 0.0250 - 0.0122 \, M = 0.0128 \, M$$

From the definition of alpha zero in a solution containing a metal chelate:

$$\alpha_{0_H} = \frac{[Y^{4-}]}{C'_{EDTA}} = \frac{2.04 \times 10^{-12}}{1.28 \times 10^{-2}} = 1.60 \times 10^{-10}$$

Interpolating in Appendix 2 gives a pH $= 3.22$ for this α_{0_H}. If the pH of the solution is any higher than this, more than 0.1% of the magnesium present in the solution will exist as the EDTA chelate.

Similarly, let us assume that all of the zinc ion has been chelated when $[Zn^{2+}] = 0.1\% \, C_{Zn}$. (Again other assumptions, such as $[Zn^{2+}] = 1.0 \times 10^{-6} \, M$ could be made instead, and these will determine the value obtained for the minimum pH to be used.) Making this assumption, then 99.9% of the zinc will be chelated with the EDTA.

$$[Zn^{2+}] = 0.1\% \, C_{Zn} = (1.00 \times 10^{-3})(1.22 \times 10^{-2} \, M)$$
$$= 1.22 \times 10^{-5} \, M$$

The material balance for the zinc present in the solution is:

$$C_{Zn} = [Zn^{2+}] + [ZnY^{2-}] = 1.22 \times 10^{-2} \, M$$

Rearranging this to solve for $[ZnY^{2-}]$

$$[ZnY^{2-}] = 1.22 \times 10^{-2} - 1.22 \times 10^{-5} \, M = 1.22 \times 10^{-2} \, M$$

Substituting these two zinc concentrations into the stability constant expression for the Zn–EDTA chelate, and solving for the molar concentration of the Y^{4-} anion gives:

$$[Y^{4-}] = \frac{1.22 \times 10^{-2}}{(1.22 \times 10^{-5})(3.2 \times 10^{16})} = 3.12 \times 10^{-14} \, M$$

Substituting this value and the value for C'_{EDTA} calculated before into the definition of α_{0_H}:

$$\alpha_{0_H} = \frac{3.12 \times 10^{-14}}{1.28 \times 10^{-2}} = 2.44 \times 10^{-12}$$

Again, interpolating the values given in Appendix 2, it is found that the solution pH necessary to give rise to this α_{0_H} is 2.52.

Thus, between a pH of 2.52 and 3.22 EDTA will chelate less than 0.1% of the magnesium ion and yet more than 99.9% of the zinc ion. Below pH 2.52, not all of the zinc will be masked, and above pH 3.22 too much of the magnesium will be complexed to make a separation feasible.

EDTA is very frequently used in basic media. Most of the metal ions that react with EDTA will precipitate from solution as their hydroxides long before a pH of 10.00 is reached. In order to avoid this precipitation when using EDTA as a titrant, the metal ion must be complexed initially so as to hold it in a soluble form in solution. Ammonia is very commonly used as the auxiliary complexing agent in EDTA titrations. It forms ammine complexes with many metals that are sufficiently stable so as to prevent the metal hydroxide from precipitating at a pH of 10.0, but the ammine complexes are sufficiently weak so as to enable EDTA to replace the ammonia molecules and form the EDTA chelate with the metal ion. In the presence of ammonia at a pH of 10, the overall reaction that occurs may be written as:

$$M(NH_3)_4^{2+} + HY^{3-} \rightleftharpoons MY^{2-} + NH_4^+ + 3NH_3$$

The extent to which this reaction will go to completion depends not only upon the pH of the solution, but also upon the concentration of free ammonia in the solution. Breaking this overall reaction down into a more revealing diagram of the equilibria involved gives:

$$
\begin{array}{ccc}
 & & K_{st} \\
M^{2+} & + & Y^{4-} \rightleftharpoons MY^{2-} \\
+ & & + \\
4NH_3 & & H_3O^+ \\
K_{st} \updownarrow & & \updownarrow K_{a4} \\
M(NH_3)_4^{2+} & & HY^{3-}
\end{array}
$$

Apparent or Conditional Stability Constants

In accordance with Equation (5–43), the stability constant for the formation of the metal–EDTA chelate is written as:

$$K_{st} = \frac{[MY^{(n-4)+}]}{[M^{n+}][Y^{4-}]}$$

The use of this constant alone in systems containing auxiliary complexing agents at differing pH values is very complicated. The stepwise stability constants for the metal complexes must be solved for $[M^{n+}]$ and the acid dissociation constants for EDTA must be solved for $[Y^{4-}]$. The use of the degree of ionization (α) that is available both for weak acids and a sequence of complexes simplifies the calculations considerably. Thus, for the system diagrammed:

$$\alpha_{0_H} = \frac{[Y^{4-}]}{C'_{EDTA}}$$

$$\alpha_{0_L} = \frac{[M^{2+}]}{C'_M}$$

$$C'_{EDTA} = C_{EDTA} - [MY^{2-}] \quad \text{and} \quad C'_M = C_M - [MY^{2-}]$$

Rewriting the alpha expressions in terms of the concentration of the free species:

$$[Y^{4-}] = \alpha_{0_H} C'_{EDTA} \qquad [M^{2+}] = \alpha_{0_{NH_3}} C'_M$$

Substituting these concentration terms into the stability constant expression for MY^{2-}:

$$K_{st} = \frac{[MY^{2-}]}{\alpha_{0_H} C'_{EDTA}\, \alpha_{0_{NH_3}} C'_M} \tag{5-71}$$

where α_{0_H} pertains to the loss of protons by the ligand and α_{0_L} pertains to the formation of the auxiliary complex by the metal ion. Both α_{0_H} and α_{0_L} are considered to be a measure of side reactions occurring in the solution. Rearranging this expression to collect all of the constants on the left-hand side of the equation:

$$\alpha_{0_H} \alpha_{0_{NH_3}} K_{st} = \frac{[MY^{2-}]}{C'_{EDTA} C'_M} = K'_{st} \tag{5-72}$$

K'_{st} is called the *conditional* or *apparent stability constant* for the metal chelate. K'_{st} is not a true constant for it varies with the pH of the solution as well as with the ammonia concentration. For a series of systems, however, where these two values are unvariable, K'_{st} will remain unchanged. During a series of repetitive calculations where only the metal ion concentration is changing, the use of conditional stability constants saves a lot of time. The determination of the apparent stability constant for a metal–EDTA chelate under specified conditions and then its use in solving a problem provides a very simple way to solve problems involving competing equilibria. Let us illustrate this simplicity.

Example. Calculate the concentration of zinc remaining unchelated by EDTA in 75.0 ml of a solution that is 0.0125 M EDTA, 0.0125 M zinc, 0.100 M NH$_3$, and has a pH of 10.00.

The equilibria involved in this problem are:

$$Zn(NH_3)_4^{2+} + HY^{3-} \rightleftharpoons ZnY^{2-} + NH_4^+ + 3NH_3$$

which when diagrammed reveals:

$$
\begin{array}{ccc}
 & & K_{st} \\
Zn^{2+} & + & Y^{4-} \rightleftharpoons ZnY^{2-} \\
+ & & + \\
4NH_3 & & H_3O^+ \\
\beta\text{'s} \updownarrow & & \updownarrow K_{a4} \\
Zn(NH_3)_4^{2+} & & HY^{3-}
\end{array}
$$

The conditional stability constant expression for this system is:

$$K'_{st} = \frac{[ZnY^{2-}]}{C'_{Zn}C'_{EDTA}} = K_{st}\,\alpha_{0_H}\,\alpha_{0_{NH_3}}$$

From Appendix 8, the stability constant for ZnY^{2-} is 3.2×10^{16}. From Appendix 2, α_{0_H} for EDTA at a pH of 10.0 = 0.355. From Appendix 6, $\alpha_{0_{NH_3}}$ for $Zn(NH_3)_4^{2+}$ in 0.1 M NH_3 is 1.0×10^{-5}. From these constants the numerical value of the conditional stability constant is:

$$K'_{st} = (3.2 \times 10^{16})(0.355)(1.0 \times 10^{-5}) = 1.1 \times 10^{11}$$

The problem asks that the concentration of unchelated zinc be calculated. This is C'_{Zn}. Note that the problem does not ask for the amount of zinc ion that is uncomplexed by anything, $[Zn^{2+}]$, although this could be found readily. In order to calculate the value of C'_{Zn} numerical values for $[MY^{2-}]$ and C'_{EDTA} must be known.

The material balance for zinc in this solution is:

$$C_{Zn} = [Zn^{2+}] + [Zn(NH_3)_4^{2+}] + [ZnY^{2-}] = 0.0125\ M$$

In a solution containing two excellent complexing agents, NH_3 and EDTA, there just won't be any uncomplexed zinc ions to speak of. Therefore, let us assume that the concentration of the uncomplexed zinc can be neglected in the above expression. Since the K'_{st} is large, 10^{11}, it is reasonable to assume that all of the zinc in the solution will exist as the EDTA chelate, so that $[ZnY^{2-}] = 1.25 \times 10^{-2}\ M$.

The statement of the problem gives the total concentration of zinc as being identical to the total concentration of EDTA in the solution.

$$C_{EDTA} = C_{Zn}$$

Since the chelate formed is a 1:1 chelate, from the formula of ZnY^{2-} it follows that:

$$C'_{EDTA} = C_{EDTA} - [ZnY^{2-}] = C_{Zn} - [ZnY^{2-}] = C'_{Zn}$$

Thus we have the concentrations and interrelationships needed. Substituting them into the expression for the conditional stability constant:

$$1.1 \times 10^{11} = \frac{1.25 \times 10^{-2}}{(C'_{Zn})^2}$$

which when solved gives:

$$C'_{Zn} = (1.25 \times 10^{-13})^{\frac{1}{2}} = 3.5 \times 10^{-6}\ M$$

This is the number requested in the statement of the problem, but in arriving at it, two assumptions were made that must now be verified. Comparison of C'_{Zn} ($3.5 \times 10^{-6}\ M$) with $[ZnY^{2-}]$ ($1.25 \times 10^{-2}\ M$) shows that almost all of the zinc does exist as the EDTA chelate, so that assumption is a valid one.

The concentration of the zinc ions uncomplexed by anything can be calculated from the definition of $\alpha_{0_{NH_3}}$.

$$[Zn^{2+}] = \alpha_{0_{NH_3}}\,C'_{Zn}$$
$$= (1.0 \times 10^{-5})(3.5 \times 10^{-6}\ M) = 3.5 \times 10^{-11}\ M$$

This value is so very small that the initial assumption about $[Zn^{2+}]$ being negligible is valid also.

The Effect of Complexation on Solubility

In the presence of a ligand that will complex with one of the ions of a precipitate, the molar solubility of the precipitate will be greater than it is in pure solvent. The ability to form a precipitate with only one ion in a mixture of several ions in a solution containing a complexing agent, permits many separations to be achieved by precipitation (for example, nickel with dimethylglyoxime in ammoniacal solution). The equilibria present can be treated mathematically from the stability constant expression and the solubility product expression. The techniques involved in solving problems are identical to those used in treating pH effects on complexation. To illustrate this, let us solve such a problem.

Example. Calculate the molar solubility of silver iodide in 0.500 M ethylenediamine.

The equilibria involved in this problem are:

$$AgI(s) \overset{K_{sp}}{\rightleftharpoons} Ag^+ + I^-$$
$$+$$
$$2en$$
$$\updownarrow K_{st}$$
$$Ag(en)_2^+$$

with the equilibrium constants:

$$K_{sp} = [Ag^+][I^-] = 8.30 \times 10^{-17}$$

$$K_{st} = \frac{[Ag(en)_2^+]}{[Ag^+][en]^2} = 6.0 \times 10^7$$

The problem asks for the molar solubility of the precipitate and this should be expressed in terms of the iodide ion concentration, since this does not undergo any complicating side reactions. Therefore, the solubility product constant expression should be solved for [I$^-$]. In order to do this, the uncomplexed silver ion concentration in the solution must be known. This can be found from the material balance and electroneutrality principle.

The electroneutrality principle expression for this solution is:

$$[Ag^+] + [Ag(en)_2^+] = [I^-]$$

The material balance for ethylenediamine in the solution is:

$$[en] + 2[Ag(en)_2^+] = C_{en} = 0.500 \ M$$

Let us assume that the molar solubility of the precipitate is very low compared to the high ethylenediamine concentration. Then the amount of the ethylenediamine that is consumed in the formation of the silver chelate can be considered to be negligible so that:

$$[en] = C_{en} = 0.500 \ M$$

The material balance for silver ion in the solution is:

$$[Ag^+] + [Ag(en)_2^+] = C_{Ag} = [I^-]$$

Since the concentration of ethylenediamine in the solution is very high and since the stability constant for $Ag(en)_2^+$ is relatively large, let us assume that almost all of the silver exists as the silver ethylenediamine complex. Then:

$$[Ag(en)_2^+] = C_{Ag} = [I^-]$$

We have obtained the two needed concentrations, so now it is possible to solve the stability constant expression for the free silver ion concentration:

$$[Ag^+] = \frac{[Ag(en)_2^+]}{K_{st}[en]^2} = \frac{[I^-]}{(6.0 \times 10^7)(5.0 \times 10^{-1})^2}$$

$$= \frac{[I^-]}{1.50 \times 10^7}$$

Substituting this concentration into the solubility product constant expression gives:

$$K_{sp} = \left(\frac{[I^-]}{1.50 \times 10^7}\right)[I^-] = 8.30 \times 10^{-17}$$

Solving this for the iodide ion concentration:

$$[I^-]^2 = 12.4 \times 10^{-10}$$

$$[I^-] = 3.5 \times 10^{-5} \, M = s$$

This is the molar solubility requested by the problem. Now let us check the validity of the two assumptions made in arriving at this value. From the preceding material balance on silver ion, it is found that the concentration of iodide is equal to the concentration of the silver ethylenediamine complex. Therefore, the amount of ethylenediamine consumed in forming the complex ion is $2 \times 3.2 \times 10^{-5} \, M = 6.4 \times 10^{-5} \, M$. Comparison of this value with the total concentration of ethylenediamine in the solution, 0.500 M, reveals that this is indeed a negligibly small concentration, so the first assumption about the amount of ethylenediamine consumed in the complexation reaction is a valid one.

Substituting the value for the iodide ion concentration into the K_{sp} expression gives 2.6×10^{-12} for the concentration of the uncomplexed silver ion. This is negligibly small compared to the $3.2 \times 10^{-5} \, M$ complexed silver ion, so the second assumption that all of the silver ion in solution exists as its ethylenediamine complex is also a valid one.

Separation of Mixtures of Ions by Complexation and Precipitation

Earlier in this chapter (p. 181) we discussed separation of a pair of ions by precipitating the more insoluble one, filtering it off, and then precipitating the less insoluble one. A common precipitant was used. When there is insufficient difference in the solubilities of the two precipitates, this method will not be feasible. One excellent way to overcome this problem is to mask one of the ions with a complexing agent, and then precipitate the other one with the precipitant. An illustration of the technique and the considerations that must be investigated is given in the next example.

Example. A solution is 0.0125 M in $Pb(NO_3)_2$ and 0.0381 M in $Ba(NO_3)_2$, and has a pH of 8.00. Show that by making the solution 0.100 M in EDTA these two ions can be separated by precipitation as their sulfates. The chemical reactions involved in this problem are:

masking
$$Ba^{2+} + HY^{3-} \rightleftharpoons BaY^{2-} + H^+ \tag{1}$$
$$Pb^{2+} + HY^{3-} \rightleftharpoons PbY^{2-} + H^+ \tag{2}$$

precipitation
$$Ba^{2+} + SO_4^{2-} \rightleftharpoons BaSO_4(s) \tag{3}$$
$$Pb^{2+} + SO_4^{2-} \rightleftharpoons PbSO_4(s) \tag{4}$$

According to the statement of the problem, solution conditions are arranged so that reactions (1), (2) and (3) must occur. Reaction (2) must occur completely to prevent reaction (4). In order to ensure that reaction (3) predominates, reaction (1) must be minimized; that is, the equilibrium position must lie further to the left than that of reaction (2). The equilibrium constant expressions for these reactions are:

$$K_{st} = \frac{[BaY^{2-}]}{[Ba^{2+}][Y^{4-}]} = 6.0 \times 10^7 \qquad K_{st} = \frac{[PbY^{2-}]}{[Pb^{2+}][Y^{4-}]} = 1.1 \times 10^{18}$$

$$K_{sp} = [Ba^{2+}][SO_4^{2-}] = 1.1 \times 10^{-10} \qquad K_{sp} = [Pb^{2+}][SO_4^{2-}] = 1.7 \times 10^{-8}$$

This example is almost identical to the one solved earlier—the example dealing with the separation of silver and thallium by precipitation as their iodides—and it is solved in a similar manner. First, we must find out which ion will precipitate first. Since the numerical values of the solubility constants are within two powers of ten of one another, and the forms of their expressions are identical, it should be apparent that in the absence of any masking agents, a complete separation of these two ions cannot be made. Since their K_{st} values are high, when the EDTA is added to the solution both Pb^{2+} and Ba^{2+} will react completely with it and exist as the EDTA chelate. To find out which ion will precipitate first, the concentration of the uncomplexed lead and barium must be found from the expressions for the stability constants. Since any homogeneous solution can have only a single concentration of any ion, the concentrations calculated from the K_{st} must also satisfy the solubility product constants. The amount of sulfate needed to begin the precipitation of each ion can be calculated from the two K_{sp} expressions. After the order of precipitation is determined, one can calculate the concentration of the first ion to precipitate which still is unprecipitated in the solution when the second ion begins to precipitate. If the first ion's concentration remaining unprecipitated is sufficiently low, the two ions can be separated.

In the preceding solution of the metal ions, EDTA will complex both, so that a material balance for the EDTA in the solution is:

$$C_{EDTA} = [H_2Y^{2-}] + [HY^{3-}] + [Y^{4-}] + [PbY^{2-}] + [BaY^{2-}]$$

or

$$C_{EDTA} = C'_{EDTA} + [PbY^{2-}] + [BaY^{2-}] = 0.100 \ M$$

The material balances for the two metal ions are:

$$C_{Pb} = [Pb^{2+}] + [PbY^{2-}] = 0.0125 \ M$$

$$C_{Ba} = [Ba^{2+}] + [BaY^{2-}] = 0.0381 \ M$$

Since both EDTA chelates are quite stable, it should be safe to neglect the concentration of the unchelated metal ion in comparison to the concentration of the chelated metal ion. Doing this gives:

$$[PbY^{2-}] = 0.0125 \ M \qquad [BaY^{2-}] = 0.0381 \ M$$

By substituting these values into a rearranged EDTA material balance equation we find that:

$$C'_{EDTA} = 0.100 \ M - 0.0125 \ M - 0.0381 \ M = 0.0494 \ M$$

The concentration of the unprotonated EDTA anion, Y^{4-}, at a pH of 8 can be calculated from the equation for the definition of alpha zero in a solution containing a metal chelate. The value of alpha zero at pH = 8.0 is obtained from Appendix 2.

$$[Y^{4-}] = \alpha_{0H} C'_{EDTA} = (5.38 \times 10^{-3})(4.94 \times 10^{-2} \ M)$$
$$= 2.66 \times 10^{-4} \ M$$

We now have found the numerical values for the concentration of the unprotonated anion, Y^{4-}, and for each of the metal chelates. Substituting these values into the respective stability constant expressions for each ion and calculating the concentration of the uncomplexed metal ion we find that:

$$[Ba^{2+}] = \frac{3.81 \times 10^{-2}}{(6.0 \times 10^{7})(2.66 \times 10^{-4})} = 2.40 \times 10^{-6} \ M$$

$$[Pb^{2+}] = \frac{1.25 \times 10^{-2}}{(1.1 \times 10^{18})(2.66 \times 10^{-4})} = 4.28 \times 10^{-17} \ M$$

Since each of these concentrations is so low, the assumption that essentially all of each metal ion exists in solution as its EDTA chelate is valid.

Now let us find out the sulfate concentration at which each of the ions starts to precipitate. The concentration of sulfate ion present in the solution that is necessary to just begin the precipitation of $BaSO_4$ and of $PbSO_4$ can be found from the respective solubility product constant expressions:

for barium:

$$[SO_4^{2-}] = \frac{K_{sp}}{[Ba^{2+}]} = \frac{1.1 \times 10^{-10}}{2.4 \times 10^{-6}} = 4.6 \times 10^{-5} \ M$$

for lead:

$$[SO_4^{2-}] = \frac{K_{sp}}{[Pb^{2+}]} = \frac{1.7 \times 10^{-8}}{4.3 \times 10^{-17}} = 4.0 \times 10^{8} \ M$$

It should be obvious from the difference in the magnitude of these two concentrations that all of the barium can be precipitated without beginning to precipitate $PbSO_4$. As a matter of fact, it would be impossible to get the concentration of sulfate ions in a solution to this abnormally high concentration. To confirm this mathematically, all that needs to be done is to calculate the concentration of barium ions remaining in the solution unprecipitated when the $PbSO_4$ just begins to precipitate. As was shown in the earlier example, this can be done by substituting the sulfate ion concentration required to begin precipitation of $PbSO_4$ into the solubility constant expression for barium sulfate:

$$[Ba^{2+}] = \frac{1.1 \times 10^{-10}}{4.0 \times 10^8} = 2.5 \times 10^{-19}\ M$$

This is unquestionably a negligible amount of barium. Either of the two criteria that have been used indicate that a separation is feasible.

This example illustrates that a separation can be effected in the presence of EDTA whereas it could not be performed in the absence of the chelating agent.

Complexometric or Chelatometric Titrations

In addition to being used in separation procedures, another very widespread use of the aminopolycarboxylic acids such as EDTA, NTA, and DTPA is as titrants for metal ions. Such titrations are called either *complexometric* or *chelatometric titrations*. Since these ligands form 1:1 chelates of moderately high stability with most metal ions, a rapid change in the concentration of the metal ion will occur near the equivalence point of the titration, so that end-point indicating techniques are sensitive. EDTA is the chelon most commonly used as a titrant because it is readily available in a form that is sufficiently pure and convenient to use and it gives excellent end-point breaks. In addition, there are several widely accepted end-point detection techniques that are applicable to EDTA titrations—visual indicators, mercury electrodes for potentiometric end points, and photometric end-point detection.

Let us see how the changes in the concentration of the metal ion during the course of a chelatometric titration can be calculated from the known equilibria and their stability constants. The usual coordinates of a titration curve for an EDTA titration are pM (ordinate) and volume of EDTA added (abscissa). To illustrate the techniques used in the calculation of chelatometric titrations curves, let us consider the titration of 50.00 ml of 0.0100 M zinc ion with 0.0100 M Na$_2$H$_2$Y · 2H$_2$O in a 0.100 M NH$_3$–0.100 M NH$_4$Cl buffer at a pH of 10.00.

The actual reaction that occurs during the titration is:

$$Zn(NH_3)_4^{2+} + HY^{3-} \rightleftharpoons ZnY^{2-} + NH_4^+ + 3NH_3$$

The details of the equilibria involved have been diagrammed already (p. 213). The numerical values of the equilibrium constants necessary to solve this equilibrium constant expression are found in the Appendices. From Appendix 7, the stability constant of ZnY^{2-} is 3.2×10^{16}. From Appendix 5, β_4 for Zn(NH$_3$)$_4^{2+}$ is 4.2×10^8. From Appendix 2, α_{0H} for EDTA at a pH of 10.00 is 0.355 and from Appendix 6, α_{0NH_3} for Zn(NH$_3$)$_4^{2+}$ is found to be 2.0×10^{-5} at a pH of 10.0. Calculations of titration curves for EDTA titrations provide a very practical application of the conditional stability constants.

Initially. Before any EDTA is added to the zinc solution, the solution is nothing more than a solution of zinc ions in 0.100 M NH$_3$ at a pH of 10.00. The concentration of the uncomplexed zinc is needed to calculate pZn ($= $ -log [Zn^{2+}]). This concentration can be calculated quite simply from α_{0NH_3}, which takes into account that lower ammine complexes still exist at this ammonia concentration and the effect of pH on the ammonia concentration.

$$[Zn^{2+}] = \alpha_{0_{NH_3}} C_{Zn} = (2.0 \times 10^{-5})(1.00 \times 10^{-2} \ M)$$

$$= 2.0 \times 10^{-7} \ M$$

$$pZn = -\log[Zn^{2+}] = 6.70$$

Before the equivalence point. During the titration, the EDTA added to the zinc solution removes the zinc ions from their ammine complexes. Up to the equivalence point of the titration, the amount of zinc present will exceed the amount of EDTA in the solution so that, with no qualms, at each point it can be assumed that the titration reaction goes essentially to completion. (*Note*: the value of K'_{st} that is calculated later confirms this.) Therefore, for any point on the titration curve after EDTA addition has begun and up to the equivalence point, the concentration of the zinc ions not chelated with EDTA but complexed with ammonia can be calculated quite readily from the stoichiometry of the reaction. The concentration of the zinc ions not complexed by either EDTA or ammonia then can be calculated from the definition of $\alpha_{0_{NH_3}}$ in the presence of two complexing agents. In all of these calculations, account must be taken of the dilution effects caused by adding the EDTA solution. To illustrate the technique, which is identical for all points up to the equivalence point, let us calculate pZn after the addition of 1.00 ml of 0.0100 ml EDTA.

The total amount of zinc present in all forms in the solution, C_{Zn} is:

$$\text{amount of Zn} = 50.00 \ \text{ml} \times 0.0100 \ M = 0.500 \ \text{mmol of zinc}$$

When 1.00 ml of EDTA has been added, the amount of EDTA added is:

$$\text{amount of EDTA added} = 1.00 \ \text{ml} \times 0.0100 \ M = 0.0100 \ \text{mmol of EDTA}$$

According to the stoichiometry of the titration reaction, this will react with 0.0100 millimoles of zinc, leaving untitrated:

$$\text{untitrated zinc} = 0.500 - 0.010 = 0.490 \ \text{mmol}$$

The concentration of zinc ions in the solution that have not been chelated by EDTA is C'_{Zn}:

$$C'_{Zn} = \frac{0.490 \ \text{mmol}}{51.0 \ \text{ml}} = 9.60 \times 10^{-3} \ M$$

But the zinc is complexed by ammonia, and for pZn we need $[Zn^{2+}]$. The concentration of uncomplexed zinc is calculated from $\alpha_{0_{NH_3}}$.

$$[Zn^{2+}] = \alpha_{0_{NH_3}} C'_{Zn} = (2.0 \times 10^{-5})(9.60 \times 10^{-3} \ M)$$

$$= 1.92 \times 10^{-7} \ M$$

$$pZn = 6.72$$

Table 5-9 gives the values of pZn as EDTA is added throughout the titration.

The values of pZn in Table 5–9 before the equivalence point have been calculated as illustrated here.

At the equivalence point. When the equivalence point of the titration has been reached, there is no excess of either EDTA or unchelated zinc. The amount of zinc that is not chelated by the EDTA can be calculated from the conditional stability constant for the overall reaction. This conditional stability constant is evaluated by means of Equation (5–72):

$$K'_{st} = \alpha_{0_H} \alpha_{0_{NH_3}} K_{st}$$

$$= (0.355)(2.0 \times 10^{-5})(3.2 \times 10^{+16}) = 2.28 \times 10^{11}$$

$$= \frac{[ZnY^{2-}]}{C'_{Zn} C'_{EDTA}}$$

From the stoichiometry of the titration reaction, it can be seen that at the equivalence point, $C'_{Zn} = C'_{EDTA}$. Nothing is stated about the forms in which the zinc and the EDTA exist in the solution, but since the values of the equilibrium constants are not the same for the zinc–ammine complexes and the protonation of Y^{4-}, it definitely is true that $[Zn^{2+}] \neq [Y^{4-}]$. The total amount of the two substances that are not chelated with one another must be equal, however.

At the equivalence point the assumption is made that essentially all of the zinc has been chelated by EDTA; that is, C'_{Zn} is negligibly small compared to $[ZnY^{2-}]$. Since K_{st} is large, this assumption is a valid one. The solution has been diluted so that:

$$[ZnY^{2-}] = \frac{0.500 \text{ mmol}}{100.0 \text{ ml}} = 0.00500 \ M$$

Substituting this and the relationship between C'_{Zn} and C'_{EDTA} into the expression for the conditional stability constant:

$$2.28 \times 10^{11} = \frac{5.00 \times 10^{-3}}{C'_{Zn} C'_{Zn}}$$

and solving for the concentration of zinc not in the EDTA chelate:

$$C'_{Zn} = \sqrt{2.20 \times 10^{-14}} = 1.48 \times 10^{-7} \ M$$

The amount of uncomplexed zinc is calculated again from the definition of $\alpha_{0_{NH_3}}$.

$$[Zn^{2+}] = \alpha_{0_{NH_3}} C'_{Zn} = (2.0 \times 10^{-5})(1.48 \times 10^{-7} \ M)$$

$$= 2.96 \times 10^{-12} \ M$$

$$pZn = 11.53$$

Beyond the equivalence point. Once the equivalence point has been passed, all that is occurring is that excess EDTA is being added to the solution. Knowing the amount of this excess EDTA and the extent of the dilution that it causes, the concentration of the zinc that is unchelated by EDTA can be calculated by solving the conditional stability constant expression. Then, from this, the concentration of uncomplexed zinc can be calculated from $\alpha_{0_{NH_3}}$. To illustrate how this is done, let us calculate pZn when 55.00 ml of EDTA has been added to the solution. To reach the equivalence point required 50.00 ml of EDTA, so there now is an excess of 5.00 ml of EDTA.

$$C'_{\text{EDTA}} = \frac{5.00 \text{ ml} \times 0.0100 \ M}{105.0 \text{ ml}} = 4.75 \times 10^{-4} \ M$$

The concentration of the zinc–EDTA chelated at this volume is:

$$[\text{ZnY}^{2-}] = \frac{0.500 \text{ mmol}}{105.0 \text{ ml}} = 4.75 \times 10^{-3} \ M$$

Substituting these values into the conditional stability constant expression and solving for C'_{Zn}:

$$C'_{\text{Zn}} = \frac{4.75 \times 10^{-3}}{(2.28 \times 10^{11})(4.75 \times 10^{-4})} = 4.39 \times 10^{-11} \ M$$

$$[\text{Zn}^{2+}] = (2.0 \times 10^{-5})(4.39 \times 10^{-11}) = 8.8 \times 10^{-16} \ M$$

All of the points on the titration curve past the equivalence point are calculated in an identical fashion. The points in Table 5–9 past the equivalence point have been calculated in the way illustrated here.

Fig. 5–8 is a graph of the data calculated in the preceding manner and tabulated in Table 5–9. It is the titration curve for the titration of zinc with EDTA under the conditions specified here. Fig. 5–8 shows that there is a relatively large and sharp break in pZn in the immediate vicinity of the equivalence point. Eriochrome black T has a transition color in this titration at a pH of 10.00 at pZn = 12.2, so that eriochrome black T can be used satisfactorily as a visual indicator for the titration.

Table 5–9. DATA FOR THE TITRATION OF 50.00 ml OF 0.0100 M Zn(NH$_3$)$_4$$^{2+}$ AT A pH OF 10.0 WITH 0.010 M Na$_2$H$_2$Y·2 H$_2$O

ml 0.010 M EDTA Added	pZn	ml 0.010 M EDTA Added	pZn
0.00	6.70	49.90	9.70
1.00	6.71	49.99	10.70
5.00	6.79	50.00	11.53
10.00	6.88	50.01	12.36
20.00	7.08	50.10	13.36
30.00	7.30	50.50	14.06
40.00	7.65	51.00	14.35
45.00	7.99	55.00	15.06
48.00	8.39	60.00	15.36
49.00	8.69	70.00	15.66
49.50	9.00	80.00	15.84
		90.00	15.96

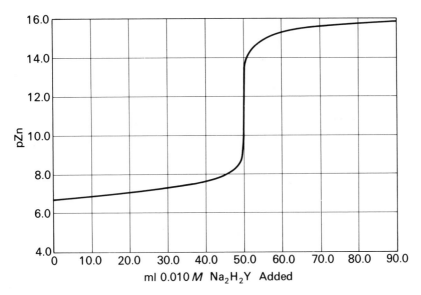

Fig. 5–8. Titration of 50.00 ml of 0.010 M $Zn(NH_3)_4^{2+}$ at pH $= 10.0$ with 0.010 M $Na_2H_2Y \cdot 2H_2O$.

Metallochromic Indicators

The chemical compounds used as visual indicators in chelatometric titrations are called *metallochromic indicators*. These indicators are organic dye molecules that form chelates with metal ions. In order for a dye to be suitable as a metallochromic indicator: (1) the color of the metal–dye chelate must be different from the color of the unchelated dye molecule; (2) the metal–dye chelate must be formed rapidly and reversibly; and (3) the color transition must occur at the pM value of the equivalence point of a specific titration. The psychodynamic aspects of color vision determine the practical utility of any indicator.

Initially, a small amount of indicator is added to the metal ion solution. This indicator will form the colored metal–dye chelate with about 0.01% of the metal ions present. The chelon is then titrated into the solution. It reacts initially with the metal ions that are not tied up in the indicator chelate. As the end point of the titration is approached, the titrant begins to remove metal ions from the metal–indicator chelate, thus liberating the free dye. At this time the solution begins to change from the pure color of the metal–indicator chelate. The color that is seen in the solution goes through the transition colors as the ratio of the concentration of free dye to that of the chelated dye increases. Finally, just at the equivalence point of the titration, the last of the metal ions is removed from the metal–indicator chelate and the solution takes on the color of the pure unchelated dye. Addition of excess chelon can have no further effect upon the color of the solution, since all of the metallochromic indicator present already is in the free, unchelated form.

The restrictions placed upon dyes in order to be used as metallochromic indicators are fairly stringent. They must form chelates with metal ions that are stronger than those of any masking agents present (for example, NH_3, en) or the metallated form of the indicator will not form initially. Yet, they must form chelates that are weaker than the titrant so that the titrant (for example, EDTA, NTA, DTPA) can displace them from the metal ion near the equivalence point. If the metal–indicator chelate is too weak, the titrant will displace it too early in the titration, and the end point will appear too soon. When the metal–indicator chelate is too strong, the titrant will not replace it until well past the equivalence point, if at all, so the end point of the titration will appear too late.

In addition to undergoing color reactions with metal ions, metallochromic indicators are usually tri- or tetraprotic acids. Frequently, each of the protonated forms of the indicator has a slightly different color from the others. Thus, the pH of the titrated solution is doubly important, since not only will it affect the degree of complexation of the metal by the indicator, but it will also affect the color change observed at the end point.

To be more specific: consider the equilibria involved in the complexometric titration of a metal, M, with a chelon, HX; for example, the titration of zinc with EDTA. The metal ion is masked with an auxiliary complexing agent, HL, (for example, NH_3, en) in order to prevent the precipitation of metal hydroxide. The indicator, added in very small amounts, is the dye $Na^+H_2In^-$ (for example, eriochrome black T).

Initially, at some constant pH, the solution will contain the metal–masking agent complex, ML_m. When the indicator is added to the solution the following equilibria are established (ignoring all attempts to balance charges or reactions):

$$ML_m + In^{3-} \rightleftharpoons MIn + ML_m + mL^-$$

$$\underset{\text{color}_1}{} \qquad \underset{\text{color}_2}{}$$

$$+$$
$$H_3O^+$$
$$\updownarrow$$
$$HIn^{2-}, \text{etc.}$$

During the initial stages of the titration, the titrant reacts only with the metal ions in the complex with the auxiliary ligand:

$$ML_m + MIn + X^- \rightleftharpoons MX + mL^- + MIn$$

$$\underset{\text{color}_2}{} \qquad\qquad\qquad\qquad \underset{\text{color}_2}{}$$

$$+$$
$$H_3O^+$$
$$\updownarrow$$
$$HX, \text{etc.}$$

Just before, and at, the equivalence point, all of the ML_m has been consumed so the titrant begins to react with the metal in the metal–indicator chelate:

$$MIn + X^- \rightleftharpoons MX + In^{3-}$$

$$\underset{\text{color}_2}{} \qquad\qquad\qquad \underset{\text{color}_1}{}$$

$$+ \qquad\qquad\qquad +$$
$$H_3O^+ \qquad\qquad H_3O^+$$
$$\updownarrow \qquad\qquad \updownarrow$$
$$HX, \text{etc.} \qquad HIn^{2-}, \text{etc.}$$

$$\qquad\qquad\qquad\qquad \underset{\text{color}_3}{}$$

Past the equivalence point there is no metal ion present in the solution that has not been chelated with the titrant, so nothing further happens:

$$MX + In^- \quad + \quad X^- \rightleftharpoons MX + In^- \quad + \quad X^-$$

$$\begin{array}{cccc}
\underset{\text{color}_1}{In^-} & & & \underset{\text{color}_1}{In^-} \\
+ & + & + & + \\
H_3O^+ & H_3O^+ & H_3O^+ & H_3O^+ \\
\updownarrow & \updownarrow & \updownarrow & \updownarrow \\
\underset{\text{color}_3}{HIn^{2-}, \text{ etc.}} & HX, \text{ etc.} & \underset{\text{color}_3}{HIn^{2-}, \text{ etc.}} & HX, \text{ etc.}
\end{array}$$

Fig. 5–9 shows the behavior of eriochrome black T as a metallochromic indicator for magnesium. The dotted vertical lines represent the pH values at which the uncomplexed dye changes from one color to another. At pH 6.91 eriochrome black T turns from red to blue and at 11.50 it turns from blue to orange. The solid line represents the effect of pH on the concentration of pMg in equilibrium with MgIn. The line is calculated and drawn at the color transition of the dye. Below the solid line the dye has the color of MgIn (red), and above the solid line the dye has the color of the unmetallated dye. Now let us see how the dye will function as a metallochromic indicator for the titration of magnesium. From Fig. 5–9, it can be seen that below a pH of 6.9, no observable color change occurs since the free dye exists as red H_2In^- and the metallated form of the dye, $MgIn^-$, is red also. Between a pH of 6.9 and 11.5, the unchelated indicator exists as the mono-protonated form, HIn^{2-}, which is blue. Within this pH interval the color change at the equivalence point of a titration will be from the red, $MgIn^-$ chelate, through varying shades of purple, to the blue HIn^{2-}. Above a pH of 11.5 the indicator exists in solution as the orange In^{3-}. The color change of an equivalence point at pH values above 11.5 would be from the red, $MgIn^-$ to the orange In^{3-}. This would be an extremely difficult, if not impossible, color transition to observe accurately.

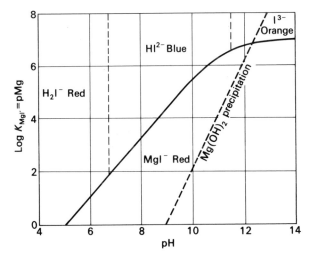

Fig. 5–9. Eriochrome black T as indicator for Mg. (*Redrawn from Ref. 19, by permission of John Wiley & Sons, Inc.*)

Thus, eriochrome black T will only function as a metallochromic indicator between pH values of 6.9 and 11.5. Notice from Fig. 5–9, that magnesium hydroxide begins to precipitate at about a pH of 9, so that above this pH value, some masking agent must be used to keep magnesium ions in solution. The titration of magnesium with EDTA using eriochrome black T as an indicator is usually carried out at a pH of 10 in an ammonia–ammonium chloride masking agent-buffer.

Fig. 5–10 shows the color change-pH diagram for the metallochromic indicator

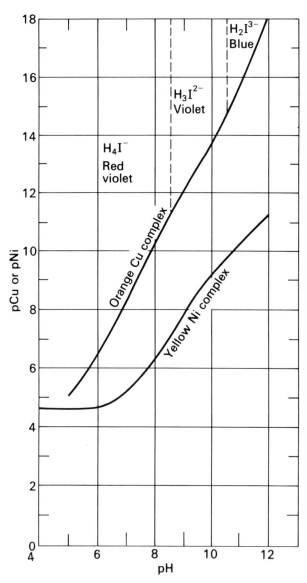

Fig. 5–10. Murexide as indicator for nickel and copper. (*Redrawn from Ref. 19, by permission of John Wiley & Sons, Inc.*)

murexide with the divalent metal ions nickel and copper, drawn analogously to Fig. 5–9. Below a pH of 8.7 murexide exists in solution as a red-violet H_4In^-. Between 8.7 and 10.3 the triprotonated form, H_3In^{2-}, is the predominant species so the solution is violet. Above a pH of 10.3, the blue, diprotonated form, H_2In^{3-}, of murexide exists in solution.

Fig. 5–10 indicates that the color of the nickel–murexide chelate is yellow. For a titration of nickel with a chelon using murexide as the indicator at pH values below 8.7, the color change at the end point will be from yellow to red-violet. Between pH 8.7 and pH 10.3, the color change at the end point of the titration will be from yellow to violet, and above a pH of 10.3, the color change will be from yellow to blue.

Fig. 5–10 indicates that the copper–murexide chelate is orange. For a titration of copper with a chelon using murexide as the indicator, the initial color of the solution will be orange. The end point color change is orange to red-violet below pH = 8.7, orange to violet between pH 8.7 and 10.3, and from orange to blue above pH 10.3.

In practice, things are not so simple. The initial color of the solution being titrated will vary with the concentration of any colored species present, for example, Ni^{2+}, $Ni(NH_3)_4^{2+}$, Cu^{2+}, $Cu(NH_3)_4^{2+}$. The color of the solution changes as the colored metal chelate is formed in increasing amounts during the titration, for example, Ni–EDTA, Cu–EDTA. At the end point the color change will pass

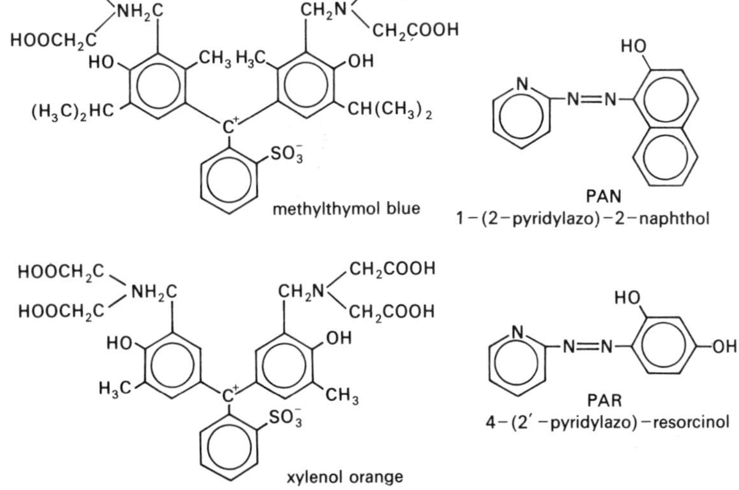

Fig. 5–11. Structures of some commonly used metallochromic indicators.

Table 5–10. RECOMMENDED INDICATORS FOR THE DIRECT TITRATION OF SELECTED METAL IONS WITH EDTA

Metal Ion	log K_{st} of EDTA Chelate	Recommended Indicators
Al(III)	16.3	No direct titration
Ag(I)	7.2	No direct titration
Ba(II)	7.76	No direct titration
Bi(III)	27.94	Methylthymol blue, pyrocatechol violet, xylenol orange
Ca(II)	10.6	Eriochrome black T, methylthymol blue, calcein
Cd(II)	16.50	Eriochrome black T, PAN, methylthymol blue, xylenol orange
Ce(III)	15.98	Chrome azurol S, methylthymol blue, xylenol orange
Co(II)	16.31	Pyrogallol red, pyrocatechol violet
Co(III)	40.7	No direct titration
Cr(III)	23	No direct titration
Cu(II)	18.80	Murexide, glycinethymol blue
Eu(III)	17.35	Chrome azurol S, methylthymol blue, xylenol orange
Fe(III)	25.1	No direct titration
Hg(II)	21.8	Methylthymol blue, xylenol orange
La(III)	15.50	Chrome azurol S, methylthymol blue, xylenol orange
Li(I)	2.79	No direct titration
Mg(II)	8.7	Eriochrome black T, methylthymol blue, calcein
Mn(II)	13.8	Eriochrome black T, methylthymol blue
Na(I)	1.66	No direct titration
Ni(II)	18.62	Murexide, chrome azurol S, methylthymol blue
Pb(II)	18.0	Eriochrome black T, methylthymol blue, pyrocatechol violet, xylenol orange
Sc(III)	23.10	Chrome azurol S, methylthymol blue, xylenol orange
Sn(II)	22.1	Methylthymol blue, Pyrocatechol violet
Sr(II)	8.63	No direct titration
Th(IV)	23.20	Methylthymol blue, xylenol orange
Tl(III)	22.5	PAN, PAR, xylenol orange
Zn(II)	16.50	Eriochrome black T, PAN, pyrocatechol violet, xylenol orange

SOURCE: Ref. 18.

rapidly through various continuously changing shades of color as the ratio of the metallated to the protonated dye changes continuously. The color of the solution past the equivalence point will be a mixture of the protonated-dye color and the metal-titrant chelate color. In spite of this, many metallochromic indicator color changes at the end point are remarkably sharp and easily detected. The sharpness of the color change will be determined by the steepness of the rise in pM at the equivalence point and the kinetics of the exchange reaction between the metal indicator chelate and the metal titrant chelate. Some of the color changes, such as those with eriochrome black T, are very difficult to judge.

The structures of some of the metallochromic indicators commonly used are given in Fig. 5–11. Appendix 9 gives the acid stability constants $(1/k_a)$ and the stability constants with various metal ions for these and additional metallochromic indicators. R. Pribil[18] has reviewed the titration of metal ions with EDTA and its analogs in a series of articles. The information in Table 5–10 is taken from his papers. Table 5–10 gives the recommended metallochromic indicators for the direct titration of many different metal ions with EDTA.

EXPERIMENT 5–8
Preparation and Standardization of 0.010 M EDTA

The disodium dihydrate of EDTA, $Na_2H_2Y \cdot 2H_2O$ commonly is used to prepare standard EDTA solutions. This salt is quite readily available from many commercial sources, often in such a high state of purity that, for routine work, its solutions need not be standardized. For most titrations, however, it is preferable to prepare a solution of the approximate concentration desired, and then to standardize the solution against some primary standard. Primary standard calcium carbonate can be used, but since high purity zinc permits a faster titration and exhibits a much sharper end point, zinc is preferred for the standardization.

The chelate formed between zinc and EDTA has a stability constant of 3.16×10^{16}. Thus titrations of zinc with EDTA can be performed from a pH of 3 upward. Procedures exist in the literature for titrations at various pH values (see Pribil's review[18] for references to these). The most widely used procedure involves the titration of zinc in an ammonia–ammonium chloride buffer at a pH of 10, using eriochrome black T as the indicator. The solubility product of zinc hydroxide is 7.1×10^{-18}. In zinc solutions of the concentrations usually used for EDTA standardizations, zinc hydroxide begins to precipitate around a pH of 7. The use of eriochrome black T requires an alkaline medium for the titration, so that some masking agent must be used to prevent zinc from precipitating. β_4 for the zinc tetraammine complex is 4.2×10^8, which is sufficiently large that a solution containing 1.0 M ammonia will not precipitate zinc hydroxide at a pH of 10.

The titration reaction is between the zinc tetraammine complex and HY^{3-}, that form of EDTA predominating in solution at a pH of 10.

$$Zn(NH_3)_4^{2+} + HY^{3-} \rightleftharpoons ZnY^{2-} + NH_4^+ + 3NH_3$$

The conditional stability constant for this titration reaction under the experimental conditions (pH = 10, $[NH_3]$ = 0.5 M) is 2.3×10^9. The stability constant for the zinc–eriochrome black T chelate is 8.8×10^{12}, but under the experimental conditions for the standardization titration, the conditional stability constant for the zinc–eriochrome black T chelate is only 5.6×10^6. Thus this indicator forms a weaker chelate with the zinc ions than does EDTA, so it will be replaced at the end point, causing the color change to occur at the appropriate time.

Preparation of approximately 0.01 M EDTA.   Weigh between 3.6–3.7 g of disodium ethylenediaminetetraacetate dihydrate into a liter plastic bottle (Note 1). To this add 1000 ml of deionized water. EDTA dissolves very slowly, so shake the solution vigorously to aid this process. Because of this slowness in dissolution of this salt the preparation of the $Na_2H_2Y \cdot 2H_2O$ solution should be started several hours before its use is anticipated. If necessary, the solution may be warmed to about 50–60°C to hasten the process. After all of the salt has dissolved, shake the solution thoroughly to ensure homogeneity.

Preparation of standard zinc solution.   Using an analytical balance, weigh 0.5000 g of high-purity zinc metal into a 150-ml beaker. The actual weight is not critical, but is should be reasonably close to the value specified and known to four significant figures. Slowly add 10 ml of 6 M HCl to the beaker, cover rapidly with a small watch glass, and allow the zinc metal to dissolve completely. Initially the reaction is quite vigorous and much of the zinc solution will be lost by splattering if the beaker is not covered quickly. When it appears that the dissolution has been completed, check carefully to make certain that all of the small particles of metallic zinc have disappeared. This dissolution may take as long as an hour, for the process slows down after its initial vigor. Heating the solution on a steam bath when the reaction slows down will speed up the dissolution.

After all of the zinc metal has dissolved, transfer the solution quantitatively into a 500-ml volumetric flask. Dilute to the mark with deionized water and mix thoroughly by upending the flask slowly at least ten times (Note 2).

Standardization of the EDTA solution.   Pipette 25.00 ml of the standard zinc solution into a 250-ml Erlenmeyer flask. Using dilute NaOH (less concentrated than 0.1 M) raise the pH of the solution until a very slight turbidity begins to persist (Note 3). Add 10 ml of the 8.5 M NH_3–NH_4Cl, pH = 10.0 buffer (Note 4), 50 ml of deionized water, and one or two drops of eriochrome black T indicator solution (Note 5). Warm the solution slightly (30–40°C), and titrate the zinc with the EDTA solution until the color of the zinc solution changes from wine red, through purples to a pure rich blue color. At the end point, the last traces of pink in the solution will have just disappeared. This color change is extremely sharp and should be able to be observed within a fraction of a drop of EDTA. The color change is almost impossible to observe under fluorescent light, so the titration must be carried out during daylight or using tungsten light. If the reaction seems to proceed slowly near the equivalence point, after each addition of titrant wait a few seconds before adding the next drop (Note 6).

Repeat the titration with two additional aliquots of the standard zinc solution. Three titrations agreeing within 0.04 ml of EDTA must be obtained. Do not consume all of the EDTA in standardizing it, for while the purpose of this experiment is to determine the molarity of the EDTA solution, the purpose of preparing the EDTA is to be able to use it in subsequent experiments.

From the known weight of zinc, its atomic weight, and the volume to which it was diluted in the volumetric flask, calculate the molarity of the zinc solution.

$$\text{molarity of zinc} = \frac{\dfrac{\text{weight of zinc metal}}{\text{atomic weight of zinc}}}{0.500 \text{ liter}}$$

From this molarity, the volume of the aliquot of the zinc solution taken, and the volume of the EDTA used to titrate it, calculate the molarity of the EDTA solution obtained in each titration.

$$\text{molarity of EDTA} = \frac{M_{Zn} \times \text{volume Zn taken}}{\text{volume of EDTA}}$$

From these molarities, calculate the average molarity, the standard deviation, and the relative standard deviation for the standardization of the EDTA.

NOTES

1. EDTA is capable of leaching metal ions from soft glass bottles so it should never be stored in them. The metals leached from the glass chelate with the EDTA prevent EDTA from reacting with other metals, thus causing an apparent decrease in the concentration of the EDTA. Borosilicate containers are less apt to be leached by EDTA, but when plastic bottles are used there are no errors due to leaching.
2. The zinc solution should not be stored in glass containers either. It should be transferred to a plastic bottle.
3. The amount of sodium hydroxide solution added at this point will depend upon the amount of acid that was necessary to dissolve the zinc (but is around 25 ml of 0.1 M NaOH). The addition of NaOH should be stopped at the first appearance of a permanent precipitate of zinc hydroxide. If too much sodium hydroxide is added, the stable zincate ion will form.
4. The ammonia–ammonium chloride buffer is prepared by dissolving 35 g of ammonium chloride and 300 ml of concentrated ammonia up to 500 ml with deionized water. This solution will readily attack glass containers, leaching out metal ions which will interfere in subsequent titrations with EDTA. Therefore, it too should be stored in plastic bottles.
5. Aqueous solutions of eriochrome black T may be prepared, but they are unstable and should not be kept for more than a week of two. A more satisfactory, and very stable, solution of the indicator is prepared by dissolving 1 g of the solid eriochrome black T in 100 ml of diethanolamine or triethanolamine. These solutions appear to be stable for several years.
6. The indicator is blacked by any traces of iron, copper, or aluminium that may be present in the solution. Pribil[18] recommends that the titration of zinc with EDTA be carried out at a pH of 5.0–5.5 with a urotropine buffer using either xylenol orange or methylthymol blue as the indicator. With reference to the use of eriochrome black T as an indicator, Pribil[18] states, "a surprisingly large number of workers are unable to recognize the endpoint. This will probably apply to other indicators as well when the colour change is from wine red through violet to blue."

The experiments involving the use of this standard EDTA solution can be found at the end of the chapters on adsorption (8), partition (9), and ion-exchange chromatography (12).

EXPERIMENT 5-9
Determination of the Formula and Stability Constant of the Chelate Formed Between Iron(III) and Tiron

In acid solution, iron(III) reacts with 4,5-dihydroxybenzene-1,3-disulfonic acid (Tiron) to produce a blue color. The object of this experiment is to find out the composition of the species causing the blue color and then to determine the stability constant(s) for this chelate. The general reaction can be written as:

$$\text{(5--73)}$$

for which the following series of stepwise stability constants are possible:

$$\beta_1 = \frac{[\text{Fe(Tiron)}^-]}{[\text{Fe}^{3+}][\text{Tiron}^{4-}]} \qquad \beta_2 = \frac{[\text{Fe(Tiron)}_2^{5-}]}{[\text{Fe}^{3+}][\text{Tiron}^{4-}]^2} \qquad \beta_3 = \frac{[\text{Fe(Tiron)}_3^{9-}]}{[\text{Fe}^{3+}][\text{Tiron}^{4-}]^3}$$

A classical technique for the evaluation of n in Equation (5–73) and for determining some of the beta values (under specialized conditions) was introduced by P. Job in 1925.[7] Commonly, the technique is called *the method of continuous variations* or *Job's method*. For successful application of Job's method, the complex species formed must have some property (color, conductance, optical rotation) that is considerably different from that of either of its constituents. A series of solutions containing different ratios of the components, and hence different amounts of the complex, is prepared. This property is measured on each solution. Both the value of n and the numerical value of the stability constants can be obtained from these measurements.

Let us see how the method of continuous variations works. The general reaction for the formation of a complex ion can be written (ignoring charges):

$$M + nL \rightleftharpoons ML_n \qquad \text{(5--74)}$$

The overall stability constant expression for this complex is:

$$K_{st} = \frac{[ML_n]}{[M][L]^n} \qquad \text{(5--75)}$$

To perform Job's method, stock solutions of M and L with identical concentrations are prepared. While the technique can be used without equimolar solutions, the mathematics of the method becomes unnecessarily complicated. From these stock solutions, a series of mixtures of M and L is prepared. Each solution in this series contains different amounts of M and of L, but all solutions have the same total concentration of M plus L. Thus, for each individual solution and for all solutions in the series:

$$C_M + C_L = C_T$$

For the purposes of this particular experiment, let us assume that ML_n absorbs light at a wavelength at which neither M nor L have any appreciable absorption. Thus, measurement of the absorbance of each solution at this wavelength will measure the concentration of ML_n present in the solution.

First of all, how can we find out what the formula for the complex is (that is, the value of n in the formula) from the amount of light absorbed by each solution? To do this, let us call f the fraction of the total concentration, C_T, of each solution that is contributed by L. Then $(1 - f)$ is the fraction of the total concentration of each solution contributed by M. Stated mathematically:

$$C_L = fC_T \quad \text{and} \quad C_M = (1 - f)\, C_T$$

The stock solutions of M and L are mixed, and the reactions allowed to occur. At equilibrium the amount of uncomplexed metal will be the difference between the initial amount of metal taken and the amount of it that has been consumed in forming the complex ion. Rearranging the material balance for the metal, we can write:

$$[M] = C_M - [ML_n]$$
$$[M] = (1 - f)\, C_T - [ML_n]$$

Similarly, the equilibrium concentration of the uncomplexed ligand is the initial concentration of the ligand taken minus the concentration of it that has been used up in forming the complex ion. Again, from the material balance on the ligand, we can write:

$$[L] = C_L - n[ML_n]$$
$$[L] = fC_T - n[ML_n]$$

From the equations it should be obvious that as the value of f changes from one solution to the next, the amount of complex ion formed varies from one solution to the next, starting at zero in solutions of pure M, rising to go through a maximum value, and then decreasing to zero again in solutions of pure L. Thus, in going from $f = 0$ to $f = 1$, $[ML_n]$ varies from zero, through a maximum value, and back to zero again.

To find the value of n, we must find the mathematical relation expressing the change in $[ML_n]$ as f is changed. To do this, substitute the values for the equilibrium concentrations of each of the species present into Equation (5–75).

$$K_{st} = \frac{[ML_n]}{\{(1 - f)C_T - [ML_n]\}\{fC_T - n[ML_n]\}^n} \tag{5–76}$$

Equation (5–76) is differentiated to obtain the derivative, $d[ML_n]/df$. This derivative, the change in the concentration of the complex formed with the change in f throughout the series, provides the desired expression. Since only the point at which the maximum concentration of complex formed is of interest to us, this derivative is set equal to zero. Simplification and rearrangement of the resulting equation gives the amazingly simple expression:

$$n = \frac{f}{1 - f} \tag{5–77}$$

at the maximum of the $[ML_n]$ vs. f function.

In the laboratory we have decided to use the absorption of light by ML_n to measure its concentration. Beer's law states that $A = ab[ML_n]$. Therefore, the measured absorbance of the series of solutions will increase from zero at $f = 0$ through some maximum value and back to zero again at $f = 1$. The maximum absorbance will occur where $[ML_n]$ is a maximum. Consequently, a graph of the absorbance of the series of solutions as a function of f will have its maximum at a position that is dependent upon the value of n in the formula of the complex, since upon rearrangement of Equation (5–77)

$$f = \frac{n}{n + 1}$$

For a 1:1 chelate, $n = 1$, and the maximum occurs at $f = 0.50$. For a 1:2 chelate, $n = 2$, so the maximum will occur at $f = 0.67$. Similarly, for a 1:3 complex, $n = 3$, and the maximum occurs at $f = 0.75$; and for a 1:4 complex, $n = 4$, and the maximum occurs at $f = 0.80$. Typical curves of absorbance as a function of f for 1:1, 1:2, 1:3, and 1:4 complexes are shown in Fig. 5–12. From experimental curves of this type, the value of n in ML_n can be calculated using Equation (5–77).

Job's method is valid only when a single complex is formed, since the technique involves preparing solutions of all possible ratios of components from pure metal ion to pure ligand. If a different complex is formed in each of these solutions, the above assumptions would no longer hold. For further discussion of this method, see the papers by M. M. Jones.[10]

Once the formula of the complex is known, the value of the exponent n, in the denominator of Equation (5–75) is also known. The form of the stability constant expression will be known, so that it now is possible to evaluate the constant.

If the complex-forming reaction of Equation (5–74) went to completion, the shape of the graph of absorbance vs. f would be triangular, as shown by the dotted line in Fig. 5–13. In actuality, the complex formed dissociates to some extent, so the actual concentration of the complex is always less than its theoretical concentration assuming a complete reaction. One result of this is that for any value of f, the measured absorbance of the experimental solution is less than the theoretical absorbance of the dotted line in Fig. 5–13. This produces a rounded curve below the

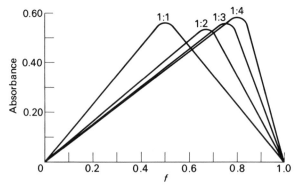

Fig. 5–12. Method of continuous variations plots for complexes.

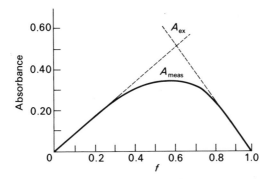

Fig. 5–13. An experimental Job's method plot.

straight lines, as shown by the solid line in Fig. 5–13. For any value of f, the difference between the two curves (that is, the two absorbances: theoretical for complete reaction, A_{ex}; and experimental, A_{meas}) is a measure of the extent of the dissociation of the complex under the experimental conditions. These differences in absorbance are used to obtain the stability constant for the complex. The way in which this is done is illustrated for the iron(III)-Tiron chelate studied in this experiment.

Tiron, as is the case for many ligands, is a weak acid. The two protons on the sulfonic acid groups are so strong that they are completely ionized, so that initially the ligand contains only the two protons on the hydroxyl groups [see Equation (5–73)]. Taking this into consideration, Equation (5–74) can be rewritten into a generalized reaction involving protons:

$$M + n\,H_xL \rightleftharpoons ML_n + nx\,H^+ \tag{5–78}$$

where the equilibrium constant for this reaction is:

$$K_{eq} = \frac{[ML_n][H^+]^{nx}}{[M][H_xL]^n} \tag{5–79}$$

The first part of the experiment for the determination of the stability constant of the iron(III)–Tiron chelate, involves the evaluation of this equilibrium constant, Equation (5–79). Once the value of this has been found, it is very easy to obtain the value of the stability constant, K_{st}, given by Equation (5–75).

Since Equation (5–78) liberates protons, in order to obtain meaningful data, the reaction must take place in a buffered solution. Under these conditions, $[H^+]$ for Equation (5–79) is known. x is known from the formula of the ligand at the pH involved. n has just been determined. Only the equilibrium concentrations of the complex ion, the free metal ion, and the uncomplexed ligand remain to be evaluated.

We have assumed that only the complex ion absorbs light at the wavelength used in the experiment. Therefore, the molar concentration of the complex ion present in the solution can be obtained from Beer's law. From $f = 0$ up to the value of f at the maximum in the curve, the concentration of the complex formed is limited by the concentration of the ligand, H_xL, present in the solution. There is always more metal ion present than there is ligand on the ascending side of the curve. The material balance on the ligand says that

$$n[ML_n] = C_{H_xL} - [H_xL]$$

When the metal ion is present in large excess, the concentration of the unchelated ligand is negligibly small, $[H_xL] \simeq 0$, so that $[ML_n] = (1/n)C_{H_xL}$. On the extrapolated line where $A = A_{ex}$, which assumed no dissociation, the concentration of the complex ion formed at any point, therefore, is equal to $(1/n)C_{H_xL}$. Inserting this into Beer's law:

$$A_{ex} = \frac{a\,b\,C_{H_xL}}{n} \tag{5-80}$$

from $f = 0$ up to the value of f at the maximum in the curve.

From the value of f at the maximum in the curve to $f = 1$, the amount of complex ion formed in the solution is limited by the concentration of metal ion present, since the ligand is present in excess. As before, from the material balance:

$$[ML_n] = C_M - [M]$$

When the ligand is present in large excess, the concentration of the unchelated metal ion is negligibly small, $[M] \simeq 0$, so that $[ML_n] = C_M$. On the extrapolated curve, which assumes complete reaction, the concentration of the complex formed at any point, therefore, is equal to C_M. From Beer's law for the extrapolated absorbance:

$$A_{ex} = a\,b\,C_M \tag{5-81}$$

from the value of f at the maximum in the curve to $f = 1$.

The experimental curve admits that dissociation does occur, so that the measured absorbance values are determined by $[ML_n]$. At any point on the curve, the fraction of the complex ion that is not dissociated and exists in solution as the complex ion is measured by A/A_{ex}. Therefore, before the maximum in the curve:

$$\frac{A}{A_{ex}} = \frac{[ML_n]}{\frac{1}{n}C_{H_xL}} \quad \text{or} \quad [ML_n] = \frac{A}{A_{ex}n}C_{H_xL} \tag{5-82}$$

After the maximum value of f in the curve:

$$\frac{A}{A_{ex}} = \frac{[ML_n]}{C_M} \quad \text{or} \quad [ML_n] = \frac{A}{A_{ex}}C_M \tag{5-83}$$

To simplify things, let C represent the concentration of the limiting reagent in the solution. Doing this, before the maximum value of f, $C = (1/n)C_{H_xL}$, whereas after the maximum value of f, $C = C_M$. Thus we can write:

$$[ML_n] = \frac{A}{A_{ex}}C$$

For any point on the measured absorbance curve, the material balance states that the concentration of the uncomplexed metal ion is the difference between the total metal ion that was taken initially and the metal ion tied up in the complex ion, or:

$$[M] = C_M - [ML_n] = C_M - n\frac{A}{A_{ex}}C \qquad (5\text{–}84)$$

Similarly, the concentration of the uncomplexed ligand at equilibrium is the difference between the total ligand concentration taken initially and that tied up in the complex, or:

$$[H_xL] = C_{H_xL} - n[ML_n] = C_{H_xL} - n\frac{A}{A_{ex}}C \qquad (5\text{–}85)$$

These three equations give us the concentrations of the three species of Equation (5–79) in terms of measured experimental quantities. Substituting these relationships into the equilibrium constant expression, Equation (5–79):

$$K_{eq} = \frac{[H^+]^{nx}\dfrac{A}{A_{ex}}C}{\left(C_M - \dfrac{A}{A_{ex}}C\right)\left(C_{H_xL} - n\dfrac{A}{A_{ex}}C\right)^n} \qquad (5\text{–}86)$$

All of the terms in Equation (5–86) are known, either from given solution concentrations or from measured and extrapolated absorbances. Thus, it is possible to calculate the equilibrium constant. Once this is done, the next step is to calculate the value of the stability constant for the complex, Equation (5–75).

The dissociation of the weak acid ligand can be described by its dissociation constants.

$$k_{a_1}k_{a_2}\dots k_{a_x} = \frac{[H^+]^x[L^{x-}]}{[H_xL]} \qquad (5\text{–}87)$$

which when rearranged to give the concentration of the un-ionized ligand molecules:

$$[H_xL] = \frac{[H^+]^x[L^{x-}]}{k_{a_1}k_{a_2}\dots k_{a_x}}$$

Now let us find out what the difference between the stability constant for the metal–ligand complex as expressed in Equation (5–75) and the equilibrium constant for the reaction (5–78) as expressed in Equation (5–79) actually is. Equation (5–79) contains all of the concentration terms of Equation (5–75), so substituting the K_{st} in for them gives:

$$K_{st} = K_{eq}\frac{[H_xL]^n}{[H^+]^{nx}[L^{-x}]^n} \qquad (5\text{–}88)$$

Now if we substitute the relationship for $[H_xL]$ given by Equation (5–87) into Equation (5–88), we obtain:

$$K_{st} = K_{eq}\frac{1}{(k_{a_1}k_{a_2}\dots k_{a_x})^n} \qquad (5\text{–}89)$$

Consequently, the numerical value for the stability constant of the metal–ligand complex is calculated from the values of the equilibrium constant, Equation (5–78), and the stepwise dissociation constants of the weak acid ligand, by using Equation (5–89).

Preparation of solutions.   The following stock solutions will be available on the side shelf of the laboratory:

1. 0.025 M H_2SO_4, 0.050 M $(NH_4)_2SO_4$ buffer
2. 2.00×10^{-3} M $FeNH_4(SO)_{42}$ in the H_2SO_4–$(NH_4)_2SO_4$ buffer
3. 2.00×10^{-3} M Tiron in the H_2SO_4–$(NH_4)_2SO_4$ buffer

Clean, dry, and label nine test tubes. Fill a 50-ml burette with the standard Tiron solution and a second 50-ml burette with the standard iron (III) solution. In the nine test tubes, prepare a series of solutions with varying volumes of iron and Tiron, yet having a total volume of 10.00 ml. The easiest series to prepare will contain 1:9, 2:8, 3:7, 4:6, 5:5, 6:4, 7:3, 8:2, and 9:1 ml Tiron:ml iron (III). Mix each of these solutions thoroughly by corking the test tube and inverting it slowly at least ten times. You should be able to see visually the difference in the amount of complex formed as the series progresses.

Measurement of concentrations.   Measure the pH of an aliquot of the sulfuric acid–ammonium sulfate buffer and record it in your laboratory notebook.

The iron(III)–Tiron chelate has an absorption maximum at 660 nm, whereas the absorbance of pure Tiron and of pure iron(III) are very slight, if not negligible, at this wavelength. Measure the absorption of each of the nine mixtures, of an aliquot of the stock 2.00×10^{-3} M iron(III) solution, and of an aliquot of the stock 2.00×10^{-3} M Tiron solution at 660 nm. Be sure to use the sulfuric acid–ammonium sulfate buffer as the reagent blank, matched cuvettes, the same cuvette each time for the sample, and the same spectrophotometer for all measurements.

The standard iron(III) solution should not have an appreciable absorbance at 660 nm, but if it does, we must correct for its absorbance. The technique that is used actually involved *overcorrecting*. The absorbance that the iron(III) would contribute to the total absorbance of the solution if it did not react at all with the Tiron, is subtracted from the measured absorbance of each solution. Thus, if the stock iron(III) solution shows any absorbance, the absorbance readings of all nine mixtures are corrected by subtracting from each measured absorbance:

$$\left(\frac{x \text{ ml Fe(III)}}{10.00 \text{ ml solution}} \right) A_{Fe(III)}$$

where x is the number of milliliters of the standard iron present in that particular mixture.

Determination of n.   Plot the corrected absorbance of each solution as the ordinate against f (the fraction of Tiron in the solution) as the abscissa. Draw the best smooth curve through these eleven points. Do not play connect the dots! Locate the maximum absorbance value on the curve and read from the abscissa the value of f corresponding to it. From this value of f, by means of Equation

(5-77), calculate the value of n in the formula for the iron–Tiron chelate. Remember that n can only be a small, whole number, so round off the calculated value appropriately. It is highly unlikely that the calculation will give you a nice rounded number for n.

Determination of K_{st}. At the three points at either end of the series of solutions (0, 1, 2 and 8, 9, 10 ml Tiron) there is a very large excess of one of the reagents in the mixture. The common ion effect due to this excess will cause the dissociation of the complex ion to be suppressed. Thus, at the extremes of the absorbance curve, A_{ex} is essentially equal to A. A linear extrapolation of these three absorbances should produce a straight line on either side of the maximum that would contain all of the A_{ex} values for the series. Therefore, draw the best straight line through the 0, 1, 2 ml Tiron and the best straight line through the 8, 9, 10 ml Tiron points. Extrapolate these two lines until they intersect. This intersection should be over the maximum in the absorbance curve, but do not be disturbed if it is not. The absorbance values lying on these two lines are extrapolated absorbance, A_{ex}, values.

Select four values of f that are fairly close to the maximum in the experimental curve. By limiting ourselves to points that are near the maximum, we obtain the maximum dissociation of the complex and minimize uncertainties created by slight differences in two large numbers. Two of the f values selected should lie to the left of both the maximum in the experimental curve and the intersection of the two extrapolated straight lines; and two of the f values should lie to the right of both of them. For each of these values of f, read A and A_{ex} from the graph. From the values of f selected and the stated concentrations of the stock solutions of iron(III) and Tiron, calculate by dilution factors, C_{Fe} and C_{H_2Ti} for each of the solutions. To the left of the maximum value of f, C is $1/n\ C_{H_2Ti}$ while to the right of the maximum value of f, C is C_{Fe}. Substituting all of these values, as well as the measured hydrogen ion concentration into Equation (5-79) and calculate a value of K_{eq} for the solution corresponding to each of the four f values.

$K_{a_1} = 2.5 \times 10^{-8}$ and $K_{a_2} = 3.3 \times 10^{-13}$ for Tiron. Insert these values and the calculated value of K_{eq} into Equation (5-89) and for each f value calculate a stability constant, K_{st}. Calculate the average K_{st} and the standard deviation of the measurements.

DISTRIBUTION EQUILIBRIA

The separation techniques of extraction and partition chromatography involve the partition of solutes between two immiscible liquids. Thus, an understanding of partition or distribution equilibrium is essential to an understanding of the separations effected by these techniques.

If a solute is soluble in each of two liquids, which are immiscible with one another, when it is dissolved in one of the liquids and this solution is shaken with the second liquid until equilibrium is attained, the solute will be present in both liquids. The amount of solute present at equilibrium in each of the solutions can be interrelated by means of an equilibrium constant for the distribution process. Thus, for the distribution reaction:

$$X_1 \rightleftharpoons X_2$$

we can write the thermodynamic equilibrium constant:

$$\mathbf{K}_D = \frac{a_{X_2}}{a_{X_1}} \tag{5-90}$$

where X is the solute being distributed or partitioned between liquid 1 and liquid 2. The equilibrium constant, $\mathbf{K}_D$, is called the partition coefficient, or the distribution coefficient for the solute in this system. The partition coefficient is no different from any other equilibrium constant. It pertains to a specific molecular form of the solute in a specific pair of liquids. It is independent of the amount of material involved, but it is dependent upon the temperature of the two solutions.

When the partition systems consist of dilute solutions of solute and have low ionic strengths, the same assumption can be made in the case of partition equilibrium that has been made for the other types of equilibria. Namely, the activity coefficient ratio is unity, so that molar concentrations can be substituted in place of the activities of the solutes. Making this assumption:

$$K_D = \frac{[X]_2}{[X]_1} \tag{5-91}$$

Equation (5-91) has the following restrictions: (1) the concentration of the solute, X, must be low in both liquids; (2) the molecular form of the solute must be the same in both liquids; and (3) the two liquids must be mutually immiscible.

Acid–base dissociation constants, solubility product constants, and stability constants are all formulated according to accepted conventions. In formulating expressions for the partition coefficients there are no accepted conventions with regard to which concentration goes in the numerator and which concentration goes in the denominator. When one of the two liquids in the system is water, it frequently is placed in the denominator, but not always. Sometimes the partition coefficient expression is set up so that the numerical value of K_D is greater than one, but, again, not always. Therefore, when attempting to use a partition coefficient, make sure that you know which liquid is represented in the numerator and which is in the denominator. The magnitude of the numerical value of the partition coefficient provides no clue whatsoever.

Calculations involving the partition coefficient are much simpler than those involving other equilibrium constants since there are only two terms in the simple partition law. These two concentration terms are interrelated not only through their ratios, as given by the partition coefficient, but also through their sum, which must be equal to the total amount of solute in the system. To illustrate the use of the partition coefficient in its straightforward form, let us solve two problems.

Determination of the Value of the Partition Coefficient

The determination of the numerical value of the partition coefficient is straightforward. A solute is shaken in the system containing the two immiscible liquids. When equilibrium has been attained, the two phases are physically separated and concentration of the solute determined in each phase by whatever technique is appropriate.

Example. In an experiment, 50.00 ml of an aqueous iodine solution is shaken with 20.00 ml of carbon tetrachloride until distribution equilibrium is reached. The initial concentration of the iodine in the aqueous phase was 1.97×10^{-2} M but after equilibrium this aqueous concentration had decreased to 5.30×10^{-4} M. Calculate the partition coefficient for iodine between carbon tetrachloride and water.

The distribution equilibrium involved in this problem is:

$$K_D \overset{I_2}{\underset{I_2}{\Vert}} \begin{array}{l} CCl_4 \\ H_2O \end{array}$$

for which the equilibrium constant can be written as:

$$K_D = \frac{[I_2]_{CCl_4}}{[I_2]_{H_2O}}$$

The problem asks for the numerical value of K_D, so numerical values must be obtained for both concentration terms. The equilibrium concentration of iodine in water is given by the problem as:

$$[I_2]_{H_2O} = 5.30 \times 10^{-4}\ M$$

The equilibrium concentration of iodine in carbon tetrachloride can be obtained from the amount of iodine that was removed from the aqueous phase during the distribution process. This, of course, is the difference between the initial number of millimoles of iodine in water and the final number of millimoles of iodine in water.

$$\text{no. mmol } I_2 \text{ initially in } H_2O = 1.97 \times 10^{-2}\ M \times 50.00\ \text{ml}$$
$$= 0.985\ \text{mmol}$$

$$\text{no. mmol } I_2 \text{ finally in } H_2O = 5.30 \times 10^{-4}\ M \times 50.00\ \text{ml}$$
$$= 0.0265\ \text{mmol}$$

$$\text{no. mmol } I_2 \text{ in } CCl_4 \text{ at equilibrium} = 0.985 - 0.0265\ \text{mmol}$$
$$= 0.959\ \text{mmol}$$

Since this is in a volume of 20.00 ml of carbon tetrachloride:

$$[I_2]_{CCl_4} = \frac{0.959\ \text{mmol}}{20.00\ \text{ml}} = 4.80 \times 10^{-2}\ M$$

Substituting the two equilibrium concentrations of iodine into the partition coefficient expression:

$$K_D = \frac{4.80 \times 10^{-2}\ M}{5.30 \times 10^{-4}\ M} = 90.6$$

This is the value requested by the problem and it was obtained without having to make any assumptions.

Once we know the value of the partition coefficient it can be used to solve various kinds of equilibrium problems. Partition coefficient values are extremely difficult to find tabulated, so that diligence and persistence are needed to unearth the necessary numbers. In effecting separations, one aspect that must be determined is the amount of solute that will be removed from one phase into the second phase during distribution. If all of the desired solute can be removed and none of the impurity solutes accompany it, then a separation can be effected based on distribution equilibria.

Example.   75.0 ml of an aqueous iodine solution containing 0.0853 g of iodine is shaken with 25.00 ml of carbon tetrachloride. How much iodine will be found in the carbon tetrachloride layer at equilibrium?

The distribution equilibrium and the partition coefficient expression are the same as in the preceding example. Since the initial concentration of iodine in the aqueous phase can be calculated, the problem merely consists of the calculation, from the distribution coefficient expression, of the equilibrium concentration of iodine in carbon tetrachloride. In order to make this calculation, the equilibrium concentration of iodine in water must be known.

Since the volumes of the two phases are not equal there will be a change in the molar concentration of iodine as it passes from one phase into the second. Because of this, it is simpler to use an amount (millimoles or milligrams) of solute as the unknown, rather than a molar concentration of the solute. Therefore, let X be the number of grams of iodine in the carbon tetrachloride layer at equilibrium. The molar concentration of iodine in CCl_4 at equilibrium is:

$$[I_2]_{CCl_4} = \frac{\dfrac{X \text{ gram}}{253.8 \text{ gram/mole}}}{0.0250 \text{ liter}}$$

The amount of iodine remaining in the aqueous phase at equilibrium will be the difference between the initial weight of iodine and the weight found in the carbon tetrachloride at equilibrium, that is: $0.0853 - X$ gram. The molar concentration of iodine in water at equilibrium is:

$$[I_2]_{H_2O} = \frac{\dfrac{0.0853 - X \text{ gram}}{253.8 \text{ gram/mole}}}{0.0750 \text{ liter}}$$

We now have expressions for each of the two concentrations in terms of a single unknown. Substituting them into the expression for the partition coefficient:

$$K_D = \frac{\dfrac{\dfrac{X \text{ gram}}{253.8 \text{ gram/mole}}}{0.0250 \text{ liter}}}{\dfrac{\dfrac{0.0853 - X \text{ gram}}{253.8 \text{ gram/mole}}}{0.0750 \text{ liter}}}$$

Since the molecular species I_2 is the same in both phases, its molecular weight appears in both the numerator and the denominator. Thus it can be cancelled, simplifying the expression to:

$$K_D = \frac{\dfrac{X \text{ gram}}{0.0250 \text{ liter}}}{\dfrac{0.0853 - X \text{ gram}}{0.0750 \text{ liter}}} = \frac{0.0750 \, X}{2.12 \times 10^{-3} - 0.0250 \, X}$$

Solving this expression for the weight of the iodine, X:

$$X = \frac{0.192}{2.34} = 0.0821 \text{ gram } I_2$$

This is the answer that was requested in the problem, obtained without making any assumptions. It is interesting and enlightening to see just what percentage of the total amount of iodine has been removed from the aqueous phase. This is done by taking the ratio of the amount of iodine present in the carbon tetrachloride phase at equilibrium to the total amount of iodine present in the system.

$$\% \text{ removed} = \frac{0.0821 \text{ g}}{0.0853 \text{ g}} \times 100 = 96.3\%$$

Thus, 96.3% of the iodine that had been in the aqueous phase initially has been transferred to the carbon tetrachloride phase.

From the point of view of separations, the purpose of partitioning a solute is to transfer essentially all of it from one liquid into another. One variable in accomplishing this transfer is the volume of the extracting liquid that is necessary to remove all of the solute.

Example. What volume of carbon tetrachloride must be used in order to remove 99.9% of the iodine from 80.0 ml of an aqueous 0.0363 M iodine solution?

The distribution equilibrium and the partition coefficient expressions are the same as in the two previous problems. The problem asks for the volume of carbon tetrachloride. In order to obtain this, the partition coefficient expression should be solved for the equilibrium concentration of iodine in carbon tetrachloride. The amount of iodine to be dissolved in the carbon tetrachloride can be obtained from the initial amount of iodine. From the concentration of iodine and the amount in the carbon tetrachloride, the volume is easy to obtain.

$$\text{no. of mmol } I_2 \text{ initially in } H_2O = 0.0363 \, M \times 80.0 \text{ ml}$$
$$= 2.90 \text{ mmol}$$

The problem states that 99.9% of this is to be distributed into CCl_4.

$$\text{no. of mmol } I_2 \text{ in } CCl_4 \text{ at equilibrium} = 0.999 \times 2.90 \text{ mmol}$$
$$= 2.89 \text{ mmol}$$

The amount of iodine remaining in the aqueous phase at equilibrium is:

$$2.90 - 2.89 \text{ mmol} = 0.01 \text{ mmol}$$

So that we can calculate the equilibrium aqueous concentration of I_2:

$$[I_2]_{H_2O} = \frac{0.01 \text{ mmol}}{80.0 \text{ ml}} = 1.2 \times 10^{-4} \ M$$

Substituting this into the partition coefficient expression:

$$K_D = \frac{[I_2]_{CCl_4}}{1.2 \times 10^{-4}} = 90.6$$

which when solved for $[I_2]_{CCl_4}$:

$$[I_2]_{CCl_4} = 1.1 \times 10^{-4} \ M$$

We know the amount of iodine in this solution, so now we can find the volume of the solution.

$$[I_2]_{CCl_4} = 1.1 \times 10^{-4} \ M = \frac{2.89 \text{ mmol}}{\text{ml } CCl_4}$$

$$\text{ml } CCl_4 = \frac{2.89 \text{ mmol}}{1.1 \times 10^{-4} \ M} = 256 \text{ ml}$$

This is the answer requested by the problem. We must use 256 ml of CCl_4 if we wish to remove 99.9% of the iodine from 80.0 ml of 0.0363 M aqueous iodine solution.

The Distribution Ratio

It should be emphasized that the partition coefficient expression describes the equilibrium only when the same molecular species appears in both liquids. If this species is involved in any additional equilibrium reactions, in either phase, the partition coefficient will pertain only to the distribution equilibrium of the common species, not to the total concentration. This is analogous to the solubility product expression for precipitates in acidic or basic solutions. The K_{sp} pertains only to the solubility equilibrium and does not include the total concentration of the dissolved ions in all forms that they are apt to appear in the solution. Similarly, the stability constant expression applies only to the complex ion and its components, not to the total concentration of any component in solution; for example, for MY^{2-}, K_{st} only involves the chelate, the metal ion, and the unprotonated ligand. It does not include any of the protonated forms of the ligand nor any forms of the metal ion that may be complexed with an auxiliary complexing agent.

A ratio of the total concentration of all forms of a species in one phase to the total concentration of all forms of the species in the second phase is not numerically equal to the partition coefficient, nor is it a constant. Experimentally it is much simpler to measure the total concentration, C, of a solute in each liquid, rather than to determine the concentration of the specific molecular form that actually crosses the phase boundary. Because of this, it is convenient to define a new term that is based upon total concentrations in both phases. This new term is called the *distribution ratio*, given the symbol D, and defined as:

$$D = \frac{\text{total concentration of all forms of the solute in liquid 2}}{\text{total concentration of all forms of the solute in liquid 1}} \quad (5\text{-}92)$$

$$= \frac{C_{X_2}}{C_{X_1}}$$

By convention, when one of the two liquids is water and the second liquid is an immiscible organic solvent, D is written with water in the denominator and the organic liquid in the numerator; that is, $D = C_{org}/C_{H_2O}$. Once the numerical value of D is known, it can be used as a constant only when the experimental conditions are identical to those for which it was determined. The relationship between K_D and D is analogous to that between K_{st} and K'_{st}. D and K'_{st} both remain constant only when the experimental conditions for which they were determined are not altered. When the experimental conditions are changed, new values of D must be measured.

When a solute exists in more than one form in either or both of the liquids, D is not numerically identical with K_D. The magnitude of the numerical difference between D and K_D will depend upon the nature of the additional equilibria present in each liquid. These concurrent equilibria can be acid–base equilibria, complex ion formation equilibria, polymerization equilibria, oxidation–reduction equilibria, and even solubility equilibria. Let us now investigate, on a quantitative basis, the the way in which the presence of these additional equilibria determines the relationship between D and K_D.

Acid–Base Equilibria in the Aqueous Phase (Dissociation Effects)

Consider a weak acid, HA, that will distribute itself between an aqueous and an organic solvent. In the aqueous solvent, the acid will dissociate into its ions. No additional reactions occur in the organic liquid. The schematic representation of the equilibria involved in such a system is:

$$
\begin{array}{c}
\text{HA} \\
K_D \updownarrow \overline{\hspace{3cm}}\quad \substack{\text{organic}\\ \text{H}_2\text{O}} \\
\underset{K_a}{\text{HA}} \rightleftharpoons \text{H}_3\text{O}^+ + \text{A}^-
\end{array}
$$

The partition coefficient pertains only to the distribution of the molecules of the weak acid and is:

$$K_D = \frac{[\text{HA}]_{org}}{[\text{HA}]_{H_2O}}$$

Since H_3O^+ and A^- are electrically charged species they cannot cross the phase boundary and will remain in the aqueous phase. The dissociation of HA into A^- means that there will be more acid (as $HA + A^-$), in the aqueous phase than if this dissociation did not occur. According to Le Châtelier's principle, as acid molecules in the aqueous phase dissociate, more from the organic phase will cross over into the aqueous phase in an attempt to minimize this disturbance.

The distribution ratio is evaluated by a gross chemical analysis of each phase (for example, titration with NaOH) and pertains to the total concentration of the acid in each solvent.

$$D = \frac{C_{\text{HAorg}}}{C_{\text{HA}_{\text{H}_2\text{O}}}} = \frac{[\text{HA}]_{\text{org}}}{[\text{HA}]_{\text{H}_2\text{O}} + [\text{A}^-]_{\text{H}_2\text{O}}}$$

Comparison of the expressions for K_D and D reveals that the difference between the two lies in the $[\text{A}^-]$ term in the denominator of D. Because of this concentration of the anion in the water, numerical values of D always will be less than those of K_D. The extent of this difference will depend upon the extent of the ionization of the acid. The dissociation that occurs is determined by the nature of the acid and the pH of the solution. Let us see what the relationship between D, K_D, K_a, and pH is.

The acid dissociation equilibrium constant expression is:

$$K_a = \frac{[\text{H}_3\text{O}^+][\text{A}^-]}{[\text{HA}]}$$

which can be solved to give the concentration of the acid anion:

$$[\text{A}^-] = \frac{K_a[\text{HA}]}{[\text{H}_3\text{O}^+]}$$

Inserting this into the denominator of the expression for D gives:

$$D = \frac{[\text{HA}]_{\text{org}}}{[\text{HA}]_{\text{H}_2\text{O}} + \frac{K_a[\text{HA}]_{\text{H}_2\text{O}}}{[\text{H}_3\text{O}^+]}} = \frac{[\text{HA}]_{\text{org}}[\text{H}_3\text{O}^+]}{[\text{HA}]_{\text{H}_2\text{O}}([\text{H}_3\text{O}^+] + K_a)}$$

$$= \frac{K_D[\text{H}_3\text{O}^+]}{[\text{H}_3\text{O}^+] + K_a} \tag{5-93}$$

Thus we have in Equation (5-93) the relationship between K_D, D, K_a, and pH. Though it is not stated explicitly in Equation (5-93), it can be seen that while K_D for a weak acid is independent of the concentration of the acid, in unbuffered solutions D will vary with concentration. In an unbuffered solution the degree of ionization varies with concentration so that $[\text{H}_3\text{O}^+]$ will change with concentration. In buffered solutions, D is independent of the concentration of the weak acid, for the hydronium ion concentration in this case is determined by the buffer and not by the weak acid to be extracted from the solution.

An example of problems involving Equation (5-93) is the calculation of the distribution ratio of a weak acid at a specific pH value.

Example. The partition coefficient of benzoic acid between 1-octanol and water is measured as 1.88. Calculate the value of the distribution ratio of benzoic acid between these solvents at a pH of 6.00.

The equilibria involved are:

$$\begin{array}{l}
\quad\quad \text{HBz} \\
K_D \;\updownarrow \rule{5cm}{0.4pt}\; \begin{array}{l}\text{octanol}\\ \hline \text{H}_2\text{O}\end{array} \\
\text{HBz} \rightleftharpoons \text{H}_3\text{O}^+ + \text{Bz}^- \\
\quad\quad\quad\;\; K_a
\end{array}$$

with the equilibrium constants:

$$K_D = \frac{[HBz]_{oct}}{[HBz]_{H_2O}} = 1.88, \quad K_a = \frac{[H_3O^+][Bz^-]}{[HBz]} = 6.32 \times 10^{-5}$$

The problem asks that the value of D be calculated. In order to do this values must be known for K_D, K_a, and $[H_3O^+]$. We have all three of these so that it is merely a matter of plugging them into Equation (5–93).

$$D = \frac{K_D[H_3O^+]}{[H_3O^+] + K_a} = \frac{(1.88)(1.00 \times 10^{-6})}{(1.00 \times 10^{-6}) + (6.32 \times 10^{-5})}$$

$$= \frac{1.88 \times 10^{-6}}{6.42 \times 10^{-5}} = 2.93 \times 10^{-2}$$

This is the answer requested by the problem and it was obtained without having to make any assumptions. Note that the presence of appreciable concentrations of benzoate ion in the aqueous phase has reduced the equilibrium constant from a K_D of 1.88 to a D of 0.0293.

Another very useful application of Equation (5–93) is in the determination of the K_a for a weak acid. Distribution methods are frequently used to determine the acid dissociation constants. Let us see how this is done.

Example. The distribution ratio of ruthenic acid is found to be constant at 58.4 for the partition of this acid from neutral and acidic solutions into carbon tetrachloride. In 1.00×10^{-2} M NaOH, the measured value of the distribution ratio for ruthenic acid is 7.90. Calculate the value of the dissociation constant of ruthenic acid, H_2RuO_5.

The equilibria involved are:

$$
\begin{array}{c}
H_2RuO_5 \\
\overset{K_D}{\big\updownarrow} \\
H_2RuO_5 \rightleftharpoons H^+ + HRuO_5^- \\
K_a
\end{array}
\qquad
\begin{array}{c}
CCl_4 \\
\hline
H_2O
\end{array}
$$

with the equilibrium expressions:

$$K_D = \frac{[H_2RuO_5]_{CCl_4}}{[H_2RuO_5]_{H_2O}} \qquad D = \frac{[H_2RuO_5]_{CCl_4}}{[H_2RuO_5]_{H_2O} + [HRuO_5^-]}$$

In acid and neutral solution, H_2RuO_5 would not be expected to dissociate to any appreciable extent. The constancy of the distribution ratio under these conditions verifies this. Thus, in acid and neutral solution there is no dissociation occurring, no anion is present, $D = K_D = 58.4$. H_2RuO_5 behaves as a monobasic acid, so Equation (5–93) is applicable. The problem asks that this equation be solved for the acid dissociation constant, K_a. In order to do this, K_D, D, and $[H_3O^+]$ must all be known. They are. In 1.00×10^{-2} M NaOH, $[H_3O^+] = 1.00 \times 10^{-12}$ M, and $D = 7.90$. Substituting all these values into Equation (5–93) gives:

$$7.90 = \frac{(58.4)(1.00 \times 10^{-12})}{(1.00 \times 10^{-12}) + K_a}$$

Upon solving:

$$K_a = 6.40 \times 10^{-12}$$

Distribution provides an excellent method for determining the dissociation constants of very weak acids and bases.

Polymerization Equilibria in the Organic Phase

The dielectric constant of many organic liquids is much less than that of water, causing polar materials to polymerize or associate in organic solvents. Whenever association accompanies partition of a solute, the following equilibria exist:

$$
\begin{array}{c}
\overset{K_{ass}}{nX \rightleftharpoons X_n} \\
\underset{X}{K_D \; \updownarrow} \quad\quad\quad \dfrac{\text{organic}}{\text{H}_2\text{O}}
\end{array}
$$

The most prevalent aggregate encountered in the organic liquid is the dimer, where $n = 2$. Restricting our discussion to the formation of dimers only gives

$$
\begin{array}{c}
2X \rightleftharpoons X_2 \\
\underset{X}{K_D \; \updownarrow} \quad\quad \dfrac{\text{organic}}{\text{H}_2\text{O}}
\end{array}
$$

The partition coefficient expression describes only the distribution of the monomeric X molecules between the two phases:

$$K_D = \frac{[X]_{\text{org}}}{[X]_{\text{H}_2\text{O}}}$$

The distribution ratio as obtained by gross chemical analysis of each phase covers both the monomers and the dimers in the organic phase:

$$D = \frac{C_{X\text{org}}}{C_{X_{\text{H}_2\text{O}}}} = \frac{[X]_{\text{org}} + 2[X_2]_{\text{org}}}{[X]_{\text{H}_2\text{O}}}$$

The difference between these two expressions lies in the inclusion of the dimer concentration in the numerator of the distribution ratio expression. As a result of dimerization in the organic phase, the numerical value of the distribution ratio will be larger than the numerical value of the partition coefficient. The magnitude of this difference will depend upon the amount of dimer formed, which will, of course, depend upon the concentration of the monomer in the organic phase and the value of the association constant, K_{ass}. Let us see exactly what the relationship between K_D and D is when dimerization occurs.

The expression for the association equilibrium constant is:

$$K_{ass} = \frac{[X_2]^2_{\text{org}}}{[X]_{\text{org}}}$$

Solving the K_{ass} expression for the dimer concentration, $[X_2]_{\text{org}}$, and substituting into the expression for the distribution ratio:

$$D = \frac{[X]_{org} + 2 K_{ass}[X]_{org}^2}{[X]_{H_2O}} = \frac{[X]_{org}}{[X]_{H_2O}} (1 + 2 K_{ass}[X]_{org})$$

$$= K_D(1 + 2K_{ass}[X]_{org}) \tag{5-94}$$

The concentration of the monomer in the organic liquid is a very impractical concentration term to have in an equilibrium constant expression, for experimentally it is extremely difficult to determine monomers in the presence of dimers. Let us eliminate it from the equation if we can. Solving K_D for $[X]_{org}$ and inserting it into Equation (5–94) gives a more useable equation.

$$D = K_D + 2K_D^2 K_{ass}[X]_{H_2O} \tag{5-95}$$

The concentration of the solute in the aqueous phase usually is very easy to determine.

W. Nernst[17] studied the distribution of benzoic acid between water and benzene and showed that it exists as dimers in the benzene phase. From his work it is possible to arrive at a value of 1.80 for K_D and 1.76×10^2 for the association constant of benzoic acid. Let us use these values to determine the value of the distribution ratio for benzoic acid.

Example. Calculate the value of the distribution ratio for benzoic acid between benzene and water for a solution that contains 0.0520 M benzoic acid in the aqueous phase at equilibrium. Neglect any acid dissociation of the benzoic acid in the aqueous phase.

The equilibria involved are:

$$\overset{K_{ass}}{2C_6H_5COOH \rightleftharpoons (C_6H_5COOH)_2}$$

$$K_D \,\underline{\quad\quad\quad\;\updownarrow\quad\quad\quad\quad\quad\quad\quad}\, \begin{matrix} C_6H_6 \\ H_2O \end{matrix}$$

$$C_6H_5COOH$$

The problem asks for the value of D. This can be obtained by solving Equation (5–94) provided that numerical values of K_D, K_{ass} and $[C_6H_5COOH]_{H_2O}$ are all known. They are either given in the statement of the problem or available from Nernst's work. Substituting them into Equation (5–94):

$$D = 1.80 + 2(1.80)^2(1.76 \times 10^2)(5.20 \times 10^{-2})$$

$$= 61.1$$

which is the answer requested by the problem. Note the tremendous increase between K_D and D because of the presence of association in the benzene phase.

In practice, Equation (5–94) is more frequently used as a means of studying association of solutes in organic liquids and to determine the value of the association constant for the solute.

Acid–Base Equilibria in the Aqueous Phase as Well as Dimerization in the Organic Phase

In the case of most carboxylic acids, distribution between water and an organic liquid such as benzene or chloroform, is also accompanied by dissociation of the weak acid in water and dimerization of the acid in the organic liquid. The diagram of the equilibria occurring during the distribution of acetic acid between water and chloroform is given below:

$$2CH_3COOH \overset{K_{ass}}{\rightleftharpoons} (CH_3COOH)_2$$

$$K_D \, \rule[0.5ex]{1em}{0.4pt} \!\!\not\parallel\!\!\rule[0.5ex]{10em}{0.4pt} \quad \begin{matrix} CHCl_3 \\ \hline H_2O \end{matrix}$$

$$\underset{K_a}{CH_3COOH \rightleftharpoons H_3O^+ + CH_3COO^-}$$

In this system, the use of the partition coefficient is valid only for the distribution of the acetic acid molecules between chloroform and water.

$$K_D = \frac{[CH_3COOH]_{CHCl_3}}{[CH_3COOH]_{H_2O}}$$

The distribution ratio expression as determined by titration of each phase with standard sodium hydroxide includes the total amount of acid found in each of the two phases.

$$D = \frac{C_{CH_3COOHCHCl_3}}{C_{CH_3COOHH_2O}} = \frac{[CH_3COOH]_{CHCl_3} + 2[(CH_3COOH)_2]_{CHCl_3}}{[CH_3COOH]_{H_2O} + [CH_3COO^-]_{H_2O}}$$

The relationship between the distribution ratio, the partition coefficient, and the concentrations and other equilibrium constants is a combination of Equations (5–93) and (5–95).

$$D = \frac{K_D[H_3O^+](1 + 2K_{ass}K_D[CH_3COOH]_{H_2O})}{[H_3O^+] + K_a} \tag{5-96}$$

The acetic acid system has been studied very thoroughly and by measuring the variations in D with pH and with the total concentration of acetic acid present, values of K_D, K_{ass}, and K_a have been determined.

Complex Ion Formation in the Aqueous Phase

When the aqueous phase contains a ligand that is capable of forming a complex ion with the solute being distributed, the value of the distribution ratio will be less than that of the partition coefficient. A schematic representation of the equilibria involved is:

$$M$$

$$K_D \, \!\!\not\parallel\!\!\rule[0.5ex]{10em}{0.4pt} \quad \begin{matrix} organic \\ \hline H_2O \end{matrix}$$

$$\underset{K_{st}}{M + nX \rightleftharpoons MX_n}$$

The partition coefficient pertains only to the distribution of the molecules, M, and is given by:

$$K_D = \frac{[M]_{org}}{[M]_{H_2O}}$$

The distribution ratio pertains to the total concentration of solute in both phases and hence is given by:

$$D = \frac{C_{M_{org}}}{C_{M_{H_2O}}} = \frac{[M]_{org}}{[M]_{H_2O} + [MX_n]}$$

The difference between these two expressions lies in the concentration of the complex ion in the aqueous phase that occurs in the denominator of the D expression. Therefore, when a solute is complexed in the aqueous phase, the value of the distribution ratio will always be less than that of the partition coefficient. The extent of this decrease will depend upon the amount of the solute that is complexed. This is determined by the concentration of the complexing agent present in the aqueous solution and the strength of the complex formed. The expression for the overall stability constant for the complex is:

$$K_{st} = \frac{[MX_n]}{[M][X]^n}$$

To obtain the relationship between D, K_D, and K_{st}, solve the stability constant expression for the concentration of the complex ion and substitute that into the above expression for the distribution ratio.

$$D = \frac{[M]_{org}}{[M]_{H_2O} + K_{st}[M]_{H_2O}[X]^n}$$

Since $K_D = [M]_{org}/[M]_{H_2O}$, substituting this into the preceding gives:

$$D = \frac{K_D}{1 + K_{st}[X]^n} \tag{5-97}$$

Distribution studies provide an excellent technique for determining the value of the stability constant for complex ions. The distribution ratio is determined in the presence and in the absence of the complexing agent in the aqueous phase. With these quantities and the value of n, Equation (5-97) can be used to obtain the value of the stability constant of the complex ion formed. A value of 768 was obtained for the stability constant of the triiodide ion, I_3^-, by this technique.

Distribution Equilibria in Metal Chelate Systems

One very widely used technique for separating mixtures of metal ions is to extract selectively certain metals as their metal chelates. A solution of a chelating agent, HX, in an organic solvent is shaken with the aqueous solution of a metal ion that will form a chelate with the chelating agent. The chelate formed is then also partitioned between the aqueous and the organic liquids. The equilibria involved are adjusted so that only the desired metal is removed to the organic phase, the other materials are not partitioned. A diagram of the pertinent equilibria is:

$$
\begin{array}{ccc}
\text{HX} & & \text{MX} \\
K_{DHX} \updownarrow & & \updownarrow \; K_{DMX} \quad \dfrac{\text{organic}}{\text{H}_2\text{O}} \\
\text{HX} \rightleftharpoons \text{H}^+ + \text{X}^- & \text{M}^{n+} + n\text{X}^- \rightleftharpoons \text{MX}_n & \\
\quad K_a & \quad K_{st} &
\end{array}
$$

The distribution ratio for the metal refers to the total concentration of metal in all forms in both of the phases, which is given as:

$$D = \frac{C_{M_{org}}}{C_{M_{H_2O}}} = \frac{[MX_n]_{org}}{[MX_n]_{H_2O} + [M^{n+}]} \tag{5-98}$$

Since both the chelating agent and the metal chelate are partitioned between the two phases, there are two partition coefficients involved in this system. The partition coefficient of the chelating agent pertains only to the molecules of the chelating agent, HX, and does not include either $[X^-]$ or $[MX_n]$. The partition coefficient of the metal chelate pertains only to the distribution of the chelate molecules and does not include $[M^{n+}]$ or $[X^-]$. They are given by:

$$K_{D_{HX}} = \frac{[HX]_{org}}{[HX]_{H_2O}} \tag{5-99}$$

$$K_{D_{MX}} = \frac{[MX_n]_{org}}{[MX_n]_{H_2O}} \tag{5-100}$$

The stability constant for the formation of the metal chelate is given as:

$$K_{st} = \frac{[MX_n]}{[M^{n+}][X^-]^n} \tag{5-101}$$

Let us try to derive a mathematical relationship for the distribution ratio in terms of the partition coefficients, the stability constant and the acid dissociation constant. The concentration of the unchelated metal ion in the aqueous phase is a difficult term to evaluate experimentally, so let us see if we can replace it in Equation (5-98). If the stability constant expression, Equation (101), is solved for the concentration of the unchelated metal ion and this is substituted into Equation (5-98) we obtain:

$$D = \frac{[MX_n]_{org}}{[MX_n]_{H_2O} + \dfrac{[MX_n]_{H_2O}}{K_{st}[X^-]^n}} \tag{5-102}$$

This hasn't really improved matters much because the concentration of the anion of the chelate, in the aqueous phase, is also difficult to evaluate experimentally. So let us try to eliminate it from Equation (5-102). The acid dissociation constant expression for the chelating agent is:

$$K_a = \frac{[H_3O^+][X^-]}{[HX]} \tag{5-103}$$

Solving Equation (5-103) for $[X^-]$ and substituting this into Equation (5-102) gives:

$$D = \frac{[MX_n]_{org}}{[MX_n]_{H_2O} + \dfrac{[MX_n]_{H_2O}}{K_{st}\left(\dfrac{K_a[HX]_{H_2O}}{[H_3O^+]}\right)^n}} \tag{5-104}$$

Simplification of Equation (5–104) does not achieve much. Therefore, let us see if we can make some assumptions that will be reasonable and yet produce a less cumbersome relationship between D and the other equilibrium constants.

Since most metal chelates have exceptionally large stability constants, the metal ions in the system will exist primarily in the form of the metal chelate. The metal chelate, however, being an uncharged molecule will prefer the organic phase, so that very little of it will exist in the aqueous phase. Almost as soon as the metal ion is chelated, it is partitioned into the organic phase. As a result of this, in the aqueous phase the concentration of the metal chelate will be low, compared to the concentration of the unchelated metal ion. Therefore, let us assume that the first term in the denominator of Equation (5–104), which represents the concentration of the metal chelate in the aqueous phase is negligibly small in comparison with the concentration of the second term of the denominator of Equation (5–104), which represents the concentration of the unchelated metal ion in the aqueous phase; $[MX_n]_{H_2O} << [M^{n+}]$. Upon making this assumption, the first term in the denominator of Equation (5–104) is neglected and simplification of Equation (5–104) yields:

$$D = K_{D_{MX}} K_{st} K_a^n \frac{[HX]_{H_2O}^n}{[H_3O^+]^n} \tag{5–105}$$

The concentration of the chelating agent in the aqueous phase at equilibrium is not known and it is difficult to determine. Since we started off taking a solution of chelating agent in the organic phase, it would be much easier to use the equilibrium concentration of the chelating agent in the organic phase. This can be achieved by substituting the partition coefficient relationship for the chelating agent into Equation (5–105):

$$D = \frac{K_{D_{MX}} K_{st} K_a^n [HX]_{org}^n}{K_{D_{HX}}^n [H_3O^+]^n} \tag{5–106}$$

We have finally derived a relationship between the distribution ratio for the metal in a metal chelate system in terms of the known equilibrium constants for the system and experimentally measurable concentrations. This relationship is not so simple as the one encountered in Equation (5–97) for complex ions. Note that the distribution ratio is dependent upon the concentration of the chelating agent in the system, the pH of the system, and the extent to which the chelating anion is available to react with the metal ion. Equation (5–106) is an extremely important relationship that finds wide application. The implications and restrictions of it will be discussed in great detail in Chapter 6.

Other Equilibria Accompanying Partition

If there exist in the aqueous phase any other equilibria, such as oxidation–reduction reactions, involving the solute, then the amount of the solute distributed into the organic phase will be less than it would have been had the equilibria not been present. Similarly, if in the organic phase, the solute undergoes chemical reactions, such as oxidation–reduction, then more of the material will be distributed into the organic phase than there would be without the presence of these additional reactions. Treatment of these situations is made on lines analogous to those used in discussing other concomitant equilibria, and yields expressions relating D and K_D that are similar to Equations (5–93) and (5–95).

From the preceding discussions, it should be apparent that the distinction between the thermodynamic partition coefficient and the empirical distribution ratio is a useful one in separation techniques. By altering experimental conditions such as pH, concentration of solute, concentration of complexing or chelating agent, oxidant or reductant, the numerical value of the distribution coefficient can be made to increase or decrease for each solute. The extent to which the numerical value of the distribution ratio will change is a property of the chemical reactions of each solute, and hence will differ among solutes. This means that a particular change in solution conditions, such as an increase in the pH of the aqueous phase by one unit, will cause a different change in the distribution ratio for each solute present in a mixture of solutes. When this difference in D becomes great enough, separation of the solutes is feasible. This is the basis for effecting separations by the techniques of extraction and liquid–liquid chromatography.

ACTIVITY COEFFICIENT PROBLEMS

1. Calculate the mean ionic activity coefficient for the solute in each of the following solutions:
    (a) 0.137 M KCl
    (b) 0.0512 M $Mg(NO_3)_2$
    (c) 0.0512 M Na_2CO_3
    (d) 0.0375 M Na_3PO_4
    (e) 0.0248 M $Cr_2(SO_4)_3$
2. Calculate the mean ionic activity coefficient of the salt in each of the following solutions:
    (a) 0.0021 M $NaClO_4$ in 0.125 M K_2SO_4 + 0.1250 M H_2SO_4
    (b) 0.000155 M $HClO_4$ in 2.0 M $KClO_4$
    (c) 0.0500 M $CuSO_4$ in 0.10 M HNO_3 + 0.50 M KNO_3
    (d) 0.0111 M $Ce(SO_4)_2$ in 2.00 M H_2SO_4
3. Calculate the numerical value for the molar concentration dissociation constant for acetic acid that should be used in solutions with ionic strengths of:
    (a) 0.0010 M (c) 0.100 M
    (b) 0.0100 M (d) 1.00 M
    The thermodynamic dissociation constant for acetic acid is 1.754×10^{-5} at 25°C.
4. Derive the expression relating the molar concentration and the activity ionization constants in terms of ionic strength for each of the following:
    (a) HF   (c) NH_3
    (b) Oxalic Acid—k_{a_1} and k_{a_2} (d) PO_4^{3-}
5. Repeat problem 4 for the solubility product constants for each of the slightly soluble salts listed here:
    (a) AgCl   (c) $AlPO_4$
    (b) $BaSO_4$ (d) $Ag_4Fe(CN)_6$

6. Repeat problem 4 for the stability constants for each of the following complex ions:

(a) $Ag(CN)_2^-$ (c) $Zn(NH_3)_4^{2+}$
(b) CuY^{2-} (d) $Ni(DMG)_2$

where Y^{4-} represents the anion of ethylenediaminetetraacetic acid and DMG is an abbreviation for dimethylglyoxime.

7. Calculate the molar concentration of hydronium ions in pure water at $0°C$, $50°C$, and $100°C$.

ELECTRONEUTRALITY PROBLEMS

1. Write the electroneutrality principle expression for each of the following solutions:

(a) 500 ml of 0.25 M NaCl + 0.25 M $BaCl_2$
(b) 0.573 M $HClO_4$, 0.378 M H_2SO_4, and 0.416 M $NaClO_4$
(c) 0.125 M $K_4Fe(CN)_6$ and 0.250 M Na_3PO_4
(d) 375 ml of a solution containing 0.750 M $Mg(NO_3)_2$, 0.125 M $MgCl_2$, and 0.375 M HNO_3

Substitute the molar concentrations of the ions into these expressions to see if they are correct.

2. Set up the expression for the material balance for the indicated species in each of the following solutions:

(a) chloride ion in 250 ml of a solution that is 0.125 M HCl and 0.125 M NaCl
(b) formate in 0.557 M formic acid containing 0.736 M sodium formate
(c) cyanide in a solution that is 0.111 M in HCN, 0.057 M in $Ag(CN)_2^-$, and 0.373 M in NaCN
(d) pyridine in a solution containing 0.027 M pyridine and 0.025 M pyridinium chloride
(e) all forms of ethylenediamine in 0.0645 M ethylenediamine
(f) all forms of phosphate in 0.128 M phosphoric acid

3. Write expressions for the electroneutrality principle on the solutions that result at equilibrium when:

(a) 25.0 ml of 0.843 M HCl are added to 25.0 ml of 0.643 M NH_3
(b) 30.0 ml of 0.250 M HCl are added to 50.0 ml of 0.125 M $Pb(NO_3)_2$ and 0.225 M $Mg(NO_3)_2$
(c) 0.012 mole of H_2CO_3 is dissolved in 125 ml of 0.515 M acetic acid and 0.500 M sodium acetate.
(d) 0.35 M $FeCl_3$ is added to 0.600 M $FeSO_4$ that is 1.0 M in $HClO_4$
(e) a solution which contains 0.0123 M $Fe(ClO_4)_3$ and 0.0246 M $CuSO_4$ in 0.50 M $HClO_4$ is made 0.70 M in NH_3

Where possible, substitute the molar concentrations into the expression to verify it.

4. Write the material balance expression for the solutions resulting when:

(a) 25.0 ml of 0.10 M NaOH are added to 30.0 ml of 0.10 M carbonic acid
(b) 25.0 ml of 0.050 M $HClO_4$ are added to 50.0 ml of 0.050 M ethylenediamine

(c) H_2S is bubbled through a 0.025 M $CdCl_2$ solution in 0.5 M HCl

(d) 0.125 M $Ni(NO_3)_2$ is adjusted to a pH of 9.0 and then made 0.80 M in KCN

(e) 0.100 M EDTA is added to 0.125 M $Zn(NO_3)_2$ which is also 0.125 M in NH_3 at a pH of 8.5.

ACID–BASE PROBLEMS

1. Calculate the pH and the concentration of all species present in each of the following solutions:

   (a) 1.267 $\times$ 10^{-3} M propionic acid

   (b) 526 mg of barbituric acid dissolved in 350 ml of water

   (c) 475 ml of 3.75 $\times$ 10^{-3} M piperidine

   (d) 2.51 $\times$ 10^{-4} M boric acid

   (e) 6.63 $\times$ 10^{-3} M H_2SO_3

   (f) 4.87 $\times$ 10^{-2} M trimethylamine

2. (a) 64.5 mg of trichloroacetic acid are dissolved in deionized water and made up to a volume of 400 ml. The measured pH of this solution is 2.91. Calculate the K_a for trichloroacetic acid.

   (b) 0.112 ml of ethanolamine (density = 1.022) is diluted to 750 ml with deionized water. The measured pH of this solution is 10.42. Calculate the K_b for ethanolamine.

   (c) 0.396 g of hydroxylamine hydrochloride is dissolved up to 600 ml. The measured pH of the solution is 4.00. Calculate K_b for hydroxylamine.

   (d) Calculate the K_b for the borate ion if a solution prepared by dissolving 5.50 g of $NaBO_2 \cdot 4\ H_2O$ in 900 ml of water has a measured pH of 10.94.

3. Calculate the pH of the solution present at equilibrium when:

   (a) 378 mg of $NaNO_3$ is added to 225 ml of 1.25 $\times$ 10^{-4} M HNO_2

   (b) 0.0516 mole of Na_3AsO_4 is dissolved in 689 ml of water

   (c) 0.568 g of pyridinium chloride is dissolved in 248 ml of water

   (d) 3.78 ml of 0.137 M HCl are added to 63.8 mg of ethylamine dissolved in 25.0 ml of water

   (e) 24.3 ml of 0.00975 M $Ba(OH)_2$ are added to 697 ml of 0.0123 M n-butyric acid

   (f) 6.14 ml of 1.25 $\times$ 10^{-2} M HCNO are added to 83.7 ml of 0.0456 M NaCNO

4. Calculate the pH of each of the following solutions:

   (a) 0.00875 M $NaAsO_2$

   (b) 125.0 ml of 1.13 $\times$ 10^{-3} M potassium acid phthalate

   (c) 7.63 $\times$ 10^{-3} M quinoline sulfate

   (d) 5.84 $\times$ 10^{-2} M ethylenediamine hydrochloride

   (e) 4.26 $\times$ 10^{-3} M $NaHSO_4$

5. Solutions of what analytical concentration of acid or base will have the following pH values?

   (a) ethylamine—a pH of 9.50

   (b) $NaHSO_4$—a pH of 3.25

(c) NaCN—a pH of 10.00

(d) butyric acid—a pH of 4.00

6. Calculate the molar concentration of the completely unprotonated anion in each of the following acid solutions:

   (a) 300 ml of 2.07×10^{-2} M citric acid at a pH of 6.50

   (b) 1.13×10^{-3} M H_2Se at a pH of 10.00

   (c) 125 ml of 8.75×10^{-3} M lactic acid at a pH of 5.00

   (d) 7.33×10^{-3} M diethylenetriaminepentaacetic acid at a pH of 10.00

   (e) 500 ml of 4.78×10^{-2} M salicylic acid at a pH of 7.00

7. (a) How many g of solid Na_2HPO_4 must be added to 525 ml of 0.125 M NaH_2PO_4 to prepare a pH 7.00 buffer?

   (b) How many millimoles of methylammonium chloride must be added to 1.375 liters of 0.234 M methylamine to prepare a pH 10.25 buffer?

   (c) What should be the equilibrium concentration of ethanolamine in a 0.0776 M ethanolammonium sulfate solution, in order to have a pH 9.50 buffer?

   (d) How many ml of 1.00 M HCl should be added to 350 ml of 0.155 M sodium borate to produce a pH 9.00 buffer?

   (e) How many ml of 7.50 M NaOH must be added to 500 ml of 0.845 M carbonic acid to prepare a pH 10.50 buffer?

8. (a) To 190.0 ml of a solution containing 0.498 M urotropine and 0.513 M urotropine hydrochloride are added 5.00 ml of 0.110 M NaOH. Calculate the pH of the resulting solution.

   (b) To the urotropine buffer in part (a) are added 7.00 ml of 0.0983 M HCl instead of the NaOH. Calculate the resultant pH of the buffer.

   (c) To the urotropine buffer in part (a) are added 170.0 ml of deionized water. Calculate the resultant pH.

9. (a) At what pH will a 7.48×10^{-3} M HBrO solution contain 4.78×10^{-4} M BrO^-?

   (b) At what pH will a 5.67×10^{-2} M malonic acid solution contain 5.67×10^{-3} M malonate ion?

   (c) Over what pH range will 99% or more of the alanine molecules in a solution exist as the zwitterion?

10. For each of the following titrations, calculate the pH of the titrate solution when 0, 10, 25, 50, 75, 90, 95, 99, 99.9, 100, 100.1, 101, 105, 110, and 125% of the titrate has reacted. Graph the resultant data.

   (c) 75.00 ml of 0.573 M picric acid with 0.778 M KOH

   (b) 127 ml of 0.480 M potassium acid phthalate with 0.409 M NaOH

   (c) 90.00 ml of 0.0784 M trimethylamine with 0.123 M HCl

   (d) 85.00 ml of 0.0648 M iminodiacetic acid with 0.111 M KOH

11. (a) Derive the expression for α_{0_H} for diethylenetriaminepentaacetic acid.

   (b) Calculate the concentration of the completely unprotonated DTPA anion at a pH of 3.00 in 0.0222 M DTPA.

   (c) Calculate the concentration of the completely unprotonated anion, Y^{4-}, at a pH of 3.00 in 0.022 M EDTA.

   (d) Calculate the concentration of the completely unprotonated anion, X^{3-}, at a pH of 3.00 in nitrilotriacetic acid (NTA).

SOLUBILITY PROBLEMS

1. How many mg of each of the following slightly soluble salts will dissolve in 323 ml of water?
    (a) $SrSO_4$
    (b) Hg_2I_2
    (c) $Tl(OH)_3$
    (d) In_2S_3 (neglect any basicity of sulfide)
    (c) $Fe_4[Fe(CN)_6]_3$

2. Calculate the numerical value of the solubility product constant (in terms of molar concentrations) for saturated solutions each of the following slightly soluble salts which contain:
    (a) 2.97 mg of $PbSO_4$ dissolved in 75.0 ml of water
    (b) 0.00241 mmol of $Co(OH)_2$ dissolved in 350 ml of water
    (c) 0.486 mg of $Ag_4Fe(CN)_6$ dissolved in 615 ml of water
    (d) 139 mg of Ag_2WO_4 dissolved in 2698 ml of 0.00103 M $NaNO_3$
    (e) 1.56×10^{-7} mg of $CuSCN$ dissolved in 1,478 ml of 0.00555 M $KSCN$

3. Arrange the following salts in order of increasing molar solubility:
    (a) Tl_2S, NiS, La_2S_3, MnS, CdS (neglect the basicity of the sulfide ion)
    (b) $AgOH$, $Mg(OH)_2$, $Ca(OH)_2$, $Tl(OH)_3$, $Cd(OH)_2$
    (c) $Ni_3(PO_4)_2$, $AlPO_4$, $Ca_3(PO_4)_2$, Ag_3PO_4 (neglect the basicity of the phosphate ion)
    (d) $AgIO_3$, $Ba(IO_3)_2$, $La(IO_3)_3$, $Cu(IO_3)_2$

4. How many mg of $Cd(IO_3)_2$ will dissolve in 850 ml of each of the following solutions?
    (a) deionized water
    (b) 4.73×10^{-2} M $Cd(NO_3)_2$
    (c) 4.73×10^{-2} M KIO_3

5. How many mg of $Zn(OH)_2$ will dissolve in 641 ml of each of the following?
    (a) deionized water
    (b) 2.33×10^{-4} M $Zn(NO_3)_2$
    (c) 2.33×10^{-4} M HCl

6. Calculate the equilibrium pH of a saturated solution of each of the following salts when dissolved in deionized water:
    (a) $Ca(OH)_2$
    (b) $Cd(OH)_2$
    (c) $ZnCO_3$
    (d) $AlPO_4$ (neglect the acidity of aluminum ion)
    (e) Tl_2S

7. Calculate the molar solubility of each of the following salts in deionized water, including pH effects, where applicable:
    (a) $SrCO_3$ (c) Ag_2CrO_4
    (b) SrF_2 (d) Ag_3PO_4

8. Calculate the molar solubility of the following salts in 1.50 liters of the solutions stated:
    (a) $Ga(OH)_3$ in a solution with an initial pH of 1.00
    (b) FeS in a pH 5.00 buffer

    (c) Ag_2S in a solution having an equilibrium pH of 7.00

    (d) Tl_2CrO_4 in a pH 4.00 buffer

    (e) $Ni_3(PO_4)_2$ in a pH 5.00 buffer

9.   What must be the concentration of each precipitant in the solution when a precipitate just begins to form in the following solutions?

    (a)   dilute NaBr is added to 435 ml of 6.73×10^{-4} M $AgNO_3$

    (b)   dilute $K_4Fe(CN)_6$ is added to one liter of 2.55×10^{-5} M $AgNO_3$

    (c) 0.00100 M HF is added dropwise to 711 ml of 0.0245 M $BaCl_2$

    (d)   dilute $Ba(NO_3)_2$ is added to 468 ml of 0.00971 M HIO_3 at a pH of 4.00

    (e) 0.00125 M $AgNO_3$ is added dropwise to 991 ml of 1.75×10^{-4} M Na_2WO_4

10. (a)   How many ml of 5.25×10^{-3} M K_2CrO_4 must be added to 465 ml of 3.72×10^{-4} M $Pb(NO_3)_2$ to just begin precipitation of $PbCrO_4$?

    (b)   How many ml of this K_2CrO_4 will have to be added to precipitate 99.99% of the lead in the solution?

11. 3.30 ml of 8.97×10^{-3} M HCl is added to 253 ml of 4.79×10^{-5} M $Hg_2(NO_3)_2$. Calculate the molar concentration of all species present in the solution at equilibrium.

12. What must be the equilibrium concentration of ammonia in each of the following solutions at the point where the metal hydroxide precipitate just begins to form?

    (a) 4.93×10^{-4} M $AgNO_3$

    (b) 4.93×10^{-4} M $Fe(NO_3)_2$

    (c) 4.93×10^{-4} M $Tl(NO_3)_3$

13. A solution is 0.00678 M in $MnSO_4$ and 0.0222 M in NH_3. What must be the molar concentration of $(NH_4)_2SO_4$ present in the solution in order to just prevent the formation of any $Mn(OH)_2$?

14. 638 ml of a solution is 0.0483 M in $MgCl_2$ and 0.0508 M in NH_4Cl. How large can the concentration of NH_3 be in this solution before $Mg(OH)_2$ begins to precipitate?

15. What is the molar solubility of $Pb(OH)_2$ in a solution which is 0.0253 M NH_3 and 0.0471 M NH_4NO_3?

16. Show whether or not the following separations are feasible (the concentration of the less soluble salt is reduced to 10^{-6} M or less when the more soluble precipitate begins to form):

    (a) 0.00437 M $AgNO_3$ from 0.00559 M $TlNO_3$ by precipitation as their iodides

    (b) 0.0611 M $AgNO_3$ from 0.00559 M $Cu(NO_3)_2$ by precipitation as their hydroxides

    (c) 0.0481 M $Mn(NO_3)_2$ from 0.00593 M $Pb(NO_3)_2$ by precipitation as their carbonates

    (d) 0.0175 M $TlNO_3$ and 0.00573 M $Pb(NO_3)_2$ by precipitation as their iodates

17. Over what pH range (if any) is it feasible to separate the following pairs of ions; that is, to decrease the concentration of the less soluble precipitate to at least 10^{-6} M before the more soluble begins to precipitate?

    (a) 0.0345 M $Zn(NO_3)_2$ and 0.0217 M $Mg(NO_3)_2$ by precipitation as their hydroxides

(b)   0.00843 M $Cu(NO_3)_2$ and 0.00515 M $Pb(NO_3)_2$ by precipitation as their chromates from a solution that is 1.00×10^{-3} M in $KHCrO_4$

(c)   0.00634 M $FeSO_4$ and 0.0373 M $MnSO_4$ by precipitation as their sulfides

(d)   0.000598 M $Ca(NO_3)_2$ and 0.00481 M $Pb(NO_3)_2$ by precipitation as their phosphates from 0.133 M H_3PO_4. (*Hint*: you will have to do some guessing to get approximate values of α_{0_H} unless you can solve cubic equations.)

COMPLEX ION PROBLEMS

1.   Calculate the fraction of the total concentration of each of the following ions that remains uncomplexed when in the system stated:
(a)   zinc (II) in 0.00100 M ammonia
(b)   silver (I) in 0.0100 M ammonia
(c)   nickel (II) in 0.0100 M ethylenediamine

2.   Calculate the average ligand number, $\bar{n}$, for cadmium (II) in 0.000100 M ammonia, 0.00100 M ammonia, 0.0100 M ammonia, 0.100 M ammonia, and 1.00 M ammonia.

3.   Calculate the molar concentration of each of the zinc ammine species present in a solution that is 0.0250 M in $ZnSO_4$ and 0.125 M in excess NH_3.

4.   Calculate the concentration of magnesium ions remaining uncomplexed when 0.00912 M $MgSO_4$ is made 0.106 M in ammonia
(a)   neglecting the presence of lower ammine complexes than the tetraammine one
(b)   including the presence of all ammine complexes formed
What is the error involved in the neglection of lower ammine species than the tetraammine?

5.   Calculate the concentration of iron that exists as uncomplexed iron(III) in 0.00648 M $K_3Fe(CN)_6$.

6.   (a)   What must be the concentration of excess ethylenediamine present in 250 ml of 0.0552 M zinc solution to reduce the concentration of uncomplexed zinc(II) to 1.25×10^{-7} M?
(b)   What will the total concentration of ethylenediamine in the system be?

7.   25.00 ml of 0.100 M NH_3 is added to 50.00 ml of 0.00412 M $CoSO_4$. Calculate the molar concentration of all species present in the solution.

8.   Calculate the molar concentration of copper that remains uncomplexed in a solution containing 0.0246 M copper sulfate, 0.0702 M sodium tartrate, and having a pH of 9.72.

9.   What is the minimum pH value at which all but 1.00×10^{-8} M of the zinc in a 0.0111 M $ZnSO_4$ solution will be complexed with 0.0226 M NaCN?

10.   Calculate the molar concentration of uncomplexed metal ion in each of the following solutions:
(a)   0.0267 M $Ca(NO_3)_2$ containing 0.0300 M EDTA at a pH of 7.50
(b)   0.0313 M $Eu(NO_3)_3$ containing 0.0313 M EDTA at a pH of 4.00
(c)   0.00855 M $MgSO_4$ containing 0.0100 M EDTA at a pH of 8.00
(d)   0.00855 M $MgSO_4$ containing 0.0100 M EDTA at a pH of 11.00
(e)   0.00505 M $Fe(NO_3)_3$ containing 0.0100 M EDTA at a pH of 2.00
(f)   0.00505 M $Fe(NO_3)_3$ containing 0.0100 M EDTA at a pH of 10.00

11. A solution that is 0.0125 M in Al(NO$_3$)$_3$ and 0.0415 M in Ga(NO$_3$)$_3$ is to be made 0.0750 M in EDTA. Over what pH range will it be possible to mask the gallium so that the aluminum can react with a second reagent and have only a 1% interference from the gallium?

12. Calculate the molar solubility of each of the precipitates listed in the medium given:
(a) BaSO$_4$ in 0.0500 M EDTA at a pH of 9.00
(b) AgSCN in 750 ml of 0.163 M NH$_3$ at a pH of 8.00
(c) ZnS in 0.0751 M ethylenediamine (neglect pH effects)
(d) Ba(IO$_3$)$_2$ in 1200 ml of 0.00100 M EDTA at a pH of 5.00

13. For each of the following systems, calculate the numerical value of the conditional stability constant of the EDTA chelate:
(a) Ce(NO$_3$)$_3$, EDTA, pH = 3.00
(b) Pb(NO$_3$)$_2$, EDTA, pH = 8.00
(c) Co(NO$_3$)$_2$, 0.10 M NH$_3$, EDTA, pH = 8.00
(d) AgNO$_3$, 0.010 M NH$_3$, EDTA, pH = 9.00
(e) Hg(NO$_3$)$_2$, 1.00 M NH$_3$, EDTA, pH = 10.00

14. 50.00 ml of a 0.0136 M NiSO$_4$ solution is made 0.500 M in NaCN and then adjusted to a pH of 4.00. Calculate the concentration of nickel that remains out of the cyano complex.

15. Calculate the number of moles of EDTA that must be added to 825 ml of 0.0389 M La(NO$_3$)$_3$ at a pH of 3.50 in order to reduce the concentration of free lanthanum ions to 5.00 × 10^{-7} M.

16. Calculate pCu for a solution that is 0.00493 M in CuSO$_4$, 0.100 M in NH$_3$, 0.00600 M in EDTA and has a pH of 9.00.

17. A solution is 0.00525 M in ZnSO$_4$ and 0.00125 M in CuSO$_4$. Ethylenediamine is added to a total concentration of 0.100 M. Can copper be separated from zinc by precipitation as their insoluble sulfides when the solution is saturated with H$_2$S? If so, which metal ion will remain in solution? If the separation is feasible, over what pH range can it be effected?

18. Magnesium can be titrated with EDTA in a pH 10.00 NH$_3$–NH$_4$Cl buffer. Calculate pMg for the titration of 0.0125 M MgSO$_4$ when 0, 10, 25, 50, 75, 90, 95, 99, 100, 101, 105, 110, and 125% of the magnesium has reacted with the EDTA. Neglect any dilution effects.

19. The conditional stability constant for a complexation reaction must be greater than 10^6 for an accurate chelatometric titration to be effected. What is the minimum pH at which the following can be carried out?
(a) silver (I) titrated with EDTA in a noncomplexing buffer
(b) lead (II) titrated with EDTA in a noncomplexing buffer
(c) thorium (IV) titrated with EDTA in a noncomplexing buffer
(d) zinc (II) titrated with EDTA in 0.10 M NH$_3$ solution

DISTRIBUTION PROBLEMS

1. 75.0 ml of 0.1051 M FeCl$_3$ in 5.0 M HCl is shaken with 25.00 ml of isopropyl ether. At equilibrium, the concentration of FeCl$_3$ in the 5.0 M HCl phase has

been reduced to 2.94×10^{-2} M. Calculate the numerical value for the partition coefficient (isopropyl ether/water) for $FeCl_3$.

2.   The partition coefficient for bromine between carbon tetrachloride and water $(K_D—CCl_4/H_2O)$ at 25°C is 27.00. If 0.873 g of bromine dissolved in 50.0 ml of water is shaken with 15.0 ml of carbon tetrachloride, calculate the weight of bromine present in the carbon tetrachloride layer at equilibrium.

3.   (a)   What volume of carbon tetrachloride is needed to partition 90% of the bromine from 125.0 ml of 0.00284 M aqueous bromine solution into the carbon tetrachloride layer at equilibrium?
      (b)   To partition 95% of the bromine?
      (c)   To partition 99% of the bromine?

4.   The partition coefficient for acetic acid between carbon tetrachloride and water is 0.00191 $(K_D—CCl_4/H_2O)$. Calculate the numerical value of the distribution ratio when 0.0317 M acetic acid is distributed between an aqueous phase and carbon tetrachloride at the following pH values (neglect any association in the carbon tetrachloride layer):

(a)	1.00	(c)	7.00
(b)	4.76	(d)	10.00

5.   Formic acid has a partition coefficient of 0.425 between methyl isobutyl ketone and water $(K_D—MIBK/H_2O)$. The distribution ratio measured when 95.0 ml of 0.00834 M formic acid at a pH of 5.00 is shaken with 20.0 ml of methyl isobutyl ketone is 0.0227. Calculate the acid dissociation constant for formic acid.

6.   Acetic acid has a partition coefficient of 3.20×10^{-3} between carbon tetrachloride and water $(K_D—CCl_4/H_2O)$. When 75.0 ml of an aqueous solution of acetic acid is shaken with 75.0 ml of carbon tetrachloride, the distribution ratio measured at equilibrium is 9.57×10^{-3} and the aqueous phase concentration of acetic acid is 0.533 M. Neglecting acid dissociation in the aqueous phase, calculate the numerical value for the association constant for acetic acid in the carbon tetrachloride layer.

7.   Bromide ion reacts with bromine to form a complex ion. The partition coefficient for bromine between carbon tetrachloride and 0.0010 N H_2SO_4 at 21.5°C is 27.5 $(K_D—CCl_4/H_2O)$. The distribution ratio for bromine at equilibrium with 0.4904 M NaBr and carbon tetrachloride is 2.90. The distribution ratio for bromine at equilibrium with carbon tetrachloride and 0.09386 M NaBr is 10.46. What is the formula of the complex formed between bromine and bromide ion? Calculate the stability constant for this complex.

8.   Copper forms a chelate with dimethylglyoxime that has the formula $Cu(DMG)_2$. The value of β_2 for this chelate is 1.74×10^{19}. The partition coefficient for the distribution of the chelate between chloroform and water is 0.118, while the partition coefficient for the distribution of dimethylglyoxime between chloroform and water is 0.302 $(K_D—CHCl_3/H_2O)$. Calculate the value of the distribution ratio for the copper dimethylglyoximate between 1.67×10^{-3} M dimethylglyoxime in chloroform and water at each of the following pH values:

(a)	3.00	(d)	4.50
(b)	3.50	(e)	5.00
(c)	4.00		

REFERENCES

1. Beckerdike, E. L. and Willard, H. H., *Anal. Chem.*, **24,** 1026 (1952).
2. Bruckenstein, S. and Kolthoff, I. M., *J. Amer. Chem. Soc.*, **78,** 10, 2974 (1956); **79,** 5915 (1957).
3. Bruckenstein, S. and Mukherjee, L. M., *J. Phys. Chem.*, **66,** 2228 (1962).
4. Burger, K., in *Chelates in Analytical Chemistry*, H. Flaschka and A. J. Barnard, Jr., Eds., Vol. II, Dekker, New York, 1969, pp. 179–212.
5. Davies, C. W., *Ion Association*, Butterworth's, London, 1962, Chap. 3.
6. Jones, M. M., *Elementary Coordination Chemistry*, Prentice-Hall, Englewood Cliffs, N. J., 1964.
7. Job, P., *Compt. Rend.*, **180,** 928 (1925); *Ann. Chim. (Paris)*, **9,** (10), 113 (1928).
8. Dole, V., *Lab. Management*, **1969,** 30 (August).
9. Jones, M. M., *J. Amer. Chem. Soc.*, **81,** 4495 (1959).
10. Jones, M. M. and Innes, K. K., *J. Phys. Chem.*, **62,** 1003 (1958).
11. Kolthoff, I. M. and Bruckenstein, S., *J. Amer. Chem. Soc.*, **78,** 1 (1956); **79,** 1 (1957).
12. Kolthoff, I. M., Bruckenstein, S. and Chantooni, M. K., Jr., *J. Amer. Chem. Soc.*, **83,** 3927 (1961).
13. Kolthoff, I. M. and Chantooni, M. K., Jr., *J. Amer. Chem. Soc.*, **90,** 5961 (1968).
14. Kolthoff, I. M. and Reddy, T. B., *Inorg. Chem.*, **1,** 189 (1962).
15. Lyle, S. J. and Maghzian, R., *Talanta*, **14,** 1021 (1967).
16. Mukherjee, L. M., Bruckenstein, S. and Badawi, F. A. K., *J. Phys. Chem.*, **69,** 2537 (1965).
17. Nernst, W., *Z. Phys. Chem.*, **8,** 110 (1891).
18. Pribil, R., *Talanta*, **12,** 925 (1965); **13,** 1223 (1966); **14,** 613, 619 (1967).
19. Ringbom, A., *Complexation in Analytical Chemistry*, Wiley-Interscience, New York, 1963.
20. Robinson, R. A. and Stokes, R. H., *Electrolyte Solutions*, 2nd ed, Butterworth's, London, 1959.
21. Sillen, L. G. and Martell, A. E., *Stability Constants of Metal–Ion Complexes*, Special Publication No. 17, The Chemical Society, London, 1964; Supplement Vol. I, Special Publication No. 25, 1971.

CHAPTER 6

SOLVENT EXTRACTION

$\mathcal{S}$olvent extraction is undoubtedly one of the oldest known and used separation techniques in science. The practice of removing unwanted materials or obtaining the desired material by washing a solid or a liquid with an immiscible liquid has been in use since the earliest days of mankind. The first recorded instance of the use of extraction in chemistry was by E. Peligot in 1842,[32] who, in his purification of the uranyl nitrate obtained from pitchblende, extracted it from aqueous solution into ether. From his routine inclusion of this step, one can infer that by this time solvent extraction was a known and useful technique. Extraction became a routine step in the purification of reaction products in organic synthesis, especially when combined with a chemical reaction in the "wash." It is one of the most widespread of the separation methods, occurring thousands of times each day all over the world in the brewing of coffee and the steeping of tea.

In 1872, Berthelot and Jungfleisch[2] reported that "A body that can dissolve in each of them separately, simultaneously put in the presence of two liquids, never dissolves completely in one of them to the exclusion of the other . . . the solute body always partitions itself between the two solvents, following a simple relation . . . the amounts dissolved by equal volumes of the two liquids are in a constant ratio." They demonstrated this partition law with many systems, including the distribution of succinic acid between water and ether. They noted that this ratio was constant and independent of the total volume of the two liquids, but that the ratio varied with temperature and sometimes with concentration of the solute. In 1891, W. Nernst[30] extended their observations and proposed the partition law as given in Equation (5–90). Since that time this partition law has been extended to cover species more complex than the atoms and molecules of weak acids that Nernst treated, but the law still remains valid. The technique of extraction has become so widespread, that in the biannual reviews by H. Freiser[13,14] 1387 papers dealing with extraction between 1965 and 1967 were listed. Part of the enormous interest in this technique lies in the widespread application of extraction to uranium and rare earth metal processing and to nuclear technology, but its routine acceptance by the average chemist is a stronger measure of the success of this separation tool.

Separation by extraction is carried out when the analytical determination desired cannot be performed in the initial environment and hence removal to a new environment is required, if an analysis is to be feasible. While *solid–liquid extraction* (*leaching*) is a technique frequently used in chemical industry and in the laboratory, the more prevalent form of extraction is *liquid–liquid extraction*. In this technique, a mixture of substances in one liquid (often water) is brought into contact with a second liquid that is immiscible with the first. During the period of contact either the wanted or the unwanted components (*not* both) of the mixture will be preferentially distributed into the second liquid. The two liquid phases are then separated mechanically and subsequent operations performed on them. The extent of the transfer of material from one phase into the second phase is described by the distribution ratio, D. Partition is an equilibrium process, thus it is impossible to transfer every single molecule or ion pair from one phase to the second. In practice, however, when the distribution ratio is sufficiently large or when a sufficient number of phase contacts are made, for all practical purposes all of the material can be obtained in only one phase.

The two liquids may be brought into contact with one another discretely or continuously, giving rise to three common ways of performing an extraction— *batch*, *continuous*, and *countercurrent*. The way selected for any particular extraction will depend upon the relative values of the distribution ratios of the components in the original mixture, the equipment available, and convenience.

BATCH EXTRACTION

In batch extraction a liquid containing the dissolved solute sample is shaken or stirred with a second, immiscible liquid in a closed container until equilibrium has been established. The two phases are allowed to settle, and then are separated mechanically. The one with the desired constituent is then used for any subsequent operations. The usual apparatus used for this method is quite simple, a separatory funnel (Fig. 2–15) of some convenient design. When the value of D for the desired constituent is large (10 or greater for equal volumes of the two phases) and considerably different from those of the other components in the mixture, a batch extraction should be the separation method of choice. Under these conditions a very large percentage of the desired solute will pass into the extracting liquid with only a single equilibrium stage.

If V_{org} and V_{aq} are the equilibrium volumes of the organic and aqueous phases, respectively, and w_{org} and w_{aq} are the amounts of the solute (either weight or moles) present in those phases at equilibrium, then the fraction, E, of the total amount of solute in the system extracted into the organic phase in a single equilibrium stage is:

$$E = \frac{w_{org}}{w_{org} + w_{aq}} \tag{6–1}$$

when the extracted species can exist in only one form:

$$D = K_D = \frac{C_{org}}{C_{aq}} = \frac{\dfrac{w_{org}}{V_{org}}}{\dfrac{w_{aq}}{V_{aq}}} \tag{6–2}$$

where K_D is the partition coefficient for the species, C_{org} represents the total concentration of the solute in the organic phase, and C_{aq} represents the total concentration of the solute in the aqueous phase. Substituting Equation (6–2) into Equation (6–1) gives:

$$E = \frac{D V_{org}}{D V_{org} + V_{aq}} \quad \text{or} \quad \%E = \frac{100\, D V_{org}}{D V_{org} + V_{aq}} \tag{6–3}$$

Let w^o_{aq}, the amount of the solute initially in the aqueous phase, be all of the solute that is present in the system. Equation (6–2) can now be rewritten:

$$D = \frac{\dfrac{w^o_{aq} - w_{aq}}{V_{org}}}{\dfrac{w_{aq}}{V_{aq}}}$$

So that:

$$D\, w_{aq}\, V_{org} = V_{aq}\, w^o_{aq} - V_{aq}\, w_{aq}$$

or:

$$w_{aq} = w^o_{aq} \left(\frac{V_{aq}}{D V_{org} + V_{aq}} \right) \tag{6–4}$$

Equation (6–4) enables the calculation of the amount of material that will remain unextracted in a single equilibrium stage, provided the volumes of the two liquid phases at equilibrium and the distribution ratio for the solute in the system are known. In a similar fashion it can be shown that:

$$w_{org} = w^o_{aq} \frac{D V_{org}}{D V_{org} + V_{aq}} \tag{6–5}$$

Equation (6–5) enables the calculation of the amount of material that will be extracted in a single equilibrium stage, provided that the volume of the two liquid phases, as well as the distribution ratio for the solute in this system are known. If there is any mutual solubility of the two liquids, the equilibrium volumes of the two phases will not be the initial volumes unless each liquid has been presaturated with the other before it is used. When equal volumes of the two liquids are taken, the equations simplify considerably.

When the value of D is less than one hundred, less than 99% of the solute can be removed by a single extraction; several will be required in order to extract all of the desired solute. The aqueous phase remaining after a first batch extraction is shaken a second time with a fresh, equal portion of the extracting liquid. When the second equilibrium is established:

$$D = \frac{\dfrac{\left(\dfrac{w^o_{aq} V_{aq}}{D V_{org} + V_{aq}} \right) - w_{aq}}{V_{org}}}{\dfrac{w_{aq}}{V_{aq}}}$$

where w_{aq} now symbolizes the amount of the solute remaining in the aqueous phase after the second extraction. Rearranging the preceding relationship:

$$w_{aq} = w_{aq}^o \left(\frac{V_{aq}}{DV_{org} + V_{aq}} \right)^2 \qquad (6\text{–}6)$$

the amount of solute, w_{org}, extracted into the organic phase during this second extraction:

$$w_{org} = w_{aq}^o \frac{DV_{aq}V_{org}}{(DV_{org} + V_{aq})^2} \qquad (6\text{–}7)$$

For analytical purposes, Equation (6–7) is not particularly useful. What is of value is the combined amount of solute extracted during both the first and the second equilibria. Adding Equation (6–5) and Equation (6–7) together

$$\text{total amount extracted} = \frac{w_{aq}^o DV_{org}}{DV_{org} + V_{aq}} \left(1 + \frac{V_{aq}}{DV_{org} + V_{aq}} \right) \qquad (6\text{–}8)$$

Continuing in this fashion, it can be shown that when an aqueous phase is extracted with n identical volumes of fresh organic solvent, the amount of solute remaining unextracted in the aqueous phase after establishment of the nth equilibrium stage will be:

$$w_{aq} = w_{aq}^o \left(\frac{V_{aq}}{DV_{org} + V_{aq}} \right)^n \qquad (6\text{–}9)$$

The expression for the total amount of solute extracted after n extractions is excessively cumbersome. This quantity is obtained more easily by calculating the amount of solute remaining unextracted and then subtracting it from the initial amount of the solute.

In deriving Equations (6–6), (6–7), (6–8), and (6–9) it has been assumed that D is constant, that is, it does not vary with solute concentration.

Knowing the value of the distribution ratio for a solute and the volumes of the two phases, one can calculate how many times the aqueous phase must be extracted in order to obtain the desired degree of extraction.

Example. The distribution ratio for palladium(II) chloride between 3 M HCl and tri-n-butyl phosphate is 2.3. How many times must 15.0 ml of a 5.00×10^{-3} M solution of PdCl$_2$ in 3 M HCl be extracted with fresh 5.00 ml portions of TBP in order to remove 99.5% of the metal?

When 99.5% of the metal has been extracted, $w_{aq}/w_{aq}^o = 0.005$. V_{org} is stated to be 5.00 ml, and V_{aq} is given as 15.0 ml. D is 2.3. Substituting all of these into Equation (6–9):

$$0.005 = \left(\frac{15.0 \text{ ml}}{2.3 \times 5.0 \text{ ml} + 15.0 \text{ ml}} \right)^n$$

solving this for n gives:

$$n = \frac{\log 0.005}{\log 0.567} = 11$$

so that one must extract eleven times under these conditions to obtain almost all of the palladium from this solution. Not a very encouraging solution!

Table 6–1.   PERCENT OF A SOLUTE HAVING $D = 4$ EXTRACTED WITH DIFFERENT VOLUME RATIOS OF THE TWO LIQUID PHASES

	Percent of Solute Extracted, %			
Number of Extractions	$V_0 = V_{aq}$	$V_0 = 0.5\ V_{aq}$	$V_0 = 0.33\ V_{aq}$	$V_0 = 0.20\ V_{aq}$
1	80.0	66.7	57.2	44.5
2	96.0	88.9	81.6	69.0
3	99.2	96.3	92.1	82.8
4	99.8	98.9	96.5	90.4
5		99.6	98.5	94.7
6		99.9	99.4	97.0
7			99.7	98.4
8			99.9	99.2
9				99.5
10				99.7
11				99.8
12				99.9

Since extraction is an equilibrium process, each contact with fresh organic liquid removes a constant fraction of the total concentration of the solute. Table 6–1 gives the results of applying Equation (6–9) to a solute with a $D = 4$ and for different volume ratios of the two liquids. Notice that in all cases, because of the equilibrium aspect of the extraction process, removing the last 2 or 3% of the solute can take as many extractions as removing the first 97%.

From the fact that the term containing the volume ratio in Equation (6–9) is exponential in n, it follows that for a given volume of organic extractant, V_0, more solute is extracted when extracting the aqueous phase n times with V_0/n portions of the organic liquid, than when extracting once with the entire volume, V_0. (See Problem 7 at the end of this chapter for a verification of this.)

From an examination of Equations (6–4), (6–5), or (6–9) it can be seen that the larger the value of D, the greater the amount of solute that will be extracted. Fig. 6–1 shows that this is not a linear relationship. For equal volumes of the two phases, $D = \%\ E/ (100 - \%\ E)$, again showing that the relationship between the amount of solute extracted and D is not a linear one. A given change in D causes a greater change in the percent extracted when D is near one, than when D is around 0.1 or 10.

If two solutes, A and B, have different distribution ratios, D_A and D_B, then they can be separated from one another, regardless of how small the differences in D may be. The ease and completeness of the separation, however, will depend upon the magnitude of the differences in D values. In the case of extraction, the value of the separation coefficient, β, can be given by:

$$\beta = \frac{D_A}{D_B}$$

In order to achieve a separation of the two components by batch extraction with a

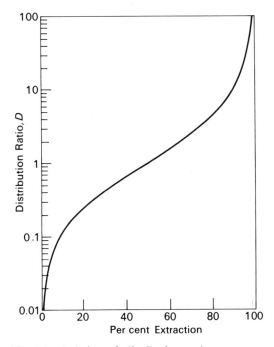

Fig. 6–1. Relation of distribution ratio to percent extraction. (*Redrawn from Ref. 26, by permission of John Wiley & Sons, Inc.*)

reasonable expenditure of time and effort, not only must β be 10^4 or 10^6 (for 99.9% extraction with only 1 p.p.t. contamination) but the absolute value of D_A must be sufficiently large (10 or greater for equal volumes of the two phases) to enable the separation to be carried out in a few equilibrium stages.

CONTINUOUS EXTRACTION

In continuous extraction the extracting liquid is passed continuously through or over the stationary liquid containing the sample, in a special apparatus, until all of the desired component has been removed. The two phases are separated physically and the one containing the desired constituent used for subsequent operations. Since the extracting liquid passes through or over the material relatively rapidly, it is probable that equilibrium is not established in continuous extraction. However, since the extraction is continued for long periods of time, all of the desired component can be extracted. When the value of D for the desired component is small (< 1) and considerably different ($\beta \geq 10^4$) from those of the other components in the mixture, continuous extraction should be the method of choice, since many batch extractions would be required for complete removal of the desired component.

The apparatus used for continuous extractions is more complex than that used for batch extractions. Its exact construction will depend upon whether the solution being extracted is heavier or lighter than the extracting liquid and whether the extracting solvent is recycled or not. Fig. 6–2 shows an extractor used when the extracting solvent is lighter than the solution containing the sample. The extracting solvent is placed in the distillation flask (A) and heated. Its vapors pass into the top of the central tube (B). There they condense in condensor, (C) The drops of condensate then fall through the long-stemmed funnel (D) to the bottom of the solution to be extracted (E). The small droplets of extractant rise up through this solution, extracting as they move, until they reach the surface. When the level of the extracting liquid in the central tube reaches the side arm (F) the extractant overflows into the distillation flask. This whole process is then repeated.

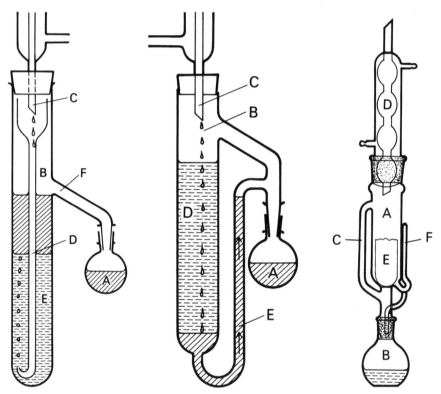

Fig. 6–2. Extractor for use with solvents lighter than water. (*Redrawn from Ref. 22, by permission of John Wiley & Sons, Inc.*)

Fig. 6–3. Extractor for solvents heavier than water. (*Redrawn from Ref. 39, by permission of John Wiley & Sons, Inc.*)

Fig. 6–4. Soxhlet extractor for solid–liquid extractions.

Fig. 6–3 shows an extractor used when the extracting solvent is more dense than the solution containing the sample. The extracting solvent is placed in distilling flask (A), and heated. Its vapors pass into the upper part of the central tube (B) where they condense in the condensor (C). In this case, the drops of condensate fall directly onto the surface of the solution to be extracted (D). Being more dense, the droplets sink through the solution to the bottom, extracting as they descend. Hydrostatic pressure will force the extractant through the narrow side arm (E) and back into the distillation flask. This process is repeated until all of the desired solute has been extracted.

When the material to be extracted is a solid, a *Soxhlet extractor*, as shown in Fig. 6–4, or some modification of it is commonly used. The powdered solid to be extracted is placed in a filter paper or cloth or paper thimble (E) in the central chamber (A). The extracting solvent is heated in the flask (B). Its vapors rise through the side arm (C) into the condensor (D) where they liquify, dropping from the tip of the condensor into the thimble (E) containing the solid. The liquid remains in this chamber increasing in volume and extracting the solid until the liquid level reaches the top of the sidearm (F). At this point, the hydrostatic pressure inside the main chamber causes the solvent to be siphoned back to the distillation flask. This process is continued until all of the solute has been dissolved (leached) out of the solid.

Continuous extractions usually extend for periods of an hour or more. The efficiency of a continuous extraction will depend upon the contact between the two phases. When this is large and lengthy, that is, many small droplets and a long central chamber in the apparatus, then an efficient extraction will occur. When the contact time is short and the interface is small, then the extraction will be quite inefficient. The solution properties that affect this contact are the relative viscosities of the two phases, the interfacial tension, the relative densities of the two liquids, the size of the area of contact between the two phases, the rate of attainment of the distribution equilibrium, the relative volumes of the two liquids, and the value of the distribution ratio.

Since a continuous extractor can be run for many hours, solutes with quite low values of D can be removed. In order to achieve a separation of the components in a mixture, the value of the separation factor, β, must still be above 10^4 and 10^6, but there is no longer any restriction on the absolute value of D_A.

COUNTERCURRENT DISTRIBUTION

In countercurrent distribution the two liquid phases essentially move in opposite directions to each other with the distribution occurring between the oppositely moving phases. When the extraction is completed, the two phases are separated physically. The liquid containing the desired constituent is used in subsequent operations. It is not necessary to reach equilibrium between the two phases for a successful extraction. This is the most efficient technique for separating mixtures containing solutes with distribution ratios very similar to one another.

Continuous countercurrent distribution is carried out in an apparatus such as that designed by Kolfenbach[20] and shown in Fig. 6–5. The liquid containing the sample to be extracted is placed in the flask in the upper left (A) and circulated through the system and contacting column (B) by a pump. The extracting liquid, which in this illustration is lighter than the sample phase, is circulated by continuous distillation, entering the contacting column at the bottom, rising through the descending solution of the mixture, extracting it as the liquids move past one another. When the extracting liquid reaches the top of the column it is syphoned off into the distillation flask. At the conclusion of the process, the extracted solute will be in the distillation flask. The authors[20] used this apparatus successfully to extract 2,3-butylene glycol into ether from an aqueous solution. D for their extraction was neither constant nor favorable, varying between 0.027 and 0.055.

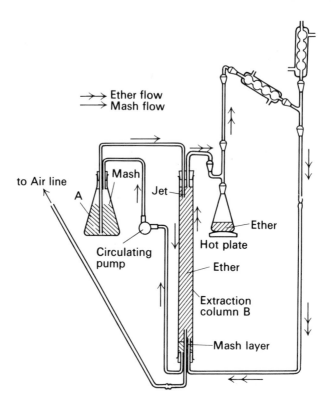

Fig. 6–5.   Extractor of Kolfenbach *et al.* (*Redrawn from Ref. 20, by permission of Analytical Chemistry.*)

When most people speak of countercurrent distribution, however, they mean discontinuous countercurrent distribution as developed by L. Craig and his co-workers at Rockefeller University. In discontinuous countercurrent distribution the two liquid phases are brought into contact with one another in a series of separate vessels in a specially constructed apparatus, shaken, the phases separated, and the phases moved on to the next vessel. The way in which the apparatus is operated causes, in effect, the movement of both phases in opposite directions to one another, stopping to attain distribution equilibrium at discrete intervals, and then moving on. The number of times that equilibrium is attained can be hundreds or thousands in a sufficiently large apparatus (see Fig. 6–6) and can be continued until the separation is effected.

In order to illustrate the mode of operation and the mathematics of the separation process in discontinuous countercurrent distribution, let us consider a series of ten separatory funnels, each filled with the same volume (say, 10 ml) of water and numbered, r, from one to ten. An eleventh separatory funnel, numbered 0, contains 10 ml of an aqueous mixture to be separated. To this funnel ($r = 0$) is added an equal volume (10 ml) of an immiscible extracting liquid that is lighter than water (for example diethyl ether). The funnel is shaken until equilibrium is reached, the two phases allowed to settle out, and the upper layer (the ether extract) is removed with a pipette and placed into funnel number 1. Ten milliliters of fresh

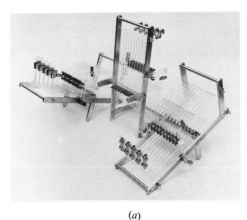
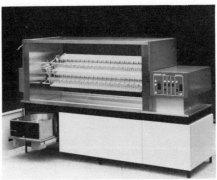

(a)   (b)

Fig. 6-6. (a) Simple, manual distribution apparatus. (b) Completely automatic countercurrent-distribution apparatus. (*Courtesy of Spectrum Medical Instruments, Inc.*)

ether are added to funnel number 0, and now both funnels 0 and 1 are shaken until equilibrium is attained. The phases are allowed to separate and the ether phase (upper) from funnel 1 is transferred to funnel 2, and the ether phase from funnel 0 is transferred to funnel 1. Ten milliliters of fresh ether is added to funnel 0. In this process n is designated as the number of times the upper phases have been transferred to the next (higher value of r) lower phase. The process at this stage can be illustrated by the following diagram:

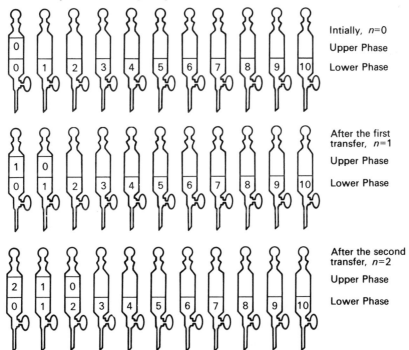

This sequence of transfer, equilibrate, settle, transfer is continued, each time moving every upper phase over to the next separatory funnel and adding 10 ml. of fresh ether to funnel 0, until all eleven of the funnels are filled with both phases (ten transfers have been made). The diagram of the process will now look like:

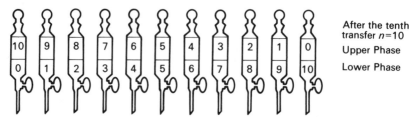

After the tenth transfer $n=10$

Upper Phase

Lower Phase

The contents of each separatory funnel are then analyzed (either each phase in each funnel separately, or both phases from each funnel together) for the concentration of the solute. The higher the value of D for a solute, the larger the number of the funnel in which it finishes.

In practice, the use of a series of funnels and pipettes for the liquid transfer is excessively cumbersome. Especially when working with 100–1000 transfers! Thus L. Craig and O. Post designed an all-glass, interconnected array of tubes to carry out discontinuous countercurrent distribution more rapidly and efficiently.

Fig. 6–7 is a diagram of a single tube, showing its positions during operation. The more dense liquid is placed in each tube to the level of the bottom of the cross arm, while the tube is in the decantation position (3). The tube is turned to the settling position (2). The unknown, in a volume of less-dense solvent equal to that of the lower phase, is added to the first tube. The apparatus is rocked, moving all the tubes back and forth from the equilibration (1) to the settling (2) positions until equilibrium is attained. The rocking is stopped with the tubes in the settling position (2). After the two layers have separated, the tubes are turned to the decantation position (3), where the upper phase runs through the cross arm into the decantation portion of the tube. The next time the apparatus is tipped into the equilibration position (1), this liquid will run up the transfer tube into the next tube

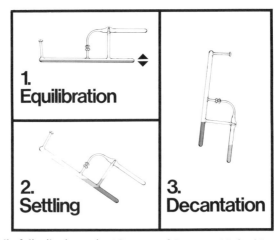

1.
Equilibration

2.
Settling

3.
Decantation

Fig. 6–7. Cell of distribution train. (*Courtesy of Spectrum Medical Instruments, Inc.*)

of the apparatus. At the same time, fresh, less-dense solvent will enter the first tube of the apparatus from the solvent reservoir.

Each tube in the apparatus may be joined to its neighbors by means of spring clamps, or the tubes can be obtained already blown together in units of ten. Equipment containing from ten to a thousand tubes can be obtained easily. An increase in the number of transfers enables better separations to be effected. The larger units usually operate automatically. With automatic operation, mixtures with β values as low as 1.2 can be separated, although a β value of 2 or 3 or better is the usual case. In most mixtures, one does not have an ideal value for a β for all of the pairs of components in the complex mixture, thus some components are easily separated from the others and some components are not. These latter unresolved pairs of components can be run through the apparatus a second or third time to separate them.

Countercurrent distribution can be a very powerful tool in effecting separations. Because of the cost and complexity of the required equipment and its operation, the amounts of solute and solvent required, and the length of time involved, the method has been replaced by chromatography in recent years. It is still the separation method of choice, however, for compounds that will interact with chromatographic column supports, because it is a very mild technique.

CLASSIFICATION OF EXTRACTION SYSTEMS

In order for a solute to be extracted from one phase into another, there must be a net decrease in the energy of the solute when it passes into the extracting phase. If, as is the case in water, the solute is strongly solvated in the initial phase, the solvation energy must be overcome, in order to transfer the solute to the second phase. In aqueous solutions the hydration energy of the solutes is quite high. In order to extract a solute from water into an organic solvent, this hydration energy can be overcome by chemical bond formation, ion-pair formation, organic phase solvation, or by some combination of these. To a certain extent, the means by which the hydration energy of the solute in the aqueous phase is overcome, establishes a general classification of extraction systems. The most important feature of any extraction system is that the species which crosses the boundary from one liquid into the second must be electrically neutral. Charged particles cannot be extracted, only neutral atoms, molecules, or ion pairs. Thus the mechanism by which the neutral species is formed from ions in aqueous systems enables the classification of extraction systems.

When the solute in the aqueous phase is an atom or nonpolar molecule it is not hydrated to any appreciable extent, so there is sufficient energy released by solvation in the organic phase to permit extraction. Such systems are the simple, nonsolvated solute, or ideal systems.

When the solute is a strongly hydrated species such as a metal ion, in order to extract it the hydration energy may be overcome by that energy released through chemical bond formation, that is, the ion is reacted to form a molecular species. The most widespread and convenient way of doing this is to form a complex ion. Hence, the enormous field of metal chelate extraction systems.

In the case of larger ions, hydration is weaker so that it is possible to form an extractable species without actual bond formation. The distinguishing feature of this class is that the species that crosses the phase boundary is not a molecule, but an ion pair. Ion-association extraction systems have subgroupings that include simple complex ion formation followed by ion-pair extraction, chelation followed by ion-pair extraction, and organic phase solvation accompanying the ion-pair extraction.

When the solvation energy between the solute and the organic solvent is greater than that between the solute and water, then a net decrease in energy results upon extraction due to the differences in solvation. Thus, the last major category is solutes that are solvated by the organic solvent. This organic phase solvation may include a total or only a partial replacement of the waters of hydration. It may also be accompanied by chelate or ion-pair formation.

The boundaries between these four categories of extraction systems are not at all clean-cut, so that if one feels obligated to place a given extraction system into a particular category it can be a highly arbitrary or exceedingly difficult chore. Many of these phenomena occur simultaneously within any extraction system, so that classification becomes a question of determining the primary mechanism of extraction. This whole problem can be avoided if the insistence upon categorization is dropped. The discussion that follows is designed to give some idea about the similarities and differences among the kinds of forces, species, reactions, problems involved in the extraction of different classes of solutes, and is not intended to be a rigid classification of the extraction systems.

Extraction of Nonsolvated Solutes

In general, nonsolvated solutes are atoms or covalent molecules that do not have large dipoles so that there is very little, if any, solvent interaction in either solvent. Consequently, these species are extracted with no molecules of solvent accompanying them across the phase boundary. The distribution behavior of nonsolvated solutes is ideal thermodynamically, describable by the simple partition law or a slight modification of it. The concomitant equilibria that exist in the system are known and straightforward. The rare gases, mercury, $HgCl_2$, HgI_2, SbI_3, $AsCl_3$, $GeCl_4$, and $InCl_3$ are typical examples of nonsolvated solutes. The solvents in the systems used differ widely in dielectric constant and are essentially immiscible, for example, water–benzene, water–carbon tetrachloride, water–toluene, and water–chloroform. Separation of mixtures of these solutes by extraction is difficult, since the distribution behavior of each solute is not very different from that of the others. For example, the partition coefficients of the inert gases between water and nitromethane are: He—5.5; Ne—6; Ar—12; and Kr—19. Extraction can be used, however, to remove these solutes from other materials that do not extract. Often for these systems no variables exist to be altered other than the identity of the extracting solvent. Changing solvents may not provide any improvement in the separation possibilities. For example, the partition coefficient of radon has been found to be 59 between water and carbon tetrachloride, 56 between water and chloroform, 80 between water and hexane, and 37 between water and methyl isobutyl ketone. Thus, there is only a factor of two in the spread between the hydrocarbon and ketone solvents. Changes in partition coefficients can be surprisingly different, however.

The partition coefficient for mercury atoms between water and the closely related hydrocarbon solvents, n-hexane and cyclohexane is 20.8 and 32.2, respectively.

Examples of solutes within this category involved in attendant equilibria are the weak acids and bases, complex molecules, and materials, such as $AlCl_3$, that will polymerize in the organic phase. The existence of these secondary equilibria provides a greater opportunity for the separation of mixtures than was available in the cases cited before. The classic example of such systems is the distribution of carboxylic acids between water and an organic liquid. In the organic phase most of these acids dimerize, whereas in the aqueous phase they will ionize. The equilibria that exist in these systems may be diagrammed as follows:

$$2R—COOH \overset{K_{ass}}{\rightleftharpoons} (R—COOH)_2$$

$$K_D \Big\updownarrow \underline{\hspace{7cm}} \quad \text{organic phase}$$
$$\text{aqueous phase}$$

$$R—COOH \underset{K_a}{\rightleftharpoons} R—COO^- + H^+$$

Equation (6–10) was derived in Chapter 5:

$$D = \frac{K_D(1 + 2K_{ass}K_D[HA]_0)}{1 + \dfrac{K_a}{[H^+]}} \tag{6–10}$$

for a monobasic acid that forms only a dimer in the organic phase. Thus, for carboxylic acids, in addition to changing the solvents, which will change K_D, K_{ass}, and $[HA]_0$, the pH of the aqueous phase and the amount of the weak acid in the system will change the value of D. All these variables can be utilized in attempting to separate mixtures. For the distribution of acetic acid between water and carbon tetrachloride, $K_D = 3.20 \times 10^{-3}$ and $K_{ass} = 5.92 \times 10^2$, while for propionic acid, K_D is 1.51×10^{-2} and $K_{ass} = 9.40 \times 10^2$. Since the acid dissociation constants for these two acids are 1.80×10^{-5} and 1.34×10^{-5}, respectively, it can be seen quite readily that the differences in extraction behavior between these two acids will be quite slight. Even with the added dividend of equilibria in excess of the distribution equilibrium, an extraction separation of such closely related compounds is exceedingly difficult. For example, for 0.0500 M solutions of both of the above acids at pH 3.0, the D values are 3.74×10^{-3} for acetic acid and 3.62×10^{-2} for propionic acid. Upon lowering the pH to 1.0, the values of D only change to 3.80×10^{-3} and 3.60×10^{-2}, respectively. Not a very helpful change.

The distribution of 8-hydroxyquinoline, C_9H_6NOH, between water and chloroform can be used as an example of the distribution of a dibasic acid. 8-Hydroxyquinoline (oxine, HOx) is a white solid with a water solubility of 3.6×10^{-3} M at 25°C, and is readily soluble in ethanol, chloroform, benzene, and other solvents. The formula of the neutral molecule is:

The proton from the hydroxyl group will dissociate in alkaline solution:

$$K_{a_2} = \frac{[H^+][Ox^-]}{[HOx]}$$
$$= 1.55 \times 10^{-10}$$

In acid solution the nitrogen in the ring will protonate:

$$+ \quad H^+ \quad K_{a_1} = \frac{[H^+][HOx]}{[H_2Ox^+]}$$
$$= 1.23 \times 10^{-5}$$

The neutral, monoprotonated form of the molecule predominates throughout most of the pH range. The neutral species is the form that is extracted into organic solvents, such as chloroform:

$$\underbrace{HOx}_{} \quad \overset{K_D}{\Updownarrow} \quad \underbrace{}_{} \quad \begin{array}{c} CHCl_3 \\ \hline H_2O \end{array}$$

$$\underset{K_{a_1}}{H_2Ox^+ \rightleftharpoons H^+ + HOx} \underset{K_{a_2}}{\rightleftharpoons Ox^- + H^+}$$

The expression for the distribution ratio for oxine can be written as:

$$D = \frac{C_{HOxCHCl_3}}{C_{HOxH_2O}} = \frac{[HOx]_{CHCl_3}}{[H_2Ox^+]_{aq} + [HOx]_{aq} + [Ox^-]_{aq}}$$

$$= \frac{[H^+]K_{a_1}K_D}{[H^+]^2 + [H^+]K_{a_1} + K_{a_1}K_{a_2}} \qquad (6\text{–}11)$$

where K_D is reported to be 205.[31]

Fig. 6–8 is a graph of the distribution ratio of oxine and the percent oxine

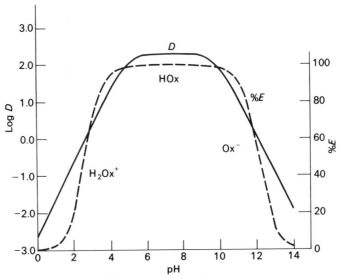

Fig. 6–8. Variation in D and $\%E$ with pH for 8-hydroxyquinoline for H_2O–$CHCl_3$.

extracted into chloroform as a function of the aqueous phase pH. At low pH values (1–2.5) the charged, doubly protonated species of oxine is the predominant form. The concentration of the neutral molecule is low and, consequently, the distribution ratio is low and very little oxine is extracted into chloroform. From pH 2.5 to about 12 where the neutral oxine molecule predominates in solution, the extraction of oxine is excellent, being essentially 100% between pH 5 and pH 10. Above pH 12 the singly charged, completely deprotonated species predominates. The neutral molecule concentration and, consequently the distribution ratio, decreases again. It is found experimentally, and it can be shown by substitution of pH values into Equation (6–11) that the maximum value of D occurs when pH $=$ $\frac{1}{2}(pK_{a_1} + pK_{a_2})$. This verifies the statement that only the neutral oxine molecule is extracted into chloroform, for this species has its maximum concentration when $K_D = D$.

The diprotonated form of the usual dibasic acid, such as succinic, malonic, or oxalic, is uncharged, so it is extracted. For common dibasic acids, Equation (6–11) is not valid. Equation (6–12) must be used instead:

$$D = \frac{[H^+]^2 K_D}{[H^+]^2 + [H^+]K_{a_1} + K_{a_1} K_{a_2}} \qquad (6\text{–}12)$$

Weak bases, such as the amines, do not polymerize in the organic phase, so that their equilibria in extraction is simpler:

$$
\begin{array}{c}
R\text{—}NH_2 \\
{\scriptstyle K_D} \updownarrow \qquad\qquad\qquad\qquad\qquad \text{organic} \\
\overline{H_2O + R\text{—}NH_2 \rightleftharpoons R\text{—}NH_3^+ + OH^-} \\
\qquad\qquad {\scriptstyle K_b}
\end{array}
$$

The expression for D for weak bases is given by Equation (6–13):

$$D = \frac{[R\text{—}NH_2]_0}{[R\text{—}NH_2] + [R\text{—}NH_3^+]} = \frac{K_D}{1 + \dfrac{K_b[H^+]}{K_w}} \qquad (6\text{–}13)$$

Ammonia has a partition coefficient of 473 between chloroform and water, so that it has a D of 0.262 at a pH of 6, and one of 404 at a pH of 10. Thus in the case of weak bases, just as in the case of weak acids, the fraction of the base present as the extractable neutral molecule can be changed by changing the pH of the aqueous phase.

One of the earliest and most thoroughly studied extraction systems is the extraction of iodine into various organic liquids. From the material in Chapter 5, the distribution ratio for iodine between aqueous iodide ion solutions and organic liquids is:

$$D = \frac{[I_2]_0}{[I_2]_{aq} + [I_3^-]_{aq}} = \frac{K_D}{1 + K_{st}[I^-]} \qquad (6\text{–}14)$$

Thus, complexation can be used to manipulate D to favorable values.

Extraction of Metal Chelates

When an aqueous solution of a metal ion is shaken with an immiscible organic solution of a chelating agent, the following overall extraction equilibrium will occur:

$$M^{n+} + n(HX)_0 \rightleftharpoons (MX_n)_0 + nH^+$$

For example, the extraction of an aqueous solution of copper ions with a chloroform solution of 8-hydroxyquinoline, forms the copper oxine chelate which is extracted into the chloroform, and the protons released increase the acidity of the aqueous phase.

The equilibrium constant expression for the general reaction can be written:

$$K = \frac{[(MX_n)]_{org}[H^+]^n}{[M^{n+}][(HX)]^n_{org}} \tag{6-15}$$

where the equilibrium constant, K, in this case is called the *extraction constant*.

If one assumes that: (1) there are no metal hydroxy species (MOH) formed in the aqueous phase; (2) there is only one species of chelate containing the metal ion in the aqueous phase; (3) the concentration of that species of metal chelate is exceedingly low in the aqueous phase; (4) no auxiliary complexing agents, such as ammonia, are present in the system; and (5) the metal chelate does not polymerize in the organic phase, then the expression for the distribution ratio of the metal ion can be written as:

$$D = \frac{C_{M_{org}}}{C_{M_{aq}}} = \frac{[MX_n]_{org}}{[M^{n+}]_{aq}} \tag{6-16}$$

Substituting Equation (6–16) into Equation (6–15) gives:

$$K = D\frac{[H^+]^n}{[HX]^n_{org}} \quad \text{or} \quad D = K\frac{[HX]^n_{org}}{[H^+]^n} \tag{6-17}$$

Comparison of Equation (6–17) with Equation (5–106):

$$D = \frac{K_{D_{MX}}K_{st}K_a^n[HX]^n_{org}}{K^n_{D_{HX}}[H^+]^n} \tag{5-106}$$

reveals that the extraction constant as defined in Equation (6–15) is a compilation of other equilibrium constants and is equal to:

$$K = \frac{K_{D_{MX}}K_{st}K_a^n}{K^n_{D_{HX}}} \tag{6-18}$$

From Fig. 6–1, Equation (6–3), and Equation (6–17) it can be seen quite clearly that as the value of the distribution ratio increases, so does the percentage of the metal ion that is extracted by the organic solution of the chelating agent. Examination of Equations (6–17), (5–106), and (6–18) will show what experimental factors in these systems can be altered to change the value of the distribution ratio to aid in separating a mixture of metal ions.

Concentration of the Metal Ion

The concentration of the metal ion being extracted does not appear in Equation (5–106) nor in Equation (6–17). So long as this metal ion concentration lies below the solubility of MX_n in water, below the solubility of MX_n in the organic liquid, and low enough so that there is sufficient ligand (HX) present in the system to complex all of the metal ion, the actual concentration of the metal ion does not have any effect on the percent extracted. The percent of a $0.00010\ M$ copper ion solution extracted under identical conditions with oxine in chloroform will be exactly the same as the percent of a $0.025\ M$ copper ion solution extracted.

Nature of the Metal Extracted

The values of both K_{DMX} and K_{st} are determined by the forces between a specific metal ion, solvent molecules, and chelating agents. Hence, both of these constants will be different for different metal ions. The way in which the distribution ratio is changed when substituting one metal ion for another can be calculated from the ratio of the partition coefficients and stability constants for two different metals M_1 and M_2.

$$\frac{D_1}{D_2} = \frac{K_{DM_1} \times K_{st_1}}{K_{DM_2} \times K_{st_2}} \tag{6–19}$$

No generalizations can be made about the nature of the change in D when going from one metal ion to a second. Both K_D and K_{st} can vary in either direction and in magnitude quite independently of one another. The result of this is that the ratio D_1/D_2 can increase, decrease, or remain constant when substitution of one metal ion for another occurs.

Nature of the Chelating Agent Used

Characteristic of any chelating agent are its acid dissociation constant, K_a, its partition coefficient, K_{DHX}, and the stability constants of its metal chelates, K_{st}. Because of the difference in the interactions between the ions involved in chelate formation, the difference in solvation, and the differences in the chelon molecules, for any particular metal in a specified solvent system at constant pH and chelon concentration, the value of the distribution ratio will change when substituting one chelon for another. Table 6–2 gives the values of the constants for 8-hydroxyquinoline, 2-methoxy-8-hydroxyquinoline, and 4-methoxy-8-hydroxyquinoline.

Even though these reagents are quite closely related there are significant differences among the constants. Notice that while K_{DHR} and K_{DMR_2} increase in going from oxine to 2-methyl oxine, K_{st} decreases. K_{DHR} increases in going from

Table 6–2. CONSTANTS OF 8-HYDROXYQUINOLINES AND THEIR COPPER CHELATES
IN THE SYSTEM WATER–CHLOROFORM

Chelon	$pK_a{}^a$	$K_{DHR}{}^b$	$K_{DMR_2}{}^b$	Log $K_{st}{}^c$
Oxine	3.76, 11.19	433	3.02×10^3	25.90
2-Methyl oxine	5.61, 10.16	1670	2.82×10^5	22.82
4-Methyl oxine	4.67, 11.62	1860	3.63×10^3	26.96

  [a] Data from Ref. 33.
  [b] Data from Ref. 29.
  [c] Data from Ref. 15. Values for log k_{st} determined in 1:1 water:dioxane.

2-methyl oxine to 4-methyl oxine, whereas K_{DMR_2} decreases. As a consequence the change in the value of D cannot be predicted from the change in any one of the constants. The ratio of all of them, to the power of n is necessary:

$$\frac{D_1}{D_2} = \frac{K_{st_1} K_{a_1}^n K_{DHX2}^n K_{DMX1}}{K_{st_2} K_{a_2}^n K_{DHX1}^n K_{DMX2}} \tag{6–20}$$

Table 6–3 lists some of the chelating agents commonly used in extractions and some of their properties.

pH of the Aqueous Phase

The hydrogen ion concentration of the aqueous phase governs the amount of dissociation of the chelon and hence the amount of the anion present in the solution to chelate with the metal ion. A low hydrogen ion concentration will favor dissociation, chelate formation, and extraction. This is shown in Equation (6–17). Thus, in general, a high pH favors metal chelate extractions. The formation of pH-influenced, nonextractable species, such as hydroxy species invalidates this generalization.

The magnitude of the change in percent of extraction with pH depends upon the formula of the metal chelate, since in Equation (6–17) the hydrogen ion concentration is raised to the nth power. Fig. 6–9 shows the effect of pH on the extraction by 0.10 M 8-hydroxyquinoline in chloroform of metal ions with $1+$, $2+$, $3+$, and $4+$ charges.

For a specific metal–chelon–solvent system, with a constant organic phase concentration of chelon, Equation (5–106) can be simplified to:

$$D = K'[H^+]^{n-} \tag{6–21}$$

where $K' = K[HX]_0^n$.

Taking logarithms of both sides of this equation:

$$\log D = \log K' + n\mathrm{pH} \tag{6–22}$$

When the concentration of the metal in the organic phase is the same as the concentration of the metal in the aqueous phase, that is, when $D = 1$, or when fifty

Table 6–3.   PROPERTIES OF SOME SELECTED CHELATING AGENTS USED IN EXTRACTION

Chelon	Molecular weight	Physical form at room temperature	pK_a	K_D	Solvent
Acetylacetone	100.11	Colorless liquid	8.94	3.3	CCl_4
				5.8	C_6H_6
				25	$CHCl_3$
Benzoylacetone	162.18	White solid	8.7	660	CCl_4
				1150	C_6H_6
				2500	$CHCl_3$
Thenoyltrifluoro-acetone (TTA)	222.2	Yellow solid	6.23	40	C_6H_6
8-Hydroxyquinoline (HOx)	145.15	Colorless solid	(1) 4.91	206	$CHCl_3$
			(2) 9.81	400	C_6H_6
8-Hydroxyquinaldine	159.17	Colorless solid	(1) 5.77	6000	$CHCl_3$
			(2)10.04		
Dimethylglyoxime	116.12	White solid	10.6	12.0	n-BuOH
				0.080	$CHCl_3$
1-Nitroso-2-naphthol	173.16	Orange-brown solid	7.63	934	$CHCl_3$
				355	MIBK
Cupferron	155.16	Buff solid	4.16	151	$CHCl_3$
				96.9	MIBK
				2190	CCl_4
1-(2-Pyridylazo)-2-naphthol (PAN)	248.26	Orange-red solid	(1) 2.9	10,000	CCl_4
			(2)11.2	2.5×10^5	$CHCl_3$
Dithizone	256.3	Violet-black solid	4.46	1.1×10^4	CCl_4
				2×10^5	$CHCl_3$
Diethyldithio-carbamic acid	149.25	White solid	3.35	343	CCl_4
				2360	$CHCl_3$
Salicylic acid	138.12	White solid	2.82	3	$CHCl_3$
				320	MIBK

SOURCE: Refs. 33–38.

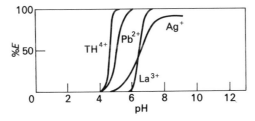

Fig. 6–9.   Effect of pH on the extraction of monovalent (Ag^+), bivalent (Pb^{2+}), tervalent (La^{3+}) and tetravalent (Th^{4+}) metal ions by 0.10 M 8-hydroxyquinoline in chloroform (*Redrawn from Ref. 35, by permission of Pergamon Press, Ltd.*)

percent of the metal ion is extracted, then log D in Equation (6–22) is zero. The pH of the solution at this point is called the pH one-half (pH$_\frac{1}{2}$) and is a constant, characteristic of the system under investigation:

$$\text{pH}_\frac{1}{2} = -\frac{\log K'}{n} \qquad (6\text{–}23)$$

For a specific chelon dissolved in an organic solvent, each metal that is extracted by it will have a different pH$_\frac{1}{2}$, since K' includes K_{st} and K_{DMX}. Thus, if a plot is made of the percent metal extracted vs. aqueous pH, a sigmoidal curve will be obtained (see Fig. 6–9). The position of this curve on the pH axis will be determined by the value of K' in Equation (6–22) and the slope of the linear portion will be determined by n (see Fig. 6–9). From such curves it is very obvious where the pH$_\frac{1}{2}$ value lies. Consequently, the determination of the pH$_\frac{1}{2}$ values for a series of metals under analogous conditions enables one to determine readily which extraction separations are feasible and which are not.

The effect of the change of the pH of the solution by one unit on the percent of metal extracted will depend upon the formula of the metal chelate, as Fig. 6–9 clearly shows. When $n = 1$ (that is, MX) an increase in the pH by one unit will cause a tenfold increase in the value of D. When $n = 2$ (MX$_2$), one pH unit increase will cause an increase in D by a factor of 100, and when $n = 3$ (MX$_3$), one pH unit increase will cause a thousandfold increase in the value of D.

The preceding discussion has neglected the formation of any hydroxy complexes such as MOH$^{(n-1)+}$ or MOHX that might form, or the precipitation of a a metal hydroxide that might begin to occur as the pH of the solution is raised. In actuality these cannot be overlooked. For metal hydroxy species, the pH at which fifty percent of the metal ion exists as the monohydroxy complex ([M^{n+}] = [MOH$^{(n-1)+}$] for various metals is: iron(III), 3.1; lead(II), 7.8; copper (II), 7.9; iron(II), 9.5; zinc(II), 9.6; cadmium(II), 10.2; silver(I), 10.2; and calcium(II), 13.6. For these same metals the pH at which the metal hydroxide precipitate just begins to form in a 0.001 M solution is: iron(III), 2.15; lead(II), 8.04; copper(II), 5.67; iron(II), 8.17; zinc(II), 7.15; cadmium(II), 8.54; silver(I), 9.28; and calcium(II), 8.36. When these hydroxy species begin to form, the value of D begins to decrease. When the hydroxy species are sufficiently stable by comparison to the metal chelate, they compete successfully for the metal ions present in the solution. When this occurs, then the value of D will fall below 100 and the percent extraction begins to be less than 100%. Fig. 6–10 shows the decrease in the percent E at high pH values for the extraction of nickel and of cadmium with 0.100 M oxine in chloroform. Metal hydroxy species begin to predominate above a pH of 9 in both systems.

The Concentration of the Chelon in the Organic Phase

The amount of any chelon that can be dissolved in the organic liquid is limited by its solubility. For most chelating agents, however, this is fairly high (8-hydroxyquinoline is soluble to the limit of 2.6 M in chloroform). Up to the solubility limit, the value of D will increase as the concentration of chelon increases, at constant aqueous phase pH. This is clearly seen in Equation (6–17). Fig. 6–11 shows the extraction curves for the extraction of manganese with 8-

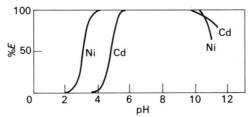

Fig. 6–10.   Effect of pH on the extraction of nickel and cadmium by 0.10 M 8-hydroxyquinoline in chloroform. (*Redrawn from Ref. 38, by permission of Pergamon Press, Ltd.*)

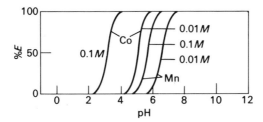

Fig. 6–11.   Effect of pH on the extraction of cobalt(II) and manganese(II) by 8-hydroxyquinoline in chloroform. (*Redrawn from Ref. 36, by permission of Pergamon Press, Ltd.*)

hydroxyquinoline in chloroform at concentrations of 0.1 and 0.01 M. The $pH_{\frac{1}{2}}$ value for manganese shifts from 6.66 to 5.66 as the concentration of the chelon increases. This shift to lower pH values with increasing chelon concentrations can be used to advantage in the extraction of metals that hydrolyze at relatively low pH values. An increase in the chelon concentration enables the extraction to be carried out at a pH low enough to prevent the hydrolysis.

Frequently the chelon will form an adduct with the metal chelate, $MX_n(HX)_r$, that is extractable. When adduct formation occurs an increase in the chelon concentration will have a greater effect than that predicted by Equation (6–17), since the dependency upon chelon concentration is now $(n + r)$ instead of just n. Cobalt oxinate and 8-hydroxyquinoline form such an adduct with the formula $Co(Ox)_2 \cdot (HOx)_2$. In the case of cobalt, increasing the oxine concentration in the chloroform phase from 0.01 M to 0.10 M causes a decrease in the $pH_{\frac{1}{2}}$ of more than one unit, namely, from 5.08 to 3.21 (see Fig. 6–11).

Solubility of the Chelate in the Organic Phase

The more soluble the metal chelate is in the organic liquid, the larger the value of K_{DMX}, other factors remaining constant during this change. Thus the value of D and the percent of the metal extracted will increase with increasing solubility in the organic liquid. Other factors, however, are not likely to remain constant with the major change occurring in the solubility of the chelon in the organic liquid. Thus K_{DHX} will be changing at the same time that K_{DMX} is changing. This change for the

8-hydroxyquinolines is shown clearly in Table 6–2. Thus, in evaluating two solvents to decide which one would be better for the extraction of a metal ion with a particular chelon, one must consider both the partition coefficient of the chelon and that of the metal chelate in order to arrive at a more realistic decision. In Equation (5–106) not only is the dependence of D upon K_{DHX} an inverse one, it is also raised to the power of n. Thus the change in the distribution ratio when substituting one solvent for another is:

$$\frac{D_2}{D_1} = \frac{K_{D_2MX} K_{D_1HX}^n}{K_{D_1MX} K_{D_2HX}^n} \tag{6–24}$$

When both the chelate formed and the chelon are more soluble in the second solvent than they are in the first solvent, and this increased solubility is approximately the same, a higher value for D for the metal chelate will be obtained when using solvent 1 than when using solvent 2. This is only true when n is greater than 1 because of the exponential relationship of K_{DHX}.

Mottola and Freiser[29] have studied the effect of different solvents on the extraction of 8-hydroxyquinolines and of their copper chelates. They compare the solvents on the basis of solvent polarity and dielectric constant and their interactions based upon the polarity and solubility of the various solutes. They report K_{DHX} for oxine to be 116 in carbon tetrachloride and 433 in chloroform. K_{DMX} for copper oxinate is reported as 112 in carbon tetrachloride and 3020 in chloroform. Substituting these values in Equation (6–24) gives $D_{CHCl_3}/D_{CCl_4} = 1.19$, even though the metal chelate is 27 times more soluble in chloroform than it is in carbon tetrachloride. In toluene, K_{DHX} is 162 for oxine and K_{DMX} for the copper oxinate is 181. The increase in both of these partition coefficients over their values in carbon tetrachloride is essentially the same, as was the condition stated before. In this case $D_{tol}/D_{CCl_4} = 0.82$, confirming the prediction that the extraction would be poorer in the solvent in which both chelon and metal chelate are more soluble by about the same amount.

Solubility of the Chelating Agent in Water

The more soluble the chelon is in the aqueous phase, the higher will be its concentration there, when starting with the same initial amount in the organic phase. Thus there will be more chelon anions available for chelate formation, and more chelate will form, so that more metal ion will be extracted. This is borne out by Equation (5–106) where the value of D increases as the value of K_{DHX} is lowered.

Acid Strength of the Chelating Agent

As the strength of the chelon as an acid increases, other factors being held constant, the value of D, and hence the percent metal extracted will increase. Since the relationship between K_a and D is an exponential one [see Equation (5–106)], acid strength can play a large role in selection of a chelon to use for a particular metal ion extraction. Table 6–2 shows that since 2-methyl-8-hydroxyquinoline has a larger value for K_{a_2} than does 4-methyl-8-hydroxyquinoline, it should give larger values of D. A second advantage that a chelon with a relatively high dissociation constant has over others, is that it can be used in more acidic solutions than chelons with lower K_a values.

Stability of the Metal Chelate

The larger the value of the stability constant, K_{st}, of the metal chelate, the greater the percent of the metal extracted at a constant pH, other factors remaining unchanged. Conversely, the pH at which a certain percentage of the metal will be extracted will be lower, the more stable the complex is.

Temperature

Although temperature is not a factor explicitly included in the mathematical relationship of Equation (5–106), it does affect the percent of metal ion that is extracted. All of the constants in the expression for D are temperature dependent. The combined effect of their temperature dependencies gives the temperature dependency of D. Whether D increases or decreases with temperature depends upon the sign and magnitude of the temperature coefficient of each constant. Hellweg and Schweitzer[16] studies the effect of temperature on the extraction of cadmium with 0.10 M 8-hydroxyquinoline in chloroform. They report that K in Equation (6–18) decreased from 4×10^{-5} at $0°C$ to 2×10^{-7} at $50°C$, and that the $pH_{\frac{1}{2}}$ for the extraction of cadmium increased as a result of this from 4.2 at $0°C$ to 5.8 at $50°C$. Over the temperature range $0–50°C$, K_{DHX} decreased slightly from 5×10^2 to 3×10^2, K_{a_2} increased from 1.2×10^{-10} to 3.2×10^{-10}, where K_{DMX_2} decreased appreciably from 9.5×10^4 to 1.0×10^3

The Effect of the Presence of Masking Agents

When a masking agent such as oxalate, cyanide, ammonia, tartrate, nitrilo-triacetic acid, or ethylenediaminetetraacetic acid is present in the aqueous phase to complex the metal ion, the extracting chelon must compete with it for the metal ion, which lowers the value of D. Thus, at the same pH and chelon concentration the percent of the metal, that is extracted is decreased in the presence of a masking agent. This decrease should not be surprising since a masking agent lowers the concentration of free metal ions available to react with the chelon and be extracted by it.

A second consequence of the presence of a masking agent in the solution is the shift of the % E–pH curve to higher pH values. The magnitude of this pH shift depends upon the strength of the metal-masking agent complexes and the concentration of the masking agent present.

Fig. 6–12 is the %E–pH curve for the extraction of copper with 0.01 M 8-hydroxyquinoline in chloroform in the presence of oxalate, tartrate, cyanide, NTA, and EDTA. From Fig. 6–12 it is clearly seen that at a pH of 4.0 in the absence of any masking agents, copper will be 100% extracted. In the presence of oxalic acid or NTA copper is only about 75% extracted at this pH, and it is essentially un-extracted in the presence of cyanide, EDTA or DCyTA. Tartaric acid is a weaker acid than oxalic acid, so that at a pH of 4.0 it will furnish fewer tartrate ions. The copper tartrate complexes are weaker than those with oxalate. Thus, one would

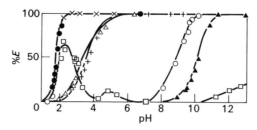

Fig. 6–12. Effect of pH on the extraction of copper(II) by 0.01 M 8-hydroxyquinoline in chloroform; ● in the absence of complexing agent, △ in the presence of 0.1 M oxalic acid, × in the presence of 0.01 M tartaric acid, □ in the presence of 0.01 M hydrocyanic acid, + in the presence of 0.01 M nitrilotriacetic acid, ○ in the presence of 0.01 M ethylenediaminetetraacetic acid, and ▲ in the presence of 1,2-diaminocyclohexanetetraacetic acid. (*Redrawn from Ref. 37, by permission of Pergamon Press, Ltd.*)

expect a greater percentage of the copper to be extracted at a pH of 4.0 from a tartrate solution than from an oxalate solution. Fig. 6–12 confirms this, in fact in the presence of tartrate essentially 100% of the copper is extracted at a pH of 4.0. The shift of the percent extracted curves to higher pH values occurs in the order: tartrate, oxalate, NTA, EDTA, DCyTA, and cyanide. This is the order of increasing strength of the copper complexes with these masking agents. The peak in the cyanide curve at about pH 2 occurs because at low pH values the very weak hydrocyanic acid ($pK_a = 9.14$) has not ionized sufficiently to provide enough cyanide ions to interfere substantially with the extraction process. Up to the pH of this maximum the copper–oxine species predominates, but above it the copper–cyano complexes begin to outnumber them.

Table 6–4 gives data ($pH_{\frac{1}{2}}$ and log K values) for the extraction of some metals with selected chelons.

Separation of Metal Ions by Extraction as Their Metal Chelates

When a solution containing two or more metal ions is extracted with an organic solution of a chelon, the metal ions may be selectively extracted if there is a large enough difference in their extraction constants, K, or their $pH_{\frac{1}{2}}$ values. The separation of two metal ions may be defined as being achieved when 99% of the extracted one is obtained with only 1% of the unextracted one present as an impurity.

For a single batch extraction, in order to achieve this separation the difference in $pH_{\frac{1}{2}}$ values between the two metal ions must be 4 when $n = 1$. When $n = 2$, a difference of only 2 pH units will suffice and for $n = 3$, a difference of 1.3 pH units is enough to enable their separation. Thus from the $pH_{\frac{1}{2}}$ values for a series of metals under analogous conditions, it is possible to determine fairly simply when a separation of two or more metal ions is feasible.

From Equation (5–106), for two metal ions under identical experimental

Table 6–4. EXTRACTION DATA FOR METAL IONS WITH SELECTED CHELATING AGENTS

Metal Ion	Acetylacetone[a]		Thenoyltrifluoroacetone[b]		8-Hydroxyquinoline[c]		Cupferron[d]		Dithizone[e]	
	log K	pH½	log K	pH½	log K	pH½	log K	pH½	log K	pH½
Ag(I)	No extraction				−4.51	6.51	Insoluble		7.18	−3.12
Al(III)	−6.48	3.30	−5.23	2.48	−522	2.87	−3.50	2.51	No extraction	
Ba(II)	No extraction		−14.4	8.0	Partial extraction*		No extraction		No extraction	
Be(II)	−2.79	2.45	−3.2	2.33	−9.62	5.81	−1.52	2.07	No extraction	
Bi(III)	No extraction		−3.21	1.80	−1.2	2.13	5.07	−0.4	9.98	0.7
Ca(II)	No extraction		−12.0	6.7	−17.89	10.38	No extraction		No extraction	
Cd(II)	No extraction		−11.4f	6.7f	−5.29	4.65	Insoluble		2.14	2.9
Co(II)	No extraction		−6.7	4.1	−2.16	3.21	−3.56	3.18	1.53	3.2
Cu(II)	−3.93	2.90	−1.32	1.38	1.77	1.51	2.66	0.03	10.53	−1.3
Fe(III)	−1.39	1.60	3.3	−0.24	4.11	1.00	9.8	−2.0	No extraction	
Ga(III)	−5.51	2.90	−7.57	3.26	3.72	1.07	4.92	−0.3	−1.3	3.6
Hg(II)	Partial extraction*		−4.34	2.20	Partial extraction*		0.91	0.85	26.85	−9.4
In(III)	−7.20	3.95	No extraction		0.89	1.54	2.42	0.50	4.84	2.4
Mg(II)	No extraction		No extraction		−15.13	9.61	No extraction		No extraction	
Ni(II)	No extraction			3.8g	−2.18	2.38	Partial extraction		1.18	3.4
Pb(II)	−10.15	6.2	−5.2	3.34	−8.04	5.04	−1.53	2.06	0.44	3.8
Sr(II)	No extraction		−14.1	7.8	−19.71	12.06	No extraction		No extraction	
Th(IV)	−12.16	4.10	0.8	0.48	−7.18	2.91	4.4	0.25	No extraction	
U(VI)			−2.26	1.79	−1.60	2.60			No extraction	
Zn(II)					−2.41	3.30	Partial extraction*		2.3	2.8

SOURCE: Ref. 34.

a 0.10 M acetylacetone in benzene.
b 0.20 M thenoyltrifluoroacetone in benzene.
c 0.10 M 8-hydroxyquinoline in chloroform.
d 0.05 M cupferron in chloroform.
e 0.0001 M dithizone in carbon tetrachloride.
f 0.10 M in chloroform.
g In 15:5 acetone:benzene.
* About 50%.

conditions of pH and chelon concentration and with identical n values, it follows that:

$$\beta = \frac{D_1}{D_2} = \frac{K_{st_1} K_{D_{M_1X}}}{K_{st_2} K_{D_{M_2X}}} \tag{6-25}$$

since all other terms will be identical and cancel out. To see whether or not a separation is feasible, a quick calculation can be made from the available stability constants and partition coefficients (or from the values of K).

Example. Can a solution containing both copper and lead ions be separated into its components by a single batch extraction with 0.10 M oxine in chloroform?

From Table 6–4 it can be seen that K for copper oxinate is 5.9×10^1 and K for lead oxinate is 9.1×10^{-9}.

$$\frac{D_{Cu}}{D_{Pb}} = \frac{K_{Cu}}{K_{Pb}} = \frac{5.9 \times 10^1}{9.1 \times 10^{-9}} = 6.5 \times 10^9$$

This does not tell the entire story, however, for the pH also has to be adjusted to a value sufficiently high to extract a large percentage of the copper with a single batch process, and yet none of the lead. In this example, calculations using Equation (6–17) show that these conditions are fulfilled between a pH of 2.51 and 4.40. Below pH 1.5 copper is less than 1.0% extracted, and above pH 6.0 both copper and lead are 100% extracted.

As can be seen from Equation (6–25), D_1/D_2 is independent of pH. Thus, when the values of n for the two chelates are the same, changing the pH of the solution will have no effect on the separation possibilities. When the value of n for the two chelates is different, pH changes will alter the value of D_1/D_2 and may be an effective means of obtaining a separation.

While most separations are based on pH changes, in the case where n differs for two metal chelates, changes in the concentration of the chelon can also be used to advantage. For example, at a given pH, extraction with 0.01 M chelon may remove one metal and none of a second. A second extraction of the solution with 0.10 M chelon this time, at the same pH can be used to remove a second metal from the solution. Often this particular technique has no advantage over a straightforward pH change, but in some cases, especially with adduct formation, it is the only way a separation can be achieved.

An excellent and widely used technique for effecting separations is the addition of a second complexing agent (masking agent) to the aqueous phase to alter the values of D. A masking agent is selected that will form nonextractable complexes of different stabilities with the two metal ions. In order for a masking agent to be effective it must form a more stable complex with the metal that is to remain unextracted than it does with the metal to be extracted. Or alternatively, there must be such a sufficient difference in the relative strengths of the masking agent–metal complexes so as to reverse completely the order of extraction of the metals. Morrison and Freiser[27] list masking agents for each element suitable for use in extractions.

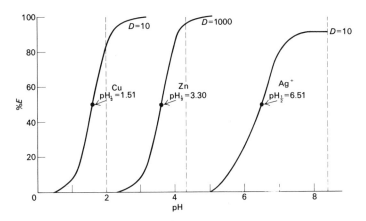

Fig. 6–13. Extraction curves with 0.10 M oxine in CHCl$_3$ for components of silver solder.

While comparison of the pH$_{\frac{1}{2}}$ values and the extraction constants for metals will give a good estimate of what separations are feasible, it is preferable to have the entire extraction curves for the metals in question. Differences in the slope and shape of the curve due to differences in n and in the formation of adducts with the reagent molecule [for example, MX$_n$(HX) and MX$_n$(HX)$_2$] will show up on the complete curves.

As an example of the use of extraction curves, consider the separation of the components of silver solder (63% silver, 30% copper, 7% zinc) by extraction with 0.10 M oxine in chloroform. The extraction curves for each of these metals are shown in Fig. 6–13. From this graph it can be seen that this separation can be accomplished quite easily since the curves are widely spaced. The acid solution of the alloy is buffered first at a pH of 2.0, and extracted with one equal volume of 0.10 M oxine in chloroform. In this single extraction 90.9% of the copper will be removed, but essentially none of the zinc or silver will be. A second extraction with oxine at this pH will bring the total copper extracted to 99.2% and a third will bring it to 99.9% of the copper. None of the other two metals will be extracted appreciably at this pH. The pH of the aqueous phase is now adjusted to 4.5, buffered, and extracted with a fresh equal volume of oxine. In this single extraction, 99.9% of the zinc will be extracted but none of the silver. Thus, at this stage there will be one chloroform solution of Cu(Ox)$_2$, a second chloroform solution containing Zn(Ox)$_2$(HOx)$_2$, and an aqueous solution of silver ion, so that these three metals have been separated. If a chloroform solution of silver is desired, the aqueous solution can be buffered at a pH of 8.5 and extracted with three equal portions of oxine in chloroform. All three of these metals can be determined colorimetrically as their oxinates in the chloroform extracts at wavelengths between 400 and 450 nm.

A second example is the attempted separation of the metals in konel, an alloy which contains nickel, cobalt, iron, titanium, and manganese. Fig. 6–14 shows the

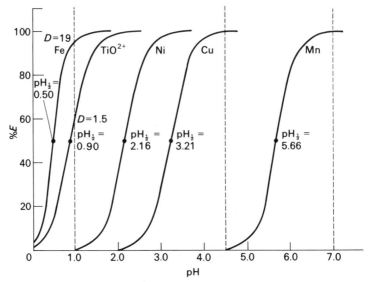

Fig. 6–14.   Extraction curves with 0.10 M oxine in CHCl$_3$ for components in konel alloy.

curves for the extraction of these metals with 0.10 M oxine in chloroform. From this graph it can be seen quite clearly that since their extraction curves are so close together, there is no pH at which iron(III) and titanium(IV) can be separated. Five repeated extractions at a pH of 1.0 will extract a mixture containing 99% of the titanium(IV) and over 99.9% of the iron(III). Likewise, nickel(II) and cobalt(II) cannot be separated from one another because their extraction curves are too close to one another. A single extraction at pH 4.5 will remove both the nickel and the cobalt, leaving only the manganese in the aqueous phase. If it is desirable, the manganese can be extracted into chloroform at a pH of 7.0. Because of the differences in oxidation state between titanium and iron, n will be different for each of these metals, and thus one could consider the change of concentration of the oxine as a possible method of attempting to separate these two metal ions. Nickel and cobalt are very difficult to separate since most of their common complexes have very similar stabilities. Since nickel chelates extract very slowly, whereas cobalt chelates extract readily, kinetic differences may provide a solution to this separation.

Extraction of Ion Pairs

In ion-association extraction systems the species that crosses the interface between water and the organic liquid is not a molecule, as was the case in the previous two categories, but an ion pair. Morrison and Freiser[28] subdivide ion-association extraction systems on the basis of the nature of the equilibrium involved in forming one of the ions of the ion pair. In their *simple-ion association* systems, both ions in the ion pair are simple ions (that is, not complex ions or chelates). This category includes the extraction into nitrobenzene of cesium or rubidium tetraphenylboride; the extraction of metal ions such as iron(III), beryllium, gallium, or indium with benzoate or high molecular weight carboxylic acids into ethyl acetate; and the extraction of HCl, HNO_3, acetic acid and other acids by long-chain amines into chloro- or nitrobenzene. In the *ion association and simple coordination* category, the substance that is to be extracted is converted first into a complex ion, which is then extracted as one of the ions in an ion pair. Examples include the extraction of iron(III) as its chloro complex from acidic solution into ethers and the extraction of iron(III), cobalt(II), tungsten, and molybdenum as their thiocyanate complexes into ethers, alcohols, or ketones. To be assigned to their *ion association and chelation* category the metal must be chelated first, after which this chelate ion is then extracted as one part of the ion pair. Examples include the extraction of the rhodamine B chelates of antimony(V) or gallium into ethyl acetate, the extraction of the phenanthroline chelates of iron and copper into amyl or hexyl alcohols, and the extraction of the 1-nitroso-2-naphthol anionic chelate of cobalt(III) into chloroform.

A feature common to all of these ion-pair extractions is the solute transfer from concentrated solutions of reagents into polar or oxygenated organic solvents, such as alcohols, ethers, or ketones. Ion-pair extraction systems include some of the earliest known extractions and some of the most widely studied systems, yet the behavior of this class of extractions still is not understood thoroughly. In general the behavior of new systems cannot be predicted nor can the behavior of familiar systems be described mathematically. The behavior is infinitely complex and nonideal.

The present inability to describe this class of extraction systems in general mathematical terms, as was done for the weak acids and bases, complexes, and metal chelate systems can be attributed to three major causes:

(1) The physical chemistry of concentrated solutions is not understood. Ion-pair extractions are carried out from solutions that are about 25% in reagent or from 3 to 8 M in strong acid, and frequently contain, in addition, high concentrations of salts. The nature of the interactions between species taking place in these systems is not known in most cases, since the solute–solute and solvent–solute interactions under these conditions of extremely high ionic strength are highly dependent upon the identity of all of the ions present as well as their concentrations. The activity of the extracted ion pair varies not only with increasing ionic strength, but also according to the identity of the salt used to obtain that ionic strength. Theories designed to operate in and to describe dilute (<0.001 M) solutions are no longer applicable in 3 to 10 M solutions. The dielectric constant of aqueous salt solutions is known to decrease with increasing salt concentrations at rates depending upon the identity of the salt. The activity of water also changes in varying ways as the amount of material dissolved in it increases. As a consequence, generalizations that could be made for other systems because they were dilute are no longer capable of being made in ion-pair extraction systems. Each extraction becomes a separate case to be described starting from scratch on the basis of the identity and concentrations of all components of the system.

(2) The chemical reactions taking place in these extraction systems are not known precisely. The exact nature of the chemical species present is not only

unknown but it is extremely variable with slight changes in its chemical environment, and the chemical identity of everything present in ion-pair systems has its effect on the extraction efficiency.

(3) The solvent systems used are not ideal. Earlier solvent pairs, such as water–carbon tetrachloride were essentially mutually immiscible (solubility of water in $CCl_4 = 0.01$ g/100 g, and of CCl_4 in water $= 0.08$ g/100 g). The solvents used as extractants for this class of extractions, however, compounds such as alcohols, ketones, and ethers, have dielectric constants close to each other and to that of water. Hence, there is an appreciable mutual solvent solubility (water in diethyl ether—1.26 g/100 g, and diethyl ether in water—6.90 g/100 g). This mutual solubility is found to change with ionic strength of the medium, causing the formation of third phases, or causing complete miscibility. In any event, volume changes and solvation effects come into play in these systems to extents that cannot be ignored. Unfortunately, in many cases they cannot be described either.

Let us look at some of the factors that were investigated in metal–chelate extraction systems to see how they operate in ion-association systems. We will see what descriptions and identifications can be made, and we will discover why such widely varying behavior cannot be generalized. Little attempt will be made to explain much of the observable behavior presented below.

The Effect of Acidity

The effect of the aqueous phase molarity of HCl on the extraction of iron(III) into diethyl ether is shown in Fig. 6–15. The value of the distribution ratio rises to a maximum around 6 M HCl and then decreases. When diisopropyl ether is used instead of diethyl ether, the curve is much steeper, the maximum occurs at a higher HCl concentration (8 M), and the maximum value of D is much greater. But even this increase to a maximum value of D followed by a decrease cannot be generalized for the extraction into bis(2-chloroethyl) ether has no maximum in its curve.

Fig. 6–16 shows the effect of HCl molarity on the percent extraction of thallium(III), thallium(I), iron(III), gallium(III), and indium(III) chlorocomplex ion pairs. To some extent the shapes and positions of these extraction curves reflect the ease of formation of the extracting ion pair.

Changing the acidity of the aqueous phase can alter the mutual solubility of the two solvents used. Fig. 6–17 shows the equilibrium volumes of diethyl ether and aqueous hydrohalic acids of different molarities after twenty ml of each are shaken together. Notice that the solubility of ether in water increases considerably as the acid molarity increases; that is, the volume of the ether phase decreases and that of the aqueous phase increases. At 8 M HCl the final ether volume is only about 5 ml and the final aqueous volume has increased to 35 ml, an increase in volume of 75%. Also note that the ether solubility in water varies with the halogen acid that is used to acidify the solutions. Solubility is greatest when HI is used, less with HBr, and least with HCl. One result of this increase in ether solubility is that there is a considerable difference between the initial solute concentration in the aqueous phase and the equilibrium concentration of that solute.

Fig. 6–18 shows the equilibrium phase HCl concentration after shaking the acid solution with an equal volume of diethyl ether as a function of the initial aqueous phase HCl concentration. Note that the equilibrium acid molarity is

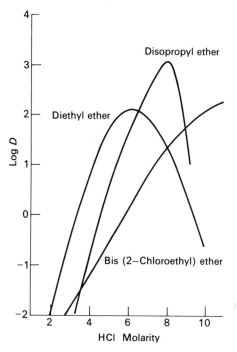

Fig. 6–15. Log *D* vs. HCl molarity for the extraction of iron(III) into diethyl ether, diisopropyl ether, and bis(2-chloroethyl) ether. (*Redrawn from Ref. 11, by permission of John Wiley & Sons, Inc.*)

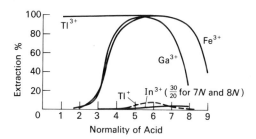

Fig. 6–16. Extraction of chlorides from hydrochloric acid. Ratios refer to V_{org}/V_{H_2O}. (*Redrawn from Ref. 19, by permission of the Society for Analytical Chemistry.*)

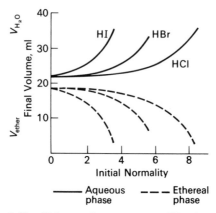

Fig. 6–17. Volume changes on equilibrating equal volumes of ether and halogen acids of various strengths. (*Redrawn from Ref. 19, by permission of the Society for Analytical Chemistry.*)

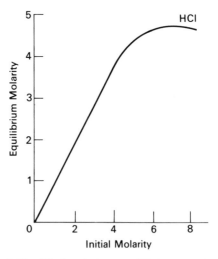

Fig. 6–18. Final molarity at equilibrium, as a function of initial molarity. (*Redrawn from Ref. 19, by permission of the Society for Analytical Chemistry.*)

always less than the initial acid molarity. As the initial acid molarity is increased, the equilibrium acid molarity increases to about 5 M, which occurs at an initial acid molarity of 7 M. Beyond this maximum concentration, the equilibrium acid molarity decreases as the initial acid molarity increases. As the acid concentration increases, so does the volume of the aqueous phase at equlibrium (see Fig. 6–17). This volume increases causes the equilibrium acid molarity to be less than the initial acid concentration. Beyond 7 M acid, the volume of the aqueous phase increases at a rate faster than the increase in the initial acid molarity, thus causing a net decrease in the equilibrium acid molarity.

The Nature of the Acid Present

The identity of the acid present in the aqueous phase has a definite influence on the extraction behavior of the system. Fig. 6–19 depicts the extraction behavior of $InCl_3$ into dibutyl ether from 10 M aqueous acid solution. The acid is initially HCl but this is replaced (keeping the hydrogen ion concentration constant) by either $HClO_4$ or HNO_3. Note the extreme differences in the values of D at the same high value of $HClO_4$ or HNO_3 concentration. Also notice the way that D varies in a completely different fashion for HNO_3 than it does for $HClO_4$. When HCl is substituted by $HClO_4$, the value of D increases continuously over a thousandfold range, whereas when the HCl is substituted by HNO_3, D rises to a maximum and then decreases, with the total change in D only a tenfold one. The absolute value of D using HNO_3 is much lower than that observed using $HClO_4$.

Fig. 6–20 shows the behavior during the extraction of various acids into 5% trilaurylamine in benzene. The strong acids (Group I)—$HClO_4$, H_2SO_4, HCl,

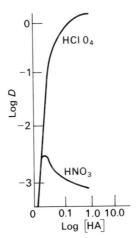

Fig. 6–19. Log D vs. log [HA] for the extraction of $InCl_3$ into dibutyl ether from 10 M acid. (*Redrawn from Ref. 10, by permission of the Journal of Physical Chemistry.*)

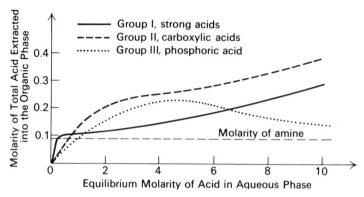

Fig. 6–20. Extraction of acids. (*Redrawn from Ref. 6, by permission of Imprimerie Gauthier-Villars.*)

and HNO_3 behave identically. The carboxylic acids, formic and acetic (Group II) do not behave too differently from the strong acids, except at low acid concentrations. Phosphoric acid (Group III) extraction rises to a maximum at 4.5 M acid and then decreases.

The Nature of the Extracting Solvent

The identity of the solvent used to extract the ion pair should be expected to have some influence on the amount of material extracted. Organic phase properties such as the solubility of the ion pair and the degree of dissociation or polymerization of the ion pair will affect the extraction behavior. Fig. 6–15 shows the differences in behavior when iron(III) chloride is extracted into three different ethers. The maximum log D value for diisopropyl ether occurs at higher acid concentrations because diisopropyl ether is less soluble in water than is diethyl ether. Relatively little bis(2-chloroethyl) ether dissolves in water, so that log D for the extraction of iron(III) into it shows no maximum at all.

Brooks and Boswell[3] studied the extraction of many metal chlorides into cyclohexanone and cyclohexanol. These two solvents should be expected to exhibit similar extraction behavior, for as Table 6–5 shows their properties are very similar.

In general this is what was observed. The percent extracted was greater in cyclohexanone for the chlorides of zinc, cadmium, mercury, gallium, indium,

Table 6–5.   PHYSICAL PROPERTIES OF CYCLOHEXANOL AND CYCLOHEXANONE

Property	Cyclohexanol	Cyclohexanone
Boiling point, °C	161	157
Density, g/cm³	0.96	0.95
Dielectric constant	15.0	18.3
Dipole moment, debye	1.9	2.8
Water solubility, g solute/100 g H_2O	3.6	2.3

thallium, antimony, and bismuth than in cyclohexanol, but the $\%E$–M HCl extraction curves had the same general shape in both solvents. In the cases of arsenic and tin, however, cyclohexanol extracted a greater percentage of the metal. Figs. 6–21(a), (b), (c), and (d) show the extraction behavior of four metals with these two solvents. Zinc and cadmium (Figs. 6–21(a) and (b), respectively) behave essentially the same in the two solvents, with bismuth (Fig. 6–21(c)) D decreases continuously with increasing acid molarity when the metal is extracted into cyclohexanone, but D increases continuously with increasing acidity when extracting into cyclohexanol. The behavior of arsenic (Fig. 6–21(d)) is analogous to that of bismuth, save that D increases in cyclohexanol and decreases in cyclohexanone. The extraction behavior using any solvent system should be confirmed experimentally since the similarity between the physical properties of two organic liquids is no assurance that their extraction behavior will be similar.

The Nature of the Ion Pair Extracted

Since ion-pair extraction systems involve interactions between an anion and a cation, it should not be surprising to find variations in extraction behavior among different ion pairs. Figs. 6–16 and 6–21 illustrate this clearly. It should also be pointed out that different oxidation states of an element will have different extrac-

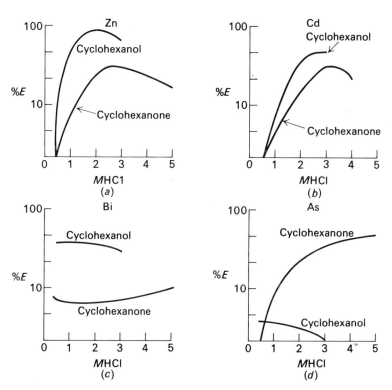

Fig. 6–21. The extraction of elements into cyclohexanone and cyclohexanol as a function of hydrochloric acid concentration: (a) zinc, (b) cadmium, (c) bismuth, (d) arsenic. (*Redrawn from Ref. 3, by permission of Analytica Chimica Acta.*)

tion behavior; for example thallium(I) and thallium(III) in Fig. 6–16. Iron(II) does not extract appreciably into ether from HCl, whereas iron(III) does, presumably because iron(II) does not form anionic halogen complex ions.

The Concentration of the Metal Ion

When the dielectric constant of the organic solvent is high, the ion pair extracted will dissociate in the organic phase causing D to depend upon the metal ion concentration. D also depends upon concentration when polymerization of the ion pair occurs in the organic phase. The distribution ratio for the extraction of molybdenum from 8.1 M HCl into bis(2-chloroethyl) ether decreases by a factor of ten as the concentration of molybdenum increases from 10^{-6} to 10^{-2} M. Fig. 6–22 shows that the distribution ratio for the extraction of iron(III) from 5.0 M HCl into diisopropyl ether increases with increasing iron(III) concentration.

The Presence of Salts in the System

The presence of other salts in the extraction system will affect the extraction behavior of ion-association extraction systems. The amount of metal halides extracted decreases in the presence of most salts. This effect is ascribed to changes in the activity coefficient of the metal ions with changes in the nature and concentration of the ionic environment.

The Extraction of Iron(III) into Ethers

One of the earliest known examples of ion-association extraction, one of the

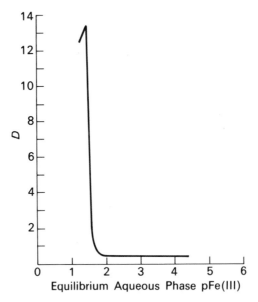

Fig. 6–22. Variation in the distribution ratio for the extraction of iron(III) from 5.0 M HCl into isopropyl ether at 25°C with iron concentration.

most thoroughly studied systems, and yet one which still is not completely explicable, is the extraction of iron(III) from aqueous HCl solutions into diethyl ether. The change in the distribution ratio with HCl concentration and with iron(III) concentration has been shown in Figs. 6–15 and 6–22, respectively. The ion pair extracted is $H^+FeCl_4^- \cdot xH_2O$, where x is between 4 and 5. $HFeCl_4$ is a stronger acid than HCl and thus does not exist as a molecular species in aqueous solutions. In organic solutions, $HFeCl_4$ is present as ion pairs, ion triplets, ion quadruplets, and so on, depending upon the concentration of iron present. The following expression for D can be written, neglecting any ether of solvation on all species:

$$D = \frac{[FeCl_4^-]_{Et_2O} + [H^+FeCl_4^-]_{Et_2O} + 2[(H^+FeCl_4^-)_2]_{Et_2O} + 3[(H^+FeCl_4^-)_3]_{Et_2O}}{[Fe(H_2O)_6^{3+}] + [FeCl(H_2O)_5^{2+}] + [FeCl_2(H_2O)_4^+] + [FeCl_3(H_2O)] + [FeCl_4^-]} \quad (6-26)$$

The observed variation of D with HCl concentration (Fig. 6–15) can be explained as follows: there is an increase in the formation of the complex $FeCl_4^-$ anion as the concentration of chloride ion increases in the aqueous phase. Consequently, as the HCl concentration increases up to the maximum value, there is more of this species present to form the extractable ion pair, $H^+FeCl_4^-$. The maximum value of D occurs around 7 M HCl because that is where the maximum equilibrium HCl concentration (see Fig. 6–18) occurs. Above 7 M HCl the molarity of HCl present at equilibrium decreases which forms less $FeCl_4^-$ than was formed at lower initial concentrations. The activity of water also decreases with increasing HCl concentration. The decrease in the value of D at high HCl concentrations cannot be due to the formation of higher iron(III) chloro complexes that are not extractable, since no higher complexes have been discovered.

If the formation constants for all of the iron–chloro species in the aqueous phase were known and the association constants for all of the ion aggregates in the organic phase were similarly known, perhaps a quantitative explanation of the change in D with iron concentration could be obtained. Fig. 6–22 shows that at low equilibrium concentrations of iron(III) (10^{-5} to 10^{-3} M), D remains essentially constant at 0.34 ± 0.02. From 1.5×10^{-2} M to 3.5×10^{-2} M iron(III), D increases rapidly from 0.56 to 13.4. Above 3.5×10^{-2} M iron(III), D begins to decrease again. Increasing polymerization of the ion pairs into triplets and quadruplets would explain the sudden rise in the curve.

Variations in the ratio of HCl to $FeCl_3$ in the system are also important. Mixed aggregates such as $H^+FeCl_4^- \cdot HCl$ form in the ethereal phase at high ratios of HCl to $FeCl_3$. The more iron(III) present, the more HCl found in the ether layer because of this adduct formation. This increased amount of HCl in turn favors increased formation of adducts, which will increase the amount of iron that is extracted.

No significant variation in D has been observed with increasing temperatures between 25 and 50°C for the extraction of iron(III) from HCl solutions into diisopropyl ether.

Other Ion-Association Systems

Simple ion-association systems involve extremely large, and thus weakly solvated, ions. These bulky ion pairs are usually extracted into low dielectric constant organic solvents such as chloroform. When solvents such as nitrobenzene that have much higher dielectric constants are used, then ion pairs formed from ions with smaller radii will also be extracted, causing a loss in the selectivity for the larger ion pairs. Examples of these systems are tetraphenylarsonium and tetra-alkylammonium cations which can be used in ion-pair systems to extract anions. The large cation is weakly hydrated. The anions usually extracted are also large and weakly hydrated, for example, tetraphenylborate, perchlorate, permanganate, and perrhenate.

Organic solutions of carboxylic acids possessing a large number of carbon atoms form extractable ion pairs with metal ions. Benzoic acid, octanoic, capric, palmetic and naphthenic acids have been used quite extensively for the extraction of all kinds of metals, such as cobalt, copper, and cesium.

High molecular-weight secondary and tertiary alkylamines are widely used for the extraction of strong acids such as HCl, H_2SO_4, and HNO_3 into chloroform or nitrobenzene. These extractions find great use in nuclear technology, so they have been investigated quite thoroughly. A metal ion that can form an anionic complex, such as $FeCl_4^-$, $UO_2(SO_4)_2^{2-}$, VO_3^-, and MoO_4^{2-} can be separated from those metals that do not exist as anions by extraction with these high molecular-weight amines. Trilaurylamine, tri-n-octylamine, diisononylamine are among the most widely used amines for this purpose. Cerium(IV) has been separated from berkelium(IV) by extraction of its hexanitrato complex, $Ce(NO_3)_6^{2-}$, into xylene with tricaprylmethylammonium nitrate.[25] The smaller berkelium(IV) ion does not form the complex nitrate anion and hence it is not extracted under these conditions.

Ion-association and simple coordination systems involve the formation of complex ions and then their extraction as acids or ammonium salts into ketones, alcohols, or ethers. Halide, thiocyanate, and nitrate complexes are the usual ones used.

One very good way to extract small, polyvalent cations is to convert them to large cationic chelates and then extract these as ion pairs with oxygen-containing anions. These comprise the ion-association and chelation systems. Thus iron(II) can be extracted into chloroform by forming the tris(phenanthroline)iron(II) cation, and extracting this in an ion pair with perchlorate as the anion. Cobalt(II) can be extracted after the formation of the bis(2,2′,2″-terpyridyl)cobalt(II) complex and then its perchlorate ion pair. Either benzene, diethyl ether or chloroform will work as the organic solvent. Another variation in this category is to convert the small, multivalent cation into a large anionic chelate, and then to extract this species as an ion pair with a large cation. Thus the anionic complex of 7-iodo-8-hydroxyquinoline-5-sulfonic acid with iron(III) can be extracted into isoamyl alcohol with the tributylammonium ion as the cation in the ion pair. The dye rhodamine B is cationic and has been used to extract the halocomplex anions of transition metals such as $FeCl_4^-$, $AuCl_4^-$, and $AuBr_4^-$ as well as $TlCl_4^-$ and $SbBr_6^-$ into benzene, diethyl ether or other low dielectric constant solvents. The use of organic dyes as the cation in the ion pair has the additional advantage of permitting analysis of the organic extract by spectrophotometry. The dyes will not be extracted themselves, the presence of a large anion is needed to obtain any of the color in the organic phase.

Table 6–6 gives some selected examples of ion-association extraction systems.

Table 6–6. ION-ASSOCIATION EXTRACTION SYSTEMS

Reagent	Materials extracted	Solvents Used
1. Simple systems		
I_3^-	Cs, Rb	Nitrobenzene
$(C_6H_5)_4As^+$	ClO_4^-, MnO_4^-, ReO_4^-, TcO_4^-	Chloroform
$(C_6H_5)_3Pb^+$	Cl^-, Br^-, I^-, AsO_4^{3-}, PO_4^{3-}, SeO_3^{2-}	Chloroform, nitrobenzene
C_7 to C_9 carboxylic acids	Ag, Al, Bi, Cs, Fe, Gd, K, La, Li, Mg, Mn, Na, Nb, Nd, Pr, Sb, Th, U, Zr	Chloroform, nitrobenzene, benzene, diethyl ether, methyl isobutyl ketone
$(n\text{-}C_{12}H_{25})_3N$	HCl, HBr, HI, $HClO_4$, HNO_3	Cyclohexane, benzene xylene, chlorobenzene
Perfluoro-octanoic acid	Ca, Fe(II), Mg, Pb, Zn	Diethyl ether
2. Ion-association and simple coordination systems		
F^-	Nb(V), Re(VII), Sn(II), Sn(IV), Ta(V)	Diethyl ether, methyl isobutyl ketone
Cl^-	As(III), Au(III), Fe(III), Ga(III), Ge(IV), Hg(II), In(III), Mo(VI), Nb(V), Pa(V), Po(II), Pt(II), Sb(V), Sc(III), Tl(III)	Diethyl ether, diisopropyl ether
Br^-	Au(III), Fe(III), Ga(III), In(III), Sb(V), Sn(II), Sn(IV), Tl(III)	Diethyl ether
I^-	Au(III), Cd(II), Hg(II), In(III), Pb(II), Sb(III), Sn(II), Tl(III)	Diethyl ether, methyl isobutyl ketone
SCN^-	Be(II), Co(II), Fe(III), Ga(III), In(III), Mo(V), Sc(III), Sn(IV), Ti(III), Zn(II)	Diethyl ether
NO_3^-	Am(VI), Au(III), Ce(IV), Fe(III), Np(VI), Pa(IV), Pu(VI), Sc(III), Th(IV), U(VI), Zr(IV)	Diethyl ether
Crystal Violet	As and Ga as their chlorides	Chloroform–acetylacetone
3. Ion-association and chelation		
Rhodamine B	$AuBr_4^-$, $AuCl_4^-$, $FeBr_4^-$, $FeCl_4^-$, $GaCl_4^-$, $SbBr_6^-$, SbI_4^-, SCN^-, $TlBr_4^-$, $TlCl_4^-$	Benzene, chloroform, diethyl ether, amyl alcohol

Extraction of Solvated Solutes

Organophosphorus compounds solvate quite strongly and because of this are excellent solvents for extractions. The P–O bond is a highly polar one, and is largely responsible for the solvating ability of these materials. Fig. 6–23 gives the classes of

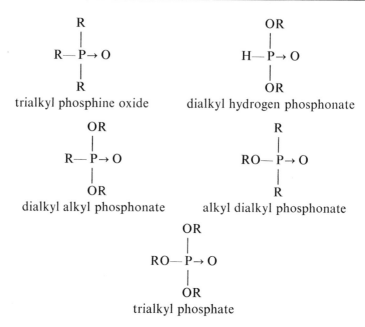

Fig. 6–23. Classes of organophosphorus compounds used as extractants.

these compounds used. The most widely used of these organophosphorus compounds is tri-n-butyl phosphate, $(nC_4H_9O)_3PO$, and this section will be devoted primarily to a discussion of it.

Tributyl phosphate (TBP) dissolves inorganic acids and the chlorides, bromides, iodides, nitrates, and perchlorates of the transition, rare earth, and actinide metals. TPB is stable to acid attack; it has a low volatility. It is relatively inexpensive and readily available. The pure liquid has a high dipole moment of 3.0 debyes and a dielectric constant of 8.0. Because of this low dielectric constant, TBP is essentially a nonionizing solvent—only perchloric acid and perchlorate salts ionize appreciably in TBP. Since it is fairly viscous, TBP often is diluted with an inert hydrocarbon, such as carbon tetrachloride or benzene to produce solutions that are easier to manipulate. This dilution does not affect its powerful extractant utility. Solutes have been found to behave ideally in TBP, allowing assumptions that activity coefficients are unity to be valid up to fairly high solute concentrations. The solubility of TBP in water is 1.5×10^{-3} M at 25°C which is low enough not to affect the aqueous solution properties. The solubility of water in TBP corresponds to the complete formation of a monohydrate, TBP · H_2O. The existence of definite TBP solvates of salts has been shown.

Tributyl phosphate has been found to extract the strong acids $HClO_4$, HCl, HBr, and H_2SO_4 as ion pairs, $H(H_2O)_4^+A^-(TBP)$, in which the proton carries four molecules of water of solvation into the TBP phase. Weak acids, such as HNO_3 and acetic acid, extract into TBP as the unhydrated molecule—HNO_3 · TBP.

Hesford and McKay[17] have studied the distribution of metal nitrates between water and TBP. They postulate the equilibrium involved as:

$$M^{n+}(aq) + n NO_3^-(aq) + m TBP(org) \rightleftharpoons (M(NO_3)_n \cdot m TBP)_{org} \qquad (6-26)$$

from which the concentration equilibrium constant can be written as:

$$K = \frac{[M(NO_3)_n \cdot m\,TBP]_{org}}{[M^{n+}][NO_3^-]^n[TBP]_{org}^m} \qquad (6\text{–}27)$$

The distribution ratio for these metal nitrate extractions is:

$$D = \frac{C_{M_{org}}}{C_{M_{aq}}} = \frac{[M(NO_3)_n \cdot m\,TBP]_{org}}{[M^{n+}]} \qquad (6\text{–}28)$$

Assuming, as appears likely, that no other species are involved in either the organic or the aqueous phases, combining Equations (6–27) and (6–28) gives:

$$D = K[NO_3^-]^n\,[TBP]_{org}^m \qquad (6\text{–}29)$$

For constant aqueous phase conditions, especially nitrate ion concentration, and using low concentrations of TBP in the organic liquid, Equation (6–29) can be simplified to:

$$D = K'\,[TBP]_{org}^m \qquad (6\text{–}30)$$

where $K' = K[NO_3^-]^n$.

Hesford and McKay studied Equation (6–30) experimentally at varying concentrations of TBP for many different metal ions and found that the relationship is a valid one. Equation (6–30) was used then to determine the number of molecules of TBP that solvate the metal nitrate species during the extraction. They reported that for M(III) nitrates there are three molecules of TBP per molecule for the metals Ce(III), Eu(III), Y(III), Am(III), Tb(III), Tm(III), and Lu(III). Tetravalent metal nitrates of Zr(IV), Th(IV), Np(IV) and Pu(IV) had only two molecules of TBP solvating them. In the cases of UO_2^{2+}, NpO_2^{2+}, and PuO_2^{2+}, there were also two molecules of TBP solvating the extracted species.

In the extraction of metal nitrates with TBP the most highly charged ions are the most readily extracted. Thus the order of increasing value of the distribution ratio would be $Na < Ca < Ce(III) < Ce(IV)$. For ions of the same charge the smaller the ion, that is, the greater the charge density, the more readily it is extracted, $Li > Na > K > Cs$, and $Ca > Sr > Ba$.

The extraction of metal chlorides of iron, gold, and cobalt from HCl solutions shows two different kinds of solvation of the iron species. In any given system, the solvation found depends upon the species of the metal being extracted. At low HCl concentrations, where the species extracted is $FeCl_3 \cdot 3TBP$, the solvation is of the metal ion. At high HCl concentrations the proton of the metallohalic acid is solvated, giving $H^+(TBP)FeCl_4^-$ as the species extracted. The trivalent rare earths have been found to have increasing values of the distribution ratio with increasing atomic numbers when extracted from HCl or HNO_3 media.

The extraction of platinum metal chlorides into pure TBP has been studied by Casey et al.[7] as a function of HCl, H^+, and Cl^- concentrations. Determination of the number of TBP molecules solvating the extracted ion pair gave values varying between 2.4 and 4.2 depending upon the solvent used to dilute the TBP making identification of the extracted species impossible. The effect of HCl concentration changes on D is shown in Fig. 6–24 for the extraction of palladium, iridium, and

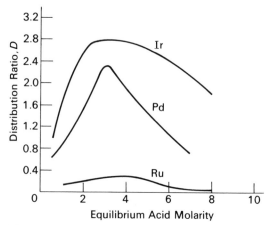

Fig. 6–24. Extraction of iridium, palladium, and ruthenium into TBP from aqueous hydrochloric acid solution. (*Redrawn from Ref. 7, by permission of North-Holland Publishing Co., 1972.*)

ruthenium. The extraction curves for the other platinum metals they studied (Pt and Os) are similar. Rhodium did not extract appreciably at any acid concentration. The value of the distribution ratio rises initially with increasing HCl concentration because increasing amounts of the dissolved TBP molecules became protonated as the H^+ ions are solvated by the TBP. These TBP solvated protons then form an ion pair with the anionic chloro complex of the platium metal, for example $[H(TBP)_x^+]_2$ $(PtCl_6^{2-})$, which is extracted into the TBP. At the maximum in the concentration curve all of the dissolved TBP is protonated and associated with either a chloride ion or a platinum metal chlorocomplex. As the HCl concentration is increased beyond this point, the competition between the chloride ion and the metal chloro complex anions for the TBP solvated protons becomes weighted in favor of the chloride ions. Not only is there more HCl than platinum metal present, but the value of D for the HCl extraction with TBP increases with increasing HCl concentration. Thus the value of D for the metal chloride decreases at higher HCl concentrations. The molarity of HCl for maximum extraction of each platinum metal and the value of its distribution ratio at that molarity are: ruthenium—4 M (0.6); palladium—3.2 M (2.3); iridium—3 M (2.8); osmium—3 M (6); and platinum—4.2 M (18.8).

Fig. 6–25 shows the effect on the extraction of palladium(II) from HCl + LiCl solutions at a constant 3 M hydrogen ion concentration but with varying chloride ion concentrations. The initial increase in D may be due to the increased formation of the extractable palladium chlorocomplex $(PdCl_4^{2-})$ or it may merely be an increase in the salting-out caused by addition of increasing amounts of LiCl. Above the maximum at about 3.5 M chloride ion, HCl is extracted in preference to the $PdCl_4^{2-}$, so that the value of D decreases.

When the chloride concentration is kept constant at 3 M and the hydrogen ion concentration varied, the curve for D as a function of the hydrogen ion concentration for the extraction of palladium(II) into pure TBP shows a maximum at

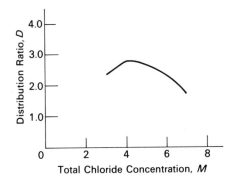

Fig. 6–25. Extraction of palladium(II) into TBP from aqueous HCl + LiCl solutions of varying chloride ion concentration at constant hydrogen ion concentrations of 3 M. (*Redrawn from Ref. 7, by permission of North-Holland Publishing Co., 1972.*)

2.8 M, as is shown in Fig. 6–26. The initial increase in D is caused by the increased protonation of TBP causing an increase in the number of extractable ion pairs. Above the maximum hydrogen ion concentration of 2.8 M, HCl is preferentially extracted, so D for the palladium extraction decreases.

The slight differences in D for the extractions into TBP of the platinum metals imply that a countercurrent distribution apparatus would be required for a separation of the metals. Casey's group tried this and found that the separation of rhodium and platinum after twenty transfers and of osmium and platinum after fifty transfers occur as predicted from the preliminary studies. Palladium could also be separated from iron(III), cobalt(II), nickel(II), copper(II), and platinum(IV) by extraction from 0.5 M HNO$_3$ by TBP ($D = 1$).

The ability of organophosphorus compounds to extract salts by means of solvation depends upon their ability to bond directly to the metal or hydrogen ion. This in turn depends upon the electron donor properties of the oxygen in the P→O bond. Molecules which have a high electron density around the oxygen should solvate better than those with lower electron densities. Different alkyl groups in the molecule will affect this bond polarity and thus the extracting ability of the compound. When phenyl groups are substituted for the n-butyl groups in tributyl phosphate, the electron density at the oxygen decreases in the sequence $(BuO)_3 > (BuO)_2PhO > BuO(PhO)_2 > (PhO)_3$. The values of D for the extraction of uranyl nitrate into these solvents are found to decrease in the same sequence.

Branching in the alkyl group also increases the electron density of the oxygen. The values of D for the extraction of uranium from $4M$ HNO$_3$ into the organophosphorus solvents increased in the order $(n\text{-}BuO)_3PO < (i\text{-}BuO)_3PO < (s\text{-}$

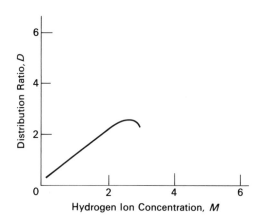

Fig. 6–26. Extraction of palladium(II) into TBP from aqueous HCl + LiCl solutions of varying hydrogen ion concentration at constant chloride ion concentrations of 3 M. (*Redrawn from Ref. 7, by permission of North-Holland Publishing Co., 1972.*)

$BuO)_3PO$. The extraction of uranium from 1 M HNO_3 was found to increase into organophosphorus solvents as the number of oxygens in the solvent molecules decreased in the sequence $(BuO)_3PO < (BuO)_2BuPO < BuO(Bu)_2PO < (Bu)_3PO$. The following sequence is also found for the extraction of uranium from 4 M HNO_3 for organophosphorus compounds $(PentO)_2Pent\ PO < (HexO)HexPO < (BuO)_2Bu\ PO < (2\text{-ethylhexyl O})_2$ ethylhexyl PO (where Pent stands for pentyl and Hex for hexyl).

Because of its importance in nuclear technology, the extraction of $UO_2(NO_3)_2$ into the organophosphorus solvents has been thoroughly investigated, especially the extraction into tributyl phosphate. This extraction into tributyl phosphate is commonly used in the purification stages of uranium and in the separation of uranium from plutonium during the reprocessing of nuclear fuels.

Table 6–7. EXTRACTION SYSTEMS OF PHOSPHORIC ACIDS AND THEIR ESTERS

Phosphate	Solvents Used	Metals Extracted
Dibutyl phosphoric acid	CCl_4, *n*-butyl alcohol	Eu, Ga, I_2, In, Nb, Pm, Sn(IV), Tb, Y, Zr
Dioctyl phosphoric acid	Benzene, cyclohexane, kerosine, chloroform	Cs, In, La, Nd, Pt, Th, Ti(IV), U(VI), Y
Tributyl phosphate	Hydrocarbons, carbon tetrachloride, benzene, xylene, chloroform	Am(V), Au(III), Bi, Ce(IV), Cf, Cm, Co, Cr(VI), Fe, In, Ir, Mo(VI), Nb(V), Np(VI), Pd, Pm, Po, Pt, Pu(IV), rare earths, Sb, Sc, Ta(V), Tc, Te, Ti(IV), U(VI), V, Zr

Examples of extractions with a few organophosphorus compounds are given in Table 6–7.

There are other organic liquids that solvate the extractable solute. The borderline between ion-association extractions and solvated solute extractions is not clearly delineated. $UO_2(NO_3)_2$ extracts readily into diethyl ether as an ion-association extraction system, yet the extractable species is $UO_2(NO_3)_2 \cdot x \ H_2O \cdot y \ Et_2O$, where x is believed to be 4 and y varies from 2 to 7 depending upon conditions. The long-chain aliphatic alcohols such as 2-octanol and n-hexanol solvate metal ions such as calcium, cobalt, magnesium, and nickel. The chlorides and nitrates of these metals are extracted into these alcohols as solvated ion pairs.

RATE OF ATTAINMENT OF EQUILIBRIUM IN EXTRACTION SYSTEMS

In all of the preceding discussion, it has been assumed that time is not a factor and that the systems were at equilibrium when the theories and equations were derived and applied. This ideal condition, however, is not always fulfilled. Some extraction systems take several hours to reach equilibrium—for example, the extraction of nickel with 8-hydroxyquinoline in chloroform. When an extraction system is not at equilibrium, the rate of attainment of equilibrium must be added to all of the factors that have been discussed.

When one examines the phenomena occurring in an extraction system, two kinds of processes are seen taking place—chemical reactions and physical movement. Either or both of these processes can be very slow and hence determine the rate at which the entire system reaches equilibrium. In other words, the rate of attainment of equilibrium in an extraction system depends upon the rate of formation of the extractable species and upon the rate of mass transfer of that species from one phase into the second phase.

The process of mass transfer can occur by two mechanisms—*diffusion* (due to concentration gradients) and *convection* (stirring, shaking). Both of these mechanisms take place in the extraction of a solute from one liquid into another. The mass transfer process, regardless of whether the driving force is diffusion or convection, can be broken down into a series of steps. The first is the movement of the solute species from the interior of the bulk of the solution to the surface layer. This is followed by the transfer of the solute from the surface layer of one liquid across to the surface layer of the second liquid. Once in the second liquid, the solute moves away from the surface layer into the interior of the solution.

The thinness of the surface layers of the liquids is important and determined by the relative velocity of the two phases past each other, for example, the rate of swirling or shaking. The rate of transfer of the solute from one surface layer to the second depends upon the size and shape of the solute, the viscosity of the two solvents, and the interfacial tension between them. In most extraction systems, the rate of mass transfer is quite rapid and hence not the rate-determining step in the extraction process. In extractions using pure tributyl phosphate, the viscosity is so great that the rate of mass transfer is exceedingly slow.

The slowest step in most extractions is believed to be the chemical reaction forming the extracting species. Chelation can be a slow process, although for most metal chelate extractions with dithizone, oxine, and diphenylcarbazone equilibrium is reached in less than two minutes. On the other hand, for certain metal chelate extractions, the slowest step in the process is the rate of formation of the dithizone, thenoyltrifluoroacetone, or 8-hydroxyquinoline chelate with the metal ion. Extractions of nickel, palladium, molybdenum, and tungsten with oxine were found to take several hours to reach equilibrium, and trivalent chromium does not react sufficiently fast to be extracted at all as its oxinate. The rate of extraction of many metals with oxine increases with increasing pH and oxine concentration, that is, with an increase in the concentration of the chelon anion involved in the chelation reaction.

The chelation reaction itself is not a single chemical reaction but consists of a sequence of steps. During many metal chelate extractions, the rate-determining step is the destruction of the bonds of the hydrated metal species between water molecules and the metal ion. These bonds must be broken before new bonds can be formed between the chelon anion and the metal ion. When, instead of being hydrated, a metal ion is already complexed with acetate, thiocyanate, or oxalate, the rate of extraction with a chelating agent increases over that found with the hydrated metal ion. Apparently the bonds between some simple complexing agents and metal ions can be broken faster than those between a metal ion and water. There are exceptions to this, of course. Tartrate and cyanide were found to have no effect on the rate of extraction of metals with 8-hydroxyquinoline. When the metal ion is chelated with masking agents NTA and EDTA, there is a considerable decrease in the rate of extraction from that of the simple hydrated metal ions. The extraction of bivalent metal ions with oxine in the presence of EDTA takes several hours to reach equilibrium, whereas the extraction of tri- and tervalent metal ions takes even longer. This slow extraction is due to the very slow rate of dissociation of the metal–EDTA chelates. Even in the case of nonhydrated solutes, the aqueous phase chemistry is responsible for the slowness of extraction. In extractions with diluted tributyl phosphate, the slow step appears to involve the formation of the TBP solvate in the aqueous phase.

L. Craig and co-workers[1] in their study of the extraction of penicillins determined the number of inversions of a test tube required to reach equilibrium. Their results are shown in Fig. 6–27 for the distribution of benzyl penicillin between a pH 4.8 phosphate buffer and diethyl ether. For the upper curve, the solute initially was all in the ether phase, and for the lower curve it initially was all in the aqueous phase. Equilibrium can be considered to be reached when the two curves merge. The graph shows that this has occurred after twenty inversions, or at the rate of their inversion, after about thirty-six seconds. Craig reports that the rate of attainment of equilibrium in penicillin systems depends upon the pH of the buffer, the relative volumes of the two phases, and the surface-active properties of the solute. In some of their studies, extraction of the benzyl penicillin initially in ether was more rapid than when the benzyl penicillin was initially in the aqueous buffer.

When the rate of attainment of equilibrium in an extraction is slow, shaking for only a short time will extract less than the equilibrium amount of solute. The effect that this has on the extraction curve is to seem to shift the curve to higher pH values. For metal chelate extractions it raises the $pH_{\frac{1}{2}}$ of the metal ion; for iron(III) extraction with oxine by about three pH units. This shift to higher $pH_{\frac{1}{2}}$ values

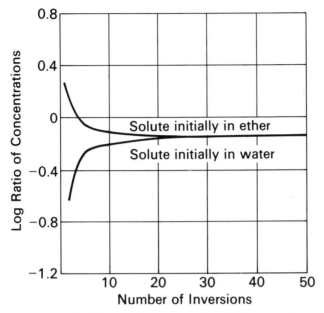

Fig. 6–27. Curves of the rate of establishment of equilibrium. (*Redrawn from Ref. 8, by permission of John Wiley & Sons, Inc.*)

caused by nonattainment of equilibrium, however, can be used to advantage in effecting separations.

CHOICE OF THE EXTRACTING SOLVENT

In attempting an extraction separation, one of the most important questions that the analyst must ask himself, and answer is, "What solvent shall I use as the extractant?" In many cases, experience and the chemical literature can provide the answer. The time spent in searching the literature for work on similar extraction systems is a valuable investment. In many other cases, however, such as when the system is a new one, or there are several possible solvents available, the analyst must choose the particular solvent by himself. Other than expediency, the factors that must be considered and usually compromised with are:

1. The solute should be very soluble in the solvent so as to have a high value of D, and thus require only one or two extractions. In metal chelate extraction systems the chelating agent is dissolved in the organic phase. Thus, in order for it to operate as an extracting reagent, it must first be extracted into the aqueous phase so that it can react. It was shown on p. 286 that the organic solvent in which both the chelating agent and the metal chelate are the least soluble extracts the most metal. For all other extraction systems, however, pick that liquid that has the greatest solvent effect on the species being extracted.

2. The solvent should be as immiscible with water as possible. One way of arriving at an excellent idea about the degree of immiscibility is through a comparison of the dipole moment of the liquid with that of water ($\mu = 1.84$ debyes).

Solvents such as benzene, hexane, and carbon tetrachloride with dipole moments of zero have very low water solubilities (less than 0.1 g/100 g), whereas solvents such as diethyl ether ($\mu = 1.2$ debyes), ethyl acetate ($\mu = 1.8$ debyes), or n-butyl alcohol ($\mu = 1.7$ debyes) have relatively high aqueous solubilities (6.90, 7.94, and 7.80 g/100 g, respectively). This generalization has its exceptions, of course—chlorobenzene with a dipole moment of 1.6 debyes has an aqueous solubility less than that of benzene.

3. The solvent should have as great a density difference from water as possible. This permits a clean-cut phase boundary between the two phases and facilitates the physical separation of the two liquids after extraction. Carbon tetrachloride (density = 1.59) is much superior in this respect to tributyl phosphate (density = 0.98). Phase separation is a real problem in pure TBP extractions.

4. The viscosity of the solvent should be low to permit good contact between the two phases while shaking and to allow rapid settling out of the two liquids after shaking. Pure TBP is very poor in this respect.

5. The solvent should have a sufficiently high boiling point so that evaporation of the solvent is not a problem. This is one of the reasons why diisopropyl ether is preferred over diethyl ether for the extraction of $H^+FeCl_4^-$.

6. The solute should be able to be recovered readily from the solvent for subsequent operations. This means that it should be easy to evaporate the solvent off the solution, easy to perform analyses in the organic solution, or easy to back-extract the solute quantitatively into the aqueous phase.

7. The solvent should not form stable emulsions with water.

8. The solvent should be readily available in a sufficient state of purity for convenient use. A rare solvent or one that requires long and elaborate purification processes before it can be used, is not going to become very popular, regardless of its extracting power.

9. The solvent should not be hazardous to the health. It should be neither toxic nor flammable.

When a single pure solvent will not separate a mixture of solutes, a mixture of two or more solvents may accomplish the separation. When a solute is highly water-soluble and relatively insoluble in water-immiscible solvents, the selection of an extracting liquid can present a considerable problem. The addition of relatively high concentrations (>2 M) of NH_4Cl, $NaCl$, or Na_2SO_4 to the aqueous phase may decrease the dielectric constant sufficiently to permit the use of methyl or ethyl alcohol or similar liquids in which the solute will be soluble, as the immiscible extracting liquid.

APPLICATIONS

Solvent extractions play important roles in chemical research, in the manufacture of chemicals and other materials, and in nuclear technology. Extractions are commonly used in chemical synthesis for the purification of the products of a reaction. Extractions are widely used in quality control, in recovery and reprocessing operations, in crime detection, and in studies of air and water pollution. Extractions may be carried out to remove the desired materials from its contaminants or conversely to remove unwanted interferrants from the sample. By extracting large volumes with small amounts of extractant, the process can be used to concentrate solutions. A few typical and interesting examples of recent applications of solvent extractions follow.

In a study of the pollution of river waters, Montgomery, Gardener, and Gregory[24] both removed and concentrated HCN from the water samples by extracting it into 1,1,1-trichloroethane. J. G. Konrad and co-workers[21] extracted organochlorine and organophosphate insecticides (aldrin, dieldrin, DDT, parathion) from lake waters into benzene. The benzene extract was then analyzed for the insecticides by gas–liquid chromatography. Higuchi and co-workers[18] have used extraction extensively in their analysis of drugs and pharmaceuticals. Laessig[23] described a rapid method for analyzing the alcohol content of blood that involves the extraction of the ethanol from the blood sample into n-butanol. Wolfsberg and co-workers[40] extracted the lanthanides and actinides from the products of underground thermonuclear explosions with tributyl phosphate and dioctylphosphoric acid. Brooks[4] used discontinuous countercurrent distribution to separate the trace elements titanium, gallium, indium, tin, molybdenum, and nickel from the major consituents in granites and silicate rocks. He used a fifty-tube automatic apparatus, extracting the elements as their ion pairs from varying concentrations of HCl into methyl isobutyl ketone. Brooks[5] also used a four hundred-tube automatic countercurrent distribution apparatus to separate lead, magnesium, molybdenum, tin, nickel, aluminum, vanadium, silver, zinc, and lanthanum from eight liters of sea water. The elements were extracted as their oxinates into chloroform over a period of twenty hours.

Fletcher[12] has given an excellent summary of the industrial uses of extraction. Tributyl phosphate is used to extract uranium from its concentrates and to separate uranium from plutonium during the reprocessing of nuclear fuels. Methyl isobutyl ketone is used as an extractant in the production of niobium and tantalum. High molecular weight carboxylic acids are used to extract copper and nickel from ores. Tertiary and quarternary amines are used in the processing of vanadium, tungsten molybdenum, and chromium. The so-called liquid ion-exchangers used in the extraction of copper and in the separation of copper from ferric iron are merely structural variants of the chelating agent α-benzoinoxime. In order to obtain europium for color television screens, dialkyl phosphoric acids are used to extract the rare earths from the ore bastaesite. Extractions are also involved in the purification of germanium for semiconductors, desalination of seawater, the manufacture of boric acid and bromine, the separation of aromatics from nonaromatics in petroleum refining, and in the removal of other important hydrocarbons from petroleum.

EXPERIMENT 6–1
Separation of Iron by Extraction into Isopropyl Ether *

The purpose of this experiment is to illustrate the extraction of an ion pair as well as to illustrate the separation of a metal from an alloy by extraction.

* Based upon material found in the papers by R. W. Dodson, G. J. Forney, and E. H. Swift, *J. Amer. Chem. Soc.*, **58**, 2407 (1936), and M. Barrachina and M. A. Villar, *J. Inorg. Nucl. Chem.*, **28**, 2407 (1966).

Removal of Iron. To a known amount of an iron sample (either an aliquot of a solution or a weighed amount of a solid iron alloy or ore dissolved in HCl, containing less than 0.5 g of iron and low in nitrate ion content) add sufficient conc. HCl to produce a solution that is between 7.5 and 8.0 M in HCl (Note 1). Transfer the solution quantitatively to a 125-ml separatory funnel, washing with 7.5 M HCl. Add 25 ml of isopropyl ether (Note 2), and shake the funnel for two minutes, venting the funnel frequently. Allow the two phases to separate, then carefully drain off the aqueous (lower) phase into a second 125-ml separatory funnel, rinsing the funnel and its stem thoroughly with 5 ml of 7.5 M HCl. Into this second separatory funnel add 25-ml of fresh isopropyl ether, shake for two minutes, venting frequently, and allow the phases to separate. If the supernatant, ether phase is colorless, extraction of iron has been complete and further extractions are unnecessary. If there is any color in the ether phase, drain the aqueous phase into a third 125-ml separatory funnel, rinsing with 7.5 M HCl. Add 25 ml of fresh isopropyl ether and extract the aqueous phase for a third time. This should be sufficient to remove all iron (Note 3).

Discard the aqueous phase. Combine all of the ether phases in a separatory funnel, rinsing the solutions into it with isopropyl ether. Add 25 ml of deionized water to the funnel, shake for two minutes, venting frequently to back-extract the iron into the aqueous phase. A single extraction will be sufficient for this.

Colorimetric determination of iron with 1,10-phenanthroline. Transfer quantitatively the aqueous phase from above to a 1-liter volumetric flask. Add 3 ml of concentrated H_2SO_4 and make up to the mark with deionized water. Upend at least ten times to mix thoroughly.

Pipette an appropriately sized aliquot of this iron solution to contain between 0.1 and 0.5 mg of iron into a 100-ml volumetric flask. Add 25 ml of pH 4.0, 0.5 M acetic acid–sodium acetate buffer. Add 5 ml of 10% aqueous hydroxylamine hydrochloride and 5 ml of 0.25% 1,10-phenanthroline in water. Dilute to the mark with deionized water, mix well by upending at least ten times, and measure the absorbance of the iron-o-phenanthroline chelate at 515 nm after ten minutes.

Pipette 3.00 ml of a standard 0.1000 mg/ml iron(III) solution into a 100-ml volumetric flask. Add 25 ml of pH 4.0, 0.5 M acetic acid–sodium acetate buffer, 5 ml of 10% aqueous hydroxylamine hydrochloride, and 5 ml of aqueous 0.25% 1,10-phenanthroline. Dilute to the mark with deionized water, mix well by upending at least ten times, and measure the absorbance of the iron-o-phenanthroline chelate at 515 nm after ten minutes.

From the measured absorbances of the standard 0.100 mg/ml iron(III) solution and of the unknown aliquot of the extract, calculate the concentration of the iron present in the aliquot. Knowing the size of the aliquot, calculate the total amount of iron extracted from the original sample. From this and the sample weight, calculate the percent of iron present in the initial solid sample.

NOTES

1. Iron(III) is extracted with a greater than 99% extraction between 6.5 M and 8.5 M HCl concentration (initial). The optimum percent extraction of iron(III) occurs between 7.7 and 8.0 M HCl (initial).
2. Technical grade diisopropyl ether will be adequate. It can be used directly with no purification necessary.

3. Under the conditions of this experiment copper, cobalt, manganese, nickel, aluminum, chromium, and zinc are not extracted.

EXPERIMENT 6–2
The Effect of pH on the Extraction of Copper as Its 8-Hydroxyquinoline Chelate into Chloroform *

Copper(II) ions will react with the organic reagent, 8-hydroxyquinoline to form the inner complex according to the reaction:

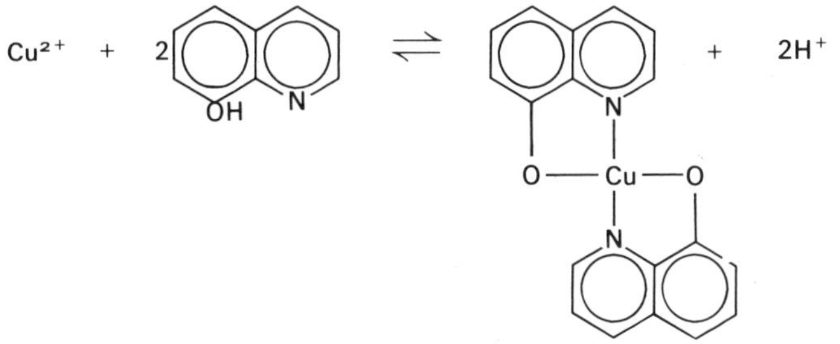

This chelate, being a neutral molecule, is extractable into chloroform. The extraction will show a pH dependence because of the production of hydrogen ions as shown in Equation (6–31). The nature of this dependence is given in Equation (6–21) and the expression for $pH_{\frac{1}{2}}$ is given in Equation (6–23).

The purpose of this experiment is to verify the pH dependence of the extraction of copper with 8-hydroxyquinoline in chloroform and to determine the $pH_{\frac{1}{2}}$ value, n, and K' for the extraction system.

Procedure. Into a 125-ml separatory funnel, pipette 1.00 ml of standard copper sulfate solution (0.500 mg Cu/ml). To this add 49 ml of distilled water and about twenty-five drops of 1 M HCl to give the solution a pH of about 1.5. Pipette 1.0 ml of 0.10 M 8-hydroxyquinoline in chloroform and 9.0 ml of pure chloroform into the funnel (Notes 1 and 2). Stopper the funnel and shake vigorously, venting frequently, for two minutes. Allow the funnel to sit for one minute, and then shake a second time for two minutes. Rest again for one minute, and shake a third time for two minutes (Note 3). Let stand until the two phases separate. Carefully drain off, through phase-separating paper or a plug of cotton barely moistened with chloroform in the neck of a small funnel, enough of the chloroform layer to fill a Spectronic 20 cuvette. With a Spectronic 20 spectrophotometer set at 450 nm (Note 7), measure the absorbance of the chloroform extract using a solution of oxine in chloroform (1.0 ml of 0.1 M oxine in chloroform plus 9 ml of pure chloroform as the reagent blank. Carefully pour the aqueous phase into a 50-ml beaker and measure its pH accurately (± 0.01 pH) with a pH meter.

Repeat the preceding procedure nine times, changing only the amount of HCl initially added (Note 5). Add about 22, 20, 15, 12, 10, 8, 5, 2, and 0 drops of 1 M HCl, respectively, in these additional extractions (Note 6).

---

* Based on the material presented by J. Stary, *Anal. Chim. Acta*, **28**, 132 (1963).

From a previously prepared calibration curve (Note 7) of absorbance at 450 nm vs. mg Cu/ml in chloroform, determine the number of milligrams of copper present in each of the chloroform layers. Using this and the initial weight of copper taken, determine the percentage of copper extracted at each of the ten pH values. Plot these data as % E (ordinate) vs. pH (abscissa) and from the resultant graph determine the $pH_{\frac{1}{2}}$ for the copper 8-hydroxyquinolate extraction. From the plotted data, determine the pH where % E is 40, 45, 50, 55, and 60, respectively. For each of these percent extraction values, calculate D and then log D. Substitute values for log D and pH into Equation (6–22) and determine n and K'.

NOTES

1. Since the solubility of water in chloroform is only 0.97 g/100 g and that of chloroform in water is only 0.800 g/100 g at 25°C, presaturation of each phase with the other, while proper technique, is unnecessary in this experiment.
2. Solutions of oxine in chloroform are not stable over long periods of time and are best prepared fresh daily.
3. In the absence of masking agents in the aqueous phase, distribution equilibrium for most metal oxinates is established within a few minutes.
4. The wavelength of maximum absorption for copper 8-hydroxyquinolate in chloroform is 400 nm. So that the absorbance readings for most of the chloroform extracts lie below 1.0, this value is not used, but the less sensitive wavelength of 450 nm was selected for the spectrophotometric measurements.
5. Specific pH values are unimportant as long as ten values are obtained that are spread more or less uniformly between a pH of 1.5 and 3.0.
6. Because of the change in the value of the distribution ratio of oxine over this pH region, and the change in the percent of the chelate extracted, in these unbuffered solutions there is no direct correlation between the number of drops of HCl added initially and the equilibrium pH measured.
7. This calibration curve may be obtained by measuring the absorbance of chloroform solutions of copper oxinate, obtained by extracting aqueous copper solutions of different concentrations at a pH of 5 with 0.010 M oxine in chloroform or by dissolving the appropriate amounts of solid copper oxinate (available from K & K Laboratories, Inc.) in chloroform. The calibration curve is linear up to 80 p.p.m. of copper in the chloroform phase.

EXPERIMENT 6–3
Separation of Copper, Lead, and Magnesium in a Mixture by Extraction with Oxine and the Spectrophotometric Determination of each Ion *

Copper, lead, and magnesium ions all form yellow chelates with 8-hydroxyquinoline that can be extracted quantitatively into chloroform. Copper oxinate has a $pH_{\frac{1}{2}}$ of 1.37, lead oxinate has a $pH_{\frac{1}{2}}$ of 5.04, and magnesium oxinate has a $pH_{\frac{1}{2}}$ of 8.57 when extracted into 0.10 M oxine in chloroform. Copper, lead, and magnesium are extracted as $Cu(Ox)_2$, $Pb(Ox)_2$, and $Mg(Ox)_2$, respectively. The $pH_{\frac{1}{2}}$ values of these chelates are sufficiently different so these ions can be separated by careful adjustment of the pH of the solution and selective extraction of each chelate. The pH of the aqueous solution is buffered at pH 3.0, where all of the copper can

---

* Based on material presented by J. Stary, *Anal. Chim. Acta.* **28**, 132 (1963) and F. Umland, W. Hoffmann, and K. U. Meckenstock, *Z. Anal. Chem.*, **173**, 211 (1960).

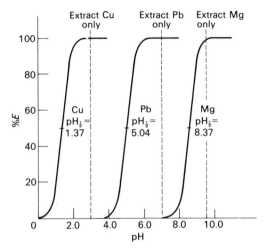

Fig. 6–28.   Extraction separation of copper, lead, and magnesium with 0.10 M oxine in chloroform.

be extracted. Raising the pH to 7.0 enables all of the lead to be removed. Finally at a pH of 9.5 all of the magnesium should be extracted. Fig. 6–28 shows the extraction curves for these three ions and the pH values at which each may be extracted selectively. Each of these metal chelates can then be determined colorimetrically in its extract by measurement of its light absorption at the appropriate wavelength. The wavelength of maximum absorption for the chloroform extract of each metal is copper—410 nm; lead—400 nm; and magnesium—385 nm.

Procedure.   Pipette a 1.00-ml aliquot of an unknown solution containing not more than 0.2 mg of each metal ion (Note 1) into a 125-ml separatory funnel, add 10 ml of deionized water, and 10 ml of 0.5 M chloroacetic acid–chloroacetate, pH 3.00, buffer. Add 10 ml of 0.10 M oxine in chloroform, and shake the funnel for two minutes, venting frequently. Allow the funnel to stand for at least two minutes to allow the layers to separate. Draw off the chloroform layer through phase-separating paper or a barely-wet-with-chloroform-cotton plug in the neck of a small funnel into a 50-ml volumetric flask. Disregard any precipitate that might be present at this stage, but keep it in the separatory funnel. The chloroform in the volumetric flask must be clear and dry, so in removing the $CHCl_3$ phase, be sure not to withdraw any of the aqueous phase. Repeat the extraction as above, using a 5-ml aliquot of the oxine solution. Continue to extract with 5-ml portions of oxine until the last chloroform extract is essentially colorless (Note 2). Less than four additional extractions should be sufficient for removal of all the copper. Make the solution in the volumetric flask up to the mark with chloroform. Mix well by upending at least ten times. Measure the absorbance of the solution at 410 nm against a 0.10 M oxine in chloroform blank. This absorbance measurement should be made within a couple of hours, since the copper oxinate solution in chloroform is not stable overnight. From the calibration curve (Note 3) posted on the bulletin board, obtain the concentration of copper corresponding to this absorbance.

(Alternatively, a standard 0.0500 mg copper in 0.010 M oxine in chloroform can be used with Beer's law.)

Transfer most of the aqueous phase into a 100-ml beaker, taking care not to spill any. Adjust the pH of the solution, using a pH meter, to about 6 with very concentrated ammonia and then very carefully raise the pH to 7.0 with dilute (1 M. NH_3. Disregard any precipitate that might be present at this point in the beaker. Quantitatively transfer the contents of the beaker back into the separatory funnel using a minimum amount of deionized water in the process. Extract the lead into 0.10 M oxine in chloroform according to the procedure given in the preceding paragraph for copper. Check to be sure the pH remains at 7.0. Readjust when necessary. First use a 10-ml portion; thereafter use 5-ml portions of the extracting chelon solution. Drain off the chloroform extract into a 50-ml volumetric flask. Be sure to filter the chloroform through phase-separating paper. Less than four extractions should also be sufficient for the removal of all of the lead. Make the extract up to the mark on the flask with chloroform, mix well by upending, and measure its absorbance at 400 nm. Determine the concentration of lead from the posted calibration curve for lead oxinate in chloroform at 400 nm (Note 4). (Alternatively, measure the absorbance of standard 0.00500 mg Pb/ml in 0.0100 M oxine in chloroform.)

Transfer the aqueous phase into a suitably-sized beaker, taking care not to spill any of the solution. Adjust the pH of this aqueous solution to about 9.5 with concentrated ammonia (15 M) forming an ammonia–ammonium ion buffer. Quantitatively return all of the solution to the separatory funnel, using such a small amount of water that the pH is not changed during the transfer process. Extract the magnesium with 10 ml of 0.10 M oxine in chloroform. Shake for less than one minute (Note 5), allow the phases to separate, and filter the chloroform layer through phase-separating paper into a 50-ml volumetric flask. Repeat the extraction with a second 10-ml portion of the oxine. Make the extract up to the mark with chloroform. Mix well by upending. Measure the absorbance of this extract at 400 nm (Note 6). From the posted calibration curve for the magnesium oxinate at 400 nm (Note 7), determine the concentration of magnesium in the chloroform extract. (Alternatively, measure the absorbance of standard 0.00500 mg Mg/ml in 0.0100 M oxine in chloroform.)

From the concentration of each of the three metals in the chloroform extracts, calculate the number of milligrams of each metal present in the initial 1.0 ml aliquot of the unknown sample.

NOTES

1. At higher metal ion concentrations, yellow precipitates of the metal oxinates form in the aqueous phase and complicate the experiment unnecessarily. Also, the calibration curve for magnesium and lead are not linear above about 7 p.p.m. of the metal in chloroform.
2. 8-Hydroxyquinoline in chloroform has a very pale, dull yellow color by itself.
3. See Note 7, p. 316 for the preparation of the copper calibration curve.
4. The calibration curve for lead is prepared by measuring the absorbance of chloroform solutions of lead oxinate, obtained by extracting aqueous lead solutions of different concentrations at a pH of 7.0 with 0.010 M oxine in chloroform. The calibration curve is linear up to about 5 p.p.m. of lead in chloroform.
5. Lengthy shaking destroys the magnesium complex.

6. The maximum absorbance, 385 nm, cannot be used because the spectrophotometer will not function below 400 nm.
7. The calibration curve should be prepared by extracting a series of aqueous solutions of known magnesium content in exactly the same manner as the unknown is extracted.

PROBLEMS

1. 0.00396 g of Br_2 is dissolved in 50.0 ml of water. This solution is shaken with 10.0 ml of carbon tetrachloride. Calculate the number of milligrams of bromine present in each of the layers at equilibrium. K_D for bromine (CCl_4/H_2O) is 27.00 at 25°C.

2. The partition coefficient for phenol between 1-octanol and water is 28.8. Calculate the percent of the phenol remaining unextracted when 0.146 g of phenol, dissolved in 125 ml of water is extracted once with a 15.0 ml portion of 1-octanol.

3. $GaBr_3$ has a distribution ratio of 1.93 when extracted from 4.5 M HBr into diethyl ether. How many times must 75.0 ml of 4.5 M HBr containing 0.478 g of $GaBr_3$ be extracted with 20.0 ml portions of ether in order to remove 99.9% of the salt?

4. Calculate the percent of 8-hydroxyquinoline extracted into an equal volume of aqueous solution from 0.100 M oxine in chloroform at a pH of:
   (a) 2.00
   (b) 7.00
   (c) 12.00

5. A weak acid, HV, has a partition coefficient between benzene and water of 4.75 and an aqueous dissociation constant of 3.91×10^{-4}. The acid does not associate in the benzene phase. Calculate the pH at which 50.0% of this acid will be extracted from water into benzene.

6. Formic acid has a distribution ratio of 0.416 between methyl isobutyl ketone and water at a pH of 2.13. Assuming no association by the formic acid in the organic layer, calculate the value of the partition coefficient for formic acid in this system.

7. The distribution ratio of niobium when extracted from 2 M HCl with a 0.25% solution of α-benzoin oxime in chloroform is 7.00. When a 50.0 ml solution of niobium is to be extracted with 50.0 ml of this chelon, show that more of the metal ion will be removed when five 10.0-ml portion are used than when a single extraction using the entire 50.0 ml of the chelon is performed.

8. Copper(II) forms a complex with thenoyltrifluoroacetone (TTA) that is extracted into 0.20 M TTA in benzene with a log $K = -1.32$. The cobalt(II)-TTA complex extracts into 0.20 M TTA in benzene with a log $K = -6.70$. What is the minimum pH value for an extraction separation ($\beta = 10^4$) consisting of a single batch extraction of these two metals with 0.20 M TTA in benzene? Which metal ion is in which phase upon completion of the separation?

9. Copper extracts into 0.100 M 8-hydroxyquinoline in chloroform with a $pH_{\frac{1}{2}}$ of 1.38. If the partition coefficient for oxine between chloroform and water is 433 and that for the copper oxinate in the same system is 3.02×10^3, calculate the overall stability constant for $Cu(Ox)_2$.

10. (a) The following metal ions are extracted into 0.100 M benzoylacetone in

benzene with the indicated extraction constants. Calculate the $pH_{\frac{1}{2}}$ values for each of these extractions, considering that the formula for the chelate in each case is $M(BzA)_2$.

Metal Ion	log K
Cd(II)	-14.11
Co(II)	-11.11
Cu(II)	-4.17
Ni(II)	-12.12
Pb(II)	-9.61

(b)   From the calculated $pH_{\frac{1}{2}}$ values, estimate which of the following pairs of metal ions can be separated by extraction with 0.100 M benzoylacetone in benzene and which cannot be separated this way: lead(II)–cadmium (II); lead(II)–copper(II); lead(II)–nickel(II); nickel(II)–cobalt(II); copper(II)–nickel(II); and cadmium(II)–nickel(II).

11.   Zinc(II) is extracted with 1.00×10^{-4} M dithizone in carbon tetrachloride with a $pH_{\frac{1}{2}}$ of 2.80. Calculate the pH at which 99.9% of the zinc in an aqueous solution will be extracted with dithizone.

12.   Zinc(II) forms a complex ion $[Zn(Ox)_2^{2-}]$ with oxalic acid (H_2Ox) that has a log β_1 of 4.9 and a log β_2 of 7.6. Calculate the value of D for the extraction of zinc(II) with 1.00×10^{-4} M dithizone in carbon tetrachloride in the presence of 0.0500 M oxalic acid at the pH value found in Problem 12.

13.   At what pH will zinc(II) be 99.9% extracted by 1.00×10^{-4} M dithizone in CCl_4 in the presence of 0.0500 M oxalic acid? (*Hint:* Assume that $\alpha_0 = 1.00$ at the pH value found. Then check this assumption after calculating the actual pH.)

REFERENCES

1. Barry, G. T., Sato, Y., and Craig, L. C., *J. Biol. Chem.*, **174**, 209 (1948).
2. Berthelot, M. and Jungfleisch, J., *Ann. Chim. Phys.*, (4) **26**, 396, 408 (1872).
3. Boswell, C. R. and Brooks, R. R., *Anal. Chim. Acta*, **33**, 117 (1965).
4. Brooks, R. R., *Talanta*, **12**, 505 (1965).
5. Ibid., p. 511.
6. Brusset, H., Hamelin, R., and Matutano, L., *Compt. Rend.*, **261**, 1979 (1965).
7. Casey, A. T., Davies, E., Meek, T. L. and Wagner, E. S., in *Proc. Intern. Conf., Solv. Extn. Chem., Gothenburg, 1966*, D. Dyrssen, J.-O. Liljenzin, and J. Rydberg, Eds., North-Holland Publishing Co., Amsterdam, 1967, pp. 327–334.
8. Craig, L. C. and Craig, D., in *Technique of Organic Chemistry*, 2nd ed., Part I, Vol. III, A. Weissberger, Ed., Wiley-Interscience, New York, 1956, p. 160.
9. Ibid., p. 253.
10. Diamond, R. M., *J. Phys. Chem.*, **61**, 1522 (1957).
11. Diamond, R. M. and Turk, D. G., in *Progress in Inorganic Chemistry*, F. A. Cotton, Ed., Vol. II, Wiley-Interscience, New York, 1960, p. 159.
12. Fletcher, A. W., in *Proc. Intern. Conf., Solv. Extn. Chem., Gothenburg, 1966*, D. Dyrssen, J.-O. Liljenzin, and J. Rydberg, Eds., North-Holland Publishing Co., Amsterdam, 1967, pp. 636–639.

13. Freiser, H., *Anal. Chem.*, **38**, 131R (1966).
14. Freiser, H., *Anal. Chem*, **40**, 522 R (1968).
15. Gutnikov, G. and Freiser, H., *Anal. Chem.*, **40**, 39 (1968).
16. Hellweg, H. E. and Schweitzer, G. K., *Anal. Chim. Acta*, **28**, 236 (1963).
17. Hesford, E. and McKay, H. A. C., *Trans. Faraday Soc.*, **54**, 573 (1958).
18. Higuchi, T., Michaelis, A., Tan, T. and Hurwitz, A., *Anal. Chem.*, **39**, 974 (1967).
19. Irving, H. M. and Rossotti, F. J. C., *Analyst*, **77**, 801 (1952).
20. Kolfenbach, J. J., Kooi, E. R., Fulmer, E. I., and Underkofler, L. A., *Ind. Eng. Chem., Anal. Ed.*, **16**, 473 (1944).
21. Konrad, J. G., Pionke, H. B. and Chesters, G., *Analyst*, **94**, 490 (1969).
22. Kutscher, F. and Steudel, H., *Z. Phys. Chem.*, **39**, 474 (1903).
23. Laessig, R. H., *Anal. Chem.*, **40**, 2205 (1968).
24. Montgomery, H. A. C., Gardener, D. K. and Gregory, J. G. G., *Analyst*, **94**, 490 (1969).
25. Moore, F. L., *Anal. Chem.*, **41**, 1658 (1969).
26. Morrison, G. and Freiser, H., *Solvent Extraction in Analytical Chemistry*, John Wiley & Sons, New York, 1957, p. 13.
27. Morrison, G. and Freiser, H., *Anal. Chem.*, **34**, 70R (1962).
28. Ibid., **36**, 95R (1964).
29. Mottola, H. A. and Freiser, H. *Talanta*, **13**, 55 (1966).
30. Nernst, W., *Z. Phys. Chem.*, **8**, 110 (1891).
31. Oosting, M., *Anal. Chim. Acta*, **21**, 397 (1959).
32. Peligot, E., *Ann. Chim. Phys.*, (3) **5**, 7 (1842).
33. Sillen, L. G. and Martell, A. E., *Stability Constants of Metal-Ion Complexes*, The Chemical Society, London, 1964.
34. Stary, J., *The Solvent Extraction of Metal Chelates*, Pergamon, Oxford, 1964.
35. Ibid., p. 23.
36. Ibid., p. 26.
37. Ibid., p. 31.
38. Ibid., p. 93.
39. Wehrli, S., *Helv. Chim. Acta*, **20**, 927 (1937).
40. Wolfsberg, K., Daniels, W. R., Ford, G. P., and Hitchcock, E. T., *Nucl. Appl.*, **3**, 568 (1967).

CHAPTER 7

CHROMATOGRAPHY

The most widely used, the most powerful, and the most effective of the separation techniques is *chromatography*. Chromatography is not a single separation method, but consists of a group of related methods that have common features. Some of the chromatographic techniques have been known and used for over one hundred years. Paper chromatography is one of the forms of chromatography that dates back farthest. F. F. Runge separated mixtures of dyes and plant extracts on unglazed paper, blotting paper, and cloth in the 1850s. Pictures of the separations he obtained are shown in his book *Die Bildungstrieb der Stoff* published in 1855. C. Schonbein, at about the same time, and F. Goppelsroeder, during the latter half of the nineteenth century, separated dyes, hydrocarbons, milk, beer, colloids, and plant and animal pigments on paper strips. A form of column chromatography was developed before the turn of the twentieth century. In 1893, L. Reed separated potassium dichromate from eosin, and ferric chloride from copper sulfate on columns of powdered kaolin. From 1898 to 1903, D. T. Day separated many crude oil samples into their components of aliphatic hydrocarbons, aromatic hydrocarbons, and nitrogen and sulfur compounds on large columns of powdered fuller's earth.

In spite of these early uses of the techniques of chromatography, Michael Tswett, a Russian botanist working at the University of Warsaw, is considered to be the originator of the methods of column chromatography as practiced today. At the age of 31 he published (in Russian) a lecture describing chromatographic separations based upon selective adsorption. In 1906 he published the first detailed paper on chromatography,[6] which showed clearly that he was quite aware of the nature of the separation tool that he was describing and of the power of its separation capabilities. In this paper, he not only named the process *chromatography* (although indicating that he was aware that it would work for colorless substances too) and the developed column a *chromatogram*, but he gave the physical basis and mechanism of operation. He cautioned that the isolation of a single zone on a chromatographic column did not guarantee purity, for two substances could appear together. Tswett drew diagrams and described the apparatus in detail. His column is still the prototype for those in use today. Tswett pointed out (1) the need for the adsorbant to be chemically inert, (2) the need to use finely divided solids to obtain effective separations, (3) the need to have the adsorbant be of intermediate strength for practical separations, and (4) the need to activate the adsorbant surface before using. He used powdered $CaCO_3$ and sucrose columns with solutions in benzene and other organic solvents. In this 1906 paper he described in detail the separation of the leaf pigments into seven zones, of which he identified five—chlorophyll a, chlorophyll b, neoxanthin, violaxanthin, and xanthophyll—along with two colorless zones.

In spite of the clarity of Tswett's descriptions and the stated potentialities of this chromatographic method, very little use of chromatography was made during the next twenty-five years. It wasn't until 1931, when Richard Kuhn separated a mixture of carrot carotenes into its components that scientists began to utilize the the method to any appreciable extent. In 1941, A. J. P. Martin and R. L. M. Synge, frustrated by their inability to separate the amino acids from wool by countercurrent distribution, developed *partition chromatography*. This was consciously patterned after countercurrent distribution. In a column, one liquid phase was suspended on the surface of a finely divided, inert solid while a second liquid phase, immiscible with the first, was allowed to flow over the stationary phase. The solute was partitioned back and forth between the two liquid phases. They developed this method so thoroughly that they were awarded the Nobel Prize in 1952 for their work in chromatography. In 1952, A. J. P. Martin and A. T. James published several papers which developed the technique of *gas chromatography*. Ettre[2] recounts elegantly the stories of Tswett, Martin, Synge, and James. In 1938 two Russians, N. A. Ismailof and M. S. Schraiber, published early work on *thin-layer chromatography*. They resolved pharmaceutical tinctures using thin layers of Al_2O_3 and other adsorbants spread on microscope slides. Not much notice was taken of this technique until 1958 when E. Stahl demonstrated the general applicability to many classes of organic compounds. He described equipment for coating the glass plates, gave logical reasons for the extreme effectiveness of the technique, and popularized the technique. Today, these and other forms of the chromatographic method are routine separation tools in organic, inorganic, biochemical, and medical science laboratories.

What constitutes chromatography? Or better still, how does one define a chromatographic method so as to include all of the known forms and, yet, exclude countercurrent distribution. It is difficult. A. I. M. Keulemans'[4] definition is widely used and highly satisfactory: "Chromatography is a physical method of separation in which the components to be separated are distributed between two phases, one of these phases constituting a stationary bed of large surface area, the other being a fluid that percolates through or along the stationary bed." He claims that the operative word is *percolate* in excluding countercurrent processes from this definition. All of the forms of chromatography do have the common features emphasized in this definition. All of them involve the physical movement of the sample through a tube or across a flat surface equivalent to the tube. In all of them, the stationary phase possesses an extraordinarily large surface area. In all of them the movement of the sample is by means of the motion of a fluid phase. All of the methods are based upon the principle of selective retardation of the movement of the components by the stationary phase. All of the methods result in the production of zones or bands of concentrated components.

Chromatographic methods are named on many different bases and there is absolutely no consistency in the names. Thus we have *paper* and *gel chromatography* —named after the medium used as the solid support; *adsorption* and *partition chromatography*—named because of the nature of the underlying physical process; *gas chromatography*—named after the state of the fluid phase; *ascending*, *descending*, *radial*, or *two-dimensional chromatography*—named after the laboratory technique used to carry out the separation; and *column chromatography*—named after the container of the stationary phase. Let us not overlook *reversed-phase* chromatography, named just to emphasize that things are backward from the "normal" mode of operation. Quite frequently these names are strung together to give formidable sounding names such as reversed-phase ascending two-dimensional paper elution chromatography. Do not be put off by this plethora of names. There are not that many different chromatographic methods.

Table 7-1.   CLASSIFICATION OF CHROMATOGRAHIC METHODS

Nature of the Distribution Process	Bulk or Mobile Phase	Stationary or Thin Phase	Kind of Chromatography
Partition	Liquid	Liquid	Partition chromatography (column) Paper chromatography
Partition	Gas	Liquid	Gas–liquid chromatography
Adsorption	Liquid	Solid	Adsorption chromatography (column) Thin-layer chromatography Ion-exchange chromatography
Adsorption	Gas	Solid	Gas–solid chromatography

In chromatography the essential process is the distribution of the solute between two phases, one stationary and the other moving. Therefore, let us tabulate the various combinations of distribution processes along with the physical nature of the two phases. This should tell us what kinds of chromatography there actually are. This is done in Table 7–1.

Table 7–1 accounts for most of the basic types of chromatography (gel chromatography being the most obvious omission) but it is very deceptive in its compartmentalization. The mechanisms of most chromatographic processes are combinations of partition, adsorption, filtration. Adsorption plays an unknown role in partition chromatography. What does occur when we call something *ion exchange*? Can we exclude partition as a mechanism in TLC? So, use Table 7–1 as a guide to the principal processes occurring, but not the sole processes involved. A knowledge of the distribution process occurring during a chromatographic separation can be of invaluable aid in improving a difficult resolution.

DESCRIPTION OF THE CHROMATOGRAPHIC PROCESS

Before becoming involved in the theory and applications of chromatography, it is worthwhile to describe the physical arrangements and the mechanical processes occurring during a chromatographic separation. In order to simplify the description and to be able to talk more specifically, let us assume that we are dealing with column chromatographic processes only. The chromatographic column (see Fig. 7–1) is plugged with glass wool to prevent the finely divided solid from running through, and then packed with powdered solid to a height of about 20 to 30 cm. The solid may or may not be wetted with a solvent. Before introduction of the sample, the column looks like the one in Fig. 7–1 (*a*).

A small aliquot (about 1 ml) of a concentrated solution of the sample is placed onto the top of the column carefully so as not to disturb the packing. The sample is allowed to drain down into the top layer of the column packing where it remains as a very narrow band. After placing the sample on the column the system will appear as in Fig. 7–1 (*b*). A solvent, called the eluent, is poured through the column at a constant rate, washing over the sample. This solvent may be the one that the sample was dissolved in originally or it may be completely different. The eluent may be a pure liquid or a mixture of liquids.

As the eluent washes over the narrow sample band, the sample will dissolve off the surface of the solid into the moving liquid. The more soluble components of the sample will dissolve first. Since the liquid is flowing, the dissolved component will move a little way down the column. There, coming in contact with fresh solid surface, the component will be attracted onto it. Fresh eluent dissolves it off the solid again. The removal of a solute from the flowing liquid by a fresh portion of solid surface and the subsequent dissolution of the solute into fresh solvent continues repeatedly as the solute passes through the entire chromatographic column. The more soluble a component is in the eluting liquid, the longer the component will

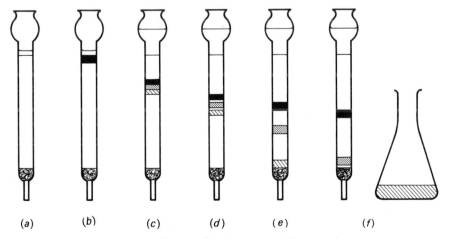

(*a*)   (*b*)   (*c*)   (*d*)   (*e*)   (*f*)

Fig. 7–1. Diagram of a chromatographic separation.

be dissolved, and, since the liquid is flowing, the faster the solute will move down the column. The less soluble a solute is in the eluting liquid, the longer it remains on the surface of the solid, and, since the solid is stationary, the slower the solute moves down the column. A solute that is completely insoluble in the eluting agent will remain in a narrow band at the top of the column and not move, no matter how many liters of solvent are passed through. A solute that is extremely soluble in the eluting liquid stays almost exclusively in the liquid phase and comes off the bottom of the column very rapidly. Solutes with intermediate solubilities take intermediate lengths of time to move down the chromatographic column.

As the solutes move down the column, their rates are determined by the distribution behavior of the solute between the surface of the solid and the moving liquid. The partition or adsorption equilibrium, will determine the rate of movement. After a short time, the sample will begin to segregate into zones in which one solute is more concentrated than another. The column now has the appearance of Fig. 7–1 (c). As elution continues, these zones of enhanced concentration gradually emerge as distinct entities, with each zone containing only a single solute [Fig. 7–1 (d)]. At a later time, these separated zones of pure component pull away from each other, allowing zones of pure solvent to appear between them, as is shown in Fig. 7–1 (e). This process of separating the components of a mixture into zones or bands of pure substance, each located at a different place on the column, is known as the *development of the chromatogram*. Eventually, the zone of the most loosely held solute emerges from the bottom of the chromatographic column. It can be collected then and analyzed. This band will be followed shortly by the band of the second most loosely held solute, and so on [Fig. 7–1 (f)], until all of the solutes have been removed from the column. This process of removing from the column and collecting each solute band is known as *elution*. The solution containing each sample component is known as an *eluate*. During the passage of the solute band down the column, the width of the band increases from the narrow strip originally at the top, to the fairly broad zone that is eventually eluted from the bottom. This process is called *band broadening*.

When working with colorless solutes separation of the solutes into bands and the movement of these bands down the column is not visible. Consequently, in order to detect each of the components, the liquid emerging from the bottom of the chromatographic column (the eluate) is collected in discrete fractions, say of ten ml. Each of these fractions is then analyzed for the components in the mixture. A graph of the concentration of each component in the eluate as a function of the volume of eluate collected (or fraction collected, or tube number) is a succession of peaks, as is shown in Fig. 7–2.

The amount of each component present in the mixture determines the area under each peak. Notice that the peaks emerging at larger volumes have a broader base; this is the consequence of the spreading of the band as it moves down the column.

The bases for the separation of the components in a mixture by chromatography lie in the differences in the chemical and physical properties of each component. The processes that occur within the chromatographic column during development of the chromatogram are all equilibrium processes. Slight differences in the components' properties are magnified enormously by the many thousands of

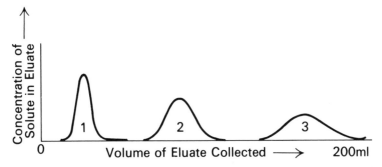

Fig. 7–2. Relationship between concentration of eluate component and volume of coilected eluate.

reversals of the equilibrium as the solute moves throughout the length of the column. Knowledge of the equilibria involved in the separation and how to shift the position of each equilibrium, enables the analyst to improve poor separations or to effect separations not otherwise possible. Lack of knowledge of the chemistry involved in a chromatographic separation cripples its effectiveness.

The debilitation of the motion of a solute compared to the motion of the flowing solvent in the column is known as the principle of *selective retardation.* Each solute in a mixture moves through the column at a rate that is determined by the position of equilibrium between the solute in the flowing solvent and the solute on the immobile solid surface. These rates of movement are characteristic of each solute, in a particular environment consisting of column packing and solvent composition. The relative length of time it takes for a solute to emerge from the bottom of a chromatographic column is used to identify the solute. Each solute will have its own degree of retardation or retardation factor. The retardation factor, R_f, for a solute is defined as:

$$R_f = \frac{\text{linear velocity of a band of the solute}}{\text{linear velocity of the flowing solvent}} \qquad (7\text{--}1)$$

$$= \frac{\text{distance moved by the solute band in time } t}{\text{distance moved by the flowing solvent in time } t} \qquad (7\text{--}2)$$

Each molecule of a solute is stationary when it is attached to the surface of the solid and mobile when it is in the solvent stream. As it progresses down the column it thus starts and stops thousands of times as it passes first from one phase into the second and then returns from the second to the first. Thus, each molecule spends only a fraction of its total time in the column moving with the solvent. Looking at it this way, another definition for the retardation factor would be:

$$R_f = \frac{\text{time spent in the mobile phase}}{\text{total time spent in the chromatographic column}} \qquad (7\text{--}3)$$

We showed above that the extent to which the solute is held back behind the solvent front depends upon the strength with which it is held onto the solid's surface (equilibrium position). Let us see if we can relate mathematically the R_f value of a solute to its equilibrium constant for the retardation phenomenon.

At any time during the development of a chromatogram, the fraction of the total number of solute molecules of any particular species that is dissolved in the moving solvent is given by:

$$\text{fraction moving} = \frac{\text{amount of solute in liquid phase}}{\text{total amount of solute present}} \qquad (7\text{--}4)$$

The amount of solute in the liquid phase at any instant is $V_l C_l$, where V_l is the volume of the liquid phase moving within the column and C_l is the concentration of the solute *at that time* in the liquid phase. Any solute not in the liquid must be stationary on the solid surface. The amount of stationary solute is $V_s C_s$, where V_s is the volume of the stationary phase holding the solute and C_s is the solute concentration in this stationary phase. Substituting these amounts into Equation (7–4) gives:

$$\text{fraction moving} = \frac{V_l C_l}{V_l C_l + V_s C_s} \qquad (7\text{--}5)$$

From Equation (7–3) the fraction of solute moving is equal to R_f, since the solute only moves with the solvent velocity when it is in the mobile phase. The fraction of the molecules in the moving phase at any time is a measure of the fraction of the time that any molecule spends in this moving phase. Thus,

$$R_f = \frac{V_l C_l}{V_l C_l + V_s C_s} = \frac{V_l}{V_l + \dfrac{C_s}{C_l} V_s}$$

$$= \frac{V_l}{V_l + K V_s} \qquad (7\text{--}6)$$

where $K = C_s/C_l$ and is an equilibrium constant. When partition is the distribution mechanism of a separation, K is the ratio of the solute concentration in the stationary liquid phase to the solute concentration in the mobile liquid phase. This, of course, is D, the distribution ratio of the solute. When adsorption is the distribution mechanism, K is the concentration of the solute adsorbed onto the surface of the solid divided by the concentration of the solute in the mobile liquid phase. This, as we shall see, includes A_s, the specific adsorptivity. In both cases the relationship between the equilibrium constant and the R_f value is identical.

Every solute will show a different R_f value for different stationary and liquid phases. This is readily understandable since the nature of the phases affects the value of K in Equation (7–6). R_f values vary with the method of preparation of the solid surface, the surface area, pore size, and so on. Composition and volume of the liquid phases affect R_f values. Temperature is always a factor to be considered in comparing R_f values. Because of variations in R_f with experimental conditions, literature R_f values should not be used for identification purposes. Experimental R_f values for the pure solutes, run on the same column and using the same chemicals and conditions as were used for the unknown should be determined. Only when using these R_f values should one attempt to identify components in an unknown mixture and even then one should be cautious. Concidence of or slight differences in R_f values may or may not be meaningful. One never knows!

PHYSICAL BASES OF CHROMATOGRAPHIC SEPARATIONS

The two kinds of equilibrium that underlie the majority of chromatographic separation processes are liquid–liquid partition and adsorption onto the surface of a finely powdered solid. Gel filtration and ion-exchange chromatographic separations involve additional principles which will be discussed at the time appropriate for each of the two techniques.

Partition of a solute between two immiscible liquids has been discussed thoroughly in Chapter 5 and its application to solvent extraction was treated extensively in Chapter 6. The principles involved, the mathematical relationships, and the methods whereby the numerical value of D can be changed, therefore, have been treated. They will not be discussed further at this time. This is not to imply that partition equilibria are insignificant.

Adsorption of a solute onto the surface of a solid has not been encountered in this book before, even though it is an equilibrium process. Since an understanding of adsorption is essential to an understanding of adsorption chromatography, let us spend a few pages in an attempt to describe the adsorption phenomenon. The electrical field surrounding the atoms, ions, or molecules in the surface layer of a solid is not symmetrical. The other atoms, ions, or molecules of the solid surround part of each one on the surface, but not all of it. Consequently, there are electrical forces at the surface of a solid which are capable of attracting particles from the surroundings. The particles attracted to a surface, and held there by such electrostatic forces are said to be adsorbed onto the surface. Thus, adsorption can be defined as an attachment of particles to an interface. Adsorption onto a solid surface may be from either a gas or a liquid. As we have seen (Table 7–1), both are encountered in chromatography. The forces holding atoms or molecules onto the surface may be van der Waals' forces, dipole interactions between polar surfaces and polar molecules, charge transfer forces, or hydrogen bonding. The first three of these forces are weaker than chemical bonding, so that when these forces are involved we call the adsorption *physical adsorption*. This is characterized by weak interactions between the solute and surface and, consequently, rapid reversibility of the adsorption equilibrium. When there is actual bonding between the solute and the surface, *chemisorption* is said to occur. Chemisorption involves strong forces, which causes a very difficult removal of the solute from the surface, often taking some of the surface layer with it.

The theory of adsorption is not fully developed at the present time, but there is sufficient information known about the process to enable a deep enough understanding to be of value in chromatographic separations. Adsorption is usually described graphically in terms of an *adsorption isotherm*. An adsorption isotherm is nothing more than a description of the change in the amount of material adsorbed onto the surface as a function of the concentration of the species in the solution. Since it is measured at a constant temperature, the graph is called an isotherm. When the adsorption onto the surface is from a gas, the partial pressure of the solute in the gaseous mixture is used instead of its molar concentration. Many types of adsorption behavior are observed. Giles[3] has classified adsorption isotherms from solution into four major types, called S (from the shape of the curve),

L (Langmuir), *H* (high affinity), and *C* (constant partition). These four types of isotherm are shown in Fig. 7–3.

The shape of the S adsorption isotherm indicates that as the adsorption from the solution progresses, it becomes easier, that is, a greater fraction of the material is adsorbed at higher concentrations than at lower concentrations. From this it can be concluded that at the surface there must be intermolecular bonding between adjacent molecules of the adsorbate, which assists the surface in holding the solute. S adsorption isotherms occur when the solute molecule is monofunctional, has moderate intermolecular interactions, and has strong competition from the polar solvent for the surface adsorption site. Giles states that S adsorption isotherms are produced when flat molecules are so adsorbed onto the surface that they stand on edge. An example of a system exhibiting an S adsorption isotherm is the adsorption of phenol onto alumina from either water or ethanol solutions.

L adsorption isotherms are the best known ones and occur in the majority of cases involving adsorption from dilute solutions. In this type of adsorption the most active adsorption sites on the surface are covered first, so that the ease with which a substance is adsorbed decreases with increasing extent of surface coverage. Hence the isotherm becomes rounded with increasing concentration in solution. When a monolayer of adsorbate covers the surface, adsorption essentially ceases. Giles believes that L adsorption isotherms are produced when molecules are adsorbed flat onto the surface and when there is no intermolecular bonding between adsorbed species. An example of a system exhibiting an L adsorption isotherm is the adsorption of phenol onto alumina from benzene.

When an H adsorption isotherm is obtained, the solute is essentially all removed from the solution at extremely low concentrations. This is not a desirable type of isotherm for chromatographic purposes. It is found during the adsorption of basic dyes onto alumina or when chemisorption occurs.

The shape of C adsorption isotherms implies that as the adsorption of the species from the solution continues, its ease of adsorption remains constant. C adsorption isotherms are found for porous solids composed of flexible molecules. The adsorbed molecules have a great ability to penetrate into the structure of the solid. The solvent does not compete successfully for adsorption sites. A system exhibiting a C isotherm is the adsorption of nonaromatic hydrocarbons onto cellulose acetate from "inert" solvents.

A quantitative relationship between the amount of material adsorbed onto a solid surface and the solution concentration was developed in 1916 by I. Langmuir.

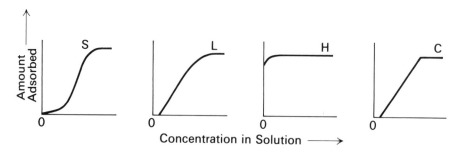

Fig. 7–3. Giles' typical isotherms[3] for adsorption from solution.

He was studying the adsorption of gases, but his results are applicable for an L adsorption isotherm from solution. Langmuir's treatment rested on three assumptions:

(1) All potential sites for adsorption onto a surface are equal in energy and probability of being occupied by a molecule of adsorbate. That is, there are no "active" sites to which the adsorbate is preferentially adsorbed. Hence, no dependence of the extent of adsorption on the fraction of the surface that is covered with adsorbed molecules.

(2) There are no interactions among the molecules adsorbed on the surface of the solid. That is to say, no intermolecular forces exist.

(3) Every molecule of the gas that, upon approaching the surface, strikes a molecule that is already adsorbed onto the surface, will bounce off, returning to the fluid phase rather than being adsorbed. This is another way of saying that there is only a monolayer of adsorbed molecules covering the surface.

Let N_0 be the number of molecules capable of being adsorbed onto the solid when the surface is completely covered with a monolayer. Let N be the number of molecules actually adsorbed onto the surface at equilibrium with the fluid phase. Let C be the concentration of molecules in the fluid phase and/or P be the pressure of the gas over the surface. The fraction of the surface area that is covered by absorbed molecules at equilibrium is θ, and θ is equal to N/N_0.

At equilibrium the rate at which adsorbed molecules leave the surface and return to the fluid phase depends upon the number of molecules adsorbed on the surface, which means the fraction of the surface that is covered by adsorbed molecules, that is,

$$\text{rate of leaving surface} = k_d \theta$$

where k_d is the proportionality constant.

At equilibrium the rate of condensation of molecules upon the surface will be dependent upon the number of molecules in the fluid phase (the concentration or partial pressure) and the surface of the solid that is available for adsorption:

$$\text{rate of adsorption} = k_a P(1 - \theta) = k_a C(1 - \theta)$$

where k_a is the proportionality constant.

Since we are considering the equilibrium condition, these two rates are equal:

$$k_d \theta = k_a P(1 - \theta)$$

Rearranging this in order to solve for the fraction of the surface covered by adsorbed species:

$$\theta = \frac{k_a P}{k_d + k_a P}$$

Calling $k_a/k_d = b$, and using solution concentrations, C, instead of partial pressures, gives:

$$\theta = \frac{bC}{1 + bC} \tag{7-7}$$

which is one expression for the Langmuir adsorption isotherm.

When explaining or predicting adsorption chromatographic separations, frequently it is desirable to use a term called the specific adsorption, A_s, which is defined as the quantity of solute, s, adsorbed per unit weight (usually per gram) of adsorbant, w. Thus:

$$A_s = \frac{s}{w} \tag{7-8}$$

At equilibrium, the specific adsorption is a measure of the fraction of the surface of the solid that is covered by adsorbed species so that, $A_s = k\,\theta$. If we call $kb = K$, then we can write the Langmuir adsorption isotherm equation in another form, one that is a bit more useful for adsorption chromatography.

$$A_s = \frac{KC}{1 + bC} \tag{7-9}$$

Equation (7–9) describes the curve shown as the L adsorption isotherm in Fig. 7–3. At low solution concentrations the L adsorption isotherm is essentially a linear one. That this should be true can be obtained from Equation (7–9). At very low concentrations, bC will be much less than 1 and can be neglected in relation to it. When this is done Equation (7–9) becomes:

$$A_s = KC$$

describing the observed linear relationship.

At high concentrations of solute in solution, the L adsorption isotherm levels off to a value independent of concentration. Equation (7–9) also describes this, for as C increases a region is reached where the value of bC becomes very much greater than 1. For this region Equation (7–9) can be rewritten:

$$A_s = \frac{KC}{bC} = \frac{K}{b}$$

which describes the saturation of the surface adsorption, beyond which no more material can be adsorbed onto it.

The relation C/A_s is completely analogous to the distribution ratio D; it is the ratio of the concentration of solute in two immiscible phases. In fact, adsorption isotherms can be considered to be nothing more than a plot analogous to those of the distribution ratios as a function of solute concentration. As is found for D at low concentrations in solution, when bC is much less than unity, the ratio C/A_s is a constant, but at higher concentrations deviations from linearity begin to arise. In Equation (7–6), K is either C/A_s or D, depending upon the distribution process.

In 1909, Freundlich proposed a general relationship between the amount of material adsorbed upon the surface of a solid and the concentration of the material in solution.

$$A_s = k_1 C^{1/N} \tag{7-10}$$

where k_1 and N are arbitrary parameters chosen so as to fit the experimental data, and C is the concentration of the solute in the solution. This general expression can describe most isotherms by judicious selection of values for N. When N equals one, the linear relationship between the amount of solute adsorbed and its concentration in solution, as found in the C isotherm and in the dilute regions of the L adsorption isotherm, is described. When N is greater than one, the L isotherm, that is, Langmuir-type adsorption is described. When N is less than one, the convex, early portion of the S adsorption isotherm is described.

For adsorption from solution, the assumptions Langmuir made in deriving his equation, are not always valid. In order to explain S adsorption isotherms Langmuir's conditions must be discarded. Measurements of heats of adsorption as a function of θ, have shown experimentally that there are sites on the surface of a solid that are "active," that is, show a preference over other sites for the adsorption of molecules and, hence, are occupied first. Certainly, there are intermolecular forces existing between molecules adsorbed on the surface of solids. These intermolecular forces reduce the ability of molecules to leave the surface, or, conversely, to make it easier to adsorb onto partially covered surfaces. While second and third layers of molecules adsorbed onto surfaces are less strongly held than the first layer, they have been found.

Band or Zone Spreading

As a band or zone of solute moves through a chromatographic media, it becomes more diffuse. The band or zone occupies a larger volume (area for two-dimensional forms of chromatography) and at every point within the initial zone, the concentration of solute becomes lower. Figs 7–1 and 7–2 show this broadening clearly. Fig. 7–2 is known as an *elution curve*. If the system were at equilibrium at all times and in all places on a chromatographic column, then the narrow band of solute that was placed at the top of the column would remain a narrow band and emerge in the eluate from the bottom of the column in a small volume. In practice, the fluid flows too rapidly for equilibrium always to be achieved. This lack of establishment of equilibrium causes the narrow band to spread out as it proceeds down the column. The leading side of the Gaussian peak has a higher solute concentration in the flowing fluid than on the stationary column. The direction of the distribution process primarily is the partition (or adsorption) of the solute from the mobile to the stationary phase. When equilibrium is not attained, and the mobile phase continues to move, the solute proceeds just a bit further along the column before it is stopped than it would have under equilibrium conditions.

On the trailing side of the Gaussian peak, the solute concentration on the stationary phase is greater than in the moving fluid. The direction of the distribution process primarily is the removal of the solute from the solid into the moving eluent stream. Since equilibrium is not attained, the solute will remain on the surface a bit longer than under equilibrium conditions, and will lag behind. Thus, because of the nonattainment of equilibrium, a band of concentrations has its front edge moving further along the column than it should, while at the same time the rear edge lags further behind on the column than it should. Consequently, there is a broadening or spreading of the band as it moves along the medium.

Shapes of Elution Peaks

The analogy between adsorption and partition chromatography and countercurrent distribution is an excellent one. Martin and Synge used it effectively when they developed partition chromatography. In countercurrent distribution, solute movement through the apparatus produces a Gaussian distribution of concentrations. In chromatography, solutes also move through the columns (or their equivalents) so as to produce a Gaussian distribution of concentrations in the eluate.

In practice, however, all elution peaks are not Gaussian in shape; but some are skewed in one direction or another, as is shown in Fig. 7–4. The explanation for these distortions can be found in the adsorption or partition behavior of the solute. The discussion that follows will be exclusively in terms of adsorption behavior, although completely analogous arguments can be made for the distortion of elution peaks in partition chromatography, based upon changes in the distribution ratio with concentration.

Let us consider a solute exhibiting an L adsorption isotherm, which can be described by the Langmuir equation in the form of Equation (7–9). As was discussed on p. 332, Equation (7–9) predicts that at very high solute concentrations A_s becomes constant. Thus, for large values of C, the ratio, C/A_s, will cease to remain a constant and will increase. Rewriting Equation (7–9) shows this more exactly:

$$\frac{C}{A_s} = \frac{1 + bC}{K} \tag{7–11}$$

Since b and K are constants, C/A_s increases as the value of C increases. Since C is the solute concentration in the mobile phase, in effect, what Equation (7–11) is saying is that the higher the concentration of solute present in the system, the greater its relative concentration in the liquid or moving phase. Since the solute spends more time in the moving phase it moves through the column faster. Consequently, Equation (7–11) predicts that high concentrations of solute will move through a chromatographic column faster than lower concentrations. Thus, an L adsorption isotherm produces an elution peak with the highest concentration of solute at the front of the curve. The peak then "tails" off, down to lower concentrations (see Fig. 7–4).

Now let us look at a solute exhibiting an S adsorption isotherm, the lower

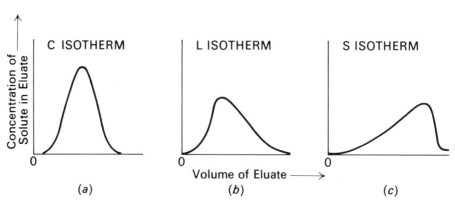

Fig. 7–4.   Shapes of elution peaks: (*a*) ideal, (*b*) tailing. (*c*) bearding.

portion of which can be described by the Freundlich equation [Equation (7–10)] with a value of N less than one. The shape of an S isotherm was explained on the basis of intermolecular interactions. This means that the more solute there is on the surface, the more strongly will the solute be held there. Equation (7–10) for N less than one predicts that low solute concentrations will move faster through the column, for they spend less time on the stationary adsorbed site. The elution peaks when S adsorption isotherms occur, as is shown in Fig. 7–4, have slow rising fronts and then very sharp rears. This effect has been called "bearding."

TECHNIQUES OF COLUMN DEVELOPMENT

There are three different methods by which a column chromatogram can be developed—*frontal analysis*, *displacement analysis*, and *elution analysis*. While all three of these methods have value in chromatography, today almost all development is carried out by elution analysis or some modification of it, that is, gradient elution analysis or programmed temperature operation.

Frontal Analysis

Frontal analysis was one of the earliest methods of column chromatography. Today it is chiefly of historical interest. The main reason that it is not widely used is that it does not give effective separations. Only one solute of a mixture (the first one appearing at the bottom on the column) can be obtained in a pure condition, but even the recovery of that solute is not 100%. A short chromatographic column which is presaturated with the solvent is used. A very large volume of the sample solution is poured continuously into the top of the column. The liquid emerging from the bottom of the column is analyzed continuously, and when its composition becomes identical to that of the sample being poured in at the top of the column, the analysis is complete. The most weakly adsorbed or partitioned component of the mixture emerges alone from the column first, followed by a sharp front separating it from a mixture of the second weakest and the weakest. This mixture comes off the column until a second front is reached. The second front is followed by a mixture of the three most weakly adsorbed or partitioned components, and so on. The resulting chromatogram is very difficult to interpret and, since there are definite disadvantages in that no complete separation of all components is obtained, the method is not used in most laboratories.

Displacement Analysis

In displacement analysis, the sample, small in volume, is placed in a narrow band at the top of the chromatographic column. A second solution containing a solute that is very strongly adsorbed or partitioned (more strongly than any of the components in the mixture to be separated) is slowly poured through the column. This solution is called the *displacing agent* or the *developer*. The developer can be a pure, strongly adsorbed solvent, but more frequently it is a solution. As the developer passes through the column, it displaces all of the components of the sample from their positions on the stationary phase, forcing them into the mobile

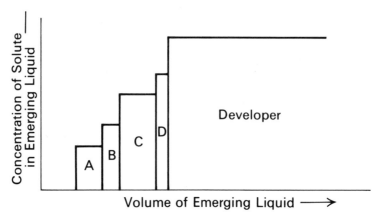

Fig. 7–5.   Analysis curve for displacement analysis.

liquid. At the same time, each of the components of the sample begins to displace those other components more weakly adsorbed or partitioned than it. Each solute is pushed along the column by a substance that is more strongly held to the solid surface. As they move reluctantly through the column, the components gradually separate into contiguous, sharp bands of pure components which eventually emerge from the bottom of the column. Analysis of the emerging liquid for a displacement analysis yields a graph having the appearance of Fig. 7–5.

The height of each band of solute is determined by the specific adsorption or distribution ratio of that solute, and since the solutes are displaced in order of increasing A_s or D, the graph has a steplike appearance. The width of each of the bands depends upon the solute concentration in the sample.

Displacement analysis is usually restricted to adsorption chromatography (or ion exchange) and, even then, used only for samples having L adsorption isotherms. The actual steps are not so sharp as indicated in Fig. 7–5; overlapping of solute bands is common. This means that a displacement analysis can never give a truly quantitative separation. When the analysis has been completed, the column is saturated with the displacing agent. If this has been chosen properly it will be exceedingly difficult, if not impossible, to remove the displacing agent from the column. Hence, a given column packing can only be used one time. One advantage of the method, however, is that the sample is concentrated during the separation process, instead of being diluted as is the case in elution analysis.

Elution Analysis

The technique of elution analysis is the one that was described earlier (p. 325). An elution curve is shown in Fig. 7–2, and the description of the process amplified in the discussion on band broadening. Elution chromatography is much more widely used today than any other mode of operation because the components of a mixture can be separated quantitatively and the columns can be used repeatedly for successive analyses. The eluting liquid must be less strongly adsorbed onto the column than any of the components in the sample.

Frequently, when attempting an elution chromatographic analysis, a single solvent will not be adequate to remove all of the components from the column. When there are very large differences among the distribution ratios or the specific adsorbances of the components of the sample, one component will come off the column quite rapidly, whereas a second component barely moves down the column. Removal of the second component using the original solvent could take many liters of solvent. If after complete removal of the first component the solvent is changed to one in which the second component is more soluble, the second component can be eluted rapidly and with a relatively small volume of the solvent, for example, 100 ml.

One widely used modification of elution analysis, designed to overcome the problems of long elution times, tailing, and poor resolution for certain components in mixtures, is *gradient elution analysis*. Two solvents are used, a weak eluting agent and a strong eluting agent. However, instead of an abrupt discontinuous shift from one solvent to the other, as described in the preceding paragraph, the composition of the eluting solution is changed continuously during elution. The eluent starts out as the pure weak solvent and then progressively increases in concentration of the strong eluting agent, until, at the completion of the analysis, the solvent is pure strong eluting agent. This continual change in composition of the eluting agent is done in a mixing chamber at the top of the column. Fig. 7–6 shows two experimental arrangements used to mix solvents for gradient elution analysis.

Not only does gradient elution analysis shorten the time of development of the chromatogram, it also improves peak shapes for it minimizes tailing. The technique of gradient elution is not limited solely to the gradual introduction of a second solvent into the eluent, but can also encompass a continuously changing eluting agent pH, a gradually increasing ionic strength, an increasing concentration of a chelating agent, and so on. Anything that continuously increases the power of the eluent to remove the solutes from the column (such as gradually increasing the

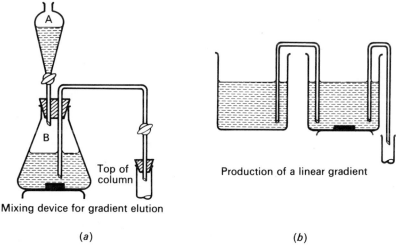

Mixing device for gradient elution

Production of a linear gradient

(a)   (b)

Fig. 7–6. Experimental arrangements for gradient elution analysis: (*a*) mixing device for gradient elution, (*b*) production of a linear gradient.

temperature of a column in gas chromatography) can be considered as a modification of gradient elution chromatography.

Zone Detection

One very critical aspect of chromatography is to be able to locate the bands or zones of solutes as they are separating on the column, so that the fractions containing the pure substances can be collected, the number of components in the mixture identified, and the concentration of each solute ascertained. Almost all of the stationary solid phases used in chromatography are white or light colored, so that when the solutes possess color, the bands and zones can be seen clearly on the columns. Unfortunately, only a small fraction of the mixtures separated chromatographically consist of colored components. Hence, the detection of bands of solute possessing no color is a common problem.

The ideal detection system is one that can be used in the column or placed in the effluent as it emerges from the bottom of the column. The detector system should not consume the components, so that they can be used for other purposes. The response of the detector should be rapid, giving almost instantaneous detection of an emerging solute band. The basis of the detection system should be some general physical or chemical property of compounds, so that the detector will be widely applicable to all mixtures and be able to discover an unexpected component in a mixture. The detector should be sensitive, so that it is capable of detecting very small concentrations of solute in relatively large volumes of solution. During the elution process, the sample is generally diluted by a factor of about one hundred. All of these characteristics are usually not available in a single detection system. One of the reasons that gas chromatography is such a popular and powerful separation technique is that several general detectors are available for use with it that do fulfill the above conditions—thermal conductivity, flame ionization, and others. A recent renewed interest in liquid chromatography has led to the development of detection systems, such as refractive index detectors, that are moderately broad in their application. Even so, when using column chromatographic techniques, a wide variety of detection systems must be considered; the one selected for a particular separation will depend upon the chemical identities of the compounds being separated.

When visual location of the chromatographic bands is not feasible under incandescent light, the column may be irradiated with ultraviolet light. Ultraviolet radiation excites many organic compounds and causes them to fluoresce. This fluorescence can then be followed as it separates into several bands and moves down the column. A modification of this technique is used in commercial thin-layer chromatographic sheets, where the solid adsorbent is treated with a fluorescent indicator, so that the stationary phase will fluoresce. Under these conditions, when the ultraviolet radiation shines on the TLC sheet during the development of the chromatogram, zones of the solutes will appear as dark spots upon a fluorescent background.

Another widely used technique when separating a mixture of colorless, non-fluorescent solutes is to collect the eluate in discrete aliquots, say of 10 ml each,

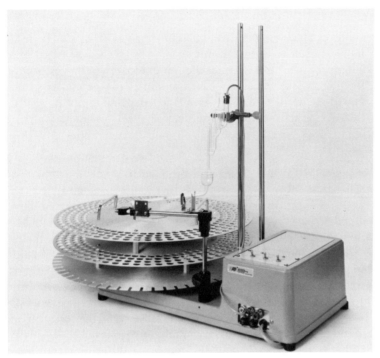

Fig. 7–7.   A commercial fraction collector for use in column chromatography. (*Courtesy of Scientific Manufacturing Industries.*)

using an automatic fraction collector (see Fig. 7–7). After completion of the separation, the analyst may have several hundred tubes of the 10-ml fractions of the eluate. Identification of the composition of these individual fractions can be based upon absorption spectroscopy (IR, UV, visible) or the specific chemistry of each component (spot tests). This is a long and tedious method, but it is necessary when the identity and column position of solutes are totally unknown.

Streak reagents or general developers may be used for zone location. The chromatogram is developed, but the separated components are left on the solid phase, not eluted from the column. The solid phase is removed from the column and then brushed or sprayed with one or more of a series of color-producing reagents. The streak reagent may be specific for a single component, such as dimethylglyoxime is for nickel, or it may react with all of the components in the mixture, such as dithizone will with most metals. Ninhydrin is commonly used as such a streak reagent to detect amino acids, forming purple or pinkish colors when amino acids are present. For quantitative analyses, the zones must be removed from the solid phase once they have been located. This is readily done by cutting the column packing into pieces and extracting the desired component from each piece. In thin-layer and paper chromatography, the detection of the zones is generally all that is required, so that component removal and concentration analyses become unnecessary. Hence, the use of streak reagents, spot tests, and general color-producing chemicals is the standard practice in these forms of chromatography.

Continuous Analysis of Effluent Components

Continuous analysis of the effluent as it emerges from the bottom of the column is more difficult to carry out, for such analysis must be based upon some general solute property. Commercial liquid chromatographs incorporate five different detection systems which are based on more or less common physical and chemical properties—refractive index, electrical conductivity, heat of adsorption, ionization in flames, and absorption of visible or ultraviolet radiation.

Refractive Index

The refractive index of a chemical compound is almost a characteristic property of it. There are only a few cases where two compounds have the same refractive index. When a solute appears in the eluate, the refractive index of the resulting solution will differ slightly ($\sim 1.0 \times 10^{-4}$ units) from the refractive index of either the pure solvent or the pure solute. Thus, continuous monitoring of the refractive index of an eluate will not only tell when the components of the mixture are coming off the column, but it will give an indication of the compounds. The refractive index of the effluent is measured by either determining the angle of bending of a ray of monochromatic light as it passes through the eluent stream, or by measuring the change in the intensity of a beam of light that is reflected by the eluent stream. Both systems respond rapidly to small changes in refractive index. The sensitivity of this type of detection system depends upon the magnitude of the difference between the refractive index of the solute and solvent.

When using a refractive index detector, the temperature of the cell must be held constant within $\pm 0.001°C$, because the refractive index of any compound is temperature dependent. Many organic liquids have temperature coefficients of 3×10^{-4} refractive index units per degree centigrade. Since most detectors respond to changes as small as 1×10^{-5} units, even slight changes in temperature will cause a change in the readings. The refractive index of water is 1.33300 at 20°C and 1.3337 at 10°C, whereas the refractive index at 18°C of 0.1 M HBr is 1.33452 and of 0.5 M HBr is 1.33952. The temperature changes and concentration changes in the refractive index can therefore be of the same order of magnitude.

Measurement of refractive index as a means of detection of solutes in the eluate has the advantages of being applicable to all classes of compounds, possessing

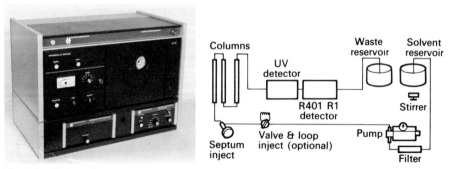

Fig. 7-8. Schematic diagram of high-speed liquid chromatograph. (*Courtesy of Waters Associates, Inc.*)

a high sensitivity, being simple and easy to automate, being nondestructive, and providing a rapid response to changes in concentration. It has the drawbacks of needing excellent thermostatting and of not being applicable when gradient elution analysis is carried out. Fig. 7–8 shows a schematic diagram of a commercial column chromatograph that has a refractive-index detector system.

Electrical Conductivity

The appearance of ions in the eluate will cause an increase in the electrical conductivity of the solution over that of the pure solvent. This change in conductance is proportional to the change in concentration and the specific conductance of the solute. Electrolytic conductivity of the eluete can be measured by placing two platinized platinum electrodes in the eluent stream, applying a 60 cycle ac voltage across the electrodes, and measuring the conductance with a Wheatstone bridge. The sensitivity will depend upon the difference between the specific conductance of the solute and the solvent. Electrical conductivity as a detection system is limited to ionic solutions, usually aqueous solutions. It has been used most successfully in gel-filtration chromatography of proteins.

Heat of Adsorption

The heat of adsorption of a solute is a property possessed by all chemical compounds. The use of this property as a chromatographic detector depends upon careful measurements of small changes in the surface temperature of the adsorbant when the solute molecules displace the solvent molecules from the surface. A cell filled with an adsorbant is placed in the effluent stream. One sensitive thermistor is placed on the surface of the adsorbant while a second thermistor is placed in an adjacent cell containing a nonadsorbing solid. This second thermistor is the reference. The temperature difference between the two surfaces is measured as the eluate passes through the cell. Whenever a solute is adsorbed onto the surface, the temperature of the adsorbant surface will rise. The total thermistor response for a solute looks like the first derivative of an S-shaped curve (rising exponentially to a maximum peak and then falling exponentially to the initial value) for the temperature will decrease during desorption of the solute. Detectors based on measurement of the heat of adsorption are not capable of measuring solute concentrations unless repeated calibrations are made, but they are excellent for locating the emerging solute bands. Very careful temperature control of the measuring cell is required, so that a large capacity water bath is required. The major advantage of this method lies in its ability to detect all adsorbable compounds. The disadvantages are its need for a very rigorous control of the temperature of the solution, its need for a very constant flow rate, and its inability to be used for quantitative work. Heat of adsorption detectors cannot be used during gradient elution analyses.

Flame Ionization

The ability of flames to ionize organic and inorganic compounds can also be used as a means of detecting the presence of solutes in an eluate. Flame ionization detectors are used very extensively in gas chromatography and, for a thorough discussion of the technique as applied to this form of chromatography, see Chapter 14. In order to adapt flame ionization to liquid chromatography, some means had to be found to remove the solvent, to vaporize the solute, and to inject the solute vapor into the flame.

The flow of liquid eluate from the chromatographic column is usually very large, so that the liquid solution cannot be injected directly into a flame. This difficulty is overcome, by diverting a small fraction of the eluate stream onto a moving chain or wire. This wire passes through a chamber, heated slightly above room temperature, where a stream of inert gas evaporates the solvent. The solute residue on the wire is then injected continuously into the flame, where it is volatilized and ionized by the temperature of the flame. The ions produced cause a flow of electrical current between the top of the burner and a wire loop in the flame. This current flow is proportional to the amount of solute in the eluate. There have been three methods used so far to get the solid solute injected into the flame: (1) burn it directly off the moving wire; (2) volatilize it off the wire and then pass the gas into the flame; and (3) burn it off the wire in a separate chamber and then pass the combustion products into the flame. Naturally, the simplest of these three—direct burning—gives variable and nonreproducible results, so it cannot be used conveniently.

Flame ionization detectors have the advantages of high sensitivity, wide applicability, quantitative response to solute concentration, no need for temperature control, and being able to be used during gradient elution analysis. The major disadvantages lie in the necessity for solvent removal and the problems created in this step. Current methods of solvent removal limit the application of flame ionization detectors to those solutes that are nonvolatile at approximately room temperature. Nevertheless, these detectors are used for protein, lipid, polymer, and other high boiling compound separations.

Absorption of Visible and UV Radiation

The absorption of visible or ultraviolet radiation by a compound is a charac-

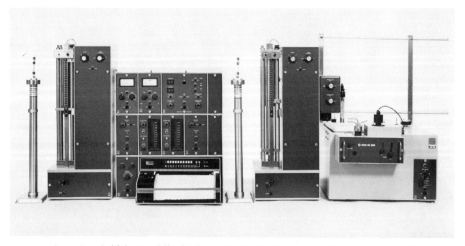

Fig. 7–9. A high-speed liquid chromatograph. (*Courtesy of Varian Aerograph.*)

teristic property of that compound. Thus, in order to use this property successfully in a chromatographic detection system, knowledge of the absorption spectra of the solutes is necessary. Once the appropriate wavelengths are determined, continuous detection and quantitative determination of concentrations are readily accomplished as the eluate flows through a spectrophotometer cell. This type of detector has the advantages that no temperature control is required, the flow rate need not be controlled closely, and it can be used during gradient elution analysis. Veening[7] gives more detailed descriptions of photometric detectors in his discussion of liquid chromatography detectors. Krejci and Pospisilova,[5] in comparing detectors used in high-speed liquid chromatographs, have determined the sensitiveness of differential refractometers and UV spectrophotometers under identical conditions.

Fig. 7–9 shows a commercial liquid column chromatograph with a forced, constant eluent flow and three interchangeable detectors—refractive index, micro adsorption, and photometric.

Other Continuous Detection Systems

In addition to the five detectors already discussed that at this time have been incorporated into commercial instruments, there are four other continuous detection systems used in research laboratories. Three of these are restricted to specific types of separations.

When the compounds to be separated are radioactive, *scintillation counters* can be used to detect their appearance in the effluent. Scintillation detectors are very useful for tracer studies, with isotopically labelled compounds. The effluent is passed into a cell that is packed with a scintillator which will respond to ^{14}C beta rays, such as CaF_2. The pulses of light emitted by the scintillator when struck by the beta rays are detected by a photomultiplier tube, whose current output is recorded continuously. The appearance of solutes is indicated by an increase in the current flowing in the circuit.

Polarography can be used to detect metal ions in aqueous eluates. A pair of platinum microelectrodes is placed in the eluate stream. A voltage that is on the diffusion plateau of the metals is applied across the electrodes. When a metal ion appears in the eluate stream, current will flow between the two electrodes, and the magnitude of the current is a measure of its concentration. A polarographic detector can detect as low as 10^{-7} M metal ion per second.

The *fluorescence* of a solute can be used in continuous analysis, just as it was used to detect zones on chromatographic columns. The techniques needed to adapt this to flowing systems are analogous to those used in visible and ultraviolet light absorption. Fluorescence has the advantage of being much more sensitive than light absorption.

The *dielectric constant* of an eluate will change when a solute appears in it. This general solution property is caused by differences in the polarizability of different solutes. Two parallel plates are placed close together, and the eluate flows between them. An ac potential is applied across the plates and the capacitance of the cell is monitored continuously. The response of the cell is linear with changes in the solute concentration. This detection system has the advantage of being nondestructive. It is not applicable when gradient elution analysis is being used, unless there is no change in the polarizability of the solvent system as its composition changes.

The application of these detectors to continuous eluate analyses has been brought about by a recent increase in the application of liquid column chromatographic techniques. Liquid chromatography is necessary to separate high-molecular-weight compounds that are not volatile at the temperatures used in gas chromatography and to separate compounds that are thermally unstable. Conlon[1] has written an excellent review of detection systems for continuous analysis of eluates.

The specific method used to detect a zone of solute will be highly dependent upon the nature of the compounds in the sample, for the detector must respond to some property common to each of the components in a specific mixture (color, fluorescence, refractive index, and so on) and the form of chromatography used to separate the mixture. There is no one general detection system applicable to all forms of chromatography. Experience and/or the library are the best guides in selecting the detection system for a particular chromatographic separation.

PROBLEMS

1. Why must a sample be added to a chromatographic column so as to produce a narrow, concentrated band of solutes?
2. What is meant by the following terms?
    (a)   development of a chromatogram
    (b)   selective retardation
3. Define R_f value. What does this term represent physically? Of what value, if any, is an R_f value in chromatography?
4. Why can literature R_f values not be used in the laboratory for experimental work?
5. What are the two equilibrium processes that underlie a large portion of the chromatographic separation processes?
6. Sketch an adsorption isotherm of the type L. Of the type C.
7. What assumptions did Langmuir make when considering adsorption equilibria?
8. Explain how a band of solute becomes broader and less concentrated as it moves through a chromatographic medium.
9. Why do only certain chromatographic peaks show tailing?
10. Distinguish clearly between development and frontal analysis.
11. When would it be desirable to use gradient elution analysis instead of plain elution analysis?
12. List four techniques used to detect solutes as they emerge from a chromatographic column.
13. What is meant by high-speed liquid chromatography? Does this technique offer any advantages over conventional chromatographic operation to warrant purchase of the expensive equipment?

REFERENCES

1. Conlon, R. D., *Anal. Chem.*, **41** (4), 107A (1969).
2. Ettre, L. S., *Anal. Chem.*, **43** (14), 20A (1971).

3. Giles, C. H., MacEwan, T. H. Nakhwa, S. N., and Smith, D., *J. Chem. Soc.*, **1960,** 3973.
4. Keulemans, A. I. M., *Gas Chromatography*, Van Nostrand Reinhold Co., New York, 1959, p. 2.
5. Krejci, M., and Pospisilova, F., *J. Chromatogr.*, **73,** 105 (1972).
6. Tswett, M., *Ber. Deut. Botan. Ges.*, **24,** 394 (1906); translated by H. H. Strain and J. Sherma, *J. Chem. Educ.*, **44,** 238 (1967).
7. Veening, H., *J. Chem. Educ.*, **47,** A549, A675 (1970).

CHAPTER 8

COLUMN ADSORPTION CHROMATOGRAPHY

The chromatographic separation of the components in a mixture by adsorption from a moving liquid stream onto the surface of a powdered solid confined in a column is called *column adsorption chromatography* or simply *adsorption chromatography*. This modification of chromatography is the one that was developed by M. Tswett in 1906, the one that was used by Kuhn and Lederer, and the one that was advocated by A. Tiselius. Column adsorption chromatography was one of the most widely used separation methods during the 1940s and early 1950s. Although the advent of gas and thin-layer chromatography decreased the extent of its applications, adsorption chromatography is still an important, powerful, and frequently applied separation tool.

THE EXPERIMENTAL VARIABLES

The theory of adsorption and of adsorption chromatography has been presented in Chapter 7. The pertinent experimental factors that determine the success of a column adsorption chromatographic separation are: (1) the nature of the adsorbent; (2) the nature of the solvent used to elute the sample; (3) the rate of flow of solvent through the column; (4) the geometry of the column containing the adsorbent-sample-eluent system; (5) the temperature. Let us investigate several of these, to discover why and how they are critical.

Adsorbents

The feature that distinguishes an adsorbent from any other solid, is the magnitude of its surface area per unit weight. An *absorbent* is defined as any finely divided solid possessing an extremely large surface area that is capable of attracting molecules to its surface. Large surface areas are those from 5 to 200 square meters/ gram (recall that 100 square meters = 0.025 acres). Chemically, adsorbents can consist of anything from carbon through powdered glass to such polar materials as calcium phosphate. Several hundred compounds have been used as adsorbents

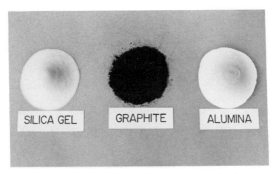

Fig. 8–1. Piles of silica gel, graphite, and alumina (Al_2O_3). (*Photograph by Stephen Daugherty.*)

in adsorption chromatography, but only a handful are commonly used and need to be discussed. The three most widely used adsorbents are shown in Fig. 8–1.

The characteristics of a solid that must be considered when selecting an adsorbent to effect a particular chromatographic separation are: (1) the surface area, (2) the particle size, (3) the linearity of the adsorption isotherms of the solutes to be separated, (4) the average surface energy, and (5) the adsorbent class. It should not be too surprising to find that all of these properties are interrelated so that one cannot adjust each to its optimum independently of the others. Compromises are necessary.

Surface Area

It was shown in Chapter 7 that adsorption isotherms are apt to be linear when the specific adsorption of the solute is low. Translating this into conditions for a chromatographic separation, one should have a surface area so large as to keep the specific adsorption (A_s = grams solute adsorbed per gram of adsorbent) as low as is practical. A rough rule of thumb is that there should be less than 1 g of sample for each 50 g of adsorbent. This guideline assumes that the surface area of the adsorbent is at least 50 m^2/g adsorbent.

The term surface area is misleading as commonly used—it probably does not refer to the geometric area of the solid surface. In practice, there is no way to determine the actual geometric area; it cannot be calculated because the number, size, and shape of all the small adsorbent particles are not known. Surface area is measured by adsorbing a gas onto the solid surface, and determining the amount of gas that is adsorbed from the dimensions of the gas molecules. What is measured by this technique is the *effective surface area*—namely the surface area that is available for adsorption of a solute from the sample solution. The total surface area may be much greater than this, since portions of the surface can be covered by some strongly adsorbed (usually chemisorbed) nondesorbable material.

Particle Size

As a rough approximation, for a given weight of adsorbent the diameter of the particles will determine the surface area. The smaller the particle diameter, the more extensive is the area per gram of solid available for adsorption. The separation efficiency in adsorption chromatography increases with decreasing particle size.

Unfortunately, in addition to surface area, there is a second factor affected by the size of the solid particles—the *permeability* of the column, or the resistance to the flow of the solvent. The smaller the size of the adsorbent particles, the harder it is to have the eluent flow through the column at a reasonable or even practical rate. In order to obtain a workable flow rate through a chromatographic column packed with very small particles, very high pressure differentials are required. These high pressures are undesirable, as well as dangerous, when working with glass columns. Particles in the range 100 to 200 mesh (149 to 74μ) provide a minimum resistance to flow with the maximum surface area. Thus, most chromatographic grade adsorbents sold commercially are of this particle size. Although the efficiency of a separation depends upon the mean diameter of the particles, the range of the spread of particle diameters around this mean does not seem to affect the separation efficiency. A finely divided solid whose particles have a very broad spread in diameters will give the same separation efficiency as a solid whose particles are uniform in size and have the same average diameter as the first solid. A wider distribution of diameters, however, will decrease the rate of solvent flow more than a narrow one.

Adsorption Isotherm Linearity

Two solutes exhibiting considerably different specific adsorptivities, can be separated regardless of the linearity of their adsorption isotherm (S, L, or C isotherms will all permit separation). But when two solutes have very similar specific adsorptivities, tailing or bearding can prevent a clean-cut separation. Theories of adsorption chromatographic separations assume linear adsorption isotherms (C). In order to maintain a linear adsorption isotherm ($\pm 10\%$) the specific adsorption cannot be greater than 2.5×10^{-4} g solute/g adsorbent. The linearity of the isotherm is dependent upon the surface area, the homogeneity of the distribution of adsorption energies among sites, temperature, and power of eluent. Provided one stays within the linear adsorption region, sample size does not affect the efficiency of a separation. When the sample is too large, its size does play a role in the separation.

Surface Activity

The activity of the surface of an adsorbent describes the distribution of the surface energy of the adsorbent. Some sites on a surface will be more "active" than others; that is, these sites will be the first to adsorb solutes from the liquid phase. The number of these active sites, as well as their energies, determine the activity of the adsorbent. To a very great extent, the activity is determined by the water content of the surface. When an adsorbent is first received from the manufacturer, it will have fairly large amounts of water adsorbed upon its surface, making it relatively inactive. If the solid is spread out in a shallow pan and heated between 200 and 400°C for several hours, the adsorbed moisture is driven off. The adsorbent is "activated."

Experimentally it has been found that adsorbents of very high surface activity give low separation efficiencies, probably because the solutes are bound too long and too firmly to the surface sites. Polar solutes can be chemisorbed on very active sites and never eluted. Thus, it is desirable to limit or control the activity of the surface. For silica and alumina, control is usually achieved by activating the surface in an oven, after which it is deactivated to the desired level of activity by adding known amounts of water. This process can increase the linear adsorption capacity of the column by as much as one hundredfold. A standard scale based on the retention volumes of test dyes eluted with standard solvents relates the water content to the surface activity of silica and alumina. In the case of charcoal, controlled deactivation uses high-molecular-weight hydrocarbons instead of water. For routine quantitative analyses, the adsorbent should always be deactivated; the more active the adsorbent surface is, the longer the retention times and the larger the retention volumes. Nonlinear adsorption, which causes tailing, is one consequence of a highly active surface.

Adsorbent Class

Historically adsorbents have been classified according to relative strength of adsorption and polarity. Strong adsorbents include alumina, silica gel, magnesium silicate (Florisil), and carbon. Intermediate adsorbents are calcium carbonate, calcium phosphate, and magnesia, whereas weak adsorbents include sucrose, starch, insulin, and talc. The strength of adsorption is determined by measuring the rate of movement of a solute band during elution analysis; for a given rate of flow, the faster the band moves down the column, the weaker the adsorbent is. Most adsorption chromatographic separations today use strong adsorbents.

Adsorbents can also be classed as either acidic or basic, depending upon the nature of the surface exposed to the flowing solvent. Silica gel and magnesium silicate are acidic adsorbents, whereas alumina is a basic adsorbent. Acidic adsorbents should be. used for the separation of acidic compounds and basic adsorbents for the separation of basic compounds. If an acidic adsorbent is used in an attempt to separate basic compounds, chemisorption may occur so the solute cannot be eluted from the column.

Common Adsorbents

The most widely used adsorbents for column adsorption chromatography are the metal oxides (alumina and silica gel), magnesium silicate (Florisil), and carbon. The metal oxides separate solutes according to their polarity; highly polar solutes are more strongly adsorbed than less polar solutes so elution occurs in order of increasing polarity. The strength of adsorption (and hence retention volume) also increases with an increase in the number of polar substituents in the molecule. The order of elution from the metal oxides is—nonpolar compounds (saturated hydrocarbons, olefins, and aromatic hydrocarbons) eluted before the moderately polar compounds (ethers, esters, and ketones) eluted before the strongly polar compounds (amines, alcohols, thiols, and acids). Carbon exhibits no preference for polar molecules, causing the strength of adsorption on carbon to be based solely on increasing solute molecular weight.

Silica or silica gel is the most widely used adsorbent in column chromatography. The surface of these particles contain hydroxyl groups attached to the silicon atoms in the silica. These hydroxyl groups hydrogen bond with polar molecules. Heating of the silica gel removes adsorbed water but does not remove the surface hydroxyl groups. The water, however, prevents other polar molecules from reaching the surface and being adsorbed upon it, hence deactivating the surface. Silica gel is readily available from laboratory supply houses at a moderate price and in a variety of particle sizes.

Alumina also is a very popular adsorbent. The nature of its surface is not established clearly; it may be predominantly aluminum atoms or hydroxyl groups or oxygen atoms. Heating of alumina at 400°C followed by the addition of a half-monolayer of water produces an adsorbing surface that is satisfactory for almost all purposes. It is as readily available and inexpensive as silica gel.

Charcoal is not used so widely at the present time as it was fifteen or twenty years ago. Carbon must be activated at temperatures over 1000°C in order to remove adsorbed polar substances and oxides, so as to make it nonreactive to polar compounds. Adsorption upon the carbon surface involves London forces. Carbon possesses a fine pore structure, which slows down the adsorption–desorption process and gives low column efficiencies. Carbon is readily available from laboratory supply houses and is much less expensive than any of the other adsorbents.

Magnesium silicate (Florisil) shows adsorptive properties intermediate between those of silica gel and alumina. Chemisorption is stronger on Florisil than on any of the adsorbents listed before, so that its use is limited. Its acidic surface restricts its use to the separation of acidic compounds. Florisil is easy to obtain at a cost comparable to silica gel and alumina. Florisil and alumina are better for separation of unsubstituted aromatic compounds than silica gel.

Other adsorbents that have been used include magnesia, diatomaceous earth, fuller's earth, sucrose, and talc. These weak adsorbents are usually used only for very polar solutes. Molecular sieves have been used recently to effect separation of molecules on the bases of their size and shape. Special adsorbents have been prepared for particular separations. For examples, in some cases a chemical complexing agent has been added to the surface so as to cause preferential adsorption of certain metal ions. Also, silver ion has been incorporated into the surface of silica gel to enhance the adsorption of olefins. Other modified adsorbents have been used for special purposes.

Solvents

The solvent in which a sample is dissolved will compete with the components of the sample for surface sites upon which to be adsorbed. Because of this, the identity of the solvent can affect not only the relative retention times of solutes, but also their order of elution. A solvent which is strongly adsorbed upon the surface (a strong eluent) will displace solutes easily and thus produce shorter retention times. Solvents which are poorly adsorbed upon the surface (weak eluents) do not compete effectively with the solute molecules, and hence do not displace them from the surface as rapidly, so that longer retention times are found when using weak eluents.

The change in the specific adsorptivity of a particular solute when substituting one solvent for a second solvent will depend upon the relative eluting strength of the two solvents as well as upon the size of the solute molecule. The molecular size of the solute determines the number of adsorption sites that the solute will occupy, and hence how many solvent molecules will be needed to displace it from the surface. If two solutes, which are not separated by adsorption chromatography in one solvent, have different sizes, changing to a second solvent of different eluting strength should cause the molecules to be separated. Exceptions to this generalization are caused by hydrogen bonding, association, and other solvent–solute or solvent–adsorbent interactions. Exceptions are found most frequently in very polar solvents such as alcohols.

The relative ability of solvents to elute a solute from an adsorbent is given by what is known as an *eluotropic series*. An eluotropic series is merely a listing of solvents according to the order in which they elute a given solute. The arrangement of solvents within an eluotropic series is essentially the same for all of the metal oxide adsorbents, but it is completely different upon carbon. Close inspection of eluotropic series upon different adsorbents will reveal that there are differences, even within the polar adsorbents. Dielectric constant, dipole moment, structure of the solvent, as well as the solvent–adsorbent interfacial tension have been studied in attempts to determine the underlying cause for the sequence of solvents within an eluotropic series. Solvent viscosity will decrease the rate of flow and decrease the separation efficiency, but it does not affect the relative order of solvent strengths. The adsorption energy of the solvent upon a particular adsorbent appears to be the predominant factor in determining the order of eluting ability. The relative strength of solvents as eluents has been put on a more quantitative basis by assigning each solvent a number, $\varepsilon°$, which is called the *adsorption energy per unit surface area* for that solvent.

Table 8–1 gives abridged eluotropic series for the four most commonly used adsorbents. Notice that, in general, the sequence of the solvents is the same for the polar solvents. The only differences between silica gel and alumina are slight inversions of order for *n*-pentane and cyclohexane and for diethyl ether and chloroform, and a possible shift in the relative eluting strength of acetone. Solvents on silica gel and Florisil show the same order of eluting ability. Solvents show essentially the same sequence of eluting power on alumina and Florisil, with the exception of the considerable displacement of diethyl ether. While the order of elution strength on carbon may appear to be that of decreasing polarity of the solvents, it is also the order of increasing molecular size of the solvent molecules. As was mentioned earlier, carbon shows no preference for polar effects, so the increase in size is the determining factor in establishing the relative eluting strengths of solvents.

The Nature of the Solute

The most important feature of an adsorption chromatographic separation is the extent of separation of the components of the sample for a given solvent–adsorbent system. In order to achieve a separation, there must be such a large difference in the retention volumes of the components that each component can be collected individually, free from contamination by any of the other components in

Table 8–1.   ELUOTROPIC SERIES FOR SOLVENTS UPON FREQUENTLY USED ADSORBENTS

Solvent	ε°	Solvent	ε°
Alumina		*Silica gel*	
n-Pentane	0.00	Cyclohexane	− 0.05
Cyclohexane	0.04	n-Pentane	0.00
Carbon tetrachloride	0.18	Carbon tetrachloride	0.14
Carbon disulfide	0.26	Carbon disulfide	0.14
Benzene	0.32	Benzene	> 0.25
Diethyl ether	0.38	Chloroform	> 0.25
Chloroform	0.40	Diethyl ether	> 0.25
Methylene chloride	0.42	Ethyl acetate	> 0.25
Acetone	0.56	Ethanol	> 0.25
Ethyl acetate	0.58	Water	> 0.25
Dimethyl sulfoxide	0.62	Acetone	> 0.25
Acetonitrile	0.65	Acetic acid	> 0.25
Isopropanol	0.82	Methanol	> 0.25
Ethanol	0.88		
Methanol	0.95		
Florisil		*Carbon*[a]	
Pentane	0.00	Water	
Carbon tetrachloride	0.04	Methanol	
Benzene	0.18	Ethanol	
Chloroform	0.20	Acetone	
Methylene chloride	0.23	n-Propanol	
Diethyl ether	0.31	Diethyl ether	
		Ethyl acetate	
		n-Hexane	
		Benzene	

SOURCE: Ref. 2, pp. 59–60.

[a] Absorbents on carbon are listed in order of increasing ε° values. (Explicit numerical values are unavailable.)

the sample. A crucial question in chromatography is: "What features of the solute molecules determine the strength with which the molecules are adsorbed onto the surface of the powdered solid?" The differences in these properties determine the order of elution of the solutes and degree of separation. Correlations of solute parameters, such as molecular size, boiling point, solute polarity, and specific adsorptivity with elution sequence have been attempted. Since adsorption involves interactions of an electrostatic nature, those molecular properties that reflect the charge distribution should be significant. For liquid adsorption chromatography, the molecular structure of the solute determines the retention volume of a particular solute.

Many attempts have been made to correlate various structural features with retention volumes. One of the most extensive and successful correlations was made by Snyder.[7] He has assigned group adsorption energies to each of the organic functional groups, using as his standard the adsorption from pentane onto alumina or onto silica gel. These adsorption energies were estimated empirically from retention-volume studies on hundreds of compounds containing that particular functional group. The compounds were adsorbed onto silica gel or alumina from pentane solutions, and their retention volumes measured. From the average retention volume of monofunctional compounds, the adsorption energy for that functional group was calculated. Once these group adsorption energies have been obtained, adsorption energies for other polyfunctional organic compounds can be calculated. The adsorption energy of a solute molecule is the sum of the adsorption energies for each of the functional groups it contains. When several different functional groups exist in the same molecule, there will be interactions between them. Their adsorption energies must then be corrected for these neighboring group effects. Corrections are applied for the acidity or basicity of the molecule, the interactions between neighboring functional groups contained in the same molecule, electronic interactions between functional groups, molecular orientation differences during adsorption, steric factors, and conjugation. From these calculated adsorption energies for solute molecules, it is possible to predict retention volumes. From the predicted retention volumes, the feasibility of a desired separation can be estimated.

In order to utilize group adsorption energies for a proposed separation from a solvent that is not pentane and upon an adsorbent that may not be silica gel or alumina, a considerable number of experimental parameters for the system must have been determined previously. The eluent strength, $\varepsilon°$, the size of the solute molecules, the volume that a monolayer of solvent occupies when adsorbed on the surface of the adsorbent, the average surface energy of the adsorbent, and the group adsorption energies for the functional groups from that solvent onto the desired adsorbent must all be known. When all of these factors have been established, excellent agreement is found between experimental and calculated retention volumes. In establishing this method, Snyder[7] has determined two thousand different adsorption energies. Values were obtained for four hundred different compounds, and from seventy different solvents for the adsorption onto alumina, silica gel, and Florisil. When such a wealth of data is available, the purely empirical approach to establishing conditions for a separation can be obviated. Usually, however, all of the necessary data for all of the functional groups from several solvents and for several adsorbents is not available. Even so, group adsorption energies can give a rough approximation of the order of elution and serve as a guide in the proper selection of solvent, and adsorbent. When all of the components in a mixture are not known (as in the workup of a product mixture in a synthesis, or the separation of protein hydrolyzates), exploratory TLC or GSC experiments are invaluable in determining the number of components present in the mixture. Table 8–2 gives the order of elution in pentane of monofunctional organic compounds as determined by Snyder for silica gel and alumina

Operating Parameters

The effect of several experimental conditions, such as method of packing, column geometry, flow rate, and temperature on the efficiency of a column adsorption chromatographic separation have been studied.[9]

Table 8–2. ORDER OF ELUTION OF ALIPHATIC COMPOUNDS
FROM ALUMINA OR SILICA GEL COLUMNS

Fluorocompounds
Chloro compounds
Iodo compounds
Organic sulfides
Ethers
Aldehydes
Esters
Ketones
Alcohols
Primary amines
Amides

Nitro compounds elute between ketones and alcohols
on alumina but between alcohols and primary amines on
silica.
Carboxylic acids are the most strongly adsorbed, and,
hence, the last compounds eluted from alumina. On
silica gel, they elute between nitro compounds and the
primary amines.

SOURCE: Ref. 2.

Packing

Very lively debates develop over the technique by which the column is best
packed. Proponents of each technique believe fervently that their method is by far
and away the optimum method. There are at least four common ways to pack a
column. The dry, powdered solid can just be poured slowly into the top of the
column, with no effort made to settle the packing. The normal procedure, however,
is to tap or vibrate the column as the dry powder is poured in. This tapping or
vibrating of the column is continued until settling has been completed, as indicated
by no further decrease in the height of the column packing. A third technique for
dry packing is to add a small amount of the powder and to tamp the adsorbent down
tightly with a dowel that is just slightly smaller than the inside diameter of the
column. More powder is added and then tamped in place, and so on. A very widely
acclaimed method is to form a slurry of the adsorbent and the solvent. When more
than one solvent is to be used, the slurry is prepared from the first solvent to be
applied to the column. This slurry is then poured into the column and the solid
allowed to settle until the desired height of adsorbent is obtained. If the stopcock
at the bottom of the column is left slightly open during the introduction of the
adsorbent slurry to the column, the packing will be much tighter.

Studies[9] as to which of these four techniques is the best have revealed that the
normal method of dry packing seems to give the best separation efficiencies. The
first method, the loose packing technique, gave the poorest operation and worst
separations. The use of a wet fill was less effective than either the normal procedure
or the tamping procedure. Frequently, it is recommended that Celite or some other

filter aid be added to the dry adsorbent in order to increase the solvent flow and to improve the separation. This is misleading advice, for it was found[9] that the addition of Celite to the powdered solid gave the poorest performance of any separation, much worse than even the loose fill method.

Column Geometry

The geometry of the adsorption column is another feature that is important to a successful separation. Snyder[9] found that for a given weight of adsorbent, the efficiency of separation was independent of column diameter up to a diameter of 1 cm. Above 1 cm there was a continual decrease in the column efficiency. Fig. 8–2 shows typical columns used in adsorption chromatography. Part (*a*) is a typical column, part (*b*) is the column used when it is necessary to increase the flow rate by applying suction and part (*c*) is the column used when it is desirable to increase the flow rate by applying pressure.

Flow Rate

The rate of flow of solvent through the column is very important in achieving a successful chromatographic separation. If the flow rate is too rapid, there will be insufficient time for the adsorption–desorption equilibrium to become established. Too rapid a flow rate can produce tailing, band overlapping, and incomplete separation. If the rate of solvent flow is too slow, diffusion of the separated solutes from the regions of higher solute concentration to those of lower solute concentrations, can undo the separation that has been effected. The optimum flow rate is a compromise involving these two factors. The efficiency of separation increases linearly as the flow rate is increased from 0.5 to 2.0 cm/sec. The optimum flow rate should be less than 0.2 ml of solvent per minute per gram of adsorbent. Generally flow rates of 1 to 3 ml per minute are used satisfactorily.

When linear adsorption isotherms (C isotherms) are found for each of the solutes, neither the nature of the components being separated nor the numerical value of the retention volume has any effect on the efficiency of the separation. In

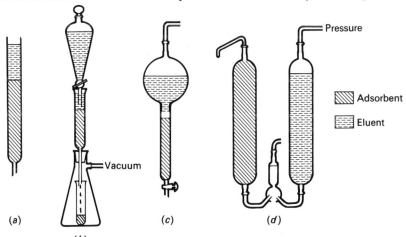

(*a*)   (*c*)   (*d*)

(*b*)

Fig. 8–2.   Column arrangements for adsorption chromatography.

other words, the compounds eluted last can be separated just as efficiently as those eluted first. Ethers can be separated from one another just as completely as amines can. This indicates that the flow rate of solvent is much slower than the rate of solute adsorption and desorption.

The weight of the adsorbent that should be used in a column depends upon the size of the sample that is to be separated; the larger the sample, the greater the weight of adsorbent. There is a limit to this, of course, for the more adsorbent present in the column, the greater the resistance to the flow of solvent, so that eventually it becomes impossible to force the solvent through the column. The capacity of the adsorbent also affects the amount of absorbent taken. A general rule of thumb is to use about fifty grams of adsorbent for each gram of sample to be separated.

Temperature

Increasing the temperature of the column will cause a slight decrease in the adsorption of all components in the sample. This decrease is on the order of one to two per cent per degree centigrade. The temperature effect is caused by a decrease in the activity of the adsorbent surface with increasing temperature. Hence, the decrease is the same for all solutes present in the sample. While an increase in temperature will give shorter retention times, the extent will be by equal amounts for all components, so that the net effect is no change in the separation efficiency or in the order of elution of the sample components. There is no valid reason for not working at room temperature, and since the temperature variations are slight, there is no need to be concerned about temperature fluctuations during the development of the chromatogram.

Retention Volumes and Times

The *retention volume* in chromatography is defined as the volume of solvent that must be used in order to elute one half of the solute in question. That is, the volume of solvent added from the start of the development of the chromatogram to the maximum in the elution peak of a solute. Fig. 8–3 shows this graphically.

The retention time is merely the time elapsed from the beginning of the development of the chromatogram to the appearance of the maximum in the elution peak of

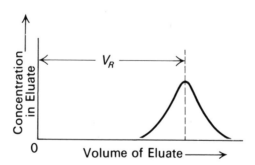

Fig. 8–3. Measurement of retention volume.

the solute. It is assumed that the rate of flow of eluent is constant throughout the development process.

In elution chromatography, the value of the retention volume, V_R, is given by:

$$V_R = KW + V^0 \qquad (8\text{--}1)$$

where V_R is the retention volume in ml, W is the total weight of the adsorbent in the column in g, V^0 is the free volume in the adsorbent column (that is the volume of the liquid phase moving through the adsorbent in the column at any instant in time) in ml. The constant, K, is the slope of the adsorption isotherm. K is equal to the specific adsorptivity, A_s, divided by the equilibrium concentration of the solute in the mobile liquid phase.

The retention time, t, is given by the formula:

$$t = \frac{V_R}{v}\left(\frac{L}{V^0}\right) \qquad (8\text{--}2)$$

where v is the velocity of the solvent in cm/sec, and L is the length of the column in centimeters. Substituting Equation (8–1) into Equation (8–2) gives:

$$t = \left(\frac{K\,W}{V^0} + 1\right)\left(\frac{L}{v}\right) \qquad (8\text{--}3)$$

From Equations (8–1) and (8–3) it can be seen that the more adsorbent present in the column the longer the retention time and the larger the retention volume will be. Similarly, for a given weight of adsorbent, a longer column will produce a longer retention time. The faster the rate of solvent flow, the shorter the retention time.

A most extensive study of the theoretical aspects of adsorption chromatography and correlations among solute structure, operating parameters, and retention times has been made by L. Snyder.[10]

APPLICATIONS

Although column adsorption chromatography is primarily used for separations in organic and biochemistry, a number of inorganic chemical applications have also been proposed. O. C. Smith[4] has devised a separation scheme for qualitative analysis based on the use of an alumina column. The group separations are made in the normal fashion with HCl and H_2S. H. Fillinger[1] developed a more rapid and usable chromatographic qualitative analysis scheme using alumina in small (6 mm i.d.) glass tubing. The Group I ions (Ag^+, Pb^{2+}, Hg_2^{2+}) are developed with K_2CrO_4 and identified by the colors of the bands formed. The copper, arsenic, aluminum, alkaline earth, and alkali metal groups are each developed by a combination of general eluents and specific reagents. Different colored bands are produced which are used to identify the ions in each group.

Snyder[6,11] and others have done extensive work on the separation of hydrocarbons and petroleum products by column adsorption chromatography. Petroleum fractions can be separated by chromatography into saturated hydrocarbons, monoaromatic, diaromatic, and other fractions. Sugars[12] have been separated on alumina, silica gel or carbon columns, and mixtures of alkaloids have been separated on alumina, silica gel or kieselguhr columns. Other applications include the separation of mixtures of dyes and pigments, vitamins, and steroid hormones.[3,13] The technique is used for the purification of antibiotics. One interesting application is the separation of isomeric compounds. DL-Mandelic acid ($C_6H_5CHOHCOOH$) has been resolved into its two enantiomers on stereospecific columns and the cis- and trans-isomers of stilbene ($C_6H_5CH{=}CHC_6H_5$) have been resolved.[8]

EXPERIMENT 8-I
Separation of Methylene Blue, Victoria Blue R, and Fluorescein by Adsorption Chromatography on Alumina *

The three dye molecules shown below are all readily adsorbed onto the surface of alumina.

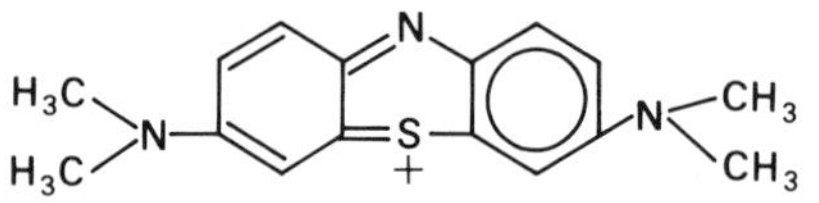

methylene blue

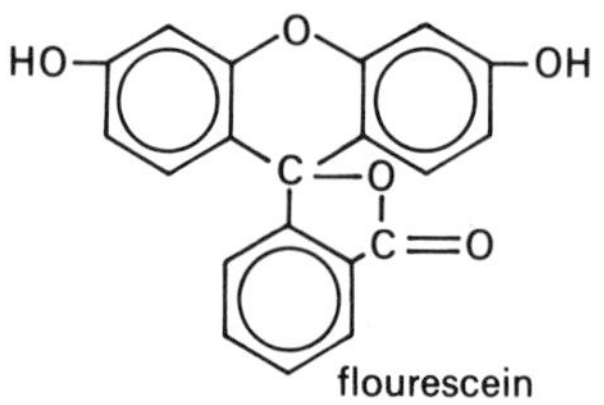

flourescein

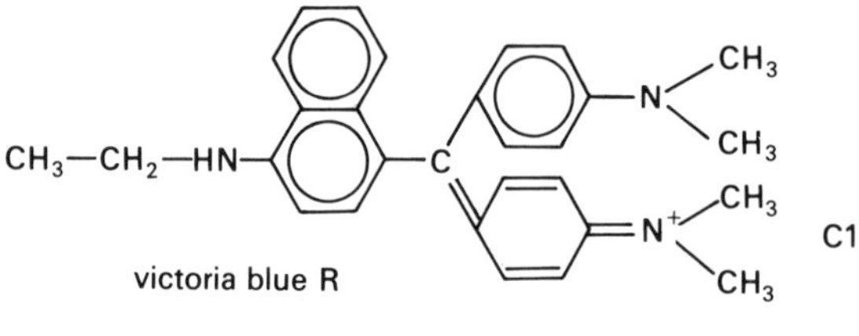

victoria blue R

Inspection of the structure of these three molecules and the use of group adsorption energies should give us some indication concerning the order of elution. Methylene blue contains twelve aromatic carbons which are weakly adsorbed on alumina. Its two tertiary amino nitrogens are only moderately strongly adsorbed. The four methyl groups are the most weakly adsorbed of all groups. The nitrogen and sulfur in the aromatic system are only weakly adsorbed. The symmetry of the structure does not lead to much polarity. Thus we should not expect methylene blue to be strongly adsorbed onto alumina. Victoria blue R like methylene blue, contains two tertiary nitrogens and four methyl groups, but it also has, however, an ethyl group and twenty-three aromatic carbons. The secondary amino nitrogen has an intermediate adsorption energy. The extensive conjugation and ionic charge will also increase the adsorptivity of the molecule. Thus, we would predict that victoria blue R will be moderately strongly adsorbed onto alumina, and more strongly adsorbed than methylene blue.

* Developed from material presented by J. Shott and H. W. Heine, *J. Chem. Educ.*, **28**, 39 (1951).

Fluorescein is composed of many oxygen-containing functional groups, all of which are very strongly adsorbed. In aromatic systems the carboxyl group has the highest adsorption energy of any group on alumina. Hydroxyl groups, of which there are two in fluorescein, are the next most strongly adsorbed groups. The ether linkage is only intermediate in adsorption energy. There are eighteen aromatic carbons but these are the only weakly adsorbed groups in the molecule. One would expect fluorescein to be very strongly adsorbed onto the alumina.

The expected order of elution of these three dyes from alumina with pentane would be methylene blue, victoria blue R, and fluorescein. The solvent used in this experiment, however, is ethanol, not pentane, so this order of elution is not observed. Since ethanol is a more polar solvent than pentane, the ionic victoria blue R is more soluble in it and hence is the most weakly adsorbed of the three dyes. Methylene blue is just slightly more strongly adsorbed and elutes from the column fairly soon after victoria blue R. Fluorescein is so strongly adsorbed onto the alumina that it does not appear to be eluted at all with ethanol. An enormous volume of ethanol would be required to remove it from the column. Thus, in order to elute the fluorescein with reasonable amounts of solvent and in practical times, a switch to water as the eluent is made. Fluorescein is not readily soluble in water, but the addition of a small amount of ammonia to it, will cause the hydrogens to ionize from the hydroxyl groups, increasing the aqueous solubility, which decreases the amount of time spent adsorbed onto the column. Thus, while the fluorescein can be eluted using pure water as the eluent, the addition of a small amount of ammonia hastens its removal.

Once the three dyes have been separated and eluted individually, their concentrations can be determined quite readily by their absorption of visible radiation. Victoria blue R absorbs strongly at 600 nm, methylene blue at 625 nm, and fluorescein at 490 nm.

Preparation of the column.   Use either a narrow chromatographic column, (one having a diameter of 1 cm or less) or a 25-ml burette. Clean and dry the tube carefully, and very gently tamp a small plug of glass wool to the bottom of the column. The glass wool should be sufficiently small and loose that it does not impede the flow of liquid through the column. Pour a layer of sand onto this to a depth less than 5 mm, and level the sand by weak tapping of the column with a ruler or wooden pencil. Carefully pour dry powdered chromatographic grade (100 to 200 mesh) alumina into the column, tapping the column gently but continuously. The tapping of the column should be continued until the alumina has settled completely and the height of the column is 20 cm and no longer decreases. It is not easy to produce a uniformly packed column the first time so that some distortion of the solute bands due to channeling is likely to occur. A continuous and uniform rate of addition of alumina to the column and an even, continuous tapping during the addition of the powder will minimize uneven packing.

Using a cork borer, cut from a piece of filter paper, a disk with a diameter slightly less than that of the internal diameter of the column. Carefully place this on the top of the column of alumina and tamp it down firmly. This filter paper disk will prevent the surface layer of the alumina from being disturbed during addition of the sample and eluting agents.

Slowly add denatured 95% alcohol to the top of the column and let it wet the alumina. It may be necessary to apply slight suction in order to obtain a reasonable flow rate. When the first drops of ethanol begin to emerge from the bottom of the column, the column is ready for use. Drain the ethanol through the column, however, until the liquid meniscus comes within 1 mm of the top of the alumina.

Addition of the sample. Pipette a 1.00-ml aliquot of the unknown dye mixture onto the top of the alumina column. During sample addition, care must be taken not to disturb the upper portion of the alumina and to apply the sample evenly. Sample addition is best done by placing the tip of the pipette against the inside wall of the column, just above the piece of filter paper. As the aliquot is draining onto the column, run the tip of the pipette around the inside of the column, being careful not to touch the packing. The column should be draining slowly during the addition of the sample. Allow the sample to drain onto the column until the liquid level is within 1 mm of the alumina surface. Rinse the inner walls of the column with 1 ml of alcohol and allow this to drain 1 mm above the top of the alumina. Repeat with 1-ml portions of alcohol, draining each to within 1 mm of the filter paper, until the supernatant liquid is colorless, indicating that all of the sample is in the narrow band at the top of the alumina.

Development of the chromatogram. Pass 95% alcohol through the column at the rate of 1 ml/min (see Fig. 3–8 for the experimental column setup with the reservoir, and Fig. 3–9 for the suction arrangement) using suction if necessary to achieve this flow rate. If suction is necessary, the eluate is collected in a large test tube suspended within the suction flask (see Fig. 3–9). Collect the eluate in a 100-ml volumetric flask if suction is not necessary. As soon as the victoria blue R begins to emerge from the bottom of the column, start collecting the eluate. When suction is used, transfer the contents of the test tube quantitatively to a 100-ml volumetric flask. Continue collecting the blue until all of the victoria blue R has been eluted from the column, which should be less than 90 ml of eluate.

Remove the volumetric flask (or large test tube) and collect the colorless eluate emerging from the column in a waste beaker until the methylene blue begins to emerge from the bottom of the column.* At this juncture start collecting the eluate in a second 100-ml volumetric flask or a second clean, dry test tube (to be transferred quantitatively to a second 100-ml volumetric flask). Continue collecting this blue eluate until all of the methylene blue has been eluted, which should be less than 90 ml of eluate. Collecting the colorless eluate in a waste beaker, drain the alcohol to within 1 mm of the top of the column.

Wash the column with 25 ml of deionized water, discarding the eluate obtained. If the fluorescein moves sufficiently rapidly during the washing so as to begin to emerge from the bottom of the column, start collecting it, even though less than 25 ml of wash liquid has been used.

Prepare 100 ml of very dilute ammonia by adding 2 drops of concentrated NH_3 to 100 ml of deionized water. Pour the ammonia through the column, being careful not to disturb the upper portion of the alumina. Allow the column to drain at the rate of 1.0 ml/min. Begin to collect the fluorescein eluate as soon as the dye

---

* Some of the methylene blue will stain the sand at the bottom of the column light blue. Do not be concerned about this; it does not appear to be a sufficient amount to affect the results. This dye cannot be eluted with alcohol or water.

begins to emerge from the bottom of the column and continue to collect it in either a 100-ml volumetric flask or a large test tube in the suction flask, until all of it has been eluted; which should be less than 90 ml of eluate.

Analysis of victoria blue R.   Dilute the eluate with 95% alcohol to the mark on the 100-ml volumetric flask and mix well by upending at least ten times. Measure the absorbance of the unknown and of a standard 1.00 mg victoria blue R/liter ethanol solution at 600 nm. Be sure to use 95% alcohol as the reagent blank.

Analysis of methylene blue.   Dilute the eluate with 95% alcohol to the mark on the 100-ml volumetric flask and mix well by upending at least ten times. Measure the absorbance of the unknown and of a standard 1.00 mg methylene blue/liter (in alcohol) solution at 625 nm. Be sure to use 95% alcohol as the reagent blank.

Analysis of fluorescein.   Dilute the unknown with deionized water to the mark on the 100-ml volumetric flask and mix well by upending at least ten times. Measure the absorbance of the unknown and of a standard 1.00 mg fluorescein/liter dilute ammonia solution at 490 nm. Be sure to use dilute aqueous ammonia as the reagent blank. Solutions of fluorescein are photosensitive so they should not be exposed to direct sunlight.

Calculation of the amount of dye present.   Beer's law applies to both the solutions of the separated dyes and to the solutions of the standards. Since the absorbances of each solute dye and its standard dye were measured at the same wavelength, the values of the molar absorptivity are the same. From the known concentration and the measured absorption of the standard dye solution a can be calculated. This calculated absorptivity can be substituted into the Beer's law expression for the separated dye. For example, in the case of victoria blue R:

for the unknown:

$$A_U = abC_U$$

for the standard:

$$A_S = abC_S$$

where, in the case $C_c = 1.00$ mg/liter.

A_S and A_U were measured at 600 nm. Both the unknown and the standard were measured in the same cuvette, so b is the same for both. The value of b need not be determined, but can be included with a. Thus, solving the Beer's law expression of the standard dye solution for ab gives $ab = A_S/C_S$. Substituting this into the Beer's law expression for the unknown dye solution gives:

$$A_U = \frac{A_S}{C_S}C_U$$

Since we are interested in determining the amount of the dye in the unknown:

$$C_U = C_S\frac{A_U}{A_S} \tag{8-4}$$

The two absorbances have been measured and the concentration of the standard is on the label of the bottle, so that it is a simple matter to calculate the concentration of the unknown. The concentration units will be whatever units the concentration of the standard is given in; in this case it is milligrams/liter.

To find the amount of each dye present in the initial aliquot (1.00 ml) of the unknown taken, it is merely necessary to multiply the concentration of the dye in the eluate by the volume of the eluate collected:

total weight of dye collected = concentration in eluate × volume of eluate

$$= C_U \times 100 \text{ ml}$$

This, of course, assumes that the separation has been successful in resolving the three dyes and that none of the dye has been left on the column or lost in any other way.

NOTE

This experiment may be performed using victoria blue B (phenyl group instead of ethyl on secondary amine nitrogen) instead of victoria blue R. The separation between victoria blue B and methylene blue is less clean. Victoria blue B has its absorption maximum at 610 nm.

PROBLEMS

1. How long will it take to elute one-half the amount of victoria blue R from an alumina column (40 cm long, 1.5 cm i.d.) on which it has a retention volume of 123 ml? Assume that this column contains 79.5 g of alumina, has a free volume of 7.0 ml, and that the solvent moves through the column with a velocity of 4.0 cm/min.

2. The absorbance of a standard solution of victoria blue B containing 1.00 milligram/liter when measured in a 1.50 cm square cuvette is 0.172. The absorbance of a 10.0 ml aliquot of 100.0 ml of victoria blue B eluted from an alumina column when measured in the same cuvette is 0.710. Calculate the total number of mg of victoria blue B eluted from the column.

3. 50.00 ml of 0.150 M acetic acid are shaken with 5.00 g of alumina until adsorption equilibrium is attained. The adsorbent is filtered off. A 25.00-ml aliquot of the solution requires 30.0 ml of standard 0.111 M sodium hydroxide to reach a phenolphthalein end point. Calculate the specific adsorption (mg/g) of acetic acid on alumina.

4. For the adsorption of methylene blue on charcoal, N in the Freundlich equation is 10.3 and k_i is 0.37. How many mg of methylene blue will be adsorbed on 4.0 g of charcoal from a solution which initially contains 1.00 mg methylene blue/liter?

5. What is the distinguishing feature of an adsorbent? List five adsorbents commonly used in column chromatography.

6. What solvent would you choose to try first for each of the column adsorption chromatographic separations given below?

    (a) separation of a mixture of hydrocarbons (more than ten CH_2 groups in a molecule, no functional groups) on alumina

(b)   a mixture of carbohydrates $[C_n(H_2O)_n]$ on charcoal

(c)   a mixture of steroids (hydrocarbon rings with hydrocarbon side chains and a small number of oxygen containing functional groups) on alumina separation of a mixture of proteins on calcium phosphate

7. What is a group adsorption energy? How are group adsorption energies used to determine elution sequences?

8. What would be the order of elution for the compounds listed below when separated on an alumina column using pentane as the eluent?

(a) $CH_3-CH_2-CH_2-COOH$, $CH_3-CH_2-CH_2-CH_2OH$,
$$CH_3-CH_2-CH_2-CHO$$

(b) $m\text{-}C_6H_4Cl_2$, $m\text{-}C_6H_4ClNH_2$, $m\text{-}CH_3-C_6H_4-Cl$, $m\text{-}CH_3-C_6H_4-OH$

(c) $C_6H_4-NH_2$, C_6H_5OH, $C_6H_5-COOCH_3$, $C_6H_5COCH_3$

REFERENCES

1. Fillinger, H. H., *Chromatographic Analysis for the Metal Ions of A First Course in Qualitative Analysis*, Hollins College, Va., 1952.

2. Heftmann, E., *Chromatography*, 2nd ed., Van Nostrand Reinhold Co., New York, 1967, Chap. 4.

3. Heftmann, E., *Anal. Chem.*, **38**, 31R (1966).

4. Smith, O. C., *Inorganic Chromatography*, D. Van Nostrand Co., New York, 1953.

5. Snyder, L. R., *J. Chromatogr.*, **5**, 430 (1961).

6. Snyder, L. R., *Anal. Chem.*, **34**, 771 (1962).

7. Snyder, L. R., in *Advances in Analytical Chemistry and Instrumentation*, C. N. Reilley, Ed., Vol. III, Wiley-Interscience, New York, 1964, pp. 251–313.

8. Snyder, L. R., in *Encyclopedia of Industrial Chemical Analysis*, F.D. Snell and C. L. Hilton, Eds., Wiley-Interscience, New York, 1966, Vol. I, pp. 78–98.

9. Snyder, L. R., *Anal. Chem.*, **39**, 698, 705 (1967).

10. Snyder, L. R. *Principles of Adsorption Chromatography*, Dekker, New York, 1968.

11. Snyder, L. R., and Roth, W. F., *Anal. Chem.*, **36**, 128 (1964).

12. Whistler, R. L., and Durso, D. F. *J. Amer. Chem. Soc.*, **72**, 677 (1950).

13. Zweig, G., *Anal. Chem.*, **40**, 491R (1968).

CHAPTER 9

LIQUID–LIQUID PARTITION CHROMATOGRAPHY

Liquid–liquid column partition chromatography, created by Martin and Synge in 1941, is an important experimental separation technique. In the late fifties the advent of gas chromatography caused a loss of interest in liquid partition techniques. In recent years, however, there has been a renewed activity, both experimental and theoretical, in column partition chromatography.[9] New equipment has been designed, and theories developed for gas chromatography are now being applied to liquid–liquid partition. This resurgence of vigor has been brought about by the realization that gas chromatography is not the panacea of separation techniques, and that liquid partition chromatography is ideally suited for separations involving delicate, thermally unstable compounds.

Martin and Synge, employed by the Wool Industries Research Association in Leeds, England, were striving to separate and analyze the amino acids present in the protein hydrolyzates of wool fibers. They developed countercurrent extraction equipment for this purpose, but it was not completely satisfactory.[14] Therefore, to solve their problem, they invented a new separation technique:

> Consideration . . . led us to try absorbing water in silica gel, etc., and then using the water-saturated solid as one phase of a chromatogram, the other one being, some fluid immiscible with water, the silica acting merely as a mechanical support. Separations in a chromatogram of this type thus depend upon differences in the partition between two liquid phases of the substances to be separated, and not, as in all previously described chromatograms, on differences in adsorption between liquid and solid phases.[15]

In their first partition chromatographic work Martin and Synge[15] used silica gel as their support, water as the stationary phase, and 1% *n*-butanol in chloroform as their mobile phase. Not only did they perfect the experimental technique, they explained the theory behind successful separations by partition chromatography. Since they deliberately patterned the technique on countercurrent distribution, the derivations of their equations—assumptions and mathematics—were analogous to countercurrent distribution. The relationship between solute concentration and distance down the chromatographic column resembles that between tube number and concentration in countercurrent distribution. Their expression for the distribution ratio in terms of the retardation factor and the surface areas of the two liquid phases is similar to Equation (7–6). Agreement between the distribution ratio obtained by extraction methods for both acetylproline and acetyl phenylalanine and that found by their new chromatographic technique was excellent— within 0.1.

While attempts to separate the amino acids by partition chromatography were not completely successful, Martin and Synge did manage to separate phenylalanine and leucine from proline, valine, and methionine. These last three amino acids could not be separated from each other. Unfortunately, while they obtained a 98% recovery of the leucine and a 101% recovery for the mixture of three amino acids, they only obtained a 79% recovery of the phenylalanine, which confused them. Nevertheless, in spite of its inadequacies in solving their particular problem, Martin and Synge did invent a significant and potent new separation technique.

The quotation from Martin and Synge's paper describes the technique very well. A finely divided solid is coated with a thin film of a liquid and packed into a column. Customarily, the more polar of the two solvents is the stationary liquid. The sample is placed in a narrow band at the top of the column. A second liquid, immiscible with the stationary one on the solid, is poured through the column, separating the components in the sample mixture by means of their differences in partition equilibrium behavior. Those solutes whose distribution ratios favor the moving liquid are eluted before those solutes whose distribution ratios favor the stationary liquid. The order of elution is roughly that of the increasing solubility in the stationary liquid. The eluate emerging from the bottom of the column is collected and analyzed by the appropriate techniques (see Chapter 7).

The conventional partition chromatographic column is a vertical glass tube, about 40 cm long and 1 to 2 cm in diameter (see Fig. 2–2). Under normal operating conditions the mobile solvent is introduced to the top of the column from a reservoir (separatory funnel) and allowed to flow through the column under the influence of gravity. The commercial liquid chromatographs recently introduced to the market at high costs, use long, narrow columns and force the liquid through the column (see below).

At the present time, partition chromatography is largely an empirical technique, although H. Vink[18] and D. C. Locke[12] have done considerable theoretical work on efficiency and separation factors. Nonetheless, there does not exist the body of correlative material on partition chromatographic separations that exists for adsorption chromatography and for gas–liquid chromatography.

THE EXPERIMENTAL VARIABLES

The experimental factors which influence a separation by liquid–liquid partition chromatography are a combination of those involved in adsorption chromatography with those important in extraction: (1) the nature of the solid phase; (2) the nature of the liquid pair; (3) the nature of the solutes; (4) the rate of solvent flow; and (5) the temperature. Let us consider each of these in some detail.

The Solid Support

The sole function of the solid in partition chromatography should be to act as a mechanical support for the stationary liquid phase. In no manner should it affect or contribute to the separation. Thus, in order for a solid to be used for a support, it should be (a) chemically inert, not reacting with either of the liquid phases or with any of the solutes; (b) nonadsorbing for substances other than the stationary liquid phase; (c) large in surface area, which probably means that it should be porous; (d) wet more readily by the stationary phase than by the mobile phase. The solids used as supports do not differ from those used in adsorption chromatography—silica gel, powdered cellulose, diatomaceous earth, starch, and powdered rubber (see Fig. 9–1).

Silica Gel

The properties of silica gel have been described in Chapter 8 and need not be repeated here. When silica gel is used as the solid support in partition chromatography, the stationary liquid adsorbed onto it is apt to be water or aqueous buffer solutions. Amounts of liquid up to 50% of the weight of the silica gel have been adsorbed. The water or buffer is mixed thoroughly with the powdered silica gel in a mortar. The resultant particles appear to be dry, but will not flow freely, sticking together. A narrow distribution of particle diameters is desirable; 100 to 200 mesh silica gel is usually used.

It is impossible to state positively that adsorption mechanisms are not involved in partition chromatographic separations involving silica gel. If the *liquid loading* (that is, the amount of liquid used to coat a given amount of stationary solid) is low, there undoubtedly will be some adsorption of solutes accompanying the partition. When using silica gel as a solid support, deactivate it (see Chapter 8) before coating with the stationary liquid phase, to minimize adsorption.

Cellulose

The structure and composition of the cellulose surface will be described in detail in Chapter 10, so that only a brief description of it will be presented here. The powdered cellulose used for column partition chromatography can be ob-

Fig. 9–1. Piles of cellulose, Celite, and silica gel (*Photograph by Stephen Daugherty.*)

tained readily, and is used with no pretreatments. Cellulose is constructed of carbohydrate chains, so that its surface layer consists of the polar hydroxyl group, OH, and less than 0.1% of carboxyl groups, COOH. These groups adsorb water from the atmosphere, continuously, coating the surface of the cellulose fibers with a thin film of water. Cellulose contains from 6 to 26% water by weight; the exact weight depends upon the temperature and humidity. Because cellulose powder requires no prior treatment, it is difficult to realize that its surface contains a liquid. Nevertheless, the chromatographic separation process occurring on cellulose is caused by partition and not adsorption. All separation phenomena cannot be attributed solely to partition processes; it is highly likely that there are both adsorption and ion-exchange mechanisms accompanying the partitioning of solutes.

Diatomaceous Earths (Celite, Kieselguhr)

Diatomaceous earths are composed of the calcified skeletons of diatoms (single-celled algae). Chemically these diatoms consist of hydrated, amorphous silica containing traces of metal oxides as impurities. A typical sample analyzes as: $\sim 90\%$ SiO_2, 3.6% Al_2O_3, 3.2% $Na_2O + K_2O$, 1.4% Fe_2O_3, 0.5% MgO, and traces of TiO_2 and CaO. When calcined, the diatom skeletons become embedded in sodium silicate glass. The diatoms are perforated with small round holes, of about 1 micron diameter, which in turn have pores in them. The average particle diameter of a diatom is 8 to 9 microns, but because of the pores, it has a surface area of about 20 m^2/g. The surface of the diatomaceous earth is composed of silanol groups, SiOH:

$$\begin{array}{cc} OH & OH \\ | & | \\ -Si-O-Si- \end{array}$$

In Celite there are 2.5×10^{19} of these groups per square meter of surface. Silanol groups adsorb water (and other polar liquids), so water is the usual stationary liquid when diatomaceous earth functions as a support. As was the case for silica gel, adsorption is believed to accompany the partition process, when the stationary liquid is not covering the surface properly. With 10% glycerol [$(CH_2OH)_2$-CHOH] on diatomaceous earth Locke[11] found retention times considerably greater than those obtained using 20 and 30% glycerol. He attributes the larger retention volumes to adsorption accompanying the solute partition, because the coverage of the surface of the solid support by glycerol is inadequate.

Reversed-Phase Supports

Normally, partition chromatographic practice has the more polar liquid phase stationary. This is the easiest method because the surfaces of the solid supports are composed of polar groups, as in silica gel, cellulose, and diatomaceous earth. Occasionally, it is desirable (see below) to immobilize the less polar liquid so as to operate the column in the *reversed-phase* mode. If the less polar liquid merely were to be adsorbed onto the polar surfaces of these supports, elution with water, alcohols, acids, or other polar liquids immediately would wash the less polar liquid off the surface, which would destroy the chromatogram. Therefore, the —OH groups on the surface of the solid must be converted into nonpolar groups that will prefer to adsorb nonpolar liquids.

One very effective conversion process that is used for silica gel and diatomaceous earths consists of exposing the surface to dimethyldichlorosilane vapor in a closed container, (for example, a desiccator). Dimethyldichlorosilane reacts with the silanol groups of the surface according to the reaction:

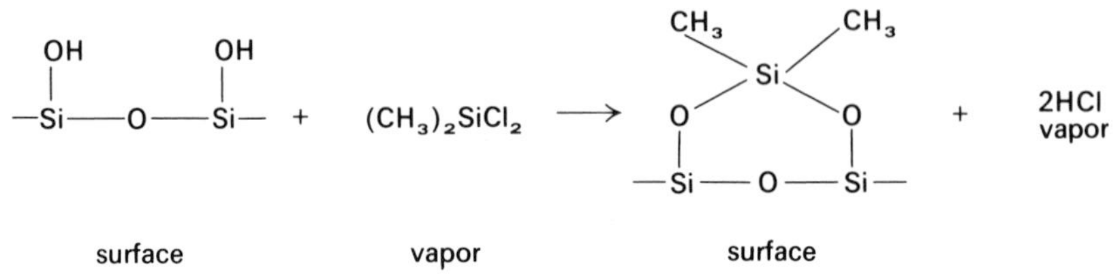

which destroys the hydroxyl groups and replaces them with methyl groups on the surface. Now nonpolar liquids will be preferentially adsorbed onto this surface, so that reversed-phase partition presents no problems. Hexamethyldisilazane, $(CH_3)_3Si$—NH—$Si(CH_3)_3$, has been used equally well to convert the surface —OH groups to —CH_3 groups.

Powdered rubber is used frequently for reversed-phase partition chromatography, Natural rubber consists of long, polymeric chains of the monomer isoprene, such as:

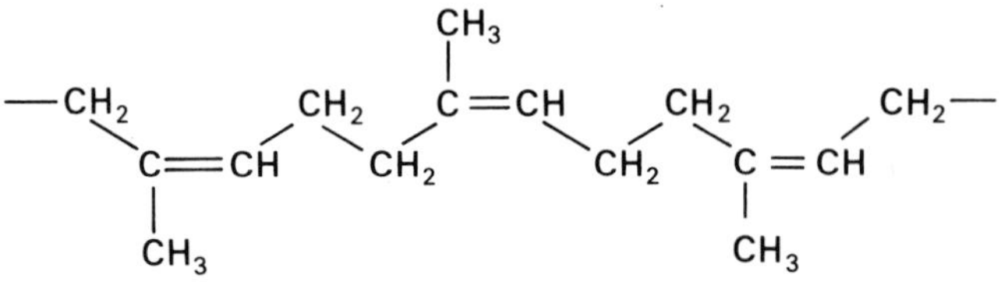

Hence, rubber is very effective in adsorbing hydrocarbons and other nonpolar liquids onto its surface.

Powdered polyethylene is also used as a support during reversed-phase partition chromatography.

Adsorption by the Solid Support

With the exception of rubber and polyethylene, the solids used as supports have polar surfaces of extremely large areas. It is to be expected that these solids also act as adsorbents. After all, they do adsorb the stationary liquid onto their surfaces. Why shouldn't they also adsorb polar solutes? As mentioned earlier, there is evidence which can be interpreted to indicate that constituents of samples, especially polar ones such as alcohols and acids, are adsorbed by the stationary phase as well as being distributed between the two liquid phases. When this adsorption occurs the elution peaks are skewed, and show tailing. Because of these distortions, adsorption accompanying the partition process is undesirable. To minimize or eliminate adsorption, the solids are deactivated by covering the more active sites with water before coating the solid with the stationary phase, or by washing the surface with mineral acids. When feasible, surfaces can be partially converted by treatment with hexamethyldisilazane (see above) to block the active adsorption sites. The most common method, although not an infallible one, is to use such a sufficiently high percentage of stationary liquid phase on the solid that the solid surface is covered completely with a fairly thick layer of liquid.

Note: Under certain conditions, especially when attempting to separate polar compounds, adsorption of the solute at the liquid–liquid interface is believed to occur.

The Liquid Phases

Stationary Liquid Phase

The amount of liquid on the solid is expressed as a fraction of the weight of the coated particles. Thus, 10% glycerol on diatomaceous earth means there are 10 g of the liquid coating 90 g of the earth.

The liquid phase is usually applied to the solid support by taking weighed amounts of the solid, and weighed amounts of the liquid to be the stationary phase and grinding them together in a mortar and pestle. Ordinarily about 0.5 to 1.0 ml of the liquid is used per g of the solid support. The resultant mixture is not wet in appearance, but it usually is not free flowing. Since the coated particles are sticky, it is frustrating, if not impossible, to use the dry technique of column packing. Thus, a wet process is always used. The particles are suspended in a small amount of the mobile phase liquid so as to form a slurry. The slurry is poured slowly through a funnel into the column. Either the solid is allowed to settle by gravity, or it is tamped down with a plunger. (The plunger is a glass rod spread at one end so that it is just slightly smaller than the inside diameter of the column.) The packed column is rinsed with the mobile phase several times before applying the sample. Cellulose usually is not wetted with water, for a sufficient amount is already adsorbed onto the surface of the solid. Instead, a slurry of cellulose in acetone is prepared and poured into the column.

Even though the stationary liquid phase usually is spread less than one mm thick over the surface of the solid, it still acts as a liquid phase. Thus, in the column we have a pair of liquid solvents between which the solutes are partitioned. Separations of mixtures of solutes depend upon the differences in the partition behavior of the compounds. As each solute is pulled down the column by the flowing liquid, it is partitioned thousands of times into the stationary phase. A partition chromatographic column is a more compact and efficient modification of a countercurrent distribution train.

Selection of the Solvent Pair

The selection of the appropriate pair of solvents for partition chromatographic separations is more difficult than the selection of the solvent for adsorption chromatography. Rather, it is quite comparable to the selection of the solvent pair for extractions. Two factors which should be borne in mind when selecting the solvent pair are: (1) the two liquids should be immiscible; and (2) in the liquid pair chosen, the components should show sufficient difference in distribution ratios to be separated effectively. The requirement for solvent immiscibility is not so rigorous as it is in extraction. If the mobile liquid contains some water, it will operate effectively and not strip the aqueous phase from the column. Thus, liquids such as acetone, *n*-butanol, and *n*-propanol have been used just as successfully as hydrocarbons, carbon tetrachloride, and chloroform.

The distribution ratio, D, in partition chromatography is defined as the ratio of the concentration of solute in the stationary liquid to the concentration of solute in the mobile liquid. Since water frequently is the stationary liquid, D for partition chromatography is the reciprocal of D in extraction. For optimum separation, the numerical values of D should be greater than one, but not too much greater. If the value of D is very small (considerably less than 1) the solutes will remain almost exclusively in the mobile phase, eluting very soon after the initial emergence of the solvent, and producing almost no separation of the solutes. If the values of D are too large (values of several hundred), the solutes will remain in the stationary phase so long that enormous quantities of solvent and time are required to remove them from the column and effect the separation. When the chemical properties of the solutes permit it, the numerical value of D can be altered by changing solution conditions. The ways of doing this were described in Chapters 5 and 6. When the solutes are weak acids or bases, buffering the stationary phase at a suitable pH takes advantage of differences in ionization. Selection of certain liquids for the mobile phase enables solute association to be used in the changing of D values. Complex ion formation in the aqueous phase is used to separate not only metal ions, but organic ligands. Details of the solution conditions required to change D can be obtained from the equations and discussions in Chapter 6.

In choosing a solvent pair for a specific separation, enormous amounts of time, energy, and chemicals can be saved by consulting the literature. The experience of others in separating the same or related compounds should be capitalized on. The selection of solvents is highly empirical, for so far only the theory of regular solutions has been applied to explain partition chromatographic separation behavior. The chemistry of the solutes should always be kept clearly in mind. Solubilities, solute–solvent interactions (chemical reactions, hydrogen bonding, and so on), and solution equilibria as discussed in Chapter 5 all can permit or prohibit partition chromatographic separations.

As mentioned earlier, in normal partition chromatography the stationary liquid phase is the more polar of the two liquids, whereas in reversed-phase partition chromatography, the less polar liquid is the stationary phase. When cellulose, diatomaceous earth and silica gel are the solid support, the stationary phase is usually water and the mobile phase a hydrocarbon. To separate acidic or basic compounds, aqueous buffers are effective as the stationary phase. To separate complexing agents, an aqueous metal ion solution makes an excellent stationary phase. Alcohols and glycols are used as stationary phases for certain applications. The mobile phases are hydrocarbons, chloroform, alcohols, and so forth. Table 9–1 gives some typical solvent pairs used.

Table 9–1. SOLVENT SYSTEMS USED IN PARTITION CHROMATOGRAPHY

Stationary Liquid	Mobile Liquid
Normal operation	
Water	Chloroform, carbon tetrachloride, methylene chloride, chloromethane, alkanes, cyclohexane, benzene, toluene
Aqueous buffers	*n*-Butanol in chloroform, *n*-propanol, ethyleneglycol monoethyl ether, hydrocarbons
Methanol, ethanol	Isooctane, glycols
Glycols	Pyridine, *n*-heptane
Aniline	Isopropanol/benzene
Formamide	Methylethyl ketone, dibutyl ether
Reversed-phase operation	
Alkanes	Water, methanol, ethanol, formamide, glycols
Cycloalkanes	Methanol
Benzene	Ethanol
n-Butanol, octanol	Water
Chloroform	Water
Silicones	Water

Structure of the Solute

Very little work has been done on the correlation between the order of the elution of a series of compounds from a partition column and the structure of the solute comparable to the group adsorption energies used in adsorption chromatography or the R_f or R_M values used in paper and thin-layer chromatography. No such terms have been proposed for partition chromatography. The feasibility of a particular separation must be determined on a highly empirical basis. With the renewed interest and activity in partition chromatographic separations, such structure-elution correlations will undoubtedly be developed.

Retention Volumes and Times

In Chapter 8 a relation between the retention volume, V_R, the weight of adsorbent, the specific absorbtivity, and the free volume of the chromatographic column was given. An analogous relationship can be written for partition chromatography:

$$V_R = DV_s + V_m \tag{9–1}$$

where, as mentioned on p. 370, the distribution ratio is defined as:

$$D = \frac{\text{concentration of solute in stationary liquid}}{\text{concentration of solute in mobile liquid}}$$

The volume of the stationary liquid phase is V_s, and V_m is the volume of the mobile liquid phase in the column. V_m is the contribution to the retention volume from the volume of the eluting liquid required to move the solute from the top to the bottom of the column if the solute never dissolved in the stationary phase at any time. DV_s is the volume of the eluting liquid necessary to move the solute from the top to the bottom of the column as the solute enters and leaves the stationary liquid. It represents the volume of liquid flowing by while the solute is in the stationary phase. Equation (9–1) shows us that the larger the value of D, the larger the retention volume. This is logical for the larger the value of D, the longer the solute remains stationary on the column, and the larger the volume of eluent that flows by without removing the solute. V_m depends upon the column geometry and the packing of the particles of solid. V_s depends upon the amount of stationary liquid used in preparing the column packing.

The *net retention volume* is the volume of eluate needed to elute one-half of the solute from the column, corrected for the volume of solvent required just to fill the interstitial space between the particles in the column. This "dead" volume is, of course, the volume of the mobile phase in the column, V_m, so that for the net retention volume we can write:

$$V_n = V_R - V_m = DV_s \qquad (9\text{–}2)$$

It would be extremely convenient to have a retention volume that does not depend on experimental parameters for its value. If we had such a number it could be used with different columns with different geometries and in different laboratories. To obtain such a number, a third retention volume is defined. This one eliminates the volume of the stationary phase from Equation (9–2), and is called the *specific retention volume*. The specific retention volume, V_g, is defined as:

$$V_g = \frac{V_n}{w_s} = \frac{DV_s}{w_s} = \frac{D}{\rho_s} \qquad (9\text{–}3)$$

where w_s is the weight of all the stationary liquid in the chromatographic column and ρ_s is the density of the liquid used to coat the solid support, that is, the stationary liquid. Equation (9–3) defines V_g, the specific retention volume, as the net retention volume per gram of stationary liquid phase. The weight of a liquid per unit volume is its density. So, the specific retention volume is equal to the distribution ratio of the solute under the experimental conditions selected divided by the density of the stationary liquid phase, ρ_s. Experimental column parameters have been eliminated from the specific retention volume since ρ_s is a physical property of the liquid and D is a conditional equilibrium constant. The specific retention volume is temperature dependent because the distribution ratio is temperature dependent. The volume of the stationary liquid will increase with increasing temperature so that ρ_s is also temperature dependent. The specific retention volume is not affected by pressure since the compressibility of liquids and solids is negligibly slight.

Locke[12] has shown thermodynamically that the specific retention volume is also given by the equation:

$$V_g = \frac{f_m M_m}{f_s M_s \rho_m} \qquad (9\text{–}4)$$

where f_m is the activity coefficient of the solute in the mobile phase at infinite dilution, f_s is the activity coefficient of the solute in the stationary phase at infinite dilution, M_m is the molecular weight of the mobile phase, M_s is the molecular weight of the stationary liquid phase, and ρ_m is the density of the mobile liquid phase.

The retention volume expressions of Equations (9–1) to (9–4) have been derived upon the following assumptions: (a) The two liquid phases are completely immiscible. (b) No adsorption occurs either on the solid support or at the liquid–liquid interface. (c) The distribution ratio remains constant throughout the length of the column. This, in effect, is saying that the distribution ratio is constant from very low concentrations of solute up to the maximum concentration of the elution curve. We have seen in Chapter 6 that this assumption is rarely a valid one. (d) The rate of establishment of the partition equilibrium is rapid in comparison to the rate of flow of solvent. (e) The volumes of the stationary and mobile liquid phases remain constant throughout the elution. (f) The resistance at the liquid–liquid interface to the transfer of the solute from one phase to the other phase is negligibly small.

Equations (9–3) and (9–4) have not been studied very thoroughly although Locke[11,12] has done some experimental work to validate Equation (9–4). Very few distribution ratios in partition chromatographic systems have been evaluated. The activity coefficients for most solutes in most solvents at infinite dilution are just not available. Decreasing the density of either the stationary or the mobile liquid phase should increase the value of the retention volume. Similarly, increasing the molecular weight of the mobile liquid should increase the value of the retention volume. It is a bit difficult to increase the molecular weight of a liquid without increasing its density, however. Decreasing the molecular weight of the stationary phase will increase the retention volume. It is exceedingly difficult, however, to change from one liquid to a second liquid with a different molecular weight, and yet keep the solute–solvent interactions (as measured by either activity coefficients or distribution ratio) the same. Perhaps with adjacent members of a homologous series this can be achieved to a slight degree.

Very few studies have been made on experimental factors that affect the volume of solvent needed to elute a particular solute. Locke[11] has studied the elution of alcohols—methanol, ethanol, 1-propanol, 2-propanol, 1-butanol, and 1-pentanol—using n-heptane as the mobile phase and glycerol on diatomaceous earth as the stationary phase. The value of the specific retention volume, V_g, for the alcohols was found to be essentially constant for flow rates of eluent between 4.4 and 10.7 cm³/min. Thus, there appears to be no effect of flow rate or of pressure drop along the column on the retention volume.

For butanol and propanol the retention volume was independent of the size of the sample taken. For methanol and ethanol a slight increase ($\sim 0.2\%/\mu l$) in retention volume with sample size was found. Hence, no generalizations can be formulated from these data.

The retention volume obtained for each alcohol in a mixture was identical to that obtained when each alcohol was chromatographed separately. Thus, there are no solute–solute interactions between different alcohol molecules, that affect the partition equilibrium.

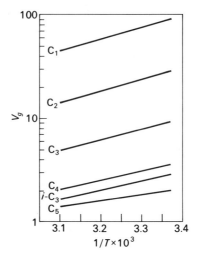

Fig. 9–2. Temperature-dependence of V_g. 30% glycerol on chromosorb P. See text for c_1, c_2, c_3 and so on. (*Redrawn from Ref. 11, by permission of the Journal of Gas Chromatography.*)

The weight of glycerol used to coat the stationary phase did not change the value of the retention volume of the alcohols, provided that there was a sufficiently large amount of glycerol in the first place. In other words, retention volumes on 20, 25, and 30% by weight of glycerol on the diatomaceous earth were identical. However, when only 10% glycerol on diatomaceous earth was used, retention volumes were increased considerably. This increase is explained on the basis of solute adsorption accompanying the partition process.

Locke pretreated his diatomaceous earth in two different ways. One sample was deactivated prior to adding the glycerol and one sample was not. No difference in the retention volumes for the alcohols was found between the two solid supports.

The temperature of the column was varied from 25 to 45°C. Fig. 9–2 is a graph of the specific retention volume for each alcohol as a function of $1/T$. c_1 is methanol, c_2 ethanol, c_3 propanol, and so on. Fig. 9–2 shows that the temperature dependence between V_g and $1/T$ is linear. The temperature coefficient for all of the alcohols was essentially the same, about 0.5% decrease in specific retention volume per degree increase in temperature. For the most accurate and reproducible partition chromatographic separations, the operating temperature of the column should be held constant in a thermostat (water bath or oven).

Fig. 9–3 shows the almost linear relationship between the number of carbons in the alcohol (including water as having no carbons) and the value of the specific retention volume. Since the aqueous solubility, molecular size, extent of hydrogen bonding, and acidity of the alcohols decrease as the number of carbons in the molecule increases, the decrease in the distribution ratio, D, with increasing molecular weight is not surprising. This, of course, causes a lowering of the specific retention volume since the alcohols spend less and less time in the stationary liquid on the solid support as their molecular weight increases.

From the specific retention volumes, the density of the glycerol used as the stationary phase, and Equation (9–3), the distribution ratios for the alcohols were

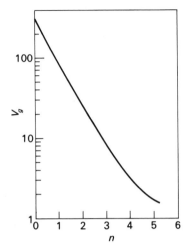

Fig. 9-3. Structure-dependence of V_g. 25% glycerol on gas chrom Q, 25°C. n is the number of carbon atoms in the alcohol. (*Redrawn from Ref. 11, by permission of the Journal of Gas Chromatography.*)

calculated: methanol—111.0; ethanol—34.02; propanol—11.01; and butanol—4.36.

Locke's work would seem to indicate that the volume of flowing solvent needed to elute a solute from a partition chromatographic column is independent of flow rate, pressure drop, sample size, solute interactions, nature of the solid support, and the amount of stationary liquid used. But until more experimental data on these points are accumulated, sweeping statements are dangerous.

For a particular solute on different stationary liquid phases from the same homologous series, using the same mobile liquid each time, the specific retention volumes decreased as the molecular weight of the stationary liquid increased, as predicted by Equation (9–4).

HIGH-SPEED OR HIGH-PRESSURE CHROMATOGRAPHY

The talents and brain power from the field of gas–liquid chromatography have turned to liquid–liquid chromatography. Their experience and techniques from gas–liquid chromatography are being adapted to liquid–liquid chromatography to speed up the separation process, to reduce the sample size, and to improve the separation efficiencies. The progress along the way to these goals is excellent, which explains why the practicing chemist and biochemist are now aware of liquid–liquid chromatography.

As was stated on p. 365, the conventional liquid–liquid partition chromatographic separation in vertical glass tubes with gravity flow of eluent consumes hours or even days in effecting a separation. The method would be more popular and perhaps more widely applicable if the same separation could be achieved in minutes. This has been accomplished. Modifications of the normal apparatus to make it more like a gas–liquid chromatograph incorporate forced solvent flow, coiled columns, and continuous detectors. Lambert and Porter,[10] Locke,[11] Kirkland,[6,9] and Felton,[3] have published descriptions of apparatus for high-speed partition chromatography. Several manufacturers have commercial liquid–liquid chromatographs for sale at prices from $4,000 to $60,000 (see Figs. 7–8 and 7–9). Quite a long way from the simple glass tube!

The columns, supports, and solvent systems used in high-performance liquid chromatography do not differ fundamentally from those discussed earlier for normal column chromatography. The columns cannot be of glass, naturally, because of the high pressures involved (500 to 5000 psi), so they are precision-bore stainless steel tubing, 50 to 100 cm long and 2 to 3 mm inner diameter. Diffusion through the porous, large surface area packings used in conventional chromatography is too slow. Specially designed packings are used, which consist of nonporous centers coated by thin layers of porous material (see Fig. 9–4).

Examples of such "superficially porous"[8] packings are Zipax (E.I. DuPont) and Corasil (Waters Assoc.); for example, Corasil I consists of a thin layer of silica gel on 37 to 50μ diameter glass beads. Its surface area (measured by N_2 adsorption) is 7 m^2/g. Kirkland[8] has written an excellent review of columns and their properties for high-performance chromatography. Solvent systems are identical.

Lower separation efficiencies are obtained with bent or spiral columns, so straight tubes are preferred. The columns are packed dry, using mechanical or electrical vibration to settle the packing. The packed column is housed in a thermostat (water jacket or oven) which holds the column temperature constant within ± 0.1°C.

Solvent is forced through these narrow columns at rates between 0.25 and 180 ml/min, although the separation efficiency has been found to be independent of flow rates between 30 and 120 ml/min. In order to force the liquids through these narrow, packed columns at such rapid flow rates, high pressure pulseless pumps are used. The pressures at the inlet end of the column can vary between 4 and 9 atmospheres, while the outlet pressure is usually atmospheric pressure.

One advantage of high-speed liquid chromatographs is that the sample size usually is very small, ranging from 0.001 to 5.0 ml, but normally from 1 to 3 μl. The liquid sample is injected from a hypodermic syringe through a rubber septum into the mobile liquid just ahead of the inlet to the column.

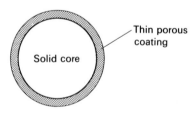

Fig. 9–4. Particle of packing for high-performance liquid chromatography.

A second advantage of high-speed liquid chromatographs is continuous monitoring of the effluent. Gone is the fraction collector and the hundreds of analyses to tell where the components are. Since narrow tubing is used, online monitoring is quite feasible. The detector, however, must be capable of responding to very small amounts of solute in a rapidly flowing liquid. The detectors used successfully so far, have been described in Chapter 7—the differential refractometer, the UV spectrophotometer, the flame ionization detector, the differential adsorpti-meter, and the conductance bridge. The dead space between the outlet of the chromatographic column and the inlet of the detector has been found to be the most critical dimension in high-speed chromatographs. If it is too large, then mixing of the separated solutes occurs. The normal volume, therefore, is about 3 μl.

The separations that have been effected by high speed liquid–liquid partition chromatography are excellent and not restricted to any particular class of chemical compounds. For instance, Kirkland[6] has separated substituted-urea herbicides by high-speed liquid chromatography. His column was 50 cm long with an i.d. of 3 mm, packed with diatomaceous earth of constant particle size and pore size, coated with 4% β,β'-oxydipropionitrile for the stationary liquid phase. Di-n-butyl ether was the eluent. He injected a 3 μl sample containing 1 μg of each of the four herbicides. At a flow rate of 0.26 ml/min the last traces of the last herbicide were eluted after 45 min. The eluent was analyzed continuously by UV spectrophoto-metry. The four herbicides separated by Kirkland are:

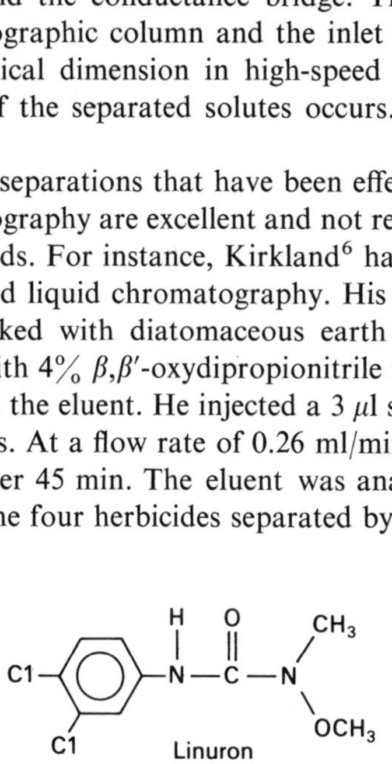

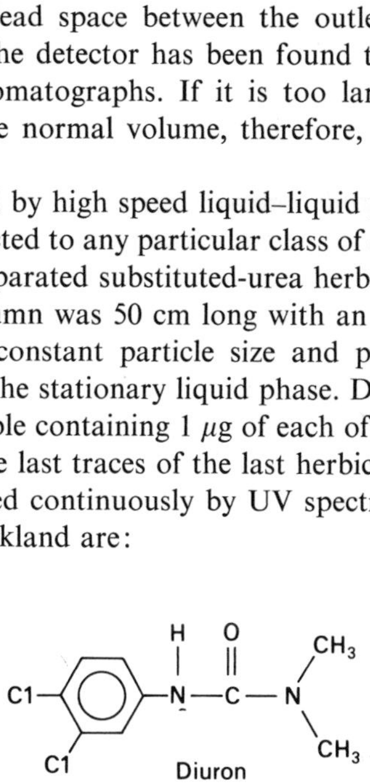

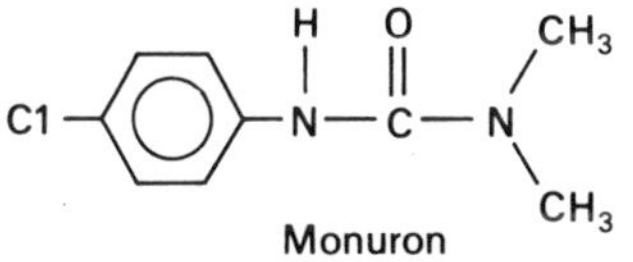

From the chemical structures it is obvious that the differences between these molecules are very slight. Among three of these herbicides the only difference is the presence or absence of a chlorine atom on the benzene ring. The difference between Linuron and Diuron is merely the replacement of a —OCH_3 group for the —CH_3 group. The herbicides were eluted in the order: Lenuron ($V_R \sim 6$ ml), Diuron ($V_R \sim 7.5$ ml), Monuron ($V_R \sim 9$ ml), and Fenuron ($V_R \sim 11$ ml). The separation is quite acceptable and certainly extremely rapid for column partition chromato-graphy.

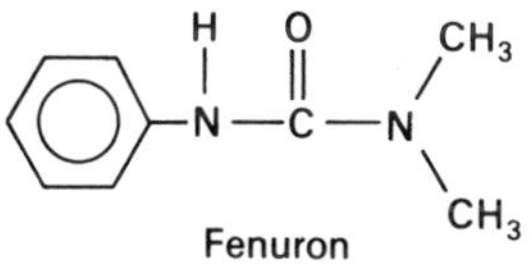

REVERSED-PHASE CHROMATOGRAPHY

In 1950, Howard and Martin,[5] while attempting to separate mixtures of long-chain fatty acids by liquid–liquid partition chromatography, could not find a suitable polar solvent to use as a stationary phase. These long-chain acids are more soluble in nonpolar liquids than in polar ones. To overcome this difficulty, the authors decided to reverse the liquid phases, using the more polar solvent as the mobile phase and the less polar solvent as the stationary phase. This was contrary to normal practices of the time. They treated kieselguhr with dichlorodimethyl silane vapor to produce a nonpolar surface, and then applied paraffin as the stationary liquid phase. Using a mixed solvent of water–methanol–n-octane as the mobile phase they were able to separate the straight-chain fatty acids, lauric (C_{12}), myristic (C_{14}), palmitic (C_{16}), and stearic (C_{18}) from one another. This was the first successful attempt to reverse the phases in partition chromatography.

In normal partition chromatography the more polar of the two liquids is held onto the polar solid support as the stationary phase and the less polar liquid is used as the eluent or mobile phase. In order to achieve a separation, the value of the distribution ratio of the solutes should be greater than one, that is, favor the stationary phase. This means that the solutes must have a greater solubility in the more polar solvent, and in order to do this the solutes usually must possess some polarity. Under these conditions it is difficult, if not impossible, to separate weakly polar or nonpolar solutes for they will favor the mobile phase and be eluted rapidly and unseparated from the column. In order to separate mixtures of nonpolar or weakly polar solutes, the stationary phase must be the one in which the solute has the greater solubility; it must be the less polar of the two liquids. Physically or mechanically this presents no problems. When the less polar liquid is the stationary phase and the more polar liquid is the mobile phase, the partition chromatographic process is called *reversed-phase chromatography*.

In order to have a solid support that will adsorb a nonpolar liquid in preference to a polar one, the surface of the solid must be nonpolar. As has been shown earlier, for diatomaceous earths this is obtained by replacing the hydroxyl groups with methyl groups. Nonpolar supports such as powdered rubber, powdered Teflon, and powdered polyethylene also are used. The stationary liquids used to coat these supports are not particularly polar, while the mobile liquids usually are polar. Examples of reversed-phase partition systems have been given in Table 7–1.

Reversed-phase column partition chromatography has been used to separate the C_{16} through C_{24} even-numbered fatty acids, the C_9 through C_{19} odd-numbered fatty acids from each other and from the even-numbered fatty acids in plasma lipids and in bovine milk fat. On a column of powdered rubber with a hydrocarbon stationary phase and a methanol–acetone–water mobile phase the mono-, di-, and triglycerides have been separated from one another. Hydroxy esters have also been separated, as have been steroids and amino acids. The C_6 through C_{20} fatty acids in ergot oil have been separated using a polyethylene powder as both the stationary phase and the solid support with water–acetone as the mobile phase.

APPLICATIONS

Partition chromatography has been used to separate mixtures of almost all classes of organic compounds—hydrocarbons, carboxylic acids, aldehydes, alcohols, phenols, amino acids, peptides, sugars, and so on. It has also been used very widely to separate lipids, steroids, penicillins, and other medicinally significant mixtures. Many applications involving the separations of inorganic ions have been reported and separation of the lanthanides has been successful.

Fritz and Frazee[4] successfully separated zirconium from hafnium (one of the most difficult separations of inorganic ions to achieve) by means of partition chromatography, obtaining a quantitative recovery of both ions. They used Teflon as their solid support, methyl isobutyl ketone as the stationary liquid phase, and aqueous ammonium thiocyanate–ammonium sulfate solutions as eluents. Zirconium was eluted in the first 20 ml of eluent, whereas hafnium had its maximum concentration at about 150 ml of eluent. Pure ammonium sulfate solution was substituted to elute the hafnium.

S. R. Ayad and J. Blamire[1] fractionated mixtures of nucleic acids by liquid–liquid partition chromatography, using diatomaceous earth with poly-L-lysine as the stationary liquid phase and aqueous NaCl as the eluent. A gradient elution technique was used, increasing the NaCl concentration from 0.4 to 4.0 M NaCl during the elution. Analysis of the four fractions obtained indicated that they were successful in separating RNA from DNA.

The Food and Drug Administration[2] uses partition chromatography to analyze for reserpine in commercial tranquilizer preparations. Using a 22×200 mm column, packed with diatomaceous earth and loaded with a 2% sodium bicarbonate buffer stationary phase, the sample, dissolved in dimethyl sulfoxide, is eluted with chloroform. This chromatography successfully separates the reserpine from the other components of the tablets, after which the quantity of reserpine is determined by ultraviolet spectrophotometry. Repeated analyses gave a 98.4 to 103.2% recovery of reserpine with a standard deviation of 1.5%.

G. R. Nakamura and H. J. Meuron[16] of the Internal Revenue Service report the separation and determination of heroin (diacetylmorphine) in illicit drug preparations. Illicit heroin preparations may include as adulterants caffein, acetylcodeine, procaine, quinine, morphine, 6-monoacetylmorphine, and methapyrilene, as well as lactose, sucrose, mannitol, or other sugars. The column is packed with diatomaceous earth coated with 0.1 M HCl as the stationary liquid. The drug mixture is dissolved in 0.1 M HCl, placed on the column after which the sample components are eluted with chloroform. Since the sugars are virtually insoluble in chloroform they remain on the column. The heroin in the eluate is analyzed by means of ultraviolet spectrophotometry.

Majors[13] separated by high-speed liquid chromatography mixtures of the aromatic amines (N-ethylaniline, N,N-diethylaniline, and others) used as antioxidants in plastics. He also separated the phthalic acid esters used to make vinyl and acrylic resins softer and more flexible. These separations cannot be accomplished by gas chromatography, yet, by high-speed liquid chromatography were completed in less than eight minutes.

A partition chromatographic separation that involves concomitant complex formation was developed by Orr[17] for the separation of alkyl sulfides. The solid support is silica gel coated with a stationary phase of a solution of mercuric acetate in aqueous acetic acid. The sample of mixed alkyl sulfides is eluted from the column with n-hexane. The equilibria involved are:

$$R_2S \overset{D}{\rightleftharpoons} R_2S \;\; + \;\; xHg(OAc)_2$$

$$\Big\updownarrow \quad K_{st}$$

$$R_2S(Hg(OAc)_2)_x$$

| mobile phase | stationary phase |

The alkyl sulfides are essentially insoluble in the aqueous, stationary phase. The formation of a mercury complex increases the aqueous solubility of these sulfides which in turn increases the value of the distribution ratio. In fact the distribution ratio is increased above one, which means the alkyl sulfide will be more soluble in the mercuric acetate solution than in n-hexane. The combination of solubility differences and complex stability differences among different alkyl sulfides enables mixtures of them to be separated. The mercury complexes of the alkyl sulfides are essentially insoluble in n-hexane, so that the uncomplexed alkyl sulfide is the species eluted from the column.

Orr found that the value of the distribution ratio decreases linearly as the number of carbons in the alkyl sulfide increased, from a value of 300 for 4-thiaheptane (six carbons) to 1.5 for 7-thiatridecane (twelve carbons). Branching of the carbon chain has little effect on the value of the distribution ratio, the number of carbons present is the predominant factor in determining the value of D. Alkyl sulfides containing up to fourteen carbon atoms are separated from hydrocarbons; alkyl sulfides containing up to twelve carbons can be separated from one another.

EXPERIMENT 9–I
Separation of Copper and Nickel on a Cellulose Column and Determination by a Chelatometric Titration *

The purpose of this experiment is to illustrate the partition chromatographic separation of inorganic ions. Burstall, Davies, and Wells developed procedures for separating and determining copper, cobalt, iron, and nickel in alloys. This experiment is a simplified modification of their separation process.

The sample of copper and nickel is dissolved in 8 M HCl, which converts both of these ions to their chloro complexes, $Ni(H_2O)_4Cl_2$ and H_2CuCl_4. While the distribution ratios for these complexes between water (the stationary phase) and acetone–HCl (the mobile phase) have not been determined, it is not unlikely to suppose that the nickel complex with its four molecules of water will have a greater solubility in the aqueous phase than will the copper chloro complex. Hence, during a partition chromatographic separation, the nickel chloro complex will spend more time in the stationary aqueous phase than will the copper chloro complex. That is

---

* Based on material presented by F. H. Burstall, G. R. Davies, and R. A. Wells, *Discuss. Faraday Soc.*, **7**, 179 (1949).

to say, the copper will be eluted from the column first, as an amber band. In order to elute the nickel from the cellulose column, its distribution ratio must be changed so as to favor the mobile phase. In this experiment this is accomplished by changing the eluting agent to aqueous 1 M HCl. In this low chloride ion medium, the nickel complex dissociates to $Ni(H_2O)_4Cl^+$, which is eluted rapidly from the column as a pale green band.

Once the two metal ions have been eluted they can be determined by any suitable method. Titration with EDTA is simple, rapid, and direct. In order for the indicators to function properly, however, the acetone must be removed from the solution. To do this, the eluates are heated on a steam bath.

Preparation of the column. The aqueous metal complex solution will creep down the walls of the column instead of passing through the cellulose unless creeping is prevented. Consequently, the 2 × 30 cm glass chromatographic tube is treated with a water-repellent silicone before being issued. Do not wash the column with water; if the tube is dirty and must be washed, be sure that it is dried thoroughly with acetone.

Using the side-shelf scales, weigh about 10 g of Whatman cellulose powder, standard grade, into a 250-ml beaker. Add 100 ml of acetone and stir until the cellulose has been wetted thoroughly. Allow the heavy fibers to settle then decant off the supernatant liquid containing all fine particles of the cellulose. Repeat with a second 100-ml of acetone, again decanting off the fine particles of cellulose. Next add about 50 ml of HCl in acetone (6 ml concentrated HCl per 300 ml acetone, which will yellow and darken on standing, so it should be made up fresh just before using) to form a slurry of cellulose in HCl–acetone.

Tamp a small wad of glass wool down to the bottom of the pretreated chromatographic column. The wad of glass wool should be sufficiently large and fit tightly enough in the column to prevent any of the cellulose powder from passing out of the bottom of the column, yet the wad should be small and loose enough so as not to impede the flow of the solvents through the column. Fill about one-fourth of the column with HCl in acetone. Pour about one-fifth of the slurry into the column. Stir up the acetone in the column to form a smooth slurry with a glass rod which has one end flattened to form a plunger of diameter slightly smaller than that of the glass column. Allow the cellulose to settle. Add the second fifth of the cellulose to the column, stirring with rapid up and down motions of the glass plunger until a uniform slurry that contains a portion of the previously added cellulose is obtained. Allow the cellulose to settle. Repeat this procedure with the third, fourth, and last fifth of the cellulose. This portionwise addition of the cellulose while stirring is essential in order to eliminate striations and obtain a uniform column packing. Gently tamp down the cellulose powder in the column, and then drain the extra solvent down to about 1 cm from the top of the cellulose. Place a disk of filter paper, just slightly smaller than the column diameter on top of the cellulose. The completed column should be about 15 cm in length. If it is not, add more cellulose. If it is longer than that, remove some of the stationary phase from the column.

Pass 50 ml of the HCl–acetone solvent through the settled column in order to remove any traces of metal ions present in the cellulose. Stop the flow of liquid when the level of its meniscus is about 0.5 cm above the top of the cellulose.

Addition of the sample.   Pipette a 2-ml aliquot of the unknown mixture of copper and nickel in 8 M HCl onto the top of the cellulose column, taking care not to disturb the powder at the top of the column. Sample addition is best achieved by placing the tip of the pipette against the inside wall of the column, just above the piece of filter paper. As the aliquot of sample is draining into the column, run the tip of the pipette around the inside of the column, being careful not to touch the packing. The liquid in the column should be draining very slowly during the addition of the sample. Allow the sample to drain onto the column until the meniscus level is within 1 mm of the cellulose surface. At no time should the eluent surface be allowed to fall below the top of the cellulose packing, or air will enter the column. Rinse the inner wall of the column with 1 ml of HCl–acetone and allow this to drain to 1 mm above the top of the cellulose. Repeat with 1 ml portions of the HCl–acetone, draining each to within 1 mm of the filter paper, until the supernatant liquid is colorless. At this time all of the sample is in the narrow band at the top of the cellulose column.

Development of the chromatogram.   Pass about 100 ml of the HCl–acetone eluent through the column. When the orange-brown copper band nears the bottom of the column, begin to collect the eluate in a 250-ml beaker. Continue to collect until all of the copper has been eluted from the column.

After all of the copper has been eluted, change the eluent to aqueous 1 M HCl. Pass about 100 ml of 1 M HCl through the chromatographic column. When the pale-green nickel band nears the bottom of the column, begin to collect the eluate in a 250-ml beaker. Continue to collect this eluate until all of the nickel has been removed from the column.

Analysis of the copper solution.   Add 50 ml of water to the copper eluate. Using 1 M NaOH adjust the pH of the solution to between 3 and 4 (pHydrion paper). Heat the solution on a steam bath for one hour to remove most of the acetone. From time to time, check the pH of the solution with pHydrion paper; if it is not between 3 and 4, add either 1 M HCl or 1 M NaOH to return the pH to this region. Cool the greenish-yellow solution. Add 5.0 ml of pH 5.00, 0.50 M acetic acid–sodium acetate buffer, a volume of ethyl alcohol equal to that of the copper solution, and three drops of 0.05% PAN indicator. Titrate the solution with 0.010 M EDTA until the color changes abruptly from deep violet to canary yellow. Approach this end point slowly and carefully as you DO NOT have another aliquot to titrate.

Analysis of the nickel solution.   Add 50 ml of water to the nickel eluate. Using 1 M NaOH, adjust the pH of the solution to between 3 and 4 (pHydrion paper). Heat the solution on a steam bath for one hour to remove all of the acetone. Cool the solution to room temperature. Add 1 M NH_3 until the solution has a pH of approximately 7 (pHydrion paper). Add 10 ml of 1 M NH_4Cl, and a small amount of the solid murexide indicator mixture. If the pH of the solution is below 7, the color of the solution will be orange. When this occurs add more 1 M ammonia until the solution becomes yellow (Note 1). Titrate the solution with 0.010 M EDTA until the end point is approached. If during the course of this titration, the color of the solution should return to orange, add more 1 M NH_3 until the color returns to yellow. Just before the end point, add 10 ml of concentrated NH_3 to raise the pH of the solution to 10 (Note 2). Warm the solution to 50–60°C (Note 3).

Continue the titration until there is an exceedingly abrupt color change from yellow to bluish violet. Again be careful in approaching the end point, do it drop by drop, because you do not have a second aliquot to titrate, and the color change occurs without warning.

Calculation of results. From the volume of standard EDTA used to reach the end point in each of these titrations and the molarity of the EDTA, the number of millimoles of each metal ion can be calculated. Since the entire amount of metal in the eluate was titrated, the number of millimoles is also the amount of metal ion present in the initial 2.0-ml aliquot. By multiplying this number of millimoles by the milliatomic weight of each metal, the number of milligrams of each metal in the original aliquot can be calculated.

no. mg Cu in original aliquot $=$ ml EDTA $\times$ molarity EDTA $\times$ at.wt. Cu in mg
no. mg Ni in original aliquot $=$ ml EDTA $\times$ molarity EDTA $\times$ at. wt. Ni in mg

NOTES

1. In the presence of nickel, murexide can be used as a pH indicator to adjust the solution to a pH of 7. Below pH 7, the species NiH_4In^+, which is orange-yellow, exists in solution. Above pH 7, the species NiH_2In^-, which is yellow, exists in solution.
2. The indicator color change at the end point is sharpest between pH 10 and 12. The solution cannot be brought to a pH in this region too early in the titration, however, because the nickel tetraammine complex is not sufficiently stable to prevent nickel hydroxide or a basic nickel salt from precipitating. Thus, only before the end point, when the nickel concentration is quite low, can the solution be raised to a pH of about 10.
3. As is the case with most nickel chelates, the rate of formation of NiY^{2-} is not very rapid. Thus, in order to increase the rate of chelate formation, and the sharpness of the end-point color change, the solution is heated.

PROBLEMS

1. Describe clearly the differences between column adsorption and column partition chromatography.
2. What role does the solid support play in partition chromatography? What properties should the solid support possess?
3. Describe three solids used as supports in partition chromatography.
4. What factors must be considered when intelligently selecting solvent systems for partition chromatography?
5. Is the distribution ratio, D, used in partition chromatography the same as the distribution ratio, D, used in solvent extraction? If it is, why is it possible to use the same term? If it is not, explain why and how the two differ.
6. Explain clearly how each of the following parameters affects the retention volume of a solute in partition chromatography:
   (a) the solubility of the solute in the stationary liquid
   (b) the density of packing of the column, assuming the total volume of the column packed constant
   (c) the amount of liquid used to coat the support material
   (d) assuming a fixed weight of solid support and a fixed volume of liquid with which it is to be coated, the particle size of the solid support
   (e) the solubility of the solute in the mobile phase
   (f) the temperature at which the column is operated

7. A mixture of straight chain alcohols $CH_3(CH_2)_nCH_2OH$ is to be separated by partition chromatography, using glycerol as the stationary liquid and heptane as the mobile liquid. What effect might each of the following experimental variables have on the retention volume of the alcohols?
   (a) the rate of the flow of the mobile solvent
   (b) the size sample taken to be analyzed
   (c) the thickness of the coating of stationary solvent on the solid support
   (d) the temperature at which the column is operated
   (e) the molecular weight of the alcohol
8. A mixture of metal ions, iron(III), nickel(II), cobalt(II), copper(II), and zinc(II), is to be separated by partition chromatography of their chloro complexes on a cellulose column. Explain the effect that each of the following could have on the effectiveness of the separation:
   (a) the stability of the metal chloro complex of each metal
   (b) the identity of the eluent used (for example, consider using pentane instead of acetone; or methyl isobutylketone instead of acetone.)
   (c) the concentration of HCl present in the eluent
9. Compare and contrast column liquid chromatography with high-speed liquid chromatography with respect to:
   (a) the size of the sample capable of being separated into its components
   (b) the efficiency of the separation
   (c) the time required to effect the separation
   (d) the apparatus needed
   (e) the means used to detect the solutes in the effluent

REFERENCES

1. Ayad, S. R. and Blamire, J., *J. Chromatogr.*, **42**, 248 (1969).
2. Barkan, S., *J. Ass. Offic. Anal. Chem.*, **52**, 113 (1969).
3. Felton, H., *J. Chromatog. Sci.*, **7**, 13 (1969).
4. Fritz, J. S., and Frazee, R. T., *Anal. Chem.*, **37**, 1359 (1965).
5. Howard, G. A. and Martin, A. J. P., *Biochem. J.*, **46**, 532 (1950).
6. Kirkland, J. J., *Anal. Chem.*, **40**, 391 (1968).
7. Kirkland, J. J., *J. Chromatogr. Sci.*, **7**, 7 (1969).
8. Kirkland, J. J., *Anal. Chem.*, **43** (12), 36A (1971).
9. Kirkland, J. J., Ed., *Modern Practice of Liquid Chromatography*, Wiley-Interscience, New York, 1971.
10. Lambert, S. M. and Porter, P. E., *Anal. Chem.*, **36**, 99 (1964).
11. Locke, D. C., *J. Gas Chromatogr.*, **5**, 202 (1967).
12. Locke, D. C. in *Advances in Chromatography*, Vol. VIII, J. C. Giddings and R. A. Keller, Eds., Dekker, New York, 1969.
13. Majors, R. E., *J. Chromatogr. Sci.*, **8**, 338 (1970).
14. Martin, A. J. P. and Synge, R. L. M., *Biochem. J.*, **35**, 91 (1941).
15. Ibid., p. 1358.
16. Nakamura, G. R. and Meuron, H. J., *Anal. Chem.*, **41**, 1124 (1969).
17. Orr, W. L., *Anal. Chem.*, **38**, 1558 (1966).
18. Vink, H., *J. Chromatogr.*, **25**, 71 (1966); **36**, 237 (1968).

CHAPTER 10

PAPER CHROMATOGRAPHY

Touch the tip of your fountain pen lightly to the end of a strip of filter paper so as to leave a spot of ink. Place the end of the strip in a dish of alcohol. Watch the spot as it moves up the paper. It is amazing to see the single spot begin to break up into several spots of different colors moving at different rates. Or place a drop of an extract from spinach leaves or grass on the end of a strip of filter paper. Dip this end into a dish of ether and watch the green spot separate into green, yellow, gray, and orange spots. These are paper chromatographic separations.

Paper chromatography has been around for a long time. Runge used a form of it as long ago as 1850. Schoenbein and Goppelsroder's "capillary analysis" (1861), similar to the modern paper chromatography, successfully separated dyes, salts, water, wine, milk, urine, and other mixtures. But the paper chromatography used today was not developed until 1944. It shouldn't be surprising at this point to learn that the technique was developed and exploited by A. J. P. Martin and his co-workers. Consden, Gordon, and Martin[5] were not satisfied with the incomplete separations and poor recovery that their new technique of partition chromatography gave for the amino acids in wool hydrolyzates. To be sure, the results were better than they had been able to achieve with countercurrent distribution but they still had not solved their problems. So they decided to combine "capillary analysis" with their partition chromatography, using a piece of filter paper as the stationary phase with various solvents as the mobile liquid. This time they were successful in separating the amino acids completely.

Just as we have seen for partition chromatography, Martin and coworkers did more than develop a new experimental method for separating amino acids. They also developed the theory of the separation process. They understood the process causing the separation, developed equations to describe the factors influencing the separation, and attempted to correlate the position of the spot on the paper with the molecular structure of the component. Consden, Gordon, and Martin state:

> The separation depends on the differences in the partition coefficient between the mobile phase and water-saturated cellulose . . . adsorption by the cellulose plays no significant part.[5]

Using the equations in their paper, Martin, *et al.*,[5] calculated distribution ratios for the partition equilibrium of glycine and alanine on the paper. These numbers agreed excellently (fortuitously they insist) with the distribution ratios for these amino acids obtained in the same solvent systems using separatory funnels. They defined the retardation factor, R_f, and reported R_f values for twenty-three different amino acids in nine different solvent systems, with a reproducibility of about four percent. In order to separate two amino acids, a ten percent difference in R_f values is required. An increase in R_f with temperature was observed (with a few anomalies, just to keep things interesting). pH increases caused some R_f values to go up and some R_f values to go down. They quite correctly explained this difference in pH behavior for different amino acids in terms of the difference in the acid dissociation constants of the various amino acids. Once again A. J. P. Martin had done an admirable piece of experimental and theoretical work in developing a new and powerful separation technique.

THE EXPERIMENTAL VARIABLES

Paper chromatography is easier to do in the laboratory than the two types of column chromatography discussed already. Once the separation has been started it can be ignored until it is finished—usually several hours later. A small spot of a concentrated solution of the mixture to be separated is placed near the edge of a piece of loose-textured filter paper and the solvent evaporated off to leave the residue dissolved in the water on the cellulose. The edge of the paper closest to the spot is placed into a trough containing a solvent that is immiscible, or partially miscible with water. The solvent trough and paper are enclosed in a container whose atmosphere is saturated with solvent vapor. The solvent moves through the paper by capillary action. As the moving solvent passes over the stationary water on the cellulose, the components of the sample are partitioned back and forth between the two liquids, exactly as is the case in column partition chromatography. The mobile liquid moves through the paper until it reaches the opposite edge. This is the development of the paper chromatogram. When the solvent has reached the edge of the paper, the paper is removed from the developing chamber and dried. The spots of solutes (hopefully separated) are located by suitable techniques. Although paper chromatography is a very powerful tool for separating complex mixtures, it is out of fashion today. This in no way minimizes its importance or ability to separate mixtures of solutes.

The liquid sample is placed on the filter paper far enough in from one edge so that the spot will be above the surface of the developing solvent in its trough. The area of the spot must be small—3 to 8 mm, so it is applied by touching a capillary pipette to the paper and allowing the liquid to flow into the paper. To obtain a concentrated solute in the spot, repeated applications are necessary—drying the spot after each touching. The solvent is evaporated off before the chromatogram is developed.

Procedural Modifications

The procedural modifications of the laboratory technique for development of

Fig. 10–1.   Development jars and tanks for descending paper chromatography. (*Courtesy of Fisher Scientific Co.*)

paper chromatograms are almost infinite in number. Some of the more common operational methods will be described.

Martin's original method uses a closed tank with the trough of solvent at the top of the tank. A rectangular sheet of filter paper is draped over a glass rod (to prevent siphoning of the solvent), one edge in the trough, the other hanging down to the bottom of the tank. The solvent, in moving through the paper, descends from the top of the tank to its bottom, consequently, this form of development is called *descending paper chromatography*. Fig. 10–1 shows jars and tanks available for developing paper chromatograms by the descending technique. The movement of the solvent is fairly rapid for gravity works favorably to aid the capillary action in moving the solvent through the paper. This is probably the most widely used development technique. The filter paper used is either 18.25″ × 22.5″ sheets or strips .5 to 1.5″ wide and about 22″ long.

Alternatively, the solvent can be placed in the bottom of the developing tank so that it rises up through the paper during development. This method of development is called *ascending paper chromatography*. The rate of movement of the solvent is slower in ascending development for gravity is working in opposition to capillary action. A chromatogram that can be developed in one hour by descending techniques is apt to require from six to eight hours to develop by the ascending technique. Fig. 10–2 shows two developing chambers for ascending development, one for small strips of filter paper, the other for sheets of paper.

In *horizontal linear paper chromatography* a flat tray is used as the developing chamber with the filter paper strips or sheets resting on a glass rack. During development the solvent moves horizontally through the length of the filter paper. Fig. 10–3 shows a typical tank. Although the tank can be made from wood, stainless steel, or glass, glass is preferable, so that the process of development can be observed without disturbing the saturation of the atmosphere by opening the tank.

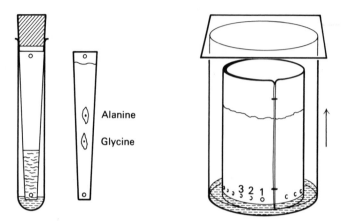

Fig. 10–2. Development jars for ascending paper chromatography. (*Redrawn from Ref. 9, by permission of Academia, Publishing House of the Czechoslovak Academy of Sciences.*)

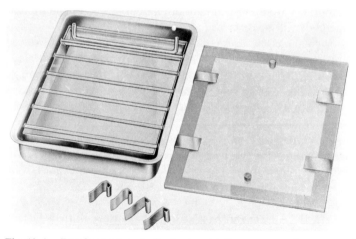

Fig. 10–3. Development tank for horizontal linear paper chromatography.

Horizontal development trays occupy less space than any of the previous chambers.

Another way to use a chamber of small volume, so as to reduce the space needed and still use long sheets of paper (19″) is by *spiral paper chromatography.* Fig. 10–4 shows the 3″ × 3″ × 2″ chamber used for this modification. The spiral of filter paper is rolled up on a Teflon sheet and then held in the solvent trough by a glass rod pressed against a glass plate. The solvent approaches the spiral of paper at a tangent, but the direction of flow is continuously changing during the development as it moves around the decreasing circles of the spiral. Because of the spiral, it is not possible to observe the development of the chromatogram.

 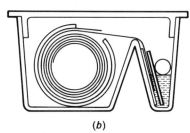

(a)   (b)

Fig. 10–4. Development tank for spiral paper chromatography: (a) Photograph. (*Courtesy of Fisher Scientific Co.*) (b) Schematic. (*Redrawn from Ref. 10, by permission of Academia, Publishing House of the Czechoslovak Academy of Sciences.*)

When a circle of filter paper is used, the sample and eluting agent are applied at the center of the disk. During development they move outward in circles of ever increasing diameter. This technique is called *radial paper chromatography* or *circular paper chromatography*. The bands of solute will appear as concentric circles in this technique rather than as spots. The apparatus for this is the simplest of that used in any of the techniques—a circle of filter paper and two petri dishes (two tops or two bottoms are used to construct the development chamber). Fig. 10–5 shows the circular development of a paper chromatogram. The paper has a narrow wick, 0.25 to .50″ wide, cut from the circumference of the circle to its center.

The use of tapering strips of filter paper combines several of these development techniques. These *wedge strips* are 2 mm wide at the bottom for a length of about 1 cm. Then over a length of about 4 cm the strip widens to 4 cm. The strip is 18 to 20 cm long at this width. The sample is spotted onto the strip at its narrow bottom which is then placed in a solvent trough for ascending development. The solvent rises in a linear fashion for a short distance along the narrow strip of paper, spreads out radially as the strip widens, and finally moves upward linearly again. The resultant bands of developed solute are arcs rather than spots or circles. These separations are cleaner than with other paper shapes.

Fig. 10–6 compares ascending, radial, and wedge-strip development of amino

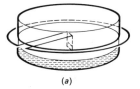 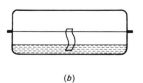

(a)   (b)

Fig. 10–5. Petri dish development for circular paper chromatography. (*Redrawn from Ref. 11, by permission of Academia, Publishing House of the Czechoslovak Academy of Sciences.*)

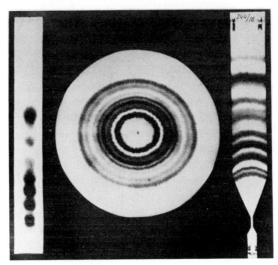

Fig. 10–6. Three types of development used in paper chromatography. *Left to right:* ascending, radial, and wedge strip. (*From Ref. 18, reproduced by permission of Springer-Verlag.*)

acids using *n*-butyl alcohol–acetic acid–water as the mobile liquid. The wedge strip gives a cleaner and more readily seen separation.

Gradient elution is extremely difficult in paper chromatography. Crudely, the same effect is achieved by multiple-development techniques. The piece of filter paper spotted with the sample is developed (ascending or descending or radial) using one solvent system as the mobile phase. When the solvent front reaches the edge of the paper, development is stopped and the chromatogram is dried. The paper is then developed in a second solvent system, during which the developed spots continue to move along the strip, but now at different rates because of the different solvent system. This technique is very good for separating closely related compounds.

A much more common way of using two solvent systems; the one used originally by Consden, Gordon, and Martin is *two-dimensional* development. Two-dimensional chromatography is an outstanding way to separate mixtures of many components that are incapable of being resolved by any one solvent system. In two-dimensional development, the sample is spotted at the lower corner of a rectangular sheet of filter paper. The liquid sample is placed on the filter paper far enough in from one edge that the spot will be above the surface of the developing solvent in its trough. To obtain a concentrated solute in the spot, repeated applications are necessary—drying the spot after each touching. The dried paper is then placed with its edge in the solvent and developed by either ascending or descending techniques. When the solvent has reached the further edge of the paper, the paper is removed from the tank and dried. The solvent system is now changed to a second liquid. The rectangle of filter paper is rotated 90° so that the edge containing the series of spots is now at the bottom, just above the solvent trough. The chromatogram is developed in this fashion until the second solvent front reaches the far edge of the paper. The resultant chromatogram contains spots of solute scattered all over the paper.

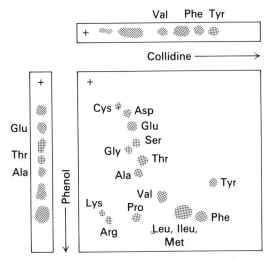

Fig. 10–7. Two-dimensional chromatographic development for amino acids. (*Redrawn from Ref. 13, by permission of Academia, Publishing House of the Czechoslovak Academy of Sciences.*)

Fig. 10–7 shows an example of two-dimensional development, clearly indicating the advantages of two-dimensional development over one-dimensional methods. Neither phenol nor collidine by itself will separate these amino acids satisfactorily. Yet, when used successively in a two-dimensional development, a very high degree of separation is obtained. Of course, all multiple-development techniques take much longer than the single development methods since the solvent is passed through the filter paper more than one time.

Detection of Spots

In paper chromatography the solutes are not eluted from the paper, so discovering their location on the paper is necessary after development. It is not a particularly difficult chore to locate and identify the solute spots by the same methods used in column chromatography. The dried sheet or strip of paper can be scanned by a strong source of ultraviolet or visible radiation. The spots are located and identified by their light absorption. Light reflection spectra can be used in the same fashion. Holding the paper under ultraviolet light will cause certain compounds to fluoresce, and hence reveal their location.

The most common technique for spot detection, however, is through the use of chemical reagents. The sheet of paper is sprayed from an atomizer (plastic window-cleaner sprayers from the local supermarket are excellent) with a developing reagent. Where spots of solute exist, a chemical reaction will occur, producing a colored reaction product. Or the paper can be exposed to a gas which will react with the components of the spots to form colored products. General reagents, those reacting with many compounds, are preferable to specific reagents, which react with only one compound. Ninhydrin, sprayed onto chromatograms, forms purple or other colored spots which locate and identify individual amino acids. Developed chromatograms of metal ions can be sprayed with solutions of dimethylglyoxime or dithizone to form colored spots or exposed to ammonia vapors to form the colored ammine complexes. Hydrogen sulfide will form colored metal sulfide precipitates in the paper. When the metals will not react with any single reagent, successive applications of a series of reagents—ammonia followed by hydrogen sulfide or followed by dimethylglyoxime—may locate all of the spots.

The Structure of Paper

The successful use of sheets of filter paper as both the supporting structure and the stationary liquid phase for partition chromatography depends upon the chemical and physical characteristics of cellulose fibers. Paper used in chromatography is made from cotton linters which are highly purified so as to be about 99% α-cellulose. Cellulose contains long chains of glucose subunits. Native cellulose has been found to have molecular weights between 57,000 and 1,500,000 depending upon its source and the pretreatment of the sample.

Fig. 10–8 shows the structure of a typical cellulose chain composed of the glucose units. Notice the hydroxyl (OH) groups plentifully strewn along the chain and distributed uniformly 360° around the circumference of the chain. The chains of cellulose are held together not only by mechanical interactions but also by hydrogen bonds formed with the hydroxyl groups. The chains, however, are not uniformly held together. In some places in cellulose fibers the chains are held so tightly they appear to be highly structured and almost crystalline—so much so that an X-ray pattern is observed from these regions. In other regions of the cellulose fibers—about forty percent of the volume—the interactions between chains are weak and disorganized so that there is no structure and the region is amorphous. Naturally, these two different types of regions impart different properties to the cellulose fibers. Since the crystalline regions are structured and dense, they cause the cellulose to be insoluble in most solvents and give the fibers their strength. The lack of structure in the amorphous regions means that there is freedom to adsorb water molecules and for the fibers to swell.

The fibers in a piece of paper are not randomly oriented. As the paper is pulled through machines during its manufacture, the fibers orient themselves in the direction of motion. Since the mobile solvent moves through the paper by capillary

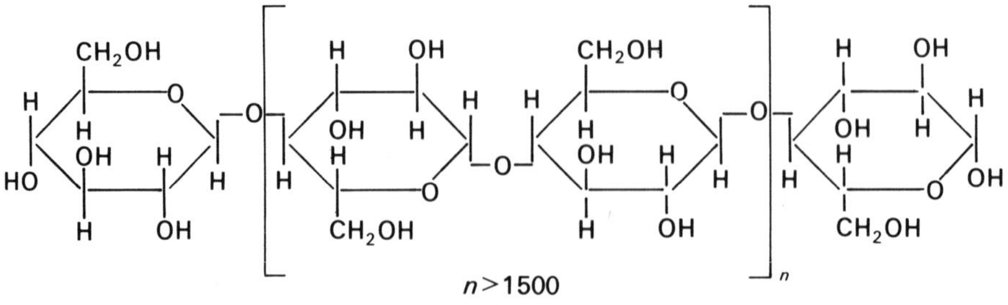

$n > 1500$

Fig. 10–8.   Structure of cellulose.

action, its rate of movement will depend upon the physical and geometric properties of the channels among the fibers. The orientation of the pores means the channels are also oriented, so the capillary flow of solvent is faster in the "machine direction" than perpendicular to it. In addition to this directional effect on solvent flow rate, there is a distance effect—the rate of solvent movement decreases with increasing path length.

The oxygens in the glucose unit of cellulose chain attract polar molecules. Since these oxygens are on the surface of the cellulose fibers, polar liquids, especially water, will be adsorbed onto the surface of the fibers. Let us start with a cellulose chain as shown in Fig. 10–8 and see what happens as water molecules are attracted to the hydroxyl groups.

First of all, water molecules comprising about six percent of the weight of the cellulose are bonded to the surface. Some of the water molecules are bonded to two of the hydroxyl groups of the glucose. Other water molecules hydrogen bond only to one hydroxyl or one oxygen. Another ten to twenty percent by weight of water is even more loosely held to the paper. These layers of water on the cellulose surface are the stationary liquid for the partitioning of solutes. When a sheet of paper is soaked in water and then the excess liquid pressed out of it, 130 to 200% additional water fills the pores of the matted fiber structure. During partition chromatography, these pores are occupied by the mobile solvent. Fig. 10–9 shows the adsorption of water by cellulose as a function of the relative humidity of the surrounding atmosphere, confirming that the maximum amount of water in paper is only about 20 to 25% by weight.

Most cellulose also contains some carboxyl groups, —COOH, which, being acidic, can lose their protons and have them replaced (neutralized) by metals or other cationic species. Thus, during paper chromatography there is always the possibility that a small amount of ion exchange (exchanging of cations for protons) takes place in the cellulose in addition to the partitioning of solutes. Since the carboxyl content is only between 0.01 and 0.10% of the weight of the cellulose, the extent of ion exchange will be exceedingly small, and thus we will consider partition as the only separation process taking place on paper.

The standard filter papers used in chromatographic work are Whatman no. 1 and S and S no. 2043b. Sheets of Whatman no. 1 have a thickness of 0.16 mm, and

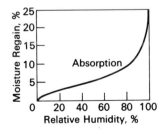

Fig. 10–9. Absorption of water vapor by cellulose at 25°C. (*Redrawn from Ref. 14, by permission of Academia, Publishing House of the Czechoslovak Academy of Sciences.*)

leave an ash of 0.06 to 0.07%. Water will rise by capillary action in it to a height of 30 cm after 140 to 220 minutes. The mixed solvent n-butyl alcohol–acetic acid–water (4:1:5) usually used in the development of amino acids, during descending development will move 35 cm in 15 to 16 hrs. S and S No. 2043b has a thickness of about 0.23 mm, an ash content of 0.04 to 0.07%, and the capillary rise of water to 30 cm takes 220 to 260 minutes. The mixed solvent n-butyl alcohol–acetic acid–water (4:1:5) will descend 35 cm in 15 hr during development at 20°C.

Retardation Factors, R_f

In Chapter 7 the retardation factor of a solute was defined as the ratio of the distance moved by the center of a spot of solute to the distance moved by the solvent front during the same time. This is the basic term used to identify solutes in paper chromatography. It is a characteristic constant for a given solute in a specified solvent system at a fixed temperature. Since we are talking about partition, it should not be surprising to learn that the R_f value depends upon the distribution ratio of a solute between the two solvents. Equation (7–6) on p. 328 states the relation as:

$$R_f = \frac{V_l}{V_l + KV_s}$$

which is valid for all chromatographic processes. V_l is the volume of the liquid or mobile phase and V_s is the volume of the stationary phase. K is the distribution ratio, D, in the case of partition chromatography and defined as stated in Chapter 9 as the solute concentration in the stationary phase over the solute concentration in the mobile phase. Paper chromatography is essentially a two-dimensional phenomenon, hence areas are more appropriate to use rather than volumes. Consden, Gordon, and Martin[5] used the symbol A_m to stand for the cross-sectional area of the moving solvent, and the symbol A_s to stand for the cross-sectional area of the stationary solvent. Everyone since then has followed this practice, so we will too. Thus, when we change our symbols, we write the above equation as:

$$R_f = \frac{A_m}{A_m + DA_s} \tag{10–1}$$

Equation (10–1) shows that the larger the numerical value of the distribution ratio, that is, the longer the solute remains in the stationary liquid phase on the paper, the less distance it will move in a given time and the smaller its R_f value will be. Equation (10–1) also tells us that anything in the experimental system that affects the area of the stationary phase, the area of the mobile liquid, or the value of the distribution ratio will affect the value of the retardation factor.

Values of R_f are used to identify solutes in paper chromatography just as retention volumes are in column chromatography. This is done as follows. It helps considerably if you have some idea as to what is present in the unknown, otherwise you have to keep guessing and chromatographing more and more knowns. A paper chromatogram is obtained for the unknown sample and the R_f values of all the spots detected are calculated. Guess (intelligently or blindly) what is in the sample. Obtain samples of these known or standard compounds. Using the exact same experimental conditions (see below) as you did for your unknown, run paper chromatograms on each known, and calculate the R_f values. The R_f values of the spots in the unknown sample are compared with the experimentally determined R_f values of the suspected components of the unknown. When the R_f of a spot of the unknown agrees with the R_f of a known, then the compound in the unknown is the same substance as the known having the identical R_f value. There are complications in this for R_f values *per se* give absolutely no indication as to chemical identity. Thus, it is not impossible that related chemical compounds could have similar R_f values and be mistaken for one another. The reproducibility of R_f values is only about five percent, so that often a clear-cut decision about identity cannot be made. In general, however, R_f values are widely used as a reliable method for the identification of components in mixtures.

Equation (10–1) describes the magnitude of the R_f value of a chemical compound as determined by the magnitude of the distribution ratio for the compound. In Chapter 5 we have seen the many factors that affect the value of the distribution ratio, while in Chapter 6 the ways in which the distribution ratio could be changed to effect separations were described. All of this is applicable and very useful in paper chromatography.

Because of the chemical structure of cellulose, water is the stationary phase in the partitioning process. This leaves only one solvent that can be altered. This is analogous to column partition chromatography. This is not to ignore reversed-phase paper chromatography, but merely to emphasize that when the more polar liquid is the stationary phase, then that liquid is usually water. The mobile liquid can be anything, preferably immiscible with water. Martin[5] reports that better separations are obtained in paper chromatography when the mobile solvent is partially miscible with water than when it is immiscible. When selecting a liquid as a solvent for paper chromatography, choose one in which the solutes are less soluble than in water. For good separations the value of the distribution ratio should be greater than one. The same types of considerations about solvents apply in paper chromatography as were discussed in Chapter 9 for partition chromatography.

In addition to the solubility of the components in the two liquid phases the equilibria occurring in both liquids should be considered. Acid–base dissociation, association, complex formation, oxidation–reduction can all be used to effect the separation. When separating mixtures of weakly acidic or basic compounds, the pH of the stationary aqueous phase will affect the R_f values of the compounds. Equation (5–93) gave the relationship between D, K_D, $[H_3O^+]$, and K_a for the distribution of weak acids. Remember that in paper chromatography the partition coefficient and distribution ratio are defined as the stationary phase (water) over the mobile phase (organic). Since this is the inverse of the definitions in Chapters 5 and 6, the relationship analogous to Equation (5–93) of Chapter 5 for paper chromatography is:

$$D = K_D\left(1 + \frac{K_a}{[H_3O^+]}\right) \tag{10–2}$$

Substituting Equation (10–2) into Equation (10–1) gives:

$$R_f = \frac{A_m}{A_m + A_sD\left(1 + \dfrac{K_a}{[H_3O^+]}\right)}$$ (10–3)

Equation (10–3) shows that as the pH of the stationary aqueous phase increases, ($[H_3O^+]$ decreases) the denominator of Equation (10–3) will increase and the R_f value will decrease. Fig. 10–10 shows the change in R_f for an acid with a K_a of 1.00×10^{-6}, with $D = 1.00$ and $A_m/A_s = 1.00$ as a function of pH. For a mixture of weak acids (for example, amino acids) with different K_a's and K_D's, a buffered stationary phase with constant pH will produce different R_f values for each acid and lead to a successful separation.

Fig. 10–11 shows R_f as a function of pK_a at a pH of 7.00 in the stationary phase, making the same assumptions about A_m/A_s and D as before. Note that on the rising portion of the curve relatively small pK_a differences produce differences in R_f of 0.1.

When the solute forms a complex with a ligand in the aqueous phase, the

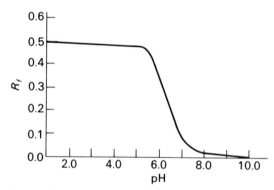

Fig. 10–10. R_f as a function of pH for a weak acid of $K_a = 1.00 \times 10^{-6}$, $D = 1.00$, $A_m/A_s = 1.00$.

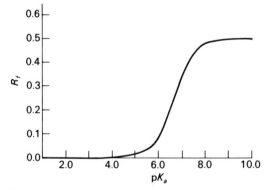

Fig. 10–11. R_f as a function of acid strength at a pH of 7.0, $D = 1.00$, $A_m/A_s = 1.00$.

relationship between D, K_D, K_{st}, and $[x]$, for paper chromatography that is analogous to Equation (5–97) of Chapter 5 is:

$$D = K_D(1 + K_{st}[x]^n)$$ (10–4)

where $[x]$ is the molar concentration of the ligand in the stationary aqueous phase and n is the number of ligand molecules in the complex. Substituting Equation (10–4) into Equation (10–1) gives:

$$R_f = \frac{A_m}{A_m + A_s K_D(1 + K_{st}[x]^n)}$$ (10–5)

Since the concentration of ligand in the stationary aqueous phase will be a constant, we can see that for complexes of the same type, as K_{st} increases, R_f decreases. Fig. 10–12 shows this for a 1:4 complex with 0.1 M ligand in the aqueous phase, assuming that $A_m/A_s = 1.00$ and $K_D = 1.00$. Note that on the descending part of the curve, a relatively slight difference in K_{st} (about a factor of two) will produce a difference of 0.1 in R_f values.

The change in solute association in the mobile phase can also be used to enhance separations; the more association in the mobile phase the higher the R_f value will be.

A major variable that can be changed to alter R_f values, and hence separations, is the solubility of the solutes in the mobile phase. For a given separation, the solutes are not variable, so solubility changes must be achieved by selection of the solvents. There are two ways solvents can be changed. The first is to change liquids completely—for example, from acetone to chloroform. The second is to change the ratio of the components in a mixed solvent—for example, from 1:1 n-butanol:acetic acid to 2:1 n-butanol:acetic acid. The latter is believed to be a more effective means of changing R_f values.

The temperature of the system will also affect the numerical value of the distribution ratio (see Chapter 5) and hence the value of the retardation factor. Burma[2] studied the effect of temperature on the paper chromatography of amino acids. In a mixture of isopropyl alcohol and water as the mobile solvent, the R_f

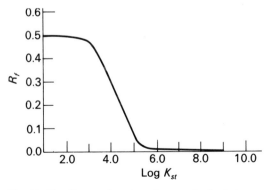

Fig. 10–12. R_f as a function of strength of a 1:4 complex at $[x] = 0.1\ M$, $K_D = 1.00$, $A_m/A_s = 1.00$.

for most amino acids increases with increasing temperature, for example, for glycine, R_f changed from 0.20 at 10°C to 0.27 at 20°C and to 0.30 at 25°C.

Naturally the chemical properties and structure of the solutes to be separated will greatly affect the value of the distribution ratio in a given solvent system. Martin[5] reports that the R_f values of amino acids increases with increasing number of carbon atoms in the main chain of the molecule. Chemically this is predictable, since the solubility of amino acids in water should decrease, the solubility in organic solvents increase, and the acid dissociation decrease as the hydrocarbon part of the molecule increases. Martin reports, however, that branching in the hydrocarbon chain causes a lower R_f value than would have been predicted from the number of carbons present and the straight chain relationship. He also reports that those amino acids containing hydroxyl groups had lower R_f values than those amino acids with the same number of carbons but no hydroxyl groups. This again follows chemical properties, for the polar hydroxyl group should increase the aqueous phase solubility, increase the distribution ratio, and hence decrease the R_f value.

As was mentioned earlier, R_f values are reproducible to about five percent within a given laboratory using the same apparatus, experimenter, and chemicals. When attempting to replicate R_f values in another laboratory, considerable differences (as high as forty percent) can be obtained. This lack of reproducibility is extremely frustrating since it means that literature R_f values are of no value *per se* in identifying unknown spots. Nevertheless, people still report R_f values in the literature to three decimal places! Much discussion about the cause of this lack of reproducibility has taken place.

The Third International Symposium on Paper and Thin-Layer Chromatography sponsored by the Czechoslovakian Chemical Society and held at Liblice in October, 1967 was devoted to the subject of reproducibility in paper and thin-layer chromatography. The papers and discussions held at this conference were published in volume 33 of the *Journal of Chromatography*. Papers by I. M. Hais,[7] A. Grune,[6] and E. Soczewinski and R. Manleo[19] were devoted to the reproducibility of R_f values in paper chromatography. The material present below is primarily taken from these three papers.

In studying the factors that affect the reproducibility of R_f values, all sorts of expected, unexpected, and bizarre things have been found. In general, these can be broken down into four categories: (a) factors involving the paper; (b) factors determined by the solvent system; (c) factors involving the sample; and (d) factors caused by the operation of the development process. Briefly let us mention these influences and discuss the reasons why some of them operate. This should give some idea of the enormous difficulties involved in trying to standardize experimental conditions so as to improve the reproducibility of the R_f values.

Factors Due to the Paper

The type of paper that is used for paper chromatography will affect the R_f value obtained experimentally. As we have seen, there is an amorphous region and a crystalline region in paper, each of which contributes to the properties of paper. The amount of each type of region in any paper will determine the extent of these properties. More dense paper will have a larger volume of the stationary liquid phase (A_s increases). In loose paper more of the mobile liquid will be able to penetrate the fiber structure so that A_m will be larger. Thus, we find that R_f values are lower in more dense paper and higher in less dense paper.

In addition to cellulose, filter paper usually has a small mineral content, the ash. For Whatman no. 1 this runs between 0.06 and 0.07% of the weight. The presence of these minerals can affect the movement of the solutes through the paper by chemical reactions. The mineral content is about 20 to 30% silicon, 40% calcium and magnesium salts, 20 to 30% alkali metal salts, 1 to 2% iron, and contains traces of aluminum, copper, and lead. For example, the presence of the traces of calcium and magnesium can disturb the separation of phosphates by forming insoluble phosphates. Copper and iron form complexes with amino acids and peptides which are strong enough to hinder separations of them. Thus in paper for chromatographic use, copper is kept below 1.5 p.p.m. and iron below 10 p.p.m.

Not only are there variations from one grade of paper to the next, there are also variations between one batch of the same paper and the next. The mineral content will be slightly different, the percent of the fibers that are crystalline will vary, the amount of water contained in the paper will be different, and the extent of fiber orientation will be different. Thus, there are differences in R_f values, even when determined on the same grade of paper, say Whatman no. 1, because of batch differences.

The storage of filter paper can affect its properties. Not only will fluctuations in the humidity change the water content, but dust, dirt, and heat can alter the properties of the paper.

Factors Due to the Solvent System

The chemical and physical properties of the solvent used to develop the chromatogram will affect the R_f value of a solute. If a pure liquid is used, the problems are less complicated. Frequently, in paper chromatography, however, the developing solvent is not a pure liquid, but a mixture. For example, the common developing solvent for amino acids is a mixture of n-butanol, acetic acid, and water. Or a mixture of butanol, ammonia, and chloroform can be used. The use of these mixed solvents creates new problems, not encountered with pure liquids, that can cause alterations in the R_f values. As we know, each substance moves along the paper at its own rate by capillary action. Thus, in a mixed solvent, each of the components moves from the starting line at its own rate. As a result the composition of the solvent changes continuously as it moves along the paper. And the further it moves the greater the change. A paper chromatogram that is fifteen centimeters long will be developed by a solvent system of different proportions than one that is thirty centimeters long, even though the initial composition of the solvent was the same for both.

Another factor which changes the composition of mixed solvents is the different vapor pressures of the components. Unless the developing chamber is saturated thoroughly before use with the solvent mixture, the rate of evaporation of each component of solvent from the paper into the atmosphere of the chamber will be different. Again, the composition of the solvent as it elutes the sample is changing with time because of this evaporation.

When chemicals are mixed together, chemical reactions should be expected to occur. Thus, when working with mixed solvents, do not be too surprised if a chemical interaction between the components alters the composition of the mixture. The most common example of this occurs in the *n*-butanol–acetic acid–water solvent mentioned before for the paper chromatographic separation of amino acids. When an acid and an alcohol are mixed together they will react to form an ester—in this case butyl acetate. To be sure, the rate of this reaction is slow, but over a period of several hours, or days, a considerable amount of *n*-butanol and acetic acid react. The amount of *n*-butyl acetate formed increases continuously, so the solvent changes from one of three components to one of four and their concentrations change with time. Chemical interactions should be avoided, if possible, when selecting mixed solvents as developing agents.

The water content of the paper is determined by the relative humidity of the atmosphere surrounding it. If the solvent used to elute the sample contains no water, not only will it remove the water layer from the paper, it will contribute nothing to the relative humidity within the developing chamber. The water of the paper will evaporate (see Fig. 10–9). To keep the stationary water layer on the paper from changing during the development of the chromatogram, most solvents contain some water, so as to saturate the atmosphere of the chamber with water vapor.

The chemical purity of reagent grade solvents is often taken for granted. It shouldn't be. The presence of impurities in the solvent will cause variations in R_f values. When different batches of the same solvent contain different impurities and in different amounts, it should not be too surprising to obtain different R_f values.

We saw back in Chapter 6 that the distribution ratio of a great many solutes varies with the concentration of the solute present in the system. *D* varies when association, complexation, solvent interactions, and many other interactions occur. Therefore, there are differences in R_f values in paper chromatography that depend upon the size of the sample that is used. More sample means higher concentrations of components in both the stationary aqueous phase and the mobile phase. And probably a variation in *D*. A rough rule of thumb is that the concentration of solutes in the sample solution should lie between 0.5 and 2%.

A very interesting factor, and one that is difficult to explain, is the effect of the volume of solvent contained in the trough in the tank. Clayton[4] reports the following R_f values for leucine using *n*-butanol–acetic acid–water as the solvent mixture for various volumes of solvent in the trough: 150 ml, $R_f = 0.81$; 300 ml, $R_f = 0.80$; 375 ml, $R_f = 0.68$; 400 ml, $R_f = 0.66$; and 700 ml, $R_f = 0.67$. The explanation for this decrease can be based on the loss of solvent vapor from the chamber when it is opened to insert the paper chromatogram. As the solvent evaporates to resaturate the chamber, the composition of the liquid phase changes because of differences in the vapor pressures of the components. The larger the volume of solvent in the trough, the smaller the change in composition due to evaporation effects. This effect of liquid volume has not been reported for pure liquids as solvents.

Factors Due to the Sample

Paper chromatography is widely used to identify components in an enormous variety of samples. Many of these samples are complex mixtures of biological origin, mixtures of reaction products for synthetic work, protein hydrolyzates, commercial products, and others. (Just look at some of the applications, p. 409.) The fluid of the unknown can contain many substances that will alter the R_f value of a particular component. Thus, for a particular compound, the R_f value obtained in the known pure solution may be different from that measured in the unknown sample. The fluid may be more viscous, reducing the capillary action rate; the components of the sample may interact to form chemical species different from those present in pure solutions; the components of the sample may interact with the solvent to form products having different R_f values. For example, the amino acids in alcoholic extracts of plant materials react with the solvent ethanol, to form amino acid esters. These esters have different R_f values from the free amino acids. Since a different chemical entity is present, the R_f value of the amino acid in an aqueous solution is not observed in these plant extracts.

Factors Due to the Development Procedure

The rate of flow of the mobile liquid is different during different forms of development. It should not be expected to find the same R_f values. Consequently, ascending, descending, radial, horizontal, and spiral development, as well as the use of wedge strips all produce slightly different R_f values for the same compounds in the same solvent systems.

It was pointed out earlier in this chapter and also in Chapter 5, that the temperature of the solutions will affect the value of the distribution ratio of a solute. Thus, the temperature will affect the R_f values that are obtained. This effect is slight. Since standards and unknown chromatograms are developed simultaneously, working at room temperature with no temperature regulation can be successful.

After the sample is spotted onto the paper, it is customary to allow the solvent in which the sample was dissolved to evaporate before beginning to develop the paper chromatogram. Frequently, in order to speed up this process, especially when multiple applications of the sample are necessary, the paper is warmed over a flame or under a heating lamp to hasten the solvent evaporation. It is quite possible to cause a chemical change in the sample components when this heat is too great. It is also possible to drive off some of the water from the paper, which lowers the amount of the stationary phase on the paper. It is also possible to cause a chemical interaction between the sample component and the cellulose which will prevent the spot from moving at all. Thus, great caution must be taken when warming the paper, so as not to change the properties of the system, otherwise, different R_f values are measured.

Another very interesting factor that has been found to cause alterations in the R_f value of a solute is the distance between the edge of the paper that is dipped into the trough of the eluting solvent and the spot where the sample is applied to the paper. The sample is usually not applied right at the edge of the paper, but several centimeters in from the edge. The R_f for a solute decreases as the distance between the spot and the reservoir increases. Fig. 10–13 shows the decrease in R_f values for two amino acids using n-butanol–acetic acid–water as the developing solvent. Note that although the extent is different, both curves descend as the distance increases.

There is a change in the composition of the solvent as it moves through the paper because the water of the solvent is adsorbed into the paper. Fig. 10–14 shows

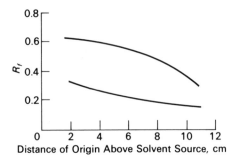

Fig. 10–13. Changes in R_f values for two dissimilar amino acids run ascending in *n*-butanol–acetic acid–water (60:15:25) at 25°C with respect to the position of the origin above the solvent source. (*Redrawn from Ref. 20, by permission of Marcel Dekker, Inc.*)

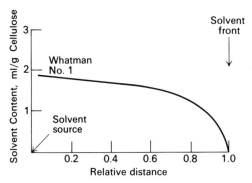

Fig. 10–14. The solvent content of a paper varies with its distance from the solvent source. (*Redrawn from Ref. 20, by permission Marcel Dekker, Inc.*)

the solvent content of Whatman no. 1 filter paper as a function of the distance on the sheet of paper away from the solvent trough. Because of this change in amount of solvent, A_m will vary with the distance. Since R_f is a function of A_m, it too will decrease with the distance from the trough. When the distance that the spot travels during development of the chromatogram is greater than the distance between the point of application of the sample and the solvent through, there is no effect of this latter distance on the R_f value measured.

Clayton[4] reports that the volume of the developing chamber affects the magnitude of the R_f obtained. Using *n*-butanol–acetic acid–water as the developing solvent for amino acids, he found that the R_f for leucine increased from 0.67 in a tank of 7 liters volume, to 0.71 in a tank of 14 liters, to 0.81 in a tank of 37 liters. The same sort of increase in R_f value with increasing volume was reported for tryptophan, valine, and tyrosine. He believes that this increase is caused by the amount of the solvent that must be evaporated in order to saturate the atmosphere, and since the components of his solvent system have different vapor pressures, the composition of the liquid in the trough changes more the larger the tank because more of the most volatile component evaporates. This explanation is consistent with his findings about the effect of solvent volume on R_f values. In both cases the R_f of leucine was higher in the solvent undergoing the greatest change in composition.

The number of factors that must be controlled and reproduced exactly in order to obtain identical R_f values is enormous. Moreover, as you can imagine, it is not easy to reproduce them from one laboratory to the next. As a result, it is only by accident that R_f values obtained by one experimenter and reported in the literature are reproduced exactly in another laboratory. For this reason, R_f values from the literature or other laboratories are never used in qualitative analysis. In order to verify the identity of the components of a sample, aliquots of compounds suspected as components are spotted on paper from the same batch used for the unknown, placed in the developing chamber along with the unknown, and developed simultaneously. Then developing conditions are identical, solvent effects will be identical, and paper and sample differences will be minimal. When knowns are spotted on the same sheet of paper as the unknown, paper effects are eliminated. Only when you obtain the R_f values yourself, in your own laboratory, using your own chemicals and apparatus, can they be considered sufficiently reliable to be used for qualitative analysis.

Prediction of R_f Values

It would be extremely convenient to be able to predict the R_f value of a compound in a solvent system, without having to determine its value experimentally. If prediction were possible, the feasibility of separating a mixture could be determined on a theoretical basis without having to resort to a trial and error method. Moderate success has been achieved in arriving at a fairly rough estimate of separation potentialities which eliminates wasting laboratory time in useless attempts.

Equation (10–1) defines the R_f value in terms of the distribution ratio. If we solve Equation (10–1) for the distribution ratio, we get:

$$D = \frac{A_m}{A_s}\left(\frac{1}{R_f} - 1\right) \tag{10–6}$$

Martin[17] has shown that the partition coefficient can be related to the free energy, $\Delta\mu$, that is required to transfer one mole of a solute from the stationary to the mobile phase:

$$\ln K_D = \frac{\Delta\mu}{RT} \tag{10–7}$$

For a specific chemical entity in a particular liquid system, $K_D = D$, so that Equations (10–6) and (10–7) can be related:

$$\frac{\Delta\mu}{RT} = \ln\left[\frac{A_m}{A_s}\left(\frac{1}{R_f} - 1\right)\right] \tag{10–8a}$$

or,

$$\Delta\mu = RT \ln\left[\frac{A_m}{A_s}\left(\frac{1}{R_f} - 1\right)\right] \tag{10-8b}$$

Martin states that the energy required to transfer the solute from one liquid to the second liquid is a function of the structure of the molecule. Therefore, the total energy can be broken down into energy contributions from different portions of the molecule. The addition of a functional group, such as —OH, to a molecule will change the free energy of the molecule, and thus the distribution ratio, by an amount that is determined by the identity of the functional group added and the two solvents involved, but that does not depend upon what the rest of the molecule is. The free energy of transfer for a molecule thus becomes the sum of the free energies of the atomic groupings that comprise the molecule, or

$$\Delta\mu = \Delta\mu_x + \Delta\mu_y + \Delta\mu_z + \ldots$$

Thus, he would rewrite Equation (10–8b) as:

$$RT \ln\left[\frac{A_m}{A_s}\left(\frac{1}{R_f} - 1\right)\right] = \Delta\mu_x + \Delta\mu_y + \Delta\mu_z + \ldots \tag{10-9}$$

where x, y, z, etc., represent the different parts of the molecule.

The significant thing about Equation (10–9) is that it relates the distribution ratio, or specifically, the retardation factor, to quantities that are presumably characteristic of different groupings of atoms and not of the combined entity of them as a molecule. Martin has established a set of building blocks, called *group constants*, which when assembled will give the retardation factor for the completed molecule. When put together differently for different molecules they give different retardation factors. So that by knowing group constants for various functional groups in various solvent systems, it is possible to add them up and obtain the retardation factor for a molecule. This is the aim that was stated at the beginning of this section.

Unfortunately, as Equation (10–9) shows, the relationship between R_f and these group constants is not a linear one. Bate-Smith[1] thought it would be much nicer if some term that did have a linear relationship with the group constants could be devised. So, for convenience only, he came up with the term, R_M, which is defined as:

$$R_M = \log\left(\frac{1}{R_f} - 1\right) \tag{10-10}$$

The symbol R_M is used because it indicates that it is the retardation as a function of group frequencies, $\Delta\mu$. M is easier to set in type than μ so it is used as the subscript. Substituting this definition into Equation (10–9):

$$2.303\, RT\left(\log\frac{A_m}{A_s} + R_M\right) = \Delta\mu_x + \Delta\mu_y + \Delta\mu_z + \ldots \tag{10-11}$$

or substituting the definition of Equation (10–10) into Equation (10–8a) gives, upon rearrangement:

$$R_M = \log\frac{A_s}{A_m} + \frac{\Delta\mu}{2.303\ RT} \qquad (10\text{--}12)$$

and substituting Equation (10–12) into Equation (10–7) gives:

$$\log K_D = R_M + \log\frac{A_m}{A_s} \qquad (10\text{--}13)$$

The advantages of using the term R_M can be seen from Equations (10–11), (10–12), and (10–13). R_M is a term that is linearly related to (1) the group constants, (2) the logarithm of the areas of the mobile and stationary liquids, and (3) the logarithm of the partition coefficient. The really significant relationship is that of Equation (10–11) which gives the desired linear relationship between R_M and constants that can be obtained for each functional group in the molecule.

Group constants ($\Delta\mu$'s) have been measured and tabulated for a great number of function groups in a wide variety of solvents. The use of these constants and Equations (10–11) and (10–10), has led to calculations of R_f values that agree remarkably well with the experimentally determined R_f values. For example, on Whatman no. 1 filter paper, using a 1:1 mixture of amyl alcohol and 5 M formic acid as the mobile solvent, the following agreement was found between calculated and experimentally measured R_f values: Lactic acid—calculated, 0.61; found, 0.62. Tartaric acid—calculated, 0.13; found, 0.14.

Group constants are obtained by measuring under identical conditions the R_f values of two compounds, which differ only by the functional group. The difference in R_f measured is due to the presence of the functional group. From this difference the group constant is calculated. As was the case for adsorption energies as discussed in Chapter 8 an enormous amount of data must be available to cover all possible functional groups and all pairs of solvent systems in use. When, however, this data has been obtained, the use of the group constants can provide a rapid method for determining the feasibility of a separation and in selecting the appropriate solvent system to use for a desired separation.

Unfortunately, R_f values do not always agree so well with the calculated ones as in the preceding illustration. Steric hindrance, hydrogen bond formation within and between molecules, optical and *cis-trans* isomerism all cause deviations between the calculated and the observed R_f values.

Selection of a Solvent

Let us suppose that you have a sample that you want to separate by paper chromatography. How do you go about deciding what solvent to use as the mobile phase? This is a problem in all forms of chromatography. As has been emphasized in Chapter 8 and 9, experience with mixtures containing similar compounds or even some of the same compounds is invaluable as a guide. Of course, if you do not have that experience yourself, then the library is the source of information that can save frustrations.

Macek and Prochazka[16] list the following qualifications that a good solvent will possess: (1) the R_f values for the components of the sample should fall between 0.05 and 0.85 in the system; (2) in the solvent the difference between R_f values of any two components must be 0.05—the minimum value necessary in order to separate any two components in the sample; (3) the distribution ratio of the components in the solvent system should be independent of concentration so as to obtain circular spots; (4) the solvent should not react chemically with any of the components of the sample mixture; (5) the solvent should not interfere with the detection of the spots on the developed chromatogram; (6) the composition of the solvent system should not change with time.

Macek and Prochazka[16] report that, in light of their experience with a wide selection of very different chemical compounds, the eleven systems presented in Table 10–1 are the best ones for separating almost all mixtures. These solvent systems are arranged in order of decreasing polarity. The ones at the top of the list are best suited for separating almost all mixtures of polar compounds and those at the bottom of the list best suited for separating nonpolar compounds.

Table 10–1. RECOMMENDED SOLVENT SYSTEMS FOR PAPER CHROMATOGRAPHY

Stationary Liquid	Mobile Liquid
Water	Isopropyl alcohol–ammonia–water (9:1:2)
Water	n-Butyl alcohol–acetic acid–water (4:1:5)
Water	Phenol saturated with water
Formamide	Chloroform
Formamide	Chloroform–benzene (from 1:9 to 9:1)
Formamide	Benzene
Formamide	Benzene–cyclohexane (from 1:9 to 9:1)
Dimethylformamide	Cyclohexane
Phenoxyethanol	Heptane
Kerosene	70% isopropyl alcohol
Liquid paraffin	Dimethylformamide–methanol–water (10:10:1)

SOURCE: Ref. 16.

There are two features of a paper chromatogram that are important for a separation of a mixture—the distance between the center of the spots and the diameter of the spots. Even when the R_f values for two components are greater than 0.05 units apart, if the spots are too large, they will overlap and be indistinguishable from one elongated spot. No separation is apparent. The R_f values will depend upon the chemistry of the solute and its interactions in the two phases—as we have seen before. The diameter of the spots depends upon the physical properties of the stationary phase. The viscosity of the liquid of the stationary phase will influence the diffusion of the solute due to concentration gradients. If the viscosity is low, diffusion occurs readily and blurry spots are obtained. As the solute moves through the paper, the size and orientation of the paper fibers will create differences in path length for different molecules. This eddy diffusion, when too large, produces large spots. The depth that the solute penetrates into the fiber depends upon the thickness of the surface layer of solvent. If the solute remains at the surface of the liquid, it will partition rapidly between the two liquids so that small spots result. But if the solute remains in the interior of the fiber very long, partition takes a longer time and the spots are larger because the second liquid continues to move along the paper. Thus, for small spots a thin layer of stationary liquid with moderate viscosity on a paper of uniform fiber structure is desirable. The improved separations by thin-layer chromatography involving layers of cellulose are due to improved physical properties of the stationary phase.

QUANTITATIVE ANALYSIS

Most people think of paper chromatography as being solely a tool for qualitative analysis, that is, good only for the separation and identification of the components of mixtures. There is no validity for this impression since paper chromatography is used widely to obtain a semiquantitative estimate of the amounts of each of the components in the mixture. There are two ways to determine the amount of solute in a spot on a paper chromatogram. Either the concentration is determined in the spot on the paper or the material is removed from the paper so its concentration is determined off the paper.

The amount of solute can be determined more easily and by a wider variety of methods when the spots are removed from the paper. There really are only two ways to remove the spots from the paper. By one technique the solvent flow is allowed to continue after the front reaches the edge of the paper; the solvent is collected in some container. The spots will continue to move and eventually will be eluted from the edge of the paper, where they are collected. For some reason, instead of calling this elution analysis, it is called "overrun." The second method for removing the spot from the paper is to take a pair of scissors and cut it out. The paper spot is placed in an appropriate solvent and the spot dissolved off the paper. Since the amount of the solute in the spot is very small, microanalytical methods must usually be employed to determine the quantity present in each spot. Titration, polarography, spectrophotometry, and radiography have all been used. As a general rule, the accuracy of analysis by the spot removal procedure is between three and five percent.

It is more difficult to obtain accurate analyses while the spot is on the paper. Since they are usually easier and faster, analyses are carried out *in situ* when they do not have to be accurate to four significant figures. One of the most commonly used techniques is *visual estimation*. A series of standard solutions of the solute with concentrations that surround the suspected concentration of the unknown are prepared. Let us say that the standards have 10, 20, 30, 40, and 50 μg of the material. The unknown and the standards are spotted on the paper, developed in the chamber, dried, and then compared. Each of the standards in the series will give a spot of increasingly larger diameter and intensity of color. By looking, the unknown can usually be placed in this series—say between the 20 and 30 μg standards. Then it is usually not too difficult to go one step further and decide whether the unknown is closer to the 20 (that is less than 25 μg) or closer to the 30 μg (that is, greater than 25 μg). In this manner a reasonable semiquantitative analysis of $\pm$ 3 μg can be performed. The concentration of solutions containing known amounts of amino acids can be determined by visual estimation to within $\pm$ 10%. When working with protein hydrolyzates and other biological sources of amino acids, the precision of the concentration determinations is considerably poorer.

Reflection or absorption spectrophotometry is an instrumental improvement on the visual estimation of amounts of solute on the paper. Paper chromatogram scanners or "readers" are available which measure the intensity of light transmitted through the spot or the reflected light from the spot. By using standards, as in the visual method, the amount of solute in the unknown spot can be ascertained. When the chemicals in the spots fluoresce, the intensity of this fluorescence can be used to measure the amount of the component. Other instrumental techniques, such as conductivity and polarography have been used to determine concentrations *in situ.*

In all of the quantitative methods the applications of the original spot of sample to the paper is the limiting factor in establishing the precision of the analysis. Great care and adroitness are required to reproduce exactly the amount of sample used.

EVALUATION OF PAPER CHROMATOGRAPHY AS A SEPARATION METHOD

At one time paper chromatography was the method of choice for separations because it was easy, fast, and provided excellent resolution in many cases. Now paper chromatography is not widely used, its position having been usurped by thin-layer chromatography and gas–liquid chromatography. Therefore, it is of value to compare paper chromatography with other forms of chromatography, especially GLC and TLC, to see where the strengths and weaknesses of paper chromatography lie.

The apparatus that is required for paper chromatography is quite simple. It certainly is much simpler and less expensive than a gas or a high-speed liquid–liquid chromatograph. It is slightly less complex than that required for column partition or adsorption chromatography. On the other hand, it is just as simple as that required for thin-layer chromatography.

Paper chromatographic separations are faster than those of column chromatography for multicomponent mixtures. They are not faster, however, than separations by either gas or thin-layer chromatography.

The expertise and attention needed to perform a paper chromatographic separation are much less than those required for gas or the column chromatographic techniques. After the sample has been spotted onto the paper and the paper placed in the development chamber, the separation can be ignored and forgotten until it has been completed.

Paper chromatography is capable of giving a better resolution among sample components that are closely related than column chromatography. On the other hand, gas and thin-layer chromatographs are just as effective in resolving complex, multicomponent mixtures of similar compounds as is paper chromatography.

The size of sample needed to effect a paper chromatographic separation is very small (less than 0.1 ml) compared to that required for conventional column separation methods (1 to 5 ml). Thus, when the amount of material is limited, the identity of its components can be obtained without wasting much of the sample, which then can be used for other purposes. Neither thin-layer nor gas chromatography, however, use samples that are any larger than those of paper chromatography. This small sample has its drawbacks. Since the success of the separation depends upon having a small sample, the method cannot be used for separation of large amounts of material. While some preparative paper chromatography has been performed, even then the sample sizes were not very large. This disadvantage can be mitigated for the information obtained from a paper chromatogram can be used to devise a column liquid–liquid chromatographic separation using cellulose as the support. This column could be considered as large scale paper chromatography capable of resolving large quantities of sample.

Since paper chromatography is carried out at room temperature, heat effects on the composition of the sample components are no problem.

APPLICATIONS

Paper chromatography was developed by Consden, Gordon, and Martin to separate amino acids, and this separation has remained its most popular application. Innumerable modifications have appeared for improving amino acid separations, for taking into consideration the problems of amino acids from various natural sources, and just for the sake of making modifications. Amino acids and protein hydrolyzates form the greatest, but not the only, use of paper chromatography.

While most people also think that paper chromatography is restricted to the separation of organic materials, there is an extremely widespread application to the separation of inorganic ions. The separation of inorganic ions is dependent upon the success in altering the values of the distribution ratios of ions in mixtures. In Chapter 6, the chemistry of altering D was described for extraction systems, and the same principles are applied in paper chromatography. The significant and critical difference when altering D for paper chromatography is, that whereas with extraction we were trying to obtain as large a value of D as possible, in the case of paper chromatography we would like a D that is around 1, or only a little higher than that. While the problem still involves finding ways to make metal ions more soluble in organic solvents, we don't want the metals too soluble. Of course, the obvious way to solubilize metal ions is to use polar organic solvents for the mobile liquid. The successful separations of inorganic materials all use ethers, ketones, alcohols, acids, esters, bases, or chloroform. The solvent miscibility restriction present in extraction systems is much less severe in paper chromatography so that quite successful separations using methanol and ethanol as the mobile phases have been accomplished, even though both of these liquids are completely miscible with water. Ion pair formation has been used to separate ions by paper chromatography, notably $HFeCl_4$ and $HAuCl_4$ have been separated from other ions by using ethers containing high concentrations of HCl as the mobile phase (compare with Chapter 6). Complex ion formation is an excellent and very widely used technique for separating mixtures of inorganic ions. Chelating agents such as acetylacetone, benzoylacetone, and 8-hydroxyquinoline have been found to be especially useful. The use of solvents that complex or solvate the cations is also widely used, pyridine and substituted pyridines are excellent solvents for separating cations.

It just is not possible to separate each of the cations from one another in the same mixture. To accomplish a separation, the cations first must be subdivided into smaller groups. This subdivision is usually done in accordance with the conventional qualitative analysis scheme, based upon solubilities of chlorides, sulfides, and hydroxides. The Group I cations (silver, thallium, mercury, lead) have been separated using 11 M methanolic HNO_3 as the developing solvent. R_f values are: silver—0.29; thallium—0.39; lead—0.51; and mercury—0.79 by ascending development. For Group II cations the anion present in the solution affects the R_f value. Using n-butanol as the solvent, the R_f values for copper in the presence of various anions are: sulfate—0.27; chloride—0.40; nitrate—0.54; and acetate—0.57. A separation by ascending development technique is effected using methyl-n-propyl ketone containing 15% 10 N HCl. The R_f values indicate a good separation: lead—0.19; bismuth—0.40; copper—0.60; cadmium—0.75; mercury—0.80. Only low-molecular-weight ketones containing HCl separate the Group III cations successfully. For acetone containing 20% HCl the R_f values are nickel—0.03; manganese—0.26; cobalt—0.51; and zinc—0.82, which ought to provide an excellent separation. The alkaline earth metal ions have been separated using radial development and 1:1 methanol–ethanol as the developing solvent, producing R_f values of barium—0.28; strontium—0.49; calcium—0.62; and magnesium—0.80. The alkali metals have been separated successfully using n-butanol: methanol (3:7) in a radial development technique, producing R_f values of potassium—0.31; sodium—0.48; NH_4^+—0.57; and lithium—0.78.

Even anion mixtures can be separated by paper chromatography. For separating anions, the solvents most frequently used are alcohols or acetone containing a base such as ammonia or pyridine. The technique has been widely applied to the separation of phosphates and polyphosphates, especially in biological systems. Using ethanol–isobutanol–ammonia as the solvent, mixtures of $Na_2H_2PO_2$, NaH_2PO_3, $NaHPO_4$, and $Na_2H_2P_2O_6$ have been separated. The halogens—fluoride, chloride, bromide, and iodide—and thiocyanate have been separated using 1.5 N NH_3 in n-butanol as the developing solvent.

The list of organic materials separable by paper chromatography is enormous in length.[8,15] Mixtures of sugars have been separated using a mixture of n-butanol–acetone–water as the solvent in circular development. When the sugars come from a naturally occurring source as, for example, from plants or body sera, the inorganic ions and organic ions are first removed by passing the solution through an ion-exchange resin. Advantage is taken of the differences in acid dissociation when attempting to separate mixtures of carboxylic acids. Acids composed of up to eight carbon atoms can be separated quite satisfactorily from one another, except the separation of formic and acetic acids, using a solvent system of 0.75 M NH_3 in n-butanol. The tobacco, opium, curare, indole, ergot, steroid, and other classes of alkaloids have provided a very large proportion of the applications of paper chromatography. Other applications include the separation of mixtures of vitamins, antibiotics, pesticides, herbicides, insecticides, dyes, and naturally occurring pigments and plastics.

Reversed-phase paper chromatography has been used to separate pesticide residues on fruits and vegetables. Soybean oil is the stationary liquid and 75:25 acetone:water is the mobile liquid. Mixtures containing DDT–DDD–Lindane have been resolved successfully as have mixtures of DDT–DDD–DDE–Kelthane. Paper chromatography is an invaluable tool in crime detection. It has been used to identify (by comparison) textile dyes, even when only a few fibers are available. By paper chromatographic comparison of inks, forgeries can be detected. Blood stains are compared and identified by paper chromatographic techniques. By analysis of urine, barbiturates can be detected.

EXPERIMENT 10-1
Separation of Amino Acids *

The purpose of this experiment is to illustrate the technique of descending paper chromatography on paper strips by means of the classic example—the method developed by Martin for the separation of amino acids. Many of the solvent systems used, especially some of Martin's, consist of phenols or substituted pyridines that are decidedly unpleasant and/or extremely hazardous to work with. This experiment uses the relatively harmless mixture of ethanol–acetic acid–water as the developing solvent system.

In this solvent system, nineteen amino acids tend to cluster themselves into groups having R_f values of 0.1, 0.2, 0.3, 0.4, 0.5, 0.6, 0.7, and 0.8. Individual acids within each of these groupings cannot be separated from one another, but acids from each of the groups, or from alternate groups can be separated quite cleanly. For example, glycine ($R_f \sim 0.28$), lysine ($R_f \sim 0.30$), serine ($R_f \sim 0.30$), and arginine ($R_f \sim 0.31$) can not be separated from one another, but they can be separated from other amino acids. With this in mind, the following amino acids have been selected to be separated, one from each of the groupings.

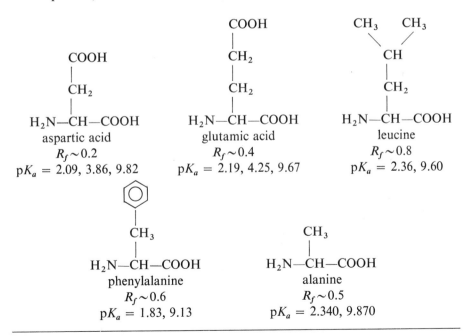

---

* Based upon material presented by L. Slaten, M. Willard, and Sr. A. A. Green, *J. Chem. Educ.* **33,** 140 (1956).

A mixture containing some or all of these acids is spotted carefully onto a strip of Whatman no. 1 filter paper and then developed with the ethanol–acetic acid–water solvent in a closed tank. After the chromatogram has been developed, the presence of the amino acids is detected by spraying the chromatogram with an alcoholic solution of ninhydrin. The individual amino acids are identified by comparison of their R_f values with those of standards run simultaneously.

Ninhydrin is the reagent that is universally used to detect amino acids. Since 1910, it has been known that ninhydrin reacts with amino acids to form colored reaction products. These are most frequently purple, although greens, reds, and yellows are encountered with some of the amino acids. The detailed chemistry of the production of these colors is not known completely, even after sixty years. The first step in the reaction has been shown to be:

ninhydrin   amino acid   hydrindantin

The ammonia released then reacts with a second molecule of ninhydrin and the hydrindantin to produce the purple coloration.

A different identity of the compound that is purple has been postulated by different authors, with no exact agreement reached. It does have an absorption maximum at 570 nm. The color-producing reaction is highly sensitive, capable of detecting as little as $0.1 \, \mu g/cm^2$ in the most favorable case with 0.5 to $5 \, \mu g/cm^2$ being the normal detection limit, depending upon the particular acid involved in the reaction. Since the chemical reaction goes to completion, by measuring the intensity of the purple color, the quantity of the amino acid present in the sample can be determined.

Developing agent.   The developing agent is a solution of 100 ml 95% ethanol, 20 ml water, and 2 ml glacial acetic acid. This solvent will esterify with time so that it should be made up fresh just before use. The solvent should be placed into developing tanks at least an hour before use so as to saturate the atmosphere in the tank with the solvent vapors.

Amino acid stock solutions.   0.10 M (or 0.5% by weight) aqueous solutions of each of the five amino acids—aspartic acid, glutamic acid, leucine, phenylalanine, and alanine. About 100 ml of each amino acid should be sufficient. In order to prevent air oxidation, each bottle should have a thin layer of toluene over the surface of the water as a preservative. It is a good idea to have a small capillary (a drawn-out commercial melting point tube works excellently) attached to each of the bottles of stock acid to prevent contamination of the stock solution and the standards on the paper.

Ninhydrin. Dissolve 0.2 g of ninhydrin in 100 ml of 95% ethanol. Store in a dark brown bottle. Commercial aerosols work just as effectively.

Caution: DO NOT touch that portion of the filter paper strip that will contain the developed chromatogram. Your hands will deposit sufficient materials (proteins, amino acids, and other contaminants) upon the paper to cause additional, spurious spots to appear when the chromatogram is sprayed with ninhydrin (purple fingerprints).

Preparation of the chromatogram. Obtain four strips of Whatman no. 1 chromatographic filter paper 1.5″ wide. Using a pencil (*Remember*: ink will chromatograph) draw a light line 8 to 9 cm from one end of each of the four strips. On each of the strips, measure 1 cm along this line from each edge of the paper and place a pencil dot there. Number each spot below the line and record in your notebook which acid is spotted at each number (see Fig. 10–15).

Chromatograph one spot of each of the standard acids and two samples of your unknown solution. Place a spot of each of the acids at one of the pencil dots. It is a good idea to place each of the two spots of the unknown on a separate strip of paper. Spot each acid by dipping a capillary pipette into the known amino acid solution, wiping the tip of the pipette clean with absorbent paper, and then momentarily touching the pipette perpendicularly to the paper, at the appropriate pencil dot. The diameter of each spot should not exceed 1.5 mm. A single application of each acid and two applications of the unknown spots should be adequate. Dry each of the spots before developing.

The developing tank is a commercial 12″ × 12″ × 24″ glass chromatographic tank. Attach the paper strips to the glass rack of the developing tank, using the plastic clips provided. The four strips will all fit on a single rack. The pencil starting line should be placed on the top of the horizontal glass rod which forms the top of the rack, with the numbers facing the short end of the rack. Cut off the excess paper at both ends of the rack.

Development of the chromatogram. Quickly place the rack containing the four paper strips in the developing tank. The lid of the tank should be opened briefly and only partially to the outside atmosphere. The atmosphere inside the developing tank is saturated with the solvent vapor which should not be allowed to become depleted.

Develop the chromatogram until the solvent front is from one-half to two-thirds of the distance down the strip. This will take from three to ten hours depending upon the paper.

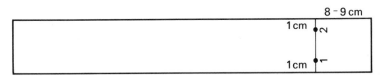

Fig. 10–15. Paper chromatographic strip.

When the solvent front has traveled about two-thirds the length of the paper, remove the rack from the developing tank and quickly mark the position of the solvent front on each of the four strips. Allow the paper to dry.

Detection of the spots.   Spray the dried strips with ninhydrin (0.2% in ethanol). Dry each sprayed strip in the oven at 80°C for three minutes. Treatment with ninhydrin should be done immediately after drying the paper and certainly no longer than twelve hours after removal of the strips from the tank. Allow the sprayed, dried paper strips to stand overnight before attempting to analyze the spots. The color of the spots will increase in intensity with time.

On each of the four strips measure:

1. the distance the solvent has traveled from the initial base line of the spots to the solvent front marked after developing the chromatogram.

2. the distance each amino acid (both standards and all in the unknowns) has travelled from the base position to the center of its developed (colored) spot. The center of the spot is taken as either the geometrical center if the color of the spot is uniform, or the point of maximum color intensity if the spot is elongated and of varying color intensity.

Determination of the unknown acids.   Calculate the R_f value for each of the acids in the standards and both unknown aliquots by dividing the distance of movement of the acid spot by the distance that the solvent front has moved during the same time. Note and record the color of each spot after being sprayed with ninhydrin. Compare the experimentally determined R_f and color of each known (standard) amino acid with the R_f and color of each spot on the chromatograms of the unknown. From the number of spots, the colors, and the R_f values for the unknown, decide which amino acids are present in your unknown sample.

EXPERIMENT 10–2
Circular Paper Chromatographic Separation of Metal Ions *

The purpose of this experiment is to illustrate the separation of metal ions by the technique of circular paper chromatography. The metals separated—copper, cobalt, iron and nickel—are encountered in steels, along with manganese. Manganese is not included in this experiment because its ring comes between those of nickel and cobalt, so it overlaps both rings. As mentioned earlier, only solutions of mineral acid in low molecular-weight-aliphatic ketones are effective as developing solvents for this mixture of ions. Burstall, Davies, Linstead, and Wells[3] have made an extensive study of metal ion separations by descending paper chromatography.

Solutions.   The standard metal ion solutions are 5% (w/v) solutions of the nitrates of copper, cobalt(II), iron(III), and nickel.

The developing solvent is prepared by mixing 87 ml of acetone, 8 ml of concentrated (12 M) HCl and 5 ml of deionized water. Since this solution deteriorates slowly it should be prepared fresh daily.

The detection solution consists of 1% dimethylglyoxime in ethanol.

---

* Taken from J. G. Surak and R. J. Martinovich, *J. Chem. Educ.*, **32**, 95 (1955).

Preparation of the chromatogram.   Prepare two 11″ circles of Whatman no. 1 filter paper in the following manner: Locate the center of the circle, and mark it with a pencil. (Why not use a ballpoint pen?) Cut a wick 1 cm wide from the circumference of the circle to its center, spacing it $\frac{1}{2}$ cm on either side of the central spot (see Fig. 10–5). Fold the wick down, so that the pencil spot marking the center of the disk is on the center of the crease. Cut the wick off to about 3 m.

Draw out an open-ended capillary melting point tube to form a capillary pipette. Use this to apply the standard solutions to one circle of filter paper and the unknown to the other. Apply one small drop of each of the standard solutions of copper, cobalt(II), iron(III) and nickel to the exact center of the filter paper. Dip the tip of the capillary pipette into the solution that is to be applied to the filter paper and allow the solution to rise by capillary action into the pipette. Withdraw the pipette and touch the tip to the side of a beaker to remove the hanging drop. Place the piece of Whatman no. 1 filter paper that has the cut wick on a piece of ordinary qualitative filter paper. At the exact center of the paper, touch the tip of the pipette perpendicularly to the paper. Allow the standard solution to flow out spontaneously until a spot 3 to 5 mm in diameter is obtained. Dry each spot. (This can be done by holding the paper very high over a very low burner flame.) When this spot has dried, in the same manner apply a drop of the second standard solution to the same spot. Continue adding standard solutions until a spot, centered in the middle of the paper contains all four cations. For best results this spot should not be diffuse or waterlogged.

On the second piece of Whatman no. 1 filter paper cut with a wick, apply four spots of the unknown solution in the same fashion as described earlier.

Development of the chromatogram.   Place the lower half of one petri dish on the desk where it will not be disturbed and where it is away from flames and direct sunlight. Pour 10 ml of the developing solvent into the dish. Rest the filter paper circle containing the standards on the rim of the dish, with the wick bent down and immersed in the solvent. Cover the paper tightly with the lower half of a second petri dish. Develop the chromatogram until the solvent has traveled almost to the edge of the dish (this should take about an hour).

Using the two upper halves of the petri dishes, set up a second development chamber and develop the chromatogram containing the unknown solution.

Detection of the spots.   When the solvent front has reached the edge of the petri dish, remove the filter paper and very rapidly, using a soft pencil, mark the extreme boundary of the solvent front. Hang the paper away from flames until the solvent evaporates completely, and the paper is dry.

Pour a few ml of 15 M NH_3 (DO THIS IN THE HOOD) into the top of one of the petri dishes and with the wick up, lay the developed chromatograms over the solution, until the fumes of ammonium salts no longer form and the blue ring of $Cu(NH_3)_4^{2+}$ appears. The boundaries of the visible rings may be marked on the filter paper at this time, if desired.

Spray the chromatogram with 1% alcoholic dimethylglyoxime. At this point nickel should appear as a reddish circle, cobalt as a dark brown circle, and iron as a brown circle. Let the paper dry.

Identification of the ions in the unknown.   Mark the boundaries of each ring on the chromatogram of the known and the chromatogram of the unknown.

Measure the distance from the center of the applied spot to the solvent front. Measure the distance from the center of the applied spot to the center of each ring. If the concentric rings are distorted, be sure that all measurements are made along the same radius.

Calculate the R_{f_c} values for each of the rings on the known and the unknown chromatogram by the definition:

$$R_{f_c} = \frac{\text{distance from center of application to center of the solute ring}}{\text{distance from center of application to solvent front}}$$

The identity of the rings on the known should be discerned from the colors of the ammine complexes and/or the dimethylglyoxime chelates. The approximate R_{f_c} values are: nickel, 0.25; cobalt, 0.65; copper, 0.80; iron(III), 1.00.

Record the colors of the rings and the R_{f_c} values for both the known and the unknown in your laboratory notebook. From the number of rings, their colors, and their R_{f_c} values, identify the components present in your unknown solution.

PROBLEMS

1. Differentiate clearly between ascending, descending, horizontal, and radial paper chromatography with respect to:
    (a) the equilibrium process responsible for the separation
    (b) the equipment required
    (c) the length of time consumed in the separation
    (d) the efficiency of the technique
2. What advantages does two-dimensional development have over one-dimensional development? Over multiple development?
3. How are colorless spots of developed solute located on paper chromatograms?
4. Why is the chief equilibrium process in paper chromatography considered to be partition? What are the two solvents involved? Which is the stationary one and which is the mobile one? Where does the stationary liquid phase come from?
5. Why is it possible to use liquid pairs that are partially or completely miscible in paper chromatography when it is not possible in extraction? Both are partition equilibria.
6. Would paper made out of glass fibers have any use in paper chromatography? Explain your answer.
7. Define the term R_f as encountered and used in paper chromatography. State the equation relating the R_f value to the areas of the liquid phases. How are R_f values used to identify solutes in paper chromatography?
8. What effect does each of the terms given below have on the R_f value of the solute specified?
    (a) the pH of the stationary liquid on the R_f values of weak acids
    (b) the pH of the stationary liquid on the R_f values of weak bases
    (c) the K_a of the acids to be separated
    (d) the concentration of a weak acid when the stationary liquid is unbuffered
9. What effect would each of the experimental variables listed below have on the R_f value measured for a particular solute?

(a)   the identity of the eluent used

(b)   the temperature of development

(c)   the concentration of complexing agent present in the eluent when separating a mixture of complexes

10. Arrange the amino acids below in order to increasing R_f values.

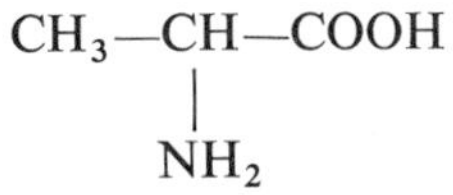

$$CH_3-CH-COOH$$
$$|$$
$$NH_2$$
alanine

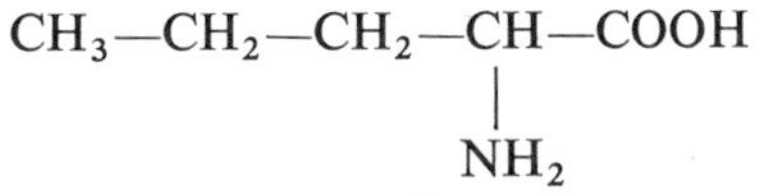

$$CH_3-CH_2-CH_2-CH-COOH$$
$$|$$
$$NH_2$$
norvaline

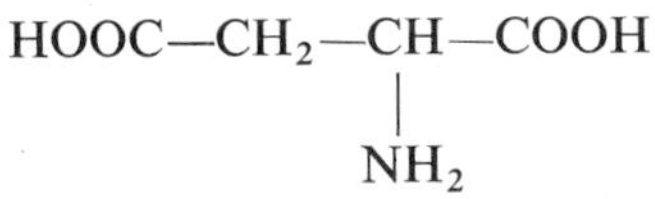

$$HOOC-CH_2-CH-COOH$$
$$|$$
$$NH_2$$
aspartic acid

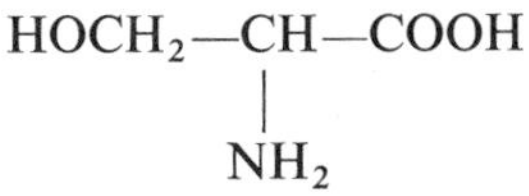

$$HOCH_2-CH-COOH$$
$$|$$
$$NH_2$$
serine

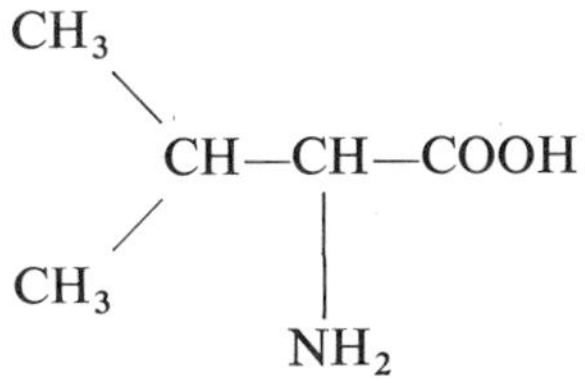

$$CH_3$$
$$\backslash$$
$$CH-CH-COOH$$
$$/ \quad |$$
$$CH_3 \quad |$$
$$NH_2$$
valine

11. Predict an order of R_f values for the paper chromatographic separation of each of the following mixtures. Justify your selection.

(a)   the amino acids valine [$NH_2-CH-CH(CH_3)_2)-COOH$], serine [$NH_2-CH(CH_2OH)-COOH$], aspartic acid [$NH_2-CH(CH_2COOH)-COOH$], cysteine [$NH_2-CH(CH_2SH)-COOH$]; using n-butanol-acetic acid–water as the developing agent

(b)   the aliphatic carboxylic acids acetic, propionic, butyric, pentanoic; using 1.5 N ammonia in n-butanol as the developing agent

(c)   the aliphatic amines methylamine, ethylamine, n-propylamine, n-butylamine; using 25% acetic acid in n-butanol as the developing agent

(d)   the alkaline earth metals barium, calcium, magnesium, strontium; using 1:1 methanol:ethanol as the developing agent.

12. Name four factors contributing to the uncertainty of measured R_f values.

13. What effect does each of the following have on the reproducibility of an R_f value for a specified solute?

(a)   variations in the mineral content of the paper

(b)   variations in the water content of the paper

(c)   the complexity of the eluent; for example, n-butanol vs. the mixture n-butanol–acetic acid–water

(d)   the size of the sample taken for analysis

14. What is a group constant, $\Delta\mu$? How is the numerical value of a group constant measured? Describe how group constants are used to obtained theoretical R_f values.

15. Why were R_M values defined? What physical quantity do they represent? Why do calculated and measured R_M values occasionally differ considerably?

16. J. H. Bremner and R. H. Kenton, *Biochem. J.*, **49**, 651 (1951) report the following R_f values for the paper chromatographic separation of aliphatic amines using *n*-butanol–acetic acid–water as the mobile solvent.

Amine	R_f Value
CH_3NH_2	0.37
$CH_3-CH_2-NH_2$	0.45
$CH_3-CH_2-CH_2-NH_2$	0.58
$CH_3-CH_2-CH_2-CH_2-CH_2-NH_2$	0.77
$H_2N-CH_2-CH_2-NH_2$	0.14
$H_2N-CH_2-CH_2-CH_2-NH_2$	0.15
$HO-CH_2-CH_2-NH_2$	0.33
$\begin{array}{c} CH_3 \\ {>}NH \\ CH_3 \end{array}$	0.43
$\begin{array}{c} CH_3 \\ {>}CH-NH_2 \\ CH_3 \end{array}$	0.57
$\begin{array}{c} CH_3 \\ {>}CH-CH_2-CH_2-NH_2 \\ CH_3 \end{array}$	0.77

Using these data, what tentative conclusions would you draw about the effect of the following structural characteristics of amines on their R_f values?
(a)   length of the carbon chain
(b)   branching of the carbon chain for the same number of carbon atoms
(c)   the number of amino groups in a molecule for the same number of carbon atoms
(d)   primary vs. secondary amines
(e)   the presence of hydroxyl groups in an amine with the same number of carbon atoms; compare this with your conclusion in (c)

17. What solvent system would you try first for the separation by paper chromatography of each of the following mixtures?
(a)   amino acids, $R-CH-COOH$
$\qquad\qquad\qquad\qquad |$
$\qquad\qquad\qquad\quad NH_2$
(b)   amines, $R-NH_2$
(c)   substituted phenols, $(R-C_6H_4-OH)$
(d)   sugars (monosaccharides)
(e)   cations

18. It is possible to separate copper from nickel by ascending paper chromatography using tartaric acid in 60% ethanol as the developing agent. Diagram the equilibria involved, and explain why this separation is feasible.
19. Outline the technique used for the quantitative analysis of a mixture by means of paper chromatography with reflectance spectroscopy to estimate the solute concentrations.
20. Compare and contrast paper chromatography and high-speed liquid partition chromatography with respect to:
    (a) the apparatus required
    (b) the size of the sample capable of being separated
    (c) the time required for the separation to be achieved
    (d) the efficiency of the separation
    (e) the facility with which quantitative results can be obtained.
21. Do you think that a qualitative analysis scheme for the common metal ions that involves paper chromatographic separations of the metal ions within the conventional groupings of metals offers any advantages over the conventional scheme involving solubility and complex ion equilibria? Explain.

REFERENCES

1. Bate-Smith, E. C. and Westall, R. G., *Biochim. Biophys. Acta.*, **4**, 427 (1950).
2. Burma, D. P., *Nature*, **168**, 565 (1951).
3. Burstall, F. H., Davies, R. G., Linstead, R. P., and Wells, R. A., *J. Chem. Soc.*, **1950**, 516.
4. Clayton, R. A., *Anal. Chem.*, **28**, 904 (1956).
5. Consden, R., Gordon, A. H., and Martin, A. J. P., *Biochem. J.*, **38**, 224 (1944).
6. Grune, A., *J. Chromatogr.*, **33**, 28 (1968).
7. Hais, I. M., *J. Chromatogr.*, **33**, 25 (1968).
8. Hais, I. M., Macek, K., Kopecky, J., and Gasparic, J., *Bibliography of Paper and Thin-Layer Chromatography 1961–1965*, Elsevier, Amsterdam, 1968.
9. Hais, I. M. and Macek, K., Eds., *Paper Chromatography*, Academic Press, New York, 1963, p. 129.
10. Ibid., p. 131
11. Ibid., p. 132
12. Ibid., p. 134
13. Ibid., p. 137
14. Ibid., p. 158
15. Heftmann, E., *Chromatography*, 2nd ed., Van Nostrand Reinhold Co., New York, 1967.
16. Macek, K. and Prochazka, Z., in *Paper Chromatography*, I. M. Hais and K. Macek, Eds., Academic Press, New York, 1963.
17. Martin, A. J. P., *Biochem. Soc. Symp.*, **3**, 4 (1949).
18. Matthais, W. *Züchter*, **24**, 313 (1954).
19. Soczewinski, E. and Manleo, R. *J. Chromatogr.*, **33**, 40 (1968).
20. Weaver, W. C. in *Advances in Chromatography*, R. A. Keller, Ed., Dekker, New York, 1966, Vol. VII, pp. 87–120.

CHAPTER 11

THIN-LAYER CHROMATOGRAPHY

Thin-layer chromatography is not a single chromatographic method, but rather a collection of chromatographic processes having in common only the physical arrangement of the stationary phase. The distinguishing experimental characteristic is a very thin coating of a powdered stationary phase on a glass, metal, or plastic sheet. This sheet merely serves as a support for the stationary phase. The mobile liquid moves through the stationary phase by capillary action. The equilibrium processes upon which separations are based can be adsorption, partition, ion exchange, or gel filtration. Thin-layer chromatography as originally developed was an adsorption equilibrium process and the majority of the applications of thin-layer chromatography use adsorption as the separation mechanism. The relationship between thin-layer chromatography and column adsorption chromatography is analogous to that between paper chromatography and column partition chromatography. The equipment needed to carry out a thin-layer chromatographic separation is remarkably simple and inexpensive, while the separation process is rapid and extremely efficient.

In spite of early papers demonstrating the utility and simplicity of thin-layer chromatography, almost twenty years elapsed before the technique became widely adopted. In 1938, Izmailov and Shraiber,[6] working in the physicochemical laboratory of the Ukrainian Institute for Experimental Pharmacy at Kharkov, USSR published their first paper on thin-layer chromatography. A slurry of alumina was spread 2 mm thick onto a glass microscope slide, dried, and then spotted with a drop of tincture of belladonna, or digitalis, or rhubarb. The drop was separated into concentric circles by dropping alcohol at the center. The components of these tinctures were identified by the colors of the circles. The appearance of the paper describing this work did not create much excitement, even among the scientists who were aware of the paper; after all, it was published in Russian and in a little-known journal.

In 1951, Kirchner, Miller, and Keller[9] set out to identify the flavoring compounds in citrus fruits. Since they had only a very small quantity of the oils containing the terpenes, a microtechnique had to be used for the separation process.

Paper chromatography was tried but would not separate the mixture. Aware of previous publications, they tried the separation on a thin layer of starch on glass plates. By this procedure they were able to separate their mixtures quite success-fully. Even though their separation was published in the leading American journal dealing with chemical analysis, it was not heralded as a great advance in separation science. The scientific world was not interested in thin-layer chromatography at this time for it was thoroughly engrossed in the fantastic new separation method—gas–liquid chromatography—that had been introduced by James and Martin in 1952.[7]

In 1955, E. Stahl of the University of Mainz in Germany was struggling to separate the components of plant glandular fibers. He tried Izmailov and Shraiber's technique, but on layers of alumina 2 mm thick he did not effect a separation. Out of necessity, he kept using thinner and thinner layers of adsorbent on his plates until finally a 20 micron-thick layer of silica gel, of very fine and carefully controlled particle diameter produced a successful separation. This separation was published in 1956,[15] but as Stahl states in his recent book, "This work, too, remained ig-nored as was that of my predecessors. The position at the time can best be summed up by the opinion that the method was 'one of the usual chromatographic gimmicks.'"[17]

Whereas the previous scientists had not been salesmen of thin-layer chromato-graphy, Stahl was. He believed in the potentialities of the technique, wanted it to catch on, and longed to know why the technique was ignored. Surprisingly enough, his investigations and reasoning said it was due to a lack of commercially available apparatus. So Stahl developed a kit of basic equipment which was introduced in 1958,[16] and soon became available commercially in Europe. Stahl's judgment and

Fig. 11–1. Simple thin-layer chromatographic equipment. (*Photograph by Stephen Daugherty.*)

salesmanship were effective for once commercial equipment became available, the technique became widely used in southern Germany and Switzerland. Until 1965, experimenters had to prepare their own thin-layer plates using Stahl's equipment, but during that year the first commercial precoated plates and sheets were put on the market. Then thin-layer chromatography blossomed. Today it is one of the most widely used separation methods. It is used by synthetic organic chemists to check the course of their reactions, and as a criteria of purity (only a single spot is produced upon development). It is used clinically as a aid in diagnosis, and in biomedical laboratories to analyze complex natural products. It is even used as another tool in crime detection. In short, thin-layer chromatography is used wherever and whenever a simple, powerful, rapid technique for separating complex mixtures can be of value.

Stahl's belief that the lack of commercially available equipment held back the acceptance of thin-layer chromatography seems startling because the performance and apparatus necessary for thin-layer chromatographic separations can be extremely simple, as is shown in Fig. 11–1. The essential pieces of equipment are a sheet or plate as a backing for the thin layer, a powdered stationary phase attached to the backing, a mobile liquid, and a closed developing chamber. Naturally, in addition to these, you need a sample and appropriate means of detecting the spots on the developed chromatogram. Stahl's kit costs around $300.

THE EXPERIMENTAL VARIABLES

Backing Sheets or Plates

The only characteristics that the backing needs to possess are a modicum of rigidity and a clean surface. Its sole function is to provide a flat surface to which the stationary phase can adhere. The most common backings are sheets of glass or microscope slides, although commercial TLC plates have stainless steel, aluminum, or plastic backings (Makrolon).

Stationary Phases

The stationary phase in thin-layer chromatography consists of a finely powdered solid. The role of the powder can be that of adsorbent, support for a thin liquid film, ion exchanger, or molecular sieve. Most frequently the solids act as adsorbents. The restrictions upon powdered solids in thin-layer chromatography are much more severe than in column chromatography. They must be purer, have a narrower range of particle sizes, and be smaller (5 to 50μ). As is the case with column adsorption and partition chromatography, surface area is the important feature of the stationary phase. The separation properties of commercial adsorbents vary as much as 50% from one manufacturer to another, and even from any single producer properties will vary from batch to batch. The flow of solvent through the thin layer will be determined by the size of the particles of the stationary phase and by the density of the packing within the layer; the flow is much slower on 0.1 to 10μ particles than on 10 to 40μ particles. A binder—plaster of paris, gypsum, or polyvinyl alcohol—is used to adhere the stationary phase to the backing.

Thin-layer chromatography plates are prepared by spreading an aqueous slurry of the solid adsorbent uniformly in a very thin layer (0.1 to 0.3 mm) over the surface of the backing. After the solvent is evaporated off, the adsorbent layer is activated by drying in the oven at 110°C. The activated plates are stored in a desiccator until ready for use.

Adsorbents

The adsorbents used in the thin layer are classified in the same manner as those used for column adsorption chromatography—from strong to weak. The same compounds are used, in general, for the thin adsorbing layer.

Silica gel is the most commonly used adsorbent in thin-layer chromatography. Its properties have been discussed in Chapter 8, p. 350.

Alumina has been discussed in Chapter 8, p. 350. When separating mixtures of weakly polar compounds, alumina is to be preferred over silica gel. When separating polar compounds such as amino acids or sugars, silica gel is to be preferred over alumina.

Magnesium silicate, calcium silicate, and activated *charcoal* have also been used as adsorbents in thin-layer separations. See Chapter 8 for their properties.

Vycor glass, powdered to particles between 60–75μ in diameter, has a surface area of 150 to 200 m^2/g because the structure contains pores of about 40 Å in diameter. It is used with 13% gypsum as a binder to form layers 0.3 mm thick. Since the surface of the glass is dirtied during the grinding process, it must be cleaned scrupulously before being used.

Polyamides such as Perlon or nylon (polyhexamethylenediamine adipate) are used as thin layers to separate polar compounds. The long-chain polymers hydrogen bond to one another so that they are essentially insoluble in water and polar solvents. The surface of the polymer, however, will have free amide groups that can adsorb. The structure of polycaprolactam (Perlon) is shown here:

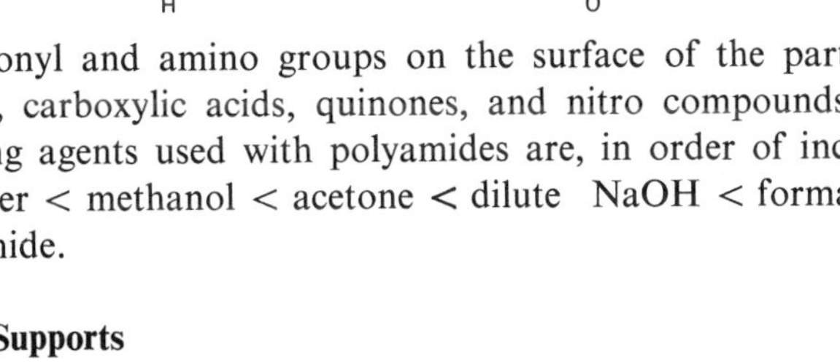

The carbonyl and amino groups on the surface of the particles hydrogen bond phenols, carboxylic acids, quinones, and nitro compounds to them very readily. Eluting agents used with polyamides are, in order of increasing eluting strength, water < methanol < acetone < dilute NaOH < formamide < dimethylformamide.

Liquid Phase Supports

Supports for the stationary liquid phases used in partition separations by thin-layer chromatography are those that have been described in Chapter 9—*silica gel, diatomaceous earth,* and *cellulose.* The fibers of naturally obtained cellulose are too long for satisfactory use in thin-layer chromatography. To reduce the length of the fibers to 2 to 20μ as well as to prepare the slurry, a 15% aqueous suspension of cellulose is stirred in a mechanical blender for 30 to 60 sec. The slurry is then spread on the backing and air dried; no binders are used with cellulose. A microcrystalline cellulose is also available that has particles that are 19 or 38μ in diameter. Because of the smaller fibers, the lack of matting present in paper, and a more even particle size, there is a more uniform distribution of the stationary liquid, which produces a more rapid and clean separation than is obtained using filter paper.

Silica gel and diatomaceous earth can be silanized to convert the surfaces to methyl groups, suitable for use in reversed-phase thin-layer chromatography.

Ion-Exchange Resins

Ion-exchange resins, such as Dowex 50W and Dowex 1, are available with particle sizes between 40 and 80μ, which are suitable for forming thin layers. The resins are usually used in the hydrogen, sodium, or chloride forms. Five grams of cellulose powder and thirty grams of ion-exchange resin are usually made into a slurry, which is then spread on the backing to produce a layer 250μ thick.

Gels

Gel-filtration thin layers are prepared from *Sephadex Superfine* which is a special dextran having more than the average cross linking. Since dextrans have great numbers of hydroxyl groups on their surfaces they swell in water to form gels. The dextran is soaked for 72 hours in water before use, and then spread as a layer between 0.2 and 0.5 mm thick. In contrast to the other forms of thin-layer plates, dextran plates are kept and stored wet. The capillary action through the dextran gel on the surface of the backing is slower than for most other thin layers moving only 1 to 2 cm/hr. Development by gel filtration takes from 8 to 10 hours as contrasted to 30 minutes for the other forms.

Plate Preparation

Precoated TLC plates are available from many commercial sources. The standard sizes are 10 × 20 cm or, preferably, 20 × 20 cm. Silica gel, alumina, and cellulose plates are available with and without fluorescent indicators incorporated into the thin layer. Polyamide and other special coatings can also be obtained. Plates that have aluminum or plastic backing can be cut to smaller sizes, for use in smaller development chambers. An extremely large proportion of the TLC separations done today use commercially precoated plates, rather than those made in the laboratory.

There are many ways to coat your own plates in the laboratory, but the two most common techniques are dipping and spreading. The ideal adsorbent layer is thin, uniform in thickness, free from cracks and lumps, and adherent to the backing.

When Peifer introduced thin-layer chromatography using microscope slides in 1962,[13] he opened the way for simple, easy, and rapid development (five minutes or so). Microscope slides are coated with the thin film by dipping. A slurry of the solid phase (about 50 g in 100 ml of water) is prepared and two microscope slides, whose flat surfaces are held firmly together, are dipped into the slurry, withdrawn slowly, and the excess slurry allowed to drain off. The two slides are separated and the solvent allowed to evaporate from the surface. This is by far and away the easiest and simplest method for coating plates, but it is only applicable to small surfaces, such as those of microscope slides.

The 20 × 20 cm plates are coated by means of commercially available spreaders. These are fairly expensive, but produce excellent layers of uniform properties. There are two types of spreaders, the *stationary trough* (or *Kirchner*) type or the *movable trough* (or *Stahl*) type. Fig. 11–2 shows the stationary type and Fig. 11–3 shows how the movable type operates. In both of these spreaders, the slurry is poured into a narrow trough that is as long as the plate width. The rear wall of the trough can be raised vertically above the plate surface to specified heights, so that as the slurry emerges from the bottom of the back wall of the trough, coating the plate, the thickness of the layer is accurately specified and controlled. Fig. 11–4 shows the trough with its adjustable wall.

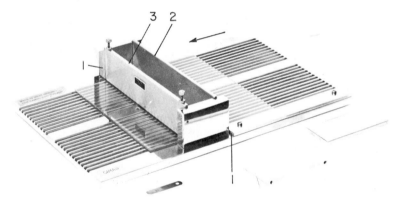

Fig. 11–2. Plate spreader with stationary trough.

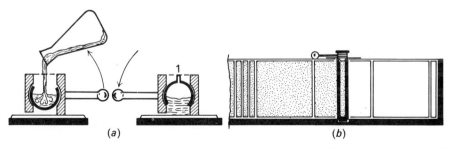

(a)   (b)

Fig. 11–3. Operation of the Stahl TLC-spreader. (*a*) Cross-section: filling with the slurry (left); position ready for spreading (right). Note the opening for entry of air (1). (*b*) Aligning tray with row of glass plates and spreader viewed from above. (*Redrawn from Ref. 17, by permission of Springer-Verlag.*)

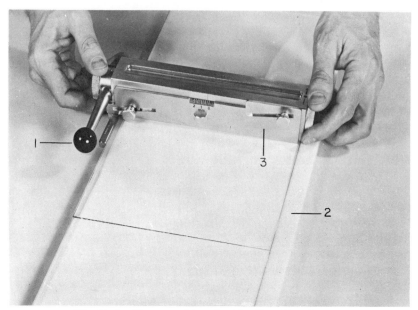

Fig. 11–4.   Close-up of trough with adjustable tail-gate.

In the Kirchner-type spreader the trough is fastened permanently at a fixed position on the bed of the apparatus. The plates to be coated are pushed under the trough, which deposits a fixed thickness of slurry on their surfaces. In the Stahl-type spreader, the plates are clamped onto the bed of the equipment and the trough is moved slowly and continuously over them, depositing an even layer of slurry on the surfaces.

Mobile Phases

The selection of the best solvent to develop a thin-layer chromatogram is based on considerations that have been discussed thoroughly in Chapters 8 and 9 when treating adsorption and partition chromatography. The eluting ability of solvents for adsorption chromatography has been given in Table 8–1, and remains the same when these solvents are used in thin-layer chromatography, going from hexane < cyclohexane < carbon tetrachloride < benzene < chloroform < diethylether < ethyl acetate < acetone.

When possible, it is preferable to use a pure liquid as the developing solvent, rather than a mixture of liquids. The components of a mixed solvent "demix" or chromatograph as they move up the thin layer. Thus, there is a continual change in the solvent composition with distance on the thin-layer plate, and the R_f values will vary according to how far the spots have traveled. When, however, a single solvent that will separate the desired mixture cannot be found and a mixture of solvents must be used, the simpler the number of components in it, the fewer problems encountered, that is, a two-component solvent is much preferred over a four-component one.

It is very essential in thin-layer chromatography that the developing solvents be of high purity. The presence of even small amounts of water or impurities can change the chromatographic behavior of the solutes and cause unreproducible separations. It should not be surprising to learn that the rate of movement of the solvent through the thin layer decreases as the viscosity of the solvent increases; which is to say, the more viscous the solvent, the longer it will take to develop the thin-layer chromatogram.

As has been emphasized in previous chapters, when first starting out to separate a mixture of compounds, the time spent in the library discovering what others have used to separate the same or similar mixtures is invaluable. In the case of thin-layer chromatography the experience of others in column adsorption as well as in thin-layer separations, is applicable.

One advantage that thin-layer chromatography has over all other chromatographic methods is the extreme shortness of time required for the separations. Using microscope slides, the chromatogram can be developed in five minutes or so, and with 20 × 20 cm plates about thirty minutes is standard. Thus, an empirical approach to solvent selection can be done very quickly, if four or five solvents are tried simultaneously the best solvent can be selected by trial and error with a minimum of wasted time.

Sample Application

To apply the sample to the thin layer properly takes much more skill and patience than it does to spot the sample into the paper in paper chromatography. Paper is more porous and flexible than is the solid adsorbent on a glass plate. Therefore, you have to be careful not to touch the adsorbent or a hole will undoubtedly result. As in paper chromatography, only a very small quantity of sample is needed, or capable of being separated. Usually from 1 to 10 μl of 1% solutions are applied, to give spots that are 3 to 5 mm in diameter.

During standardization of the technique of thin-layer chromatography it was agreed that the sample should be spotted 1.5 cm up from the lower edge of the plate, and 1.0 cm in from the edge of the plates. Since pencil lines cannot be drawn on a TLC plate to indicate the appropriate place to spot the sample, templates which have holes at the correct position for the application of the unknown and standard substances, frequently, are placed over the plate as guides.

The sample is applied from a hypodermic syringe, with a micropipette (lambda pipette), or with a platinum loop. The platinum loop is made from 0.4 mm platinum wire coiled in a circle with a diameter of 1.5 mm. It applies 10 μl of sample solution. In using all of these applicators, the drop is touched to the surface of the plate, quickly and cleanly, never allowing the tip of the needle, pipette, or loop to come in contact with the thin layer. A steady hand is needed.

Development

Ascending development is most prevalent in thin-layer chromatography. According to the standardized technique, the developing liquid is placed to a depth of 5 to 8 mm in the bottom of the closed chamber. Development is carried out at

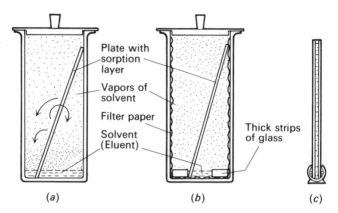

Fig. 11–5. Development chambers for ascending thin-layer chromatography: (*a*) chamber with normal saturation (NS), the arrows indicate solvent evaporation from the layer and the dots symbolize the vapor density; (*b*) chamber saturated with solvent by means of filter-paper lining, saturated with the solvent (CS); (*c*) reduction of the chamber volume using the S-chamber. (*Redrawn from Ref. 17, by permission of Springer-Verlag.*)

room temperature, with 40 to 65% relative humidity, and in a solvent vapor-saturated chamber until the solvent front has traveled 10 cm. The fastest way to saturate the developing chamber with the solvent vapor is to line the sides of the chamber with blotting paper that has been soaked in the solvent. Development chambers are made out of glass to avoid contamination of the solvent and to enable visualization of the development process. Development chambers are usually relatively small, which allows rapid saturation with solvent vapor. They range all the way from jam jars and other glass bottles to elaborate tanks. Fig. 11–5 shows several typical development chambers for ascending development. In Fig. 11–5(a) nothing special is done to increase the rate of saturation of the atmosphere. In Fig. 11–5(b) the sides of the tank are lined with blotting paper. In Fig. 11–5(c) an S-chamber is shown. (S stands for sandwich in English or *schmal* in German, meaning narrow.) In an S-chamber the 20 × 20 cm TLC plate is the rear wall of the chamber, and the cover plate of the chamber is the front wall. Side walls, which are gaskets 2 to 3 mm thick, are attached to the cover. The whole assembly is clamped together and developed by standing upright in a trough of solvent. Since there is an extremely small free space in the S-chamber, saturation problems are minimized for the atmosphere very readily becomes saturated.

Descending development, which is the most common method for paper chromatography is not used to any extent in thin-layer chromatography. Descending development is not so easy to perform as in paper chromatography, where the limp strip or sheet of paper can be hung over a glass rod and the solvent allowed to flow down it. Glass plates are not readily draped over rods! There is no reason to go to the extra trouble since in thin-layer chromatography descending development does not shorten the development time nor give better separations. Thus, since the equipment is more complex, it just isn't worth the expense.

Horizontal development is encountered occasionally in TLC. Fig. 11–6 shows

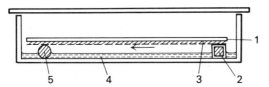

Fig. 11–6. Development chamber for horizontal thin-layer chromatography: (1) TLC plate, face down; (2) glass or metal rod, wrapped round with filter paper; (3) thin-layer; (4) solvent; (5) glass rod or tube as support. (*Redrawn from Ref. 17, by permission of Springer-Verlag.*)

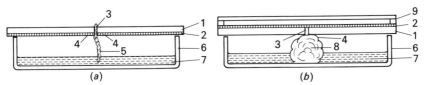

(a)   (b)

Fig. 11–7. Development chamber for circular thin-layer chromatography: (a) for separating several substance mixtures; (b) with a small preliminary separating column for a single substance mixture. (1) Supporting 20 × 20 cm plate; (2) thin layer; (3) perforation of 2 mm diameter; (4) point of application; (5) cotton-wool wick; (6) petri dish cover; (7) solvent; (8) cotton-wool pad; (9) glass strips. (*Redrawn from Ref. 17, by permission of Springer-Verlag.*)

a typical chamber for horizontal development. The glass TLC plate rests upside down on two glass rods. One (5) merely serves as a support for the plate (1). The other rod (2) is wrapped with a piece of filter paper which serves as a wick to supply the solvent to the plate.

During circular development, the TLC plate is upside down in the flat, closed container, with a wick of cotton touching the center of the spot (see Fig. 11–7).

Saturation of the Chamber

One debatable feature of thin-layer chromatogram development is whether or not the chamber should be saturated with the solvent vapor before the plate is put in to develop. The two possible practices are:

1. Place the developing solvent in the chamber (lined with blotting paper or not) about one hour before using so that the free space in the chamber becomes saturated with the vapor (saturation chambers).

2. Pour the developing solvent into the chamber immediately before placing the plate in to be developed.

The standardized development procedure specifies the use of saturated chambers. De Zeeuw[2] prefers the use of unsaturated chambers, finding that they produce better separation of hypnotics (barbitols) using ether–chloroform as the developing solvent. He claims that, in effect, the use of unsaturated chambers is a form of gradient elution since solvent front movement and saturation of the free space in the chamber occur simultaneously. As the chamber is being saturated when using mixed solvents, the more volatile component evaporates off the plate near the solvent front faster than the less volatile components. As the solvent moves up the plate the vapor in the chamber becomes increasingly saturated with the volatile components and evaporation of them from the plate is less. As a result, the composition of the eluting agent in the plate becomes increasingly more concentrated in the more volatile components as the plate develops. Of course, this only holds true when mixed solvents are used. As a result of this gradient elution, De Zeeuw contends he obtains separations improved over those in saturation chambers. The development time is longer, the spot diameter and shape are more compact, the spots are more cleanly outlined, there are no observable edge effects, and reproducible R_f values are obtained.

The degree of saturation of the chamber is an important variable in TLC because the solvent vapors are adsorbed readily onto the fine particles in the thin layer of solid. Thus, the moving liquid solvent front encounters a stationary phase that is already partially covered with the solvent. This causes a "deactivation" of the adsorption sites. One of the most polar of the liquids that can be adsorbed onto the thin layer is water. Because water deactivates adsorbents, the humidity of the room in which the plates are spotted and in the developing chamber can affect the separation. When silica gel and alumina are the adsorbents and polar solvents are used as the developing agents, there is no effect on the R_f values due to the humidity, but when nonpolar solvents are used, the amount of water adsorbed onto the plate (for example, the relative humidity in the room and chamber) does affect the R_f values—increasing humidity increases the R_f values. When nonpolar stationary phases, such as carbon, or silanized diatomaceous earth, or silica gel, are used there are no effects due to humidity in R_f values. When cellulose is used as the stationary phase in partition thin-layer chromatography, the R_f values obtained decrease as the humidity increases.

Detection of Spots

Since the same detection techniques that were discussed in Chapters 7 and 10 are used in thin-layer chromatography, only a few additional comments are needed.

Commercial TLC plates and sheets can be obtained containing a fluorescing dye. When an unused sheet is held under ultraviolet light, the entire layer fluoresces. After development, however, when the sheet is held under ultraviolet light, wherever there is a spot of the sample, the fluorescence is quenched and a dark spot appears. This is probably the most common detection technique today, for fluorescent dyes are easily and routinely added to the powdered adsorbent before preparing the slurry for homemade TLC plates.

Streak reagents and sprays are also widely used in TLC—things such as ninhydrin, H_2S, dithizone, and $SbCl_3$. Another trick, found primarily in TLC when the spots are colorless and do not fluoresce, is to expose the developed plate to iodine vapor. The iodine vapor will interact with the components in the sample by chemical reaction, by adsorption, or by solubility to produce a colored product which can be observed visually.

QUALITATIVE ANALYSIS

R_f Values

The R_f values obtained in thin-layer chromatographic separations are much less reproducible and reliable than those obtained by other techniques, including paper chromatography. To obtain meaningful identifications by thin-layer chromatography it is essential to run standards and knowns in the developing chamber at the same time as the unknown, preferably on the same plate. In order to be able to do this, 20 × 20 cm has been established as the standard TLC plate size. On a plate of this size, a few spots of the unknown and about ten spots of standards and knowns can be placed on the same plate, thus making development conditions constant, although probably not reproducible, for that particular analysis.

The magnitude of R_f values are determined by the physical and chemical properties of the chemical compounds involved—the solute, the adsorbent, the mobile liquid. The effect of the structure and properties of the compounds comprising the sample has been discussed in Chapter 8 in terms of adsorption energies and group adsorption energies. In Chapter 10 R_M values as applied to paper chromatography were discussed. The concept of R_M values can also be applied to thin-layer separations. There is no need to repeat those discussions here, so reread pp. 327–328 on R_f values and pp. 403–405 on R_M values. The discussion of the role of the adsorbent and developing solvent has been given already both in this chapter and more extensively in Chapter 8, so that it need not be repeated.

The reproducibility of R_f values becomes significant when trying to identify compounds in a mixture, and when trying to repeat separations of solutes with close R_f values. The poor reproducibility of thin-layer chromatographic R_f values is attributable to an extremely large number of factors. In order to obtain the same R_f value for successive separations, all of these factors must be reproduced exactly, which really is impossible. These factors are inherent in the four aspects of thin-layer chromatography—the adsorbent, the solvent, the sample, and the development process. Let's just look briefly at some of the most important of these experimental factors.

Adsorbent Effects on R_f Values

The adsorbent can affect the R_f values in many ways. As we know, the identity of the adsorbent gives different values—for example, R_f values on silica gel are going to be different from the R_f values obtained on magnesium silicate. But this isn't the only thing we need to worry about. Generally, TLC is dependent upon adsorption for its success and hence the surface of the adsorbent is critical to the separation efficiency and reproducibility. Adsorbents obtained from different manufacturers, or even from the same manufacturer but from different batches, will have different past histories and hence different surface properties. And as a result of this, R_f values for the same compound may differ up to 50% when different batches of the same chemical are used as an adsorbent. Remember we encountered this in paper chromatography too.

The purity and activity of the surface are important, but so are the particle size and the surface area. The effect of the surface area on the reproducibility of R_f values varies with both solvent and solutes, depending upon their relative adsorption energies. In the case of water and also of carbon tetrachloride, the value of R_f decreases with increasing surface area. It is debatable whether or not the thickness of the layer on the backing affects the numerical value of the R_f. Geiss[4] found that the value of the R_f increased by 10 percent in going from layers that were 0.1 mm thick to layers 2 mm in thickness. Dallas[1] reported that there is no effect of layer thickness in S tanks, and also that if all other experimental conditions are standardized and reproduced there is no effect of layer thickness. Janchen[8] reported that when the development chamber is saturated with solvent vapor there is no effect of layer thickness. In order to eliminate any possibility, however, the standardized layer thickness is between 0.1 and 0.3 mm, preferably 0.2 mm. Layers on the commercially available precoated plates are 100 or 150 μ thick. To summarize, the adsorption of solutes depends upon the identity, the extent, the cleanliness, the activation of the surface of the adsorbent.

Solvent Effects on R_f Values

As has been discussed in this and previous chapters, not only the identity of the solvent changes the R_f values, but its purity will have an effect also. Because of the sensitivity of TLC to small traces of compounds, only the purest liquids should be used as solvents. The influence of solvent viscosity has been mentioned earlier. Demixing occurs when using mixed solvents. Chemical interactions among the solvent components should be checked, as mentioned in Chapter 10. Because of differences in the vapor pressure and adsorption properties of the components the composition of the mixed solvent changes during use. A mixed solvent should never be reused more than twice.

Solute Effects on R_f Values

Naturally the chemical properties of the solute will affect the extent of its adsorption and hence its R_f value in TLC. But, in addition to that, other aspects of the solute or the sample influence the reproducibility of the R_f obtained. The amount of the sample used to spot the plate makes a difference if the adsorption isotherm for that sample constituent is not linear, but is one of the curved ones shown in Fig. 7–3. The presence of other materials in samples, especially samples of natural origin, can change the viscosity, chemical composition, or relative adsorption and hence change the R_f value obtained.

Effects of the Development Process on R_f Values

The effect of the extent of saturation of the atmosphere in the developing chamber with the vapors of the developing liquid, as well as the relative humidity in the room and the developing chamber, has been discussed earlier. These two experimental factors alter the number of molecules of solvent or water adsorbed onto the dry surface of the TLC plate from the gas phase, which changes the purity of the surface as well as the number of sites available for adsorption of the solute from the liquid phase.

Although Geiss and Schlett[5] studied the effect of temperature on the efficiency of the TLC separation process, it is difficult to make a clear-cut statement about temperature effects on the reproducibility of R_f values. They report that at constant water content in the chamber, the R_f value is constant over a temperature range from 5 to 60°C. At constant relative humidity, the R_f value was found to increase with increasing temperature at about 0.03 to 0.05 per degree C.

The practical effect of the influence of all these factors is that R_f values in the literature cannot be reproduced in the laboratory. While the order of movement of spots is probably not going to change, the actual distance any spot moves certainly will be different from one run to another. Thus, it is absolutely essential to develop plates using the same batch of adsorbent, in the same tank, for the same distance, and under the same conditions if any meaningful interpretations of the data are to be made.

The important characteristics of thin-layer chromatograms are the relative values of R_f and the size of the spots produced. These determine whether or not two substances can be separated. When the diameter of the spots is too great, even if the R_f values are sufficiently different, the spots will overlap, so that a separation is impossible. Fig. 11-8 shows the effect of spot size on separations. Thus, relatively small spots are needed in order not to inhibit separations.

For resolution of two compounds by thin-layer chromatography their R_f values should differ by at least 0.06. For the optimum separation, the R_f values should be about 0.33. Compounds which are adsorbed very slightly onto the surface

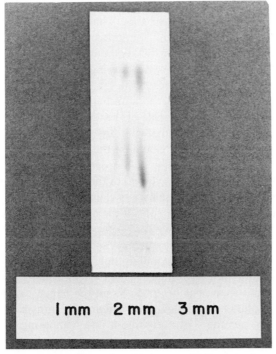

Fig. 11–8. Effect of spot size on TLC separations. (*Photograph by Stephen Daugherty.*)

of the thin layer will move very rapidly to the end of the plate and in bunches, so that no separation is possible. Similarly, compounds which are very strongly adsorbed will remain on the adsorbent layer and not be separated either.

QUANTITATIVE ANALYSIS

Almost everyone thinks of thin-layer chromatography as a separation process that is used for qualitative purposes—to see how many components are present in a mixture (in synthesis or natural product work), to determine the presence or absence of a particular substance (crime detection and clinical testing), or to identify compounds (biochemical, medical, and organic research). But thin-layer chromatography can be, and actually is, used for quantitative analysis. Naturally TLC is not so accurate or precise as gravimetric determinations or acid–base titrations, but neither is it so crude as a lot of people think.

A developed thin-layer chromatogram consists of a series of small spots of the same or different colors (see Fig. 11–8). For quantitative analysis, the problem is to find out how much material is present in each of the spots. As was the case in paper chromatography, this can be done in either of two methods—by removing the spot from the plate to analyze it, or by analyzing the spot where it is found on the plate.

To determine the amount of component in each spot while it is still on the plate you must somehow or other relate the size of the spot or the intensity of its color to a weight of the compound. This is the problem. The solution is empirical for there is no inherent theoretical relationship between the amount of material present in the spot and the area of the spot. Thus, solutions of known concentration, must be run simultaneously with the unknown and these known spots compared with the unknown spots. Various comparison techniques are possible. A series of standard solutions of known, but varying, concentrations of the substance to be determined is chromatographed on the same plate with the unknown. Visual comparison among the spots of different concentrations and the unknown gives a surprisingly good concentration estimate of the unknown. This technique is used in paper chromatography, but the judgments are more difficult to make and less precise in thin-layer chromatography because the spots are smaller. That is to say, any comparison of the size and deepness of color of spots is less reproducible.

The relationship between the size (area) of the spot and the amount of material contained in it is disputed. Some researchers claim this relationship is logarithmic, others that it depends on the square root of the area. In many cases both relationships seem to hold, whereas in others only one or the other will apply. In either case, the area of the spot must be measured. A sheet of tracing paper is placed over the developed chromatographic plate and outlines of the spot traced onto the paper. This is not as easy as it sounds for the edges of the spot usually are not distinct, but blurry. Once the spot shape has been traced on the paper, its area can be determined by use of a planimeter, by counting squares (if transparent graph paper is used), or by cutting out the spot, weighing it and comparing its weight with the weight of standard spots. No matter how it is done, some number must be obtained to represent, as accurately as possible, the area of the spot.

Sometimes the relationship between the area and the amount of material is given by the linear equation: $A = m \log w + c$; and sometimes by the relationship; $\sqrt{A} = m \log w + c$, where A is the area of the spot and w is the weight of the material in the spot. There are two constants in the linear equation, m and c, that depend upon the particular thin-layer plate and the way that the spot is detected.

In order to avoid the determination of m and c, Purdy and Truter[14] developed a self-contained method based upon a comparison standard technique. A sample of the unknown, whose concentration is to be determined, is diluted by some factor (d). Equal volumes (in replicate) of the unknown, the diluted unknown, and a standard of known concentration are spotted on the same plate, developed, detected on the plate, the outlines of the spots traced onto transparent paper, and then the area measured. The weights and areas have been found to be related by the equation:

$$\log w = \log w_s + \frac{\sqrt{A} - \sqrt{A_s}}{\sqrt{A_d} - \sqrt{A}} \log \qquad (11\text{--}1)$$

where w is the weight of the material in the spot of the unknown and w_s is the weight of the material in the known or standard. A is the area of the spot of the original unknown, and A_d is the area of the spot of the diluted unknown sample. A_s is the area of the spot of the known. d is the dilution factor of the unknown. Equation (11–1) is derived from the linear relationship given earlier between the square root of the area and the amount of material in the spot, using the standard and the diluted unknown to obtain values for c and m. By diluting the unknown, more accurate results are obtained since the interelement effects in the unknown (if present) will still be present in the dilute unknown, although to a lesser extent. The method is based upon using the same volume of the sample for the original spot each time. In checking the validity of this method, Purdy and Truter measured over 540 spots and found a standard deviation of only $\pm 2.7\%$. The method was applied to the determination of inorganic materials, acids, alcohols, esters, and other substances.

The precision of this method is limited by the reproducibility of spotting and measuring the area of the developed spot. The precision of the spotting is estimated as about 1% relative, whereas a 5% relative precision exists in measuring the area of the spot. Nonetheless, the precision quantitative TLC is given by standard deviations of 3 to 8%. Since this standard deviation applies to many hundreds of different compounds of different types, the accuracy of the method also can be considered to be between 3 and 8%.

The intensity of the fluorescence of the spot as compared to that of the thin layer outside the spot (where there would be no fluorescence) can be related to the amount of material in the spot by using comparison standards of known concentration.

The intensity of light, either absorbed through the thin layer (glass backing) or reflected from the spot, can be related to the concentration of the material in the spot through standards by means of Beer's law.

In Chapter 7 we have seen that the concentration of solute in a chromatographic band emerging from the bottom of a column varies in a Gaussian fashion with volume. The solute concentration in a spot on either a paper or a thin-layer chromatogram also increases in a Gaussian curve from zero at the edges to a

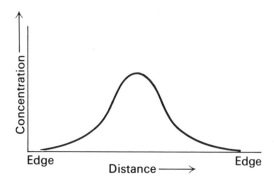

Fig. 11–9.   Concentration profile of a TLC spot.

maximum at the center (see Fig. 11–9). The area under this curve is proportional to the amount of solute in the spot. Therefore, the most accurate quantitative analysis procedure for TLC uses a recording densitometer (plate reader) to obtain the concentration profile of the spot after which the area under the Gaussian curve is measured (planimeter, triangulation, cut and weigh). A standard amount of the substance is chromatographed simultaneously, the concentration profile of this standard spot measured with the recording densitometer, and the area of this peak measured. Comparison of the two areas gives the amount of solute in the unknown spot.

$$W_u = W_s \frac{A_u}{A_s}$$

where W_u is the weight in the unknown spot, and W_s is the weight in the known spot. The area under the densitometer trace for the unknown is A_u, and A_s is the area under the densitometer trace to the known.

Lefar and Lewis[10] review the procedures for, the complications involved in, and the instrumentation available for spectrophotometric quantitative analysis of TLC plates by absorption, reflectance, and fluorescence techniques.

The spot can be removed from the thin-layer plate by a variety of techniques. One common method is to outline the spot with a razor blade and then scrape the adsorbent off the backing into a suitable container, where the constituent causing the spot is dissolved off the adsorbent. Another method elutes the spot by allowing the plate development to continue after the solvent front reaches the end of the plate. A third way consists of sucking the wet spot off and filtering out the adsorbent. The resultant solution of unknown can be analyzed by any technique that is suitable for such exceedingly small amounts of material. Ultraviolet and visible spectrophotometry and polarography have been used successfully to analyze these eluates. When the constituent is inherently radioactive or has been labeled, counting techniques may be applied to determine the concentration of the eluate.

It might seem that more accurate results would be obtained by removing the spot from the plate and analyzing it than by measuring spot areas. This, unfortunately, is not the case. Techniques involving the removal of the spot from the thin-layer chromatographic plate give quantitative results that are less accurate than analyses of the spot on the plate, because of the additional errors introduced during the removal of the spot from the plate—it is almost impossible to remove a spot quantitatively.

Interestingly, the methods of removal of the spot from the TLC plate are much more precise because of the uncertainties in measuring the area of the spot.

Lott and Hurtubise[12] present an excellent review of TLC, stressing the instrumentation needed and available commercially for plate preparation and development, zone removal, and plate scanning.

ADVANTAGES AND LIMITATIONS

The advantages that thin-layer chromatography possesses over other chromatographic methods that make it the most popular separation method at the present time have been mentioned repeatedly throughout this chapter. To recapitulate:

1. *Speed*. Separations can be accomplished routinely in from five to thirty minutes.

2. *Simple Equipment*. Microscope slides, precoated sheets, ordinary bottles, are really the usual equipment. Perhaps a commercially obtained spreader and developing tank, but even these are not complex.

3. *Efficiency*. Within a distance of 10 cm very complex mixtures of solutes can be resolved into separate spots.

4. *Power*. The technique is capable of resolving mixtures of very similar chemicals.

5. *Adaptability*. The method is excellent for preliminary or trial studies for column chromatography.

6. *Versatility*. The basis for the separation can be adsorption (most common), partition, ion exchange, or gel filtration.

7. *Microanalysis*. The normal sample size is in micrograms so that it is an excellent technique for analysis of mixtures when there is only an extremely small amount of the mixture available.

The limitations of the technique are primarily concerned with the lack of reproducibility of the R_f values and, consequently, the lack of reproducibility of certain separations. The technique is limited to microgram amounts of material, so that preparative work is not conveniently carried out by thin-layer methods. The information about adsorbents, solvents, order of elution can be used, however, to develop column chromatographic separations of large quantities of solutes.

APPLICATIONS

TLC has been applied to just about everything that you would imagine and also to an enormous number of things that you wouldn't imagine. It is used for the detection and analysis of mixtures of terpenes, natural oils, balsams, vitamins, chlorophylls, steroids, lipids, alkaloids, metabolites, amines, pharmaceuticals (antihistamines, analgesics, hypnotics, bacteriocides, diuretics, laxatives, oral antidiabetic agents, local anaesthetics, antibiotics, and other drugs), dyes, food additives (antioxidants, preservatives, artificial sweeteners, emulsifiers, and pesticide residues) and colorants, plantstuffs, amino acids, nucleic acids, inorganic salts, detergents, optical brighteners, and on, and on, and on.[17] Clinically it has been used to identify sugars in urine and feces for diagnosis of diabetes and other diseases that affect the elimination of sugars. Plasma, urine, and sera have been analyzed for amino acids, fats, lipids, cholesterol, phospholipids, steroids, and other compounds. It is used in the tests for the proper function of organs to study the rate and nature of the breakdown of metabolites. TLC is used to detect the presence of foreign materials in the blood, urine, or sera, used in the case of poisoning, and in therapy. Back in Chapter 5 we saw how TLC was involved in the methadone treatment program of drug addicts.

In forensic science, silica gel is the most frequently used adsorbent. TLC is used to detect poisons, metal ions, drugs, tranquilizers, and other substances in body fluids. It is used to identify dyes, oils, and insecticides. TLC is capable of identifying explosives in the residues and smoke of the explosion.

As stated earlier, thin-layer chromatography is used routinely by the synthetic organic chemist to see if he has prepared the compound he is attempting to synthesize and whether or not it is in a pure state.

Lincoln, Pohl, and Haworth[11] have used thin-layer chromatography to simplify the conventional qualitative-analysis scheme. The metals are separated into the conventional groups by the solubility of their chlorides, sulfides, and hydroxides. The precipitate of each group is then dissolved in acid and the metal ions separated by thin-layer chromatography on microscope slides, using a variety of solvents. The plates develop in from 35 minutes to 2 hrs, depending upon the solvent system. The metals within each group are identified by their R_f values after the use of detection reagents. K_2CrO_4 was used to detect the elements in Group I, H_2S to detect the elements in Group II, individual spot tests for the Group III and IV elements. The alkali metals were detected by the use of silver-ion and fluorescein as an adsorption indicator.

In an attempt to determine plant pigments in sea water so as to establish the geographic distributions of marine life productivity, Garside and Riley[3] developed a chromatographic method for chlorophylls in sea water. The sample of sea water is filtered and the small particles of organic material on the filter dissolved in

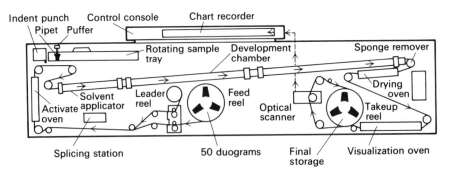

Fig. 11–10.   Schematic diagram of an automated thin-layer chromatograph. (*Redrawn from Ref. 18, by permission of the American Chemical Society.*)

methanol–acetone. This is spotted onto a silica gel TLC plate and developed with light petroleum–ethyl acetate–dimethylformamide (1:1:2). The separated spots are scanned with a recording densitometer and the area under the peaks on the paper trace correlated with the concentration of each substance. They separated chlorophylls a, b, c, carotene, xanthophylls, and other products at the 0.12 to 0.5 μg level and determined the amounts of each with an accuracy of $\pm$ 5%.

Very recently commercial instruments have been introduced at extremely high prices ($55,000) that automate the entire process of thin-layer chromatography—from activation of the plate and spotting of the sample through analyses of the developed spots (see Fig. 11–10).

EXPERIMENT 11–1
Thin-layer Chromatographic Separation of Anthraquinones *

The purpose of this experiment is to show the ability of thin-layer chromatography to separate a mixture of closely related compounds. The anthraquinone dyes were selected because each has a distinctive color, which enables the separated spots to be seen visually. The six anthraquinone derivatives to be separated are shown below.

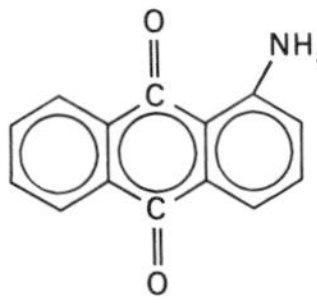

1-aminoanthraquinone 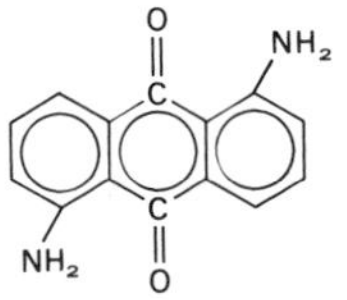   1,5-diaminoanthaquinone 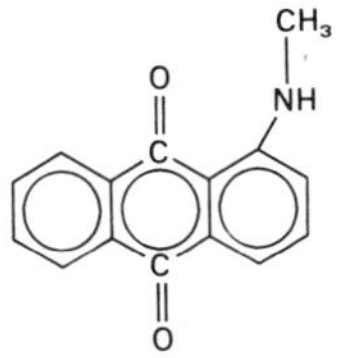   1-methylaminoanthraquinone

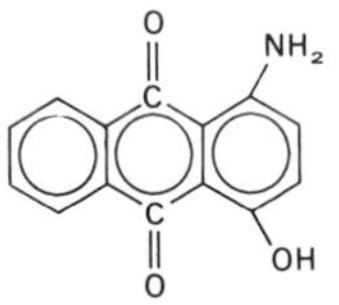

1-amino-4-hydroxyanthraquinone 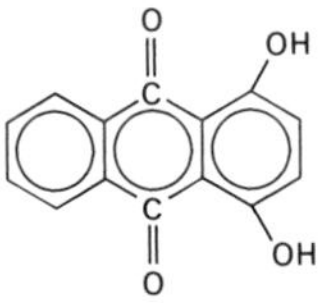   1,4-dihydroxyanthraquinone 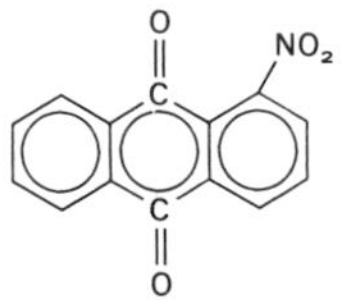   1-nitroanthraquinone

As can be seen, there are only slight differences among the structures of these molecules. There are differences in the dipole moments and adsorption energies of these molecules, so that there are differences in the rate at which the dyes migrate up a thin layer of silica gel.

Solutions.   The following solutions will be used:

a saturated solution of each of the dyes in ethanol

a saturated solution of all of the dyes in ethanol (known mixture)

* Designed and developed by Donald J. Mitchell, Juniata College, Huntingdon, Pa.

solutions of unknowns containing some or all of the dyes in ethanol
the developing solution which is a 1:15 solution of ether in benzene.

Preparation of plates.   Prepare a slurry of 25 g of Silicar 7GF* in 100 ml of
chloroform:carbon tetrachloride:methanol (10:10:1). Mix the slurry thoroughly,
and then dip into it two microscope slides or long glass plates held back to back.
Very slowly remove the plates from the slurry. Separate them and place them, glass
side down on a paper towel to dry.

Alternatively, commercially obtainable sheets (Eastman Chromatogram 6061†)
coated with silica gel (with or without fluorescent indicator) can be used. Three
strips, 4.0 cm wide and 12.0 cm long, are needed. Be very careful in handling these
sheets because the thin layer of silica gel flakes off easily and fingerprints will
affect your results.

Developing chamber.   Any jar at least fourteen cm high and having a neck
opening greater than 5.0 cm is suitable. The jar must be capable of being sealed
tightly. Each student should have his own developing jar.

Cut a piece of strip filter paper, 3 to 5 cm wide and just long enough to extend
from the bottom of the developing chamber to the lid. Crease the paper lengthwise
and stand it in the jar, near the side to serve as a wick to keep the atmosphere in the
jar saturated with solvent. Pour the developing solvent (ether in benzene) in the
bottom of the jar to a depth of 8 mm. Close the chamber and allow it to sit until
the wick is wet completely with the solvent; at least thirty minutes. For successful
and reproducible results, the atmosphere in the jar must be saturated thoroughly
with the solvent vapor.

Spotting of the plates.   Each glass plate or Chromatogram strip is spotted
with three solutions—two spots of standard dyes and one spot of the known or
unknown mixture (see Fig. 11–11). Each spot is placed 1.5 cm from one end of the
plate or sheet and 1.0 cm from both the side of the sheet and its neighboring spots.
Because the thin layer flakes off, it is impossible to mark the location of these spots
on the plates. Use a pattern drawn on a piece of paper to guide you to the correct
position for each spot. Be sure to record in your notebook, which spots are where,
on which plate. Spot the solutions with a capillary pipette (either a lambda pipette

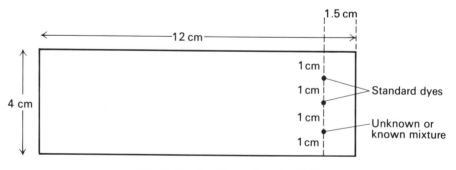

Fig. 11–11.   Spotting pattern for TLC.

* Available from Malinckrodt Chemical Company.
† Available from Eastman Kodak Company, Rochester, New York, 14650.

or one made by drawing out an open-ended capillary melting point tube). In order to avoid poking a hole in the coating while applying the samples, the tip of the capillary should not touch the surface of the layer, just the drop of liquid should touch it. The diameter of the spot should not exceed 3 mm. To obtain sufficient material, more than one drop is needed at each spot. For the seven known solutions three drops, one on top of the other are adequate. Allow each drop to dry before applying the next drop. For the unknown, use 4 to 5 spots, one on top of the other, allowing each drop to dry before applying the successive drop. Rinse the capillary pipette in the solvent and dry it before reusing it in a different solution.

Development of the chromatogram. Using forceps, place the strips in the developing chamber, spots at the bottom. Be careful not to let the thin layer touch the wick or the sides of the jar. The plates should slant backward, leaning against the jar, but they should not lean to the side, for the solvent will move vertically up from the bottom of the chamber. The spots should be above the surface of the developing solvent at the bottom of the chamber. Depending upon the size of the jar, two or more strips can be placed in it at any one time, touching only at the bottom, below the surface of the developing solvent.

Insert the plates rapidly and recap the jar quickly so the saturation in the chamber is not lost. Allow the plates to develop until the solvent front has reached the upper edge of the plate (~ 10 minutes). Remove the developed plates from the chamber. Observe the spots on the known and unknown mixtures, for the colors of the spots are clearest when the strip is still wet with the solvent. Allow the plates to dry. (*Note*: Commercial dyes are notorious for being impure, which means that some of the standard "pure" dyes will produce more than a single spot.)

Identification of the unknown. Most of these dyes are visible under ordinary light. Several of them fluoresce, so that it is advantageous, and occasionally necessary, to observe them under ultraviolet light. The short wavelength, 2537 Å causes 1-amino-4-hydroxyanthraquinone to fluoresce blue, 1,4-dihydroxy-anthraquinone to fluoresce lime green, and 1-nitroanthraquinone to fluoresce pale blue.

Measure the distance from the point of application of each spot to the top of the chromatographic plate. Measure the distance from the point of application of each spot to the center of each spot. From these two distances calculate the R_f value for each spot in the knowns and in the two aliquots of the unknown. Record the R_f value and the color observed for each known anthraquinone dye. From their R_f values and colors, identify each of the dyes in the known mixture of the dyes. Similarly, from the R_f values and colors, identify each of the anthraquinone dyes present in your unknown sample and report them to the instructor.

EXPERIMENT 11–2
Separation of *cis* and *trans*-Dichlorobisethylenediaminecobalt(III) Chloride *

The purpose of this experiment is to illustrate the power of thin-layer chroma-

---

* Based on material presented by H. Seiler, C. Biebricher, and H. Erlenmeyer, *Helv. Chim. Acta*, **46**, 2636 (1963).

tography by separating a mixture of the *cis-* and *trans*-isomers of the inorganic complex ion dichlorobisethylenediaminecobalt(III). The structures of these complexes are shown below.

cis isomer   *trans* isomer

As can be seen from these structures, even though the chemical formulas of the two isomers are identical, the dipole moments of the two compounds and hence their polarities are quite different. The *trans* isomer will not have a dipole moment, whereas the *cis* isomer will. Thus, the *cis* isomer should be adsorbed onto the surface of the silica gel in a thin layer, whereas the *trans* isomer probably will be adsorbed less strongly. Hence, the R_f value of the *trans* isomer will be greater than that of the *cis* isomer, a deduction which is verified in this experiment.

Solutions. You will use 1% methanolic solutions of each of the two isomers as well as one of a mixture containing the two isomers. These solutions are prepared by dissolving 10 mg of each isomer in a drop of water and then diluting to 1.0 ml with methanol. Since the solutions are unstable, they should be prepared by each student just before he uses them to spot his plates.

The developing solution consists of 90 ml methanol, 10 ml 0.5 M sodium acetate in methanol, 0.1 ml of 1 M acetic acid in methanol, and 1 ml of water. Since this solution is unstable, it should be prepared fresh daily.

2 M aqueous ammonia

0.1% rubeanic acid [dithiooxamide–$(C\text{-}S\text{-}NH_2)_2$] in ethanol

Preparation of plates. Commercial silica gel sheets (Chromatogram Sheet 6060 or 6061*) can be used satisfactorily. One strip 4.0 cm wide and 12.0 cm long is sufficient for this experiment. Be careful in handling these sheets because the thin layer of silica gel flakes off easily and fingerprints will affect the results. Dry the strips in the oven at 110°C for one hour before using and then store in the desiccator until cooled and ready to be used.

Developing chamber. Any jar is suitable which is at least fourteen centimeters high and has a neck opening of at least 5.0 cm that can be sealed tightly. Each student should have his own developing jar.

Cut a piece of filter paper 3 to 5 cm wide and just long enough to extend from the bottom of the developing chamber to under the lid. Crease the paper lengthwise and stand it in the jar near the side, to serve as a wick to keep the atmosphere in the jar saturated with the solvent. Place the developing solvent (methanolic pH 6 acetate buffer) in the bottom of the jar to a depth of 8 mm. Close the chamber and allow it to sit until the wick is wet completely with the solvent, at least thirty minutes. For successful and reproducible results, the atmosphere in the jar must be saturated with the solvent vapor.

---

* Eastman Kodak Company, Rochester, New York, 14650.

Spotting of the sheets. Prepare the methanolic solution of the *cis* isomer, the *trans* isomer, and the mixture of the two. Draw a capillary pipette from an open-ended capillary melting point tube or use a lambda pipette to spot the sheet. Each spot is placed 1.5 cm from one end of the plate and 1.0 cm from both the side of the sheet and its neighbors (see Fig. 11–11). Because the thin layer will be damaged, these distances cannot be marked on the plate, but must be estimated from a pattern drawn on a piece of paper. In order to avoid poking a hole in the thin coating, the tip of the capillary pipette must never come in contact with the surface of the layer. The drop is allowed to form at the tip and then touched to the desired place on the plate. Experience and a steady hand are essential for successful spotting. The diameter of each spot should not exceed 3 mm. Spot just once with each of the solutions. Rinse the capillary pipette in methanol and dry it before reusing it in each different solution.

Development of the chromatogram. Using forceps, place the dried plate in the developing chamber, spots at the bottom. Be careful not to let the thin layer touch the wick or the sides of the jar. The plate should lean backward against the wall of the jar, not sideways, as the solvent will ascend perpendicularly from the bottom of the jar. The spots should be above the surface of the developing solvent at the bottom of the chamber.

Insert the plates quickly, and recap the chamber rapidly so that the solvent saturation is not destroyed. Develop the chromatogram until the solvent front reaches the upper edge of the chromatographic sheet. Remove the developed chromatogram from the jar and allow the chromatogram to dry.

Detection of the spots. *Caution*: All-glass or plastic sprayers must be used as rubeanic acid is a very sensitive spot test for metal ions, especially copper and zinc. Windex sprayers fit on conveniently sized reagent bottles and have given excellent service.

Spray the dried chromatographic strip with 2 M aqueous ammonia. After allowing the ammonia to dry, spray the plate with 0.1% rubeanic acid in ethanol. Blue-green spots should be produced by each of the isomers.

Identification of the unknowns. Measure the distance that the solvent has traveled from the application of the sample to the upper edge of the chromatogram. Measure the distance that each spot has moved from its point of application. Calculate the R_f values from these data for each of the two isomers and the spots in the unknown. Since the *cis* isomer is more labile than the *trans*, isomerization causes some of the *trans* isomers to always show up on the *cis* chromatogram. Note the extent of the separation in the mixture of the two isomers.

EXPERIMENT 11–3
Separation of the Components of a Commercial Pharmaceutical Preparation *

Several commercial cold and headache remedies are a mixture of caffeine,

---

* Based upon material presented by H. Ganshirt and A. Malzacher, *Archiv. Pharm.*, 293/65, 925 (1960) and by E. Stahl, *Thin-Layer Chromatography*, 2nd ed, Springer–Verlag, New York, 1969, p. 556. V. T. Lieu, *J. Chem. Educ.*, **48,** 478 (1971) describes essentially the same experiment.

salicylamide, acetyl salicylic acid, and phenacetin. To check for purity and against adulteration of these remedies it is necessary to establish methods for the analysis of these preparations. One very successful method for determining the components in these cold and headache remedies has been by means of thin-layer chromatography. The purpose of this experiment is to separate and identify the components in such mixtures and to obtain a rough estimate of the amount of each one present.

caffeine
$R_f \sim 0.20$

salicylamide
$R_f \sim 0.49$

acetyl salicylic acid
$R_f \sim 0.59$

phenacetin
$R_f \sim 0.39$

The structures and polarities of these molecules differ sufficiently to produce R_f values that are satisfactorily different to enable a thin-layer chromatographic separation.

Solutions.   Prepare 1% (w/v) solutions of each of the four possible components by dissolving 50 mg in 5 ml of methanol.

The developing solvent is a mixture of methanol:acetic acid:diethyl ether: benzene (1:18:60:120). This should be prepared fresh daily.

Prepare the ferric chloride–potassium ferricyanide reagent by dissolving 0.5 g of $K_3Fe(CN)_6$ and 2.0 g of $FeCl_3$ in 100 ml of deionized water. This solution should be prepared fresh daily.

10% aqueous chloramine T

Preparation of plates.   Cut two strips of Chromatogram 6060* silica gel sheets without fluorescent indicator 4.0 × 12.0 cm as described in the preceding experiment. They need not be activated by drying in the oven.

Developing chamber.   As described in the preceding experiment. This should be filled to a depth of 8 mm with the methanol–acetic acid–ether–benzene solvent at least a half-hour before it is to be used.

Preparation of sample.   In a test tube powder two tablets of the commercial product with a glass rod. Add 5 ml of methanol to the powder and stir for five minutes to extract all of the soluble ingredients from the powder. Filter the solution through a piece of filter paper in a small funnel, into another small test tube. The clear filtrate is the sample solution.

Spotting the sheets.   Using a lambda pipette or drawn-out melting point capillary place 1 μl of each of the four known solutions (two on each sheet of Chromatogram 6060*) on the thin-layer silica gel sheets. Place 1 μl of the unknown solution on each of the plates. The spots should be placed 1.5 cm from one end of the sheet, 1.0 cm from the edge of the sheet and 1.0 cm from each other (see Fig. 11–11). Follow the precautions stated in the two previous experiments when

---

* Eastman Kodak Company, Rochester, New York, 14650.

spotting the chromatographic sheets. Be sure to rinse the spotting pipette in methanol and dry it before reusing it in each different solution.

Development of the chromatogram. Using forceps, place the two strips in the developing chamber with the spots at the bottom. The two sheets should lean backward against the wall of the jar, not sideways. The bottoms of two sheets may touch in the solvent. The spots should be above the surface of the developing solvent at the bottom of the chamber.

Using forceps, insert the plates adroitly and quickly. Close the developing chamber as soon as feasible so that the solvent saturation of the atmosphere inside is preserved. Develop the chromatogram until the solvent front teaches the upper edge of the chromatographic sheet. Remove the developed chromatogram from the jar. Allow the chromatogram to dry.

Detection of the spots. Salicylamide, acetyl salicylic acid, and phenacetin can be detected by their fluorescence under ultraviolet radiation at 254 nm. Phenacetin produces a large, uneven, dark blue-purple spot, salicylamide fluoresces with a bright, brilliant blue spot, acetyl salicylic acid gives a purplish brown spot, while caffeine leaves a dark spot on the fluorescent background.

Spray the developed chromatogram with the ferric chloride–ferricyanide reagent if there is any uncertainty after observing the chromatogram under UV light. The acetyl salicylic acid will appear as a brown spot while the phenacetin will produce a blue spot.

To detect caffeine, spray the developed chromatogram with the 10% aqueous chloramine T solution and then with 1 N HCl. Heat the sheet in the oven at 96 to 98°C until the chlorine odor has vanished. Then place the plate in ammonia vapor. Warm the exposed plate slightly. When caffeine is present, a pink-red spot will appear.

Identification of the components. For each of the standards and the two unknowns measure the distance that the solvent traveled from the application of the sample to the upper edge of the chromatogram. Measure the distance that each spot has moved from its point of application. From these data calculate the R_f values for each of the four knowns and for each of the components found in the two unknown aliquots. From the R_f values and the colors produced during the UV irradiation and spot tests, identify the components present in the unknown commercial preparation. From the known concentration of each of the four standards, estimate the concentration of each of the components present.

(It is quite probable that some salicylic acid will be produced by hydrolysis during the preparation and development of the chromatogram. This will appear as a faint spot with a R_f of around 0.85.)

PROBLEMS

1. What feature distinguishes thin-layer chromatography from other forms of chromatography?

2. Powdered adsorbents have more stringent requirements for TLC than for column adsorption chromatography. What are these requirements with regard to particle size?

3. What types of distribution processes can be used in thin-layer form to separate mixtures of solutes?

4. Which of the adsorbents used in thin-layer chromatography would you try first in attempting each of the separations listed below?
    (a) methylamine, ethylamine, n-propylamine, i-amylamine
    (b) resorcinol, phenol, 1,3,5-trihydroxybenzene
    (c) a mixture of naturally occurring lipids
    (d) a mixture of polynuclear aromatic hydrocarbons, such as biphenyl, o-triphenyl, and m-triphenyl

5. What solvent system would you try first for each of the thin-layer separations listed below?
    (a) ammonium salts of carboxylic acids ($R\text{-}COO^-NH_4^+$) on silica gel
    (b) long-chain alcohols [$CH_3(CH_2)_n\text{—}CH_2OH$] on silica gel
    (c) derivatives of barbituric acid

$$\left(\begin{array}{c} HN\text{—}C\text{=}O \\ | \quad | \\ O\text{=}C \quad CH_2 \\ | \quad | \\ HN\text{—}C\text{=}O \end{array} \right) \quad \text{on silica gel}$$

    (d) amino acids ($R\text{—}CH\text{—}COOH$) on alumina
                            |
                            NH_2
    (e) fatty acids ($R\text{—}COOH$, where R is an even number of carbons either 16 or 18, straight chain, and perhaps unsaturated) on kieselguhr

6. What disadvantages do mixed solvent systems possess when used as eluting agents in thin-layer chromatography? What advantages do they possess that cause them to be so widely used?

7. Why should the developing chamber be saturated with the vapor of the eluent, especially when using mixed solvents, before putting the thin-layer plate in it?

8. Explain how the adsorbent properties can alter the observed R_f value for a particular solute.

9. What influence does each of the factors given below have on the measured R_f value of a solute?
    (a) the thickness of the thin-layer on the plate
    (b) the purity of the eluent
    (c) the concentration of the solute in the drop used to spot the plate
    (d) the temperature of development of the plate

10. The R_f values for the thin-layer chromatography of amino acids on silica gel G using n-butanol–acetic acid–water as the developing solvent are: aspartic acid, 0.17; glycine, 0.18; alanine, 0.22; glutamic acid, 0.24; valine, 0.32; phenylalanine, 0.43; leucine, 0.44; and tryptophan, 0.47.
    (a) In terms of the structure of these compounds, explain the magnitude and sequence of these amino acid R_f values.
    (b) Using these experimental conditions, which amino acids can be separated cleanly from which others? Which amino acids cannot be separated?

11. Describe the techniques used to detect colorless spots on thin-layer chromatographic plates.

12. What two properties of a solute spot determine whether it can be resolved from its closest neighbor? What is the optimum difference in R_f values for two adjacent spots for resolution of them? What is the minimum difference between two R_f values for two adjacent spots in order to be able to resolve them?

13. Why are better (cleaner) separations of the same compounds obtained with thin layers of cellulose on glass plates than by means of paper chromatography?

14. Standard experimental operating conditions for thin-layer chromatography have been proposed [E. Stahl, *J. Chromatogr.*, **33**, 273 (1968)]. Why?

15. Which method for performing a quantitative analysis on the separated solutes on a thin-layer chromatographic plate is the more reproducible? Which is the more accurate?

16. A thin-layer chromatographic sheet is spotted with two microliter aliquots of a standard 0.150 *M* copper solution, an unknown copper solution, and the unknown copper solution diluted to one-half its initial concentration. After development and visualization the area of each of these three spots was measured. The standard copper spot had an area of 28.3 mm², the unknown copper spot had an area of 22.6 mm², and the diluted unknown copper spot had an area of 14.9 mm². Calculate the concentration of the copper in the original unknown solution.

REFERENCES

1. Dallas, M. S. J., *J. Chromatogr.*, **33**, 193 (1968).
2. De Zeeuw, R. A., *J. Chromatogr.*, **32**, 43 (1968); **33**, 222, 227 (1968).
3. Garside, C. and Riley, J. P., *Anal. Chim. Acta*, **46**, 179 (1969).
4. Geiss, F., *J. Chromatogr.*, **33**, 9 (1968).
5. Geiss, F. and Schlett, H., *J. Chromatogr.*, **33**, 208 (1968).
6. Izmailov, N. A. and Shraiber, M. S., *Farmatsiya*, **3**, 1 (1938).
7. James, A. T. and Martin, A. J. P., *Biochem. J.*, **50**, 679 (1952).
8. Janchen, D., *J. Chromatogr.*, **33**, 195 (1968).
9. Kirchner, J. K., Miller, J. M. and Keller, C. J., *Anal. Chem.*, **23**, 420 (1951).
10. Lefar, M. S. and Lewis, A. D., *Anal. Chem.*, **42** (3), 79A (1970).
11. Lincoln, S., S.H.C.J., Pohl, R. A. and Haworth, D. T., *J. Chem. Educ.*, **47**, 401, (1970).
12. Lott, P. F. and Hurtubise, R. J., *J. Chem. Educ.*, **48**, A437, A481 (1971).
13. Peifer, J. J., *Mikrochim. Acta*, **1962**, 529.
14. Purdy, S. J. and Truter, E. V., *Analyst*, **87**, 802 (1962).
15. Stahl, E., *Pharmazie*, **11**, 633 (1956).
16. Stahl, E., *Chemiker Ztg.*, **82**, 323 (1958).
17. Stahl, E., *Thin-Layer Chromatography*, Academic Press, New York, 1965, p. 4.
18. *Chem. & Eng. News*, **50** (12), 42 (1972).

CHAPTER 12

ION-EXCHANGE
CHROMATOGRAPHY

These days, when deionized water competes with distilled water in the laboratory, and water softeners are in many homes, ion exchange is probably the separation principle most frequently encountered by the student. In this technique the ions in a solution are replaced by or exchanged for different ions of the same charge. Ions of the opposite charge, usually are unaffected by ion exchange. Ion exchange is used to remove interfering ions to collect desired ions, to concentrate ionic solutions, and to separate mixtures of ionic substances. The ion-exchange process involves an ionic, insoluble polymer. One ion of the polymer is a complicated interwoven mesh—silicates, aluminates, borates, or organic polymers—that cannot dissolve in aqueous solutions. Counterbalancing the charge on these enormous networks are small ions, which diffuse readily within the network, and can be exchanged for other ions in a surrounding solution. Ion exchange is a reversible equilibrium reaction.

cation exchange:

$$R^-H^+ + Na^+ \rightleftharpoons R^-Na^+ + H^+$$

anion exchange:

$$\underset{\substack{\text{ion} \\ \text{exchanger}}}{R^+Cl^-} + \underset{\text{solution}}{NO_3^-} \rightleftharpoons \underset{\substack{\text{ion} \\ \text{exchanger}}}{R^+NO_3^-} + \underset{\text{solution}}{Cl^-}$$

where R represents the polymeric ion.

There are three modes of using ion exchange—ion removal, ion replacement, and ion-exchange chromatography. For ion removal, the ion exchanger contains both exchangeable protons and exchangeable hydroxide ions. The salt solution is percolated through a long column of the exchanger where all metal ions (or organic cations) are exchanged for protons, and all anions are exchanged for hydroxide ions. Electroneutrality is strictly obeyed at all places and all times in both the column and the solution.

448

$$R^-H^+ \ + M^+ \ \rightleftharpoons R^-M^+ + H^+$$

$$R^+OH^- + X^- \ \rightleftharpoons R^+X^- + OH^-$$

$$H^+ + OH^- \rightleftharpoons H_2O$$

These equations show that by passing aqueous solutions through ion exchangers, all ionic substances are removed from the solution and replaced by water molecules. Only ionic substances are removed. Thus the deionized water available in laboratories still contains bacteria, organic molecules, and dissolved gases (for example, CO_2, N_2, and NH_3).

Water softening does not change the ionic content of the solutions, it merely replaces one cation with an equivalent amount of another. Calcium, magnesium, and iron are the cations in ground water which when present as their carbonates or bicarbonates cause hardness. To *soften* water is to replace these cations with sodium ion by means of a synthetic inorganic or organic ion exchanger.

$$2R^-Na^+ + Ca^{2+} + 2HCO_3^- \rightleftharpoons (R^-)_2Ca^{2+} + 2Na^+ + 2HCO_3^-$$

This technique of ion replacement can be used whenever the ions in solution will interfere with a desired reaction; they are replaced by ions that do not interfere. We have used ion replacement in Chapter 5 to determine the capacity of an ion-exchange resin by replacing all of the hydrogen ions on a resin with sodium ions.

Ion-exchange chromatography takes advantage of differences in the equilibrium position of the ion-exchange reaction involving different ions to resolve ionic mixtures into solutions containing only a single ionic species.

There is a technical jargon used in discussing ion exchange that should be defined clearly to avoid confusion or misunderstanding when it is encountered or used. The following terms are frequently used.

An *ion exchanger* is an insoluble inorganic or organic polymer that is capable of replacing reversibly its ions with ions of the same charge in a solution.

The *fixed ions* of an ion exchanger are those ions that are incorporated into the insoluble skeleton of the polymer.

The *counter ions* of an ion exchanger are the ions of the polymer which are exchanged for similarly charged ions in a solution. They are opposite in electrical charge to the fixed ions.

A *cation-exchange resin* is an ion exchanger whose anions are fixed and whose cations are the counter ions.

An *anion-exchange resin* is an ion exchanger having fixed cations and exchangeable anions.

The *capacity* of an ion exchanger is the number of ions per unit quantity of exchanger that are capable of being exchanged. The capacity of an ion exchanger is usually expressed in milliequivalents per gram of dry resin and in milliequivalents per milliliter of wet resin.

The *selectivity* of an ion exchanger measures the equilibrium position of the exchange reaction among different ions. The ion exchanger is selective toward those ions whose equilibrium favors inclusion in the exchanger. Selectivity is really an ordering of exchange equilibrium constants.

ION EXCHANGERS

Ion exchangers which are inorganic polymers have been known for a much longer time than ion exchangers which are organic polymers. Inorganic polymers have low capacities, are relatively unstable, and are soluble in either acid or alkaline solutions (or in both). The naturally occurring aluminosilicates, such as the *zeolites* $(Ca,Na)(Si_4Al_2O_{12}) \cdot 6H_2O$, were used in the early days of ion exchange, but their unfavorable properties led to the manufacture of synthetic zeolites with more homogeneous structures and regulated pore sizes. These are now called *molecular sieves*. Zirconium phosphate precipitates as a polymer containing water molecules; this is capable of exchanging cations for the hydrogen ions in the structure.

In 1935, Adams and Holmes[1] showed that resins synthesized from catechol and formaldehyde were capable of removing iron from ferric chloride and cations from Thames River water, whereas resins synthesized from aniline and formaldehyde removed the anions from sulfuric, nitric, hydrochloric, and acetic acids. From their paper on the synthesis of ion exchangers the water-softening industry, deionized water, and ion-exchange chromatography are logical consequences.

Although ion exchange resins made from formaldehyde and either aromatic alcohols or amines are still available commercially, the most commonly used and best resins are synthesized from styrene and divinyl benzene.

Twisted chains of carbon atoms have benzene rings attached. Some benzene rings are connected to two chains of carbon atoms, cross-linking them together. The extent of this cross-linking is governed by the amount of divinyl benzene present in the initial polymerization mixture. Common ion-exchange resins have 2, 4, 6, 8, 10, 12, 14, or 16% divinyl benzene and hence are available as X2, X4, X6, X8, X10, X12, X14, or X16. X stands for "percent cross-linking" but really is only the percentage of divinyl benzene used initially in the synthesis. The polymer occurs as a bead. Since this polymer is nonionic it can only provide the skeleton or network for the attachment of fixed ionic groups. The identity of these fixed ions determines the ion-exchange properties of the resin.

Strong cation exchangers are prepared by treating the polymer beads with chlorosulfonic acid so as to introduce one sulfonic acid group in the para position of the nonbridging benzene rings, giving:

$$-CH-CH_2-CH-CH_2-CH-CH_2-CH-CH_2-$$

$$SO_3^-H^+ \qquad SO_3^-H^+$$

$$-CH-CH_2-CH-CH_2-CH-CH_2-CH-CH_2-$$

These sulfonic acid cation-exchange resins are available as beads having diameters between $20\,\mu$ and 2.0 mm. Those usually used are 100–200 mesh. Cation-exchange resins are available in a W grade which stands for white but means they are cream colored, rather than their usual tan or light brown. Their capacity of approximately 5.50 mequiv/g for the dry resin decreases very slightly with increasing cross-linking. The resin beads are insoluble in water, but will very slowly react with it when heated above 100°C. The dry beads are stable to 200°C. They are attacked by strong oxidizing agents. The most commonly encountered sulfonic acid cation resins are Dowex 50, Amberlite IR-120, and Purmutit Q. Most cation-exchange applications use the strong acid, sulfonate resins. Fig. 12–1 shows a typical strong cation-exchange resin.

If, instead of styrene, methyl acrylate ($CH_2 = \overset{\displaystyle CH_3}{\underset{\displaystyle |}{C}}-COO-CH_3$) is copolymerized with divinyl benzene, after hydrolysis, the polymer contains carboxyl groups as the fixed exchange sites.

$$-\overset{CH_3}{\underset{COOH}{C}}-CH_2-CH-CH_2-\overset{CH_3}{\underset{COOH}{CH}}-CH_2-CH-$$

$$-CH-CH_2- \qquad -CH-CH_2-$$

One advantage of using a weak cation exchange resins is that the carboxyl group does not ionize at low pH values. Permutit H70 is a weak cation exchanger, for example.

Resins which will exchange anions are prepared by treating the styrene-divinylbenzene polymer with chloromethyl ether, followed by treatment with trimethylamine. This produces a resin with a quarternary amino group on each of the benzene rings.

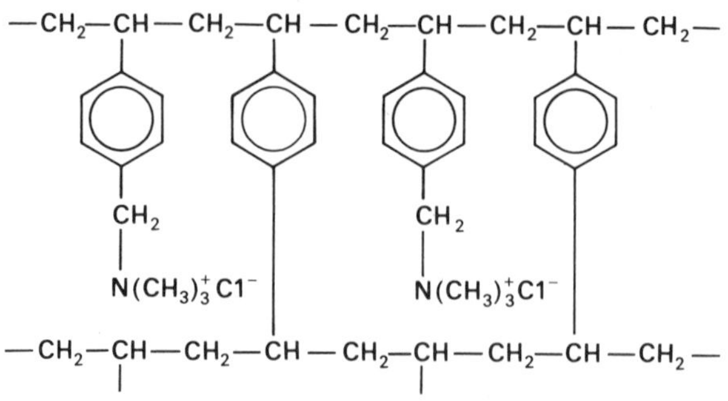

$$-CH_2-CH-CH_2-CH-CH_2-CH-CH_2-CH-CH_2-$$

$$CH_2 \qquad\qquad CH_2$$
$$N(CH_3)_3^+ Cl^- \qquad N(CH_3)_3^+ Cl^-$$

$$-CH_2-CH-CH_2-CH-CH_2-CH-CH_2-CH-CH_2-$$

Since a quarternary amine is a strong base, it readily exchanges the chloride ions for any other anions in solution. The capacity of these strong anion-exchange resins is about 4.32 mequiv/g of dry resin. Commonly encountered quarternary amine resins are Dowex-1, Amberlite IRA-400, and Permutit S1. Fig. 12–1 shows a typical strong anion-exchange resin.

Weak anion-exchange resins can be synthesized but they are usually less resistant to chemical attack and not widely used.

Although ion-exchange resins that contain both strong acid and strong base fixed exchange groups have been synthesized, they have not been either widely investigated or used. The bed of commercial water deionizers consists of a mixture of beads of cation-exchange resin and beads of anion-exchange resin, rather than a single resin containing both groups.

One extremely interesting specialized resin that has been developed and widely used in recent years, is the *chelating resin*. The styrene-divinylbenzene polymer is treated with chloromethyl ether as in the preparation of strong anion exchangers. The product is then treated with ammonia and chloroacetic acid, which produces the imidodiacetic acid group attached to the benzene ring. Each benzene ring does not acquire a chelating group. The number of groups present varies from batch to batch, so that the capacity of the resin varies from batch to batch, but averages around 3.6 mequiv/g dry resin.

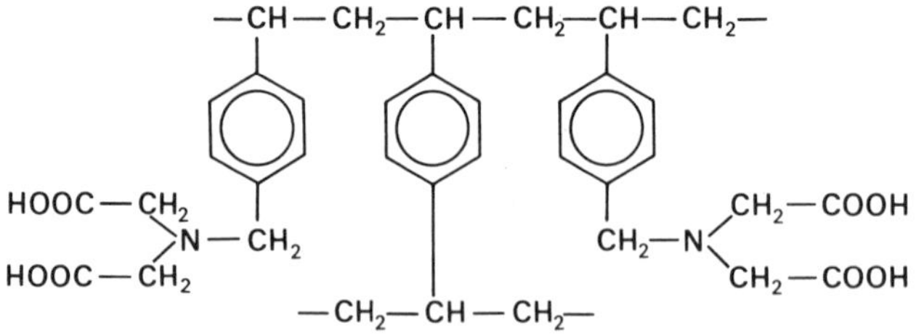

$$-CH-CH_2-CH-CH_2-CH-CH_2-$$

$$HOOC-CH_2 \qquad\qquad CH_2-COOH$$
$$\!\!>\!N-CH_2 \qquad CH_2-N\!\!<$$
$$HOOC-CH_2 \qquad\qquad CH_2-COOH$$

$$-CH_2-CH-CH_2-$$

As is obvious from the structure above, a chelating resin has one-half of an EDTA molecule attached to the ion-exchange resin. Therefore, the ion exchange behavior of chelating resins is analogous to the behavior of EDTA, both in terms of selectivity and pH effects. The pK_{a_1} of the resin is between 2.8 and 3, whereas the pK_{a_2} of the resin is between 8 and 8.6. The only commercially available chelating resin is Dowex A-1.

The capacities mentioned above for particular ion exchangers are for the com-

Fig. 12–1. Piles of Dowex 50 and Dowex 1. (*Photograph by Stephen Daugherty.*)

pletely dried resin. It is extremely difficult, however, to remove all traces of water from ion-exchange resins, so an air-dried capacity usually is determined. The air-dried capacity represents the number of exchange sites in the resin which are in equilibrium with moist laboratory air. This capacity is what was determined in Chapter 5. An air-dried resin contains about thirty percent water, which produces air-dried capacities of about 3.7 mequiv/g for the sulfonate cation-exchange resin, 3.0 mequiv/g for the quarternary ammonium anion-exchange resin, and 2.5 mequiv/g for the iminodiacetate chelating resin. Because the content of water in the air-dried resins is uncertain and variable, these capacities are only accurate to about 1 percent.

An ion exchange resin immersed in water or another solvent takes up solvent-swelling considerably. The resultant, wet resin beads have capacities from one-quarter to one-half that of the completely dry resin. The wet capacity is very dependent upon the cross-linking, which is not true for dry resins. The molality of the fixed ion-exchange groups inside the wet resin is between 5.9 and 9.3 m, depending upon the percent cross-linking of the resin. Thus behavior inside the resin beads is that of concentrated ionic solutions.

The ion-exchange resin beads in a column full of resin do not occupy all of the space, but only about 58% of it. The 42% of the volume of the column free of solid particles is occupied by the mobile liquid phase. The capacity of a packed ion-exchange column, very important in practice, is called the *bed capacity*. The bed capacity limits the amount of sample that can be chromatographed.

Dry ion-exchange resins should never be packed into a column and then wetted by water or the solvent. As the beads absorb solvent molecules they expand physically, creating enormous pressures on the column walls, which will break them. This uptake of solvent is known as *swelling* and it is dependent upon a myriad of properties of both the ion-exchange resin and the counter ions present. The fixed ionic groups within the resin hydrate in an attempt to dissolve in the solvent.

Because of the hydrocarbon skeleton and the cross-linking, they cannot dissolve. But the network stretches to accommodate the water molecules. This swelling continues until the strain on the cross-linked skeleton is sufficiently great to halt the uptake of water molecules by opposing any further stretching.

Although the primary cause of swelling is the hydration of the fixed ions, electrostatic repulsions between the fixed ions also causes expansion of the resin in a solvent. Hydration numbers of the fixed ions in an ion-exchange resin are always higher than the hydration numbers in a regular aqueous solution, so there are some solvent molecules in the resin that are not associated with fixed ions. This "free" solvent enters the ion-exchange resin bead because of osmotic pressure differences; the system attempts to dilute the highly concentrated solution within the particles.

Fig. 12–2 shows the effect of the molarity of acid and of the identity of the acid on the swelling of the ion-exchange resins. As the concentrations of electrolyte outside the particles increases, the osmotic pressure difference between the inside and the outside of the resin decreases, so the solvent uptake is less. Thus the volume of the resin decreases with increasing electrolyte concentration in the exterior solution.

Ion-Exchange Equilibria

The exchange of ions between a resin and its surrounding solution is a reversible equilibrium process, which permits the law of mass action to be applied to the exchange. If we consider that the exchange reaction is:

$$m(R^-)_n A^{n+} + nB^{m+} \rightleftharpoons n(R^-)_m B^{m+} + m\, A^{n+} \qquad (12\text{–}1)$$

we can write the thermodynamic equilibrium constant for the ion-exchange reaction as

$$K = \frac{a_{R_m B}^n \cdot a_A^m}{a_{R_n A}^m\ a_B^n} \qquad (12\text{–}2)$$

where $(R^-)_n A^{n+}$ represents the ion A^{n+} in the resin phase, and $(R^-)_m B^{m+}$ represents the ion B^{m+} in the resin phase. If we assume that there are no changes in the swelling of the resin as the ions are exchanged, the equilibrium constant of Equation (12–2) is comparable to the thermodynamic equilibrium constants that were discussed in Chapter 5. They are truly constant, varying only with temperature.

All of the uncertainties about activities and activity coefficients that were discussed in Chapter 5 are encountered in ion exchange. Ion-exchange reactions tend to be carried out in concentrated solutions which causes the activities of the ions in the aqueous phase to vary considerably from their molar concentrations. The crucial problem, and one that remains unsolved, involves the activities of the ions in the resin. The standard state, against which activities in a resin must be compared, has not been established. The measurement of activities in the resin is not possible. The result of this is, that while thermodynamic equilibrium constants for ion exchange reactions can be determined from energy measurements, the constants cannot be used for equilibrium calculations. Many different ways have been invented to circumvent this problem and to obtain a number which will indicate the equilibrium position of an ion-exchange reaction or at least give a quantitative

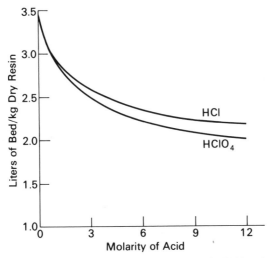

Fig. 12–2. Bed volume of Dowex 50-X4 in HCl and HClO₄ solutions. (*Redrawn from Ref. 16, by permission of Nelson, Murase, and Kraus.*)

estimate of the preference of the ion-exchange resin for one ion over another. Let us briefly define each of these, so that it will be familiar.

The simplest of these terms is the *separation factor*, α, which is defined in the following manner:

$$\alpha_A^B = \frac{[(R^-)_m B^{m+}][A^{n+}]}{[(R^-)_n A^{n+}][B^{m+}]} \tag{12-3}$$

where $[(R^-)_m B^{m+}]$ and $[(R^-)_n l^{n+}]$ are the molar concentrations of the ions, B^{m+} and A^{n+} in the resin. Because the expression for the separation factor is written without exponents, the numerical value of it is independent of the concentration units used, so molalities and mole fractions will work just as well.

It is very easy to determine the numerical value of the separation factor. Take a measured amount of ion-exchange resin of known capacity in the A form. Equilibrate this with a solution containing a known amount of B. When equilibrium has been attained, determine the molar concentration of both A and B in the solution. From the original amount of B and the capacity of the resin, it is simple to determine the molar concentration of A and B in the resin. Then, using all four concentrations, α can be calculated. From Equation (12–3) it is apparent that a value of α_A^B greater than one means that the resin will prefer B^{m+} over A^{n+}, that is, Equation (12–1) goes to the right. Conversely, a numerical value of α_A^B less than one means that the resin prefers A^{n+} over B^{m+}, that is, Equation (12–1) goes to the left. It should be apparent, also, from the form of Equation (12–3) that the separation factor is not a true constant at all, but varies according to the total ionic concentration of the solution, the fraction of A that is in the solution, as well as the temperature.

The *selectivity coefficient*, K, is analogous to the molar equilibrium constant introduced in Chapter 5,

$$K_A^B = \frac{[(R^-)_m B^{m+}]^n [A^{n+}]^m}{[(R^-)_n A^{n+}]^m [B^{m+}]^n} \tag{12-4}$$

Since concentrated ionic solutions exist both within and outside the resin bead, none of the assumptions made in Chapter 5 are valid here at all. Consequently, the selectivity coefficient does not remain constant, but varies with experimental conditions. When the charges on A and B are equal, the separation factor and the selectivity coefficient have identical numerical values. When m and n are different, however, the relationship between the separation factor and the selectivity coefficient is given by:

$$(\alpha_A^B)^m = K_A^B \left(\frac{[(R^-)_m B^{m+}]}{[B^{m+}]} \right)^{m-n} \tag{12-5}$$

In dilute aqueous solutions, activity coefficients are used to convert the molar concentrations of the ions in solution to the activities of these ions. This corrects for solution differences, making selectivity dependent upon resin properties alone. The equilibrium constant, now is called the *corrected selectivity coefficient* and is defined as:

$$K_A^{B'} = K_A^B \frac{f_A^m}{f_B^n} = \frac{[(R^-)_m B^{m+}]^n}{[(R^-)_n A^{n+}]^m} \times \frac{a_A^m}{a_B^n} \tag{12-6}$$

where f_A and f_B represent the activity coefficients of A and B, respectively, in the solution.

One frequently encountered ion-exchange term is the *distribution coefficient*, D. This is actually a distribution ratio, as defined in Chapter 5, rather than a partition coefficient. The distribution coefficient pertains to only one ion and is defined as the total concentration of all forms of the ion in the resin phase divided by the total concentration of all forms of the ion in the solution phase, or:

$$D = \frac{C_{resin}}{C_{solution}} \tag{12-7}$$

As we know from our experience with distribution equilibrium, D is not a constant but varies with the concentration of the ions present and the existence of other equilibria present in the solution. Notice that in keeping with column and paper partition chromatography, D is defined with the stationary phase over the mobile phase. The distribution ratio is related to the selectivity coefficient by the expression:

$$D_B = (K_A^B)^{1/n} \left(\frac{[(R^-)_n A^{n+}]}{[A^{n+}]} \right)^{m/n} \tag{12-8}$$

Ion-Exchange Resin Selectivity

The selectivity of an ion-exchange resin refers to its preference for one ion over a second ion. No matter which of the expressions defined in the previous section is used as a numerical quantitative measure of selectivity, the same qualitative statements and sequences of selectivity for resins apply.

1. An ion exchanger prefers counterions of higher charge. In other words, Fe^{3+} is more strongly held than is Cu^{2+} which is more strongly held than is NH_4^+. This is primarily an electrostatic effect. As the concentration of the external solution becomes more dilute and as the concentration of the ion in the resin becomes more concentrated, this preference for more highly charged species increases. Because of the definition of Equation (12–3) the charge and charge concentration effects are reflected in the numerical value of the separation factor, but not in the numerical value of the selectivity coefficient.

2. An ion exchanger prefers those counterions which have the smallest solvated volume. This preference is caused by the swelling of the resin. The smaller the volume of the solvated ion, the less swelling results when the ion enters the resin and hence, the more favored the ion. On an electrostatic basis the smaller solvated ions can get closer to the charged sites on the resin and, hence, the force of attraction between the fixed ions and the counterions is greater. This preference is more pronounced in dilute solutions and in highly cross-linked resins. This selectivity is illustrated by the alkali metals, whose order of preference for a cation-exchange resin is:

$$Li^+ < Na^+ < K^+ < Rb^+ < Cs^+$$

which is also the order of decreasing radius of the hydrated ions. This swelling pressure and cross-linking excludes large organic and complex inorganic ions from the ion-exchange resins completely and forms the basis for ion-exclusion chromatography.

3. An ion exchanger prefers counterions which form the strongest ion pairs or bonds with the fixed ionic groups. Examination of Equation (12–1) shows that this is nothing more than a restatement of Le Châtelier's principle. The more tightly the ion is bound to the resin, the more the equilibrium is shifted in that direction. It is completely analogous to precipitate formation, volatilization, etc. as means of causing reactions to go to completion. The manifestations of this in ion-exchange selectivity are not difficult to understand at all, provided that the equilibrium within the resin is understood. Thus, it should not be too surprising to discover that weak cation-exchange resins, those containing carboxyl groups, will prefer hydrogen ion to metal cations. After all, the weak acid dissociation is working in favor of the hydrogen ion. Nor should it be surprising to discover that the chelating resins prefer the transition metals for the EDTA chelates of the transition metals are much stronger than those of other metals. Similarly, thallium(I) and silver(I) are preferred over the alkali metals by strong cation resins because the transition metals are more polarizable and hence form stronger ion pairs.

4. An ion exchanger prefers counterions composed of organic groups resembling the components of the carbon matrix. This is merely a rephrasing of that old chemical saw "like prefers like" which is based on enhanced London forces between similar species. Therefore, when exchanging organic ions, polystyrene resins show a preference for ions containing aromatic groups over ions containing aliphatic groups, for example, phenyl dimethylethyl ammonium ion, because of the phenyl group it contains, is preferred over tetramethyl ammonium or tetraethyl ammonium ion.

5. An ion exchanger prefers counterions that associate less strongly with their

coions. This preference forms the basis of ion-exchange chromatography, since it is an expression of the effect of competing equilibria on the resin selectivity. We know only too well from Chapter 5, that the presence of a second equilibrium in a solution will shift the position of the first equilibrium. In terms of ion exchange:

$$R^-A^+ + B^+ \rightleftharpoons R^-B^+ + A^+$$
$$+$$
$$C^-$$
$$\updownarrow$$
$$AC$$

so that when the ion A^+ interacts with some species, C, in the solution the exchange equilibrium will be shifted to the right, and the resin will favor B^+. The equilibrium in which A^+ participates can be any of those discussed in Chapter 5—acid–base, complex ion formation, distribution, and even precipitation.

The results of these rules may be summarized by the following selectivity sequences, barring concomitant equilibria as discussed in (5) above.

For sulfonic acid resins, the selectivity for cations is:

$$Th^{4+} > Zr^{4+} > Ti^{4+}$$

$$In^{3+} > Tl^{3+} > Ga^{3+} > Al^{3+}$$

$$Ba^{2+} > Pb^{2+} > Sr^{2+} > Ca^{2+} > Ni^{2+} > Cd^{2+} > Cu^{2+} > Co^{2+} > Zn^{2+} > $$
$$Mg^{2+} > UO_2^{2+}$$

$$Tl^+ > Ag^+ > Cs^+ > Rb^+ > K^+ > NH_4^+ > Na^+ > H^+ > Li^+$$

Table 12–1. DISTRIBUTION CO-EFFICIENTS FOR CATIONS WITH DOWEX-50 X4 FROM 1 M HClO$_4$

Metal Ion	log D
Na$^+$	0.67
Cs$^+$	0.75
Mg^{2+}	1.20
UO$_2^{2+}$	1.40
Mn^{2+}	1.57
Ca^{2+}	1.87
Sr^{2+}	2.08
Hg^{2+}	2.08
Ba^{2+}	2.42
Fe^{3+}	1.60
Ga^{3+}	2.25
Eu^{3+}	2.55
Ce^{3+}	2.75
Sc^{3+}	2.70
La^{3+}	3.1
Th^{4+}	4.6

SOURCE: Ref. 14.

Table 12-1 gives distribution coefficients for metal ions on Dowex 50 from 1 M $HClO_4$.

The selectivity for anions on the quarternary ammonium ion resins is:

$$\text{citrate} > \text{sulfate} > \text{oxalate} > I^- > NO_3^- > CrO_4^{2-} > Br^- > SCN^- > Cl^-$$
$$> \text{formate} > \text{acetate} > OH^- > F^-$$

The selectivity for cations on the iminodiacetate chelating resins is:

$$Hg^{2+} > UO_2^{2+} > Cu^{2+} > VO^{2+} > Pb^{2+} > Ni^{2+} > Cd^{2+} > Zn^{2+} > Co^{2+}$$

$$Fe^{2+} > Mn^{2+} > Be^{2+} > Ca^{2+} > Mg^{2+} > Ba^{2+} > Sr^{2+}$$

with the total spread in selectivity coefficients between mercury and strontium of 3×10^4. Since the total spread of selectivity coefficients on sulfonic acid resins for the divalent metal ions is only about three, the advantages of the chelating resins should be apparent. For the trivalent metal ions the selectivity sequence on chelating resins is:

$$Cr^{3+} > In^{3+} > Fe^{3+} > Ce^{3+} > Al^{3+} > La^{3+}$$

and for the monovalent ions:

$$Li^+ > Na^+ > K^+ > Rb^+ > Cs^+$$

This is the reverse of the sequence for the monovalent ions on the strong cation-exchange resins. Table 12–2 gives separation factors for metal ion pairs on Dowex A-1.

Table 12–2. SEPARATION FACTORS OF 0.1 M METAL NITRATES ON DOWEX A-1

Metal 1	Metal 2	α_1^2
K^{1+}	Na^{1+}	1.38
Na^{1+}	Li^{1+}	1.61
Sr^{2+}	Mg^{2+}	1.3
Sr^{2+}	Ba^{2+}	1.15
Ba^{2+}	Ca^{2+}	1.5
Ca^{2+}	Mn^{2+}	4.9
Co^{2+}	Zn^{2+}	1.3
Co^{2+}	Ni^{2+}	3.65
Zn^{2+}	Cd^{2+}	1.3
Zn^{2+}	Ni^{2+}	2.6
Cd^{2+}	Ni^{2+}	1.8
Ni^{2+}	Pb^{2+}	3.0
Pb^{2+}	Cu^{2+}	3.2

SOURCE: Ref. 25.

Anything which will cause a change in the activities or molar concentrations of the ions, in or outside the resin, will shift the ion-exchange equilibrium position so as to alter the selectivity of the ion-exchange resin. In Chapter 5 these factors were treated in detail. Now let us see how they can be applied to affect the selectivity of ion-exchange resins.

As the ionic strength of a solution increases, the activity of the ions in the solution will change. Table 5–2 and Fig. 5–2 show how the activity coefficients of various ions change with increasing ionic strength. Since the separation factor, selectivity coefficient, and distribution ratio in ion exchange are all defined in terms of molar concentrations, their numerical values will change with ionic strength. As the ionic strength of a solution is increased, the activity coefficients for different ions vary differently causing the selectivity of ion-exchange resins to vary differently for different ions. Fig. 12–3 shows how the separation factor, α_A^B, changes as the total concentration of the two ions (ionic strength) increases when using solutions of metal nitrates and carrying out the exchange on Dowex A-1. Fig. 12–3 shows clearly that there is no uniform way in which the selectivity varies. For certain pairs of ions, Ba–Sr, Cd–Zn, and Co–Zn, there seems to be no change in α_A^B as the ionic strength increases. For Pb–Ni the selectivity for Pb increases up to a maximum value and then decreases as the ion concentration increases. For other ion pairs, Mn–Ca, Co–Ni, Zn–Ni, Cu–Pb, the selectivity decreases with increasing ionic strength. These changes in selectivity with ionic strength mean that separations feasible for trace amounts of metal ions, may not be feasible at higher metal ion concentrations; no separation may occur or the preference for one ion may be reversed.

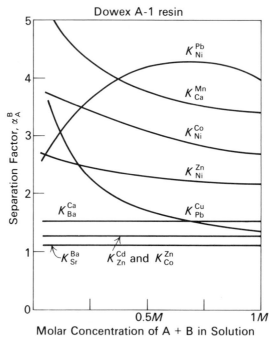

Fig. 12–3. Variation in separation factors on Dowex A-1 with increasing concentration of metal ions. (*Redrawn from Ref. 25, by permission of Springer-Verlag.*)

There is relatively little heat evolved or consumed during the ion-exchange process. Therefore, the equilibrium position, that is, resin selectivity, is dependent only slightly upon temperature, provided that no other equilibria are involved. Fig. 12–4 shows the effect of a temperature change from 2 to 145°C on the corrected selectivity coefficient of the alkali and alkaline earth metals. When additional equilibria are present the total temperature effect can be extremely large, because of the temperature effect on the acid–base, complex ion, or other equilibria involved.

It was mentioned earlier that the selectivity of an ion-exchange resin will vary as the fraction of the resin sites occupied by a particular metal ion changes. Fig. 12–5 shows the decrease of the distribution coefficient in Dowex 50 as europium(III) and thorium(IV) occupy more and more exchange sites. Activity effects within the resin produce the nonlinear relationships between D and concentration in the resin. Most theories of ion-exchange behavior are restricted to trace amounts of the metal ions exchanged in order to avoid effects due to ionic strength and extent of loading of the exchange column.

Kraus and Nelson[16] have made extensive and exhaustive studies of the ion exchange behavior of metal ions in HCl, HClO$_4$, HBr, and HNO$_3$ media. Their results are presented graphically as the change in the distribution coefficient of the metal ion on Dowex 50, as a function of the molarity of acid in the exchanging solution. The initial decrease in distribution ratio with increasing acid concentra-

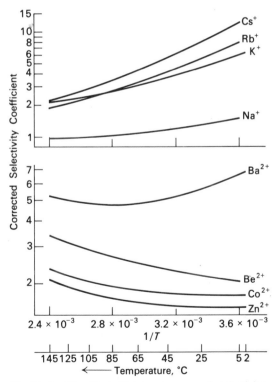

Fig. 12–4.   The effect of temperature on resin selectivity. (*Redrawn from Ref. 9 by permission of McGraw-Hill Book Co.*)

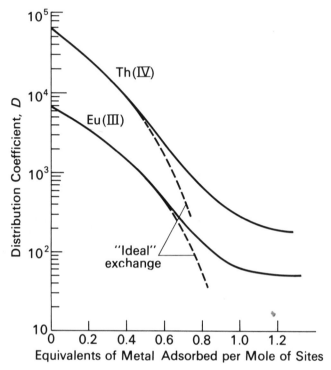

Fig. 12–5. The effect of loading on ion-exchange selectivity. (*Redrawn from Ref. 16, by permission of Nelson, Mause, and Kraus.*)

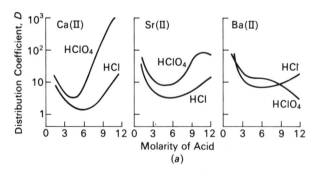

Fig. 12–6a. Adsorption of metal ions on Dowex 50-X4 from HCl and HClO$_4$ solutions at 25°C: (*a*) calcium(II), strontium(II), and barium(II); (*b*) manganese(II), cobalt(II), copper(II), zinc(II), cadmium(II), mercury(II), and lead(II); (*c*) iron(III), aluminum(III), gallium(III), indium(III), antimony(III), and bismuth(III); (*d*) scandium(III), yttrium(III), and rare earth elements; (*e*) thallium(IV), titanium(IV), hafnium(IV), and zirconium(IV); (*f*) uranium(VI), molybdenum(VI), and tungsten(VI). (*Redrawn from Ref. 16, by permission of Nelson, Murase, and Kraus.*)

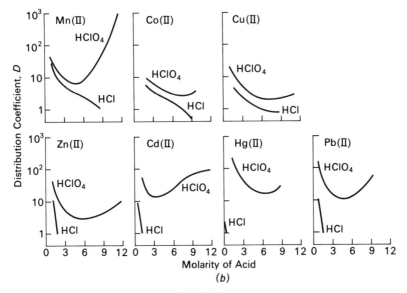

Fig. 12–6b.

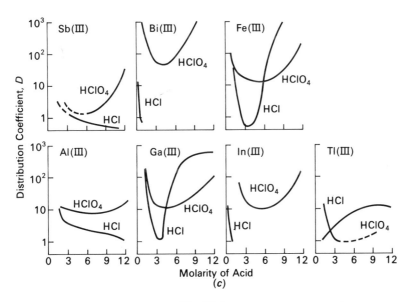

Fig. 12–6c.

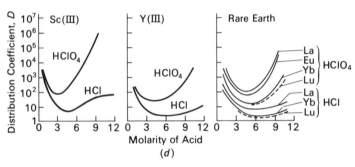

Fig. 12–6d.

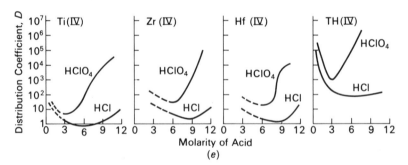

Fig. 12–6e.

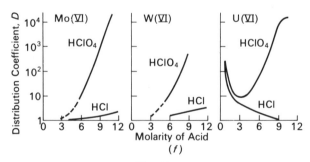

Fig. 12–6f.

tion, is explained in terms of increasing formation of chloro, bromo, or nitrato complexes of the metal ions. Since perchlorate ion is not noted for its ability to form complexes with metals, the decrease in perchlorate solutions must be attributed to activity effects. Complex ion formation is not the entire explanation for the behavior observed in hydrochloric acid solutions, for solutions of ammonium chloride of equal molarity do not cause parallel behavior in the metal ion exchange.

Figs. 12–6(a) through (f) show the effects of HCl and $HClO_4$ concentration on the distribution coefficients for metals on Dowex-50. The alkali metals have an almost negligible distribution coefficient in greater than 1 M HCl and $HClO_4$ solutions. The alkaline earth metals (see Fig. 12–6(a)) do not complex, appreciably, with chloride ion so their behavior is almost identical in HCl and in $HClO_4$. Beryllium and magnesium have distribution coefficients below one at HCl concentrations above 2 M; in $HClO_4$ solutions, their behavior is almost identical to that of copper. Fig. 12–6(b) shows the ion-exchange behavior of the divalent transition metal ions. Since these metals all form anionic complexes with chloride ion, or, as in the case of lead, precipitate, the value of D for chloride containing solutions decreases rapidly. The distribution coefficient of nickel is almost identical to that of copper in HCl solutions more concentrated than 0.2 M, and almost identical to that of cobalt in solutions of $HClO_4$ more concentrated than 0.2 M. The distribution coefficient of silver(I) decreases from 11 to 3 as the perchloric acid concentration rises from 1 to 7 M. In HCl solutions, AgCl precipitates, so D is negligibly small. Fig. 12–6(c) shows the behavior of trivalent metal ions, while Fig. 12–6(d) shows how D for scandium, yttrium, and the rare earths is affected by acid concentration. Fig. 12–6(e) depicts changes for the tetravalent metal ions of thorium, titanium, hafnium, and zirconium. Fig. 12–6(f) shows how the exchange of the hexavalent ions of molybdenum, tungsten, and uranium is affected by an increase in HCl and $HClO_4$ concentration.

At high cloride ion concentrations the chloro complexes of the transition metals are anions, MCl_4^{2-}. These anionic complexes can be exchanged for the anions of an anion-exchange resin. Let us consider the equilibrium reactions:

$$Cd^{2+} + 4Cl^- \rightleftharpoons CdCl_4^{2-}$$

$$2R^+Cl^- + CdCl_4^{2-} \rightleftharpoons (R^+)_2CdCl_4^{2-} + 2Cl^-$$

As the concentration of chloride ion in a cadmium solution is increased, the complex-ion forming equilibrium is shifted in favor of the tetrachloro cadmium(II) complex. As more of this anion is produced in the solution the ion-exchange equilibrium is shifted to the right, resulting in an increase in resin selectivity for the complex ion over the chloride ion. Fig. 12–7 shows how the distribution coefficients for cadmium and for zinc on an anion-exchange resin increase as the molality of HCl in the solution increases; that is, as the concentration of the negatively charged complex ion increases.

In Chapter 5 we have seen how hydrogen ions in the solution compete with the metal ions for the ligand during complex ion formation. Therefore, when complexes with weakly acidic or basic ligands are involved in ion exchange, the pH of the solution must be controlled. When a weak acid ligand is the fixed ion of the

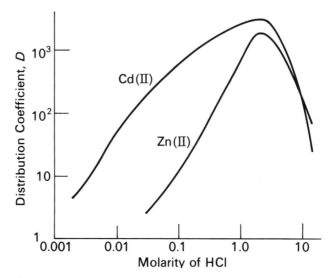

Fig. 12–7. The effect of complex ion formation on the anion exchange selectivity of the anionic chloro complexes of zinc and cadmium. (*Redrawn from Ref. 18, by permission of Pergamon Press, Inc.*)

resin (Dowex A-1), increasing the pH of the solution favors complex formation between the resin and the metal ions. The exchange equilibrium:

$$R\text{-}CH_2\text{-}N(CH_2\text{-}COOH)_2 + M^{2+} \rightleftharpoons R\text{-}CH_2\text{-}N\text{-}(CH_2\text{-}COO^-)_2M^{2+} + 2H^+$$

is shifted toward the right as the protons react with the hydroxide ion in solution. Therefore, the selectivity of a chelating resin for a metal ion increases with increasing pH. Fig. 12–8 shows the effect of pH on the distribution coefficient of transition metal ions with the resin, Dowex A-1. D increases with pH because of the increased complexation in the resin.

If, on the other hand, the chelating agent is added to the solution and the ion exchanger is a strong acid cationic resin, pH increases in the solution will have an opposite effect on the selectivity of the resin for the metal ions. Consider the equilibria involved now:

$$M^{2+} + H_2Y^{2-} \rightleftharpoons MY^{2-} + 2H^+$$

$$2R^-Na^+ + M^{2+} \rightleftharpoons (R^-)_2M^{2+} + 2Na^+$$

As the pH of the solution is increased, the formation of the complex with EDTA or any other weak base chelon is increased, shifting the equilibrium position of the first reaction to the right, leaving less uncomplexed metal ion in the solution. This decrease causes the exchange equilibrium of the second reaction to shift to the left. Consequently, the selectivity of the ion-exchange resin decreases as the

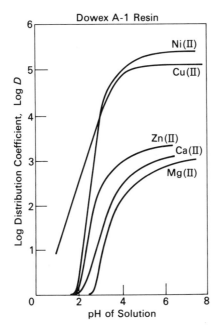

Fig. 12–8. The effect of pH on the distribution coefficient of transition metal ions with the chelating resin, Dowex A-1. (*Redrawn from Ref. 25, by permission of Springer-Verlag.*)

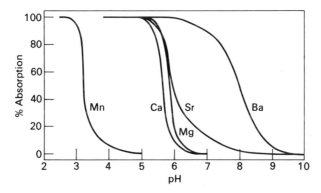

Fig. 12–9. The effect of pH on the amount of metal ion on a strong cation-exchange resin (Amberlite IR-120) from metal-EDTA solution. Concentrations of metal ion: 7.2×10^{-3} M, concentration of EDTA: 1.8×10^{-2} M. (*Redrawn from Ref. 15, by permission of Nelson and Kraus.*)

pH increases. Fig. 12–9 shows the effect of pH on ion exchange between a strong cation-exchange resin and a metal ion solution that also contains 0.018 M EDTA. The decrease in the amount of metal ion on the ion exchange resin at high pH is caused by the increase in the amount of EDTA chelate formed in the solution. Since changing the pH of a metal ion solution containing a chelon changes the extent of complexation, as well as the ion-exchange selectivity, by taking advantage of the pH effect, separations of metal ions can be effected by ion exchange, in a fashion exactly analogous to extraction. For example, according to Fig. 12–9, at a pH of 5.5, no manganese will be on the resin, but all of the calcium, magnesium, strontium, and barium will be held on the resin. Thus, at a pH of 5.5, manganese can be separated from any or all of the alkaline earth metals by ion exchange using EDTA solutions. Because repeated equilibrium processes occur as the solution passes down an ion-exchange column, calcium, magnesium, and strontium probably could be separated quantitatively from barium at a pH above 7.

Thus, as we have seen in the other forms of chromatography, by coupling equilibria, the separation possibilities are greatly enhanced. A knowledge of the chemistry of the fixed ions in the resin and of the counterions in the solution can be used very advantageously.

COLUMN OPERATION

Batch exchange processes are used when studying the equilibrium, thermodynamic, and physical properties of ion-exchange resins. Ion exchange-membranes, ion-exchange papers, and thin layers of ion exchangers are all available for separation purposes. The major mode of using ion-exchange resins, however, at the present time is in an ion-exchange column. These are conventional chromatographic columns—0.5 to 2.0 cm diameter glass tubes of sufficient length to provide a column of resin long enough to give the bed capacity needed to effect the desired separation.

Column Development

Ion-exchange columns are developed either by displacement analysis or by elution analysis; frontal analysis is rarely used. The displacement analysis operation, techniques, prerequisites, and separations are identical to those discussed in Chapter 7. In displacement development, the counterions in the developer are preferred over any counterion present either on the column initially or in the sample. Thus, as they move through the column they exchange for all ions in front of them. Because of this, the boundary between the sample components and the developing solvent is called *self-sharpening* (see Fig. 7–5). The rate of development of the sample is determined by the rate of solvent flow and the distribution coefficient of the displacing counter ion. The rate is independent of the distribution coefficients of the sample constituents for they are pushed along the column by the counter ions of the developer. Displacement development has been used by Spedding to separate mixtures of the rare earths on a production scale.

The more common method of column development is elution analysis. In elution development the counterion initially present in the resin usually is hydrogen ion or chloride ion. The fixed ions of the resin have a selectivity for the counterion in the eluting agent that is greater than or equal to that of the initial counterion but less than that of any of the components in the sample. Often the eluting counterion is identical to the initial counterion of the resin. The sample components move through the column at rates dependent upon the rate of solvent flow and their own distribution coefficients. The concentration profile of the eluate is Gaussian. Elution analysis is said to have *nonsharpening* boundaries, because the solute peaks spread as the solutes move down the column.

The selection of an eluting solution requires a knowledge of the series of selectivities of the resin for the ions present in the sample, and the effects of the pH, complexation, and concentration. When it is difficult to find a single set of operating conditions that will separate all of the ions in the unknown efficiently, change from one eluting agent to another after removing one or more of the ions from the column. Gradient elution can also be used to effect the separation—the pH of the solution can be changed continuously, the concentration of the eluting counterions can be changed continuously, the concentration of chelating ligands in the eluent can be changed continuously, the temperature of column operation can be changed continuously, or the composition of the liquid used to dissolve the solutes can be changed continuously.

Usually aqueous solutions are used in ion-exchange chromatography, but there is no reason not to use mixed aqueous-organic solvents, or pure organic solvents themselves if the solubilities of the sample and eluting solute are sufficiently high in them. Mixed solvents should consist of polar liquids such as water-alcohols, water-acetone, and water-dioxane. The shift from aqueous to mixed solvents frequently improves the selectivities of the ions. Switching from aqueous solutions to mixed solvent systems can cause changes in (1) the solvation of the counterions both in the solvent and in the resin; (2) the position of equilibrium of both ion exchange and concomitant reactions; (3) the dielectric constant of the solvent, and hence the strength of the electrostatic attraction between the fixed and counter ions. In addition, partitioning of the solutes between the mixed solvent and the aqueous resin can accompany the ion-exchange process. Thus, in certain cases, the use of mixed solvents will effect separations not accomplished in aqueous solvents.

The narrowness of an elution peak will be dependent upon the experimental conditions of column operation as well as the chemistry of the exchange processes occurring in the column. When, at a given solvent flow rate, the rate of the ion exchange reaction is slow, there is less time for the solute to attain equilibrium with the column. Since the system is not at equilibrium there will be more spreading of the solute in the column, and broader elution peaks will be obtained. The rate of attainment of ion-exchange equilibrium can be increased by decreasing the particle size of the beads so as to have a larger surface area for exchange, however, this also increases the resistance to solvent flow. Resin beads with low percentages of cross-linking have more accessible exchange sites so that the rate of exchange in them is increased. Increasing the temperature of the column or decreasing the rate of solvent flow also increases the rate of attainment of ion-exchange equilibrium and produces narrow elution peaks.

Detection of Solute Bands

Frequently, ion-exchange chromatography is used to separate mixtures of metal ions. For these applications the detection and determination of the metal ion in the eluent can be restricted to those methods that are best suited for the determination of metal ions.

The most rapid and highly sensitive methods for metals are those of flame spectroscopy. The eluate is collected and then analyzed by emission flame photometry, atomic absorption flame photometry, or atomic fluorescence flame photometry. These techniques are able to detect very slight traces (one part per billion) of one metal in the presence of others. Absorption spectrophotometry is also a reasonably rapid and quite sensitive method for determination of most metal ions. Chelatometric titration of the eluate from an ion-exchange column with an EDTA solution is a very widespread method for determination of the separated components (see the experiments at the end of this chapter). Activation analysis has also been used for determination of the metals in eluates. The chemistry of the transuranium elements has been studied by ion exchange. Kraus[16] and many other people have used radioactive isotopes in studying the properties and behavior of ion-exchange resins. When these isotopes are used, they are detected by the appropriate counting technique.

When mixtures of organic ions are separated, colorimetric or other methods specific for these ions are employed. A colorimetric determination of the intensity of the ninhydrin reaction product enables a quantitative determination of the separated amino acids present.

Theory of Column Development

The theory of ion-exchange column development was developed before Van Deempter's theory of gas chromatographic development, yet the final equations are surprisingly identical (see p. 509 of Chapter 14). Glueckauf[5] derived equations for the efficiency of ion-exchange columns on a kinetic basis. These equations are only applicable for dilute solutions of electrolytes since he assumed that the distribution coefficient did not change with ion concentration. Glueckauf's equation for the *height of a theoretical plate* (HETP) can be simplified to:

$$\text{HETP} = 1.64\,r + A r^2 \bar{v} + \frac{B r^2 \bar{v}}{1 + C r \bar{v}} + \frac{D}{\bar{v}} \tag{12–9}$$

where r is the radius of the ion-exchange particles and $\bar{v}$ is the flow rate of the solvent through the column. A, B, C, and D are constants that depend upon the properties of the resin and the counter ions being exchanged.

A theoretical plate represents one separation stage in a column. For maximum column efficiency as many theoretical plates as possible should be present in an ion-exchange column, which means that the height of a theoretical plate (HETP) should be as small as possible. The first term of Equation (12–9) predicts that the smaller the diameter of the resin beads, the more efficiently the column will operate.

The second term of Equation (12–9) describes the influence of the diffusion of the counterions within the resin particle on the efficiency of the column separation. The slower the flow rate and the faster the diffusion (smaller A), the more efficient the operation of the column. The third term states that the faster the diffusion of the counter ions in the liquid film coating the resin beads, the more efficient the operation of the column. The last term of Equation (12–9) is due to the diffusion of the solutes in the column caused by the appearance of concentration gradients during the separation. As the separated solutes concentrate into bands in the eluting agent, there is a tendency for the counterions to diffuse out of these bands into the pure solvent because of their lower concentration in pure solvent. The faster this diffusion, the poorer the separation efficiency of the ion-exchange column. As this last term shows, the size of the resin particles does not affect this process. The slower the flow of eluent through the column, the more time for diffusion and the less efficient the separation. In practice, unless the flow rate is extremely slow, this last term is negligibly small.

Unfortunately many of the terms contained in the A, B, C, and D of Equation (12–9) cannot be determined directly. This means that while the theory of ion-exchange column separations, as exemplified by Equation (12–9), is excellent for describing separations that have occurred, for the values of A, B, C, and D can be determined from the empirical curves of HETP vs. $\bar{v}$, the theory is of little value in predicting what separations may be feasible.

Factors Affecting Retention Volumes

One of the greatest achievements of ion-exchange chromatography is Hamilton's separation of the amino acids on Dowex 50–X8,[8] which led to his development of the *automatic amino acid analyzer*[7] now used routinely in most biochemical, molecular biological, and medical laboratories. To achieve this fantastic separation, Hamilton explored exhaustively the ion-exchange behavior of amino acids. He investigated the influence of experimental parameters on the retention volumes of each amino acid. Even though his work was restricted to the amino acids, many of the relationships Hamilton unearthed can be generalized safely to all ion-exchange separations. Let us look briefly, therefore, at some of his findings.

Hamilton related the volume of eluent needed to reach the peak of the solute (*retention volume*) to column dimensions and the distribution coefficient of the solute:

$$V_R = AZ(D + F_I) \tag{12–10}$$

where V_R is the retention volume, A is the cross-sectional area of the ion-exchange column, Z is the length of the bed of resin in the column, D is the distribution coefficient of the solute, and F_I is the fraction of the column volume occupied by the mobile liquid. Thus $1 - F_I$ is the fraction of the column volume occupied by the solid resin. The distribution coefficient in the expression is not the same one defined by Equation (12–7); it contains the amount of solid present in the column. It is defined as:

$$D = \frac{[X]_{\text{resin}} (1 - F_I)}{[X]_{\text{liquid}}} \tag{12–11}$$

Values for V_R, A, Z, and F_I are obtained experimentally and then Equation (12–10) is used to obtain numerical values of D.

The steps of the replacement of one ion in the solvent by one from the resin are:

1. Diffusion of ion A in the solvent to the surface of the resin bead. The effectiveness of this step is dependent upon the flow of the solution in the column and the rate at which ion A diffuses through the liquid (its diffusion coefficient).

2. Diffusion inside the resin bead of ion A to the site of the fixed ion. The effectiveness of this step is dependent upon the concentration gradient within the resin particle and the rate at which ion A diffuses within the resin.

3. The exchange of ion A by ion B at the site of the fixed ion.

4. The diffusion of ion B away from the fixed ion to the surface of the resin bead. The effectiveness is dependent upon the same factors as in (2), except they apply to ion B.

5. Diffusion in the solvent of ion B away from the surface of the resin. The effectiveness is dependent upon the same factors as in (1) except that they apply to ion B.

Step (3) is very rapid. When the concentrations of the ions being separated are very low, the extent to which steps (4) and (5) influence the separation efficiency are minimal, leaving only steps (1) and (2) to determine the separation efficiency. This is the same conclusion that Glueckauf reached in deriving Equation (12–9).

Hamilton's study of step (1) showed that band spreading and peak resolution are proportional to the number of different paths the ions can take in moving down the column (*eddy diffusion*). The solute peak width for the amino acids increased with an increase in the length of the column, the diameter of the column, solvent flow, and resin particle diameter. These findings are all in accord with the general chromatographic behavior described in Chapter 7.

The values of distribution coefficients increased as the temperature was increased from 35 to 85°C. Since, in addition to the ion-exchange equilibrium, there are an acid–base equilibria present in the amino acid separations, this increase in D with temperature is quite understandable. For the amino acids alanine, aspartic acid, glutamic acid, glycine, and valine the values of the distribution coefficient decrease as the pH of the eluting agent was increased from 2.85 to 3.25. Since all of these amino acids have their pK_{a_1} values near this range (between pK_a 2.32 and 4.25) as the pH of the solvent is increased, the amino acids lose a proton; they are transformed from a positively charged to a neutral (actually zwitterion) species. The resin has less preference for this neutral species, so D decreases with increasing pH.

To separate two components by elution chromatography, there must be sufficient difference between the retention volumes of each component to enable each to be collected free from contamination by the other. The minimum possible difference in retention volumes for separation occurs when the bases of the two elution peaks just abut one another, as is shown in Fig. 12–10.

Assuming that there are no deviations from ideal behavior (D is independent of concentration so bearding or tailing does not occur), the elution peaks will be Gaussian in shape. Gaussian curves (see Chapter 4) are four standard deviations

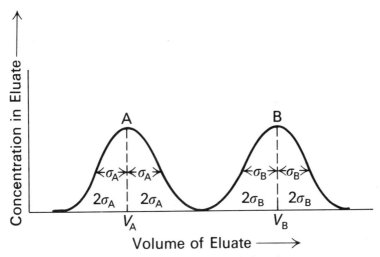

Fig. 12–10. Minimum conditions for the resolution of two components by elution chromatography.

wide at the base, as shown in Fig. 12–10. Therefore, to resolve the components A and B, the retention volume difference between A and B must at least equal that volume corresponding to one-half the sum of the peak base widths of the two peaks. That is for resolution

$$V_B - V_A \geq 2\sigma_A + 2\sigma_B \qquad (12\text{–}12)$$

The *resolution ratio*, R_R, is obtained by rearranging the above minimum condition.

$$R_R = \frac{V_B - V_A}{\sigma_A + \sigma_B} \qquad (12\text{–}13)$$

According to Fig. 12–10 and/or Equation (12–12), the numerical value of R_R must be two or greater in order to separate two components. Note that the resolution ratio takes into account both the difference in the distribution coefficient of the two solutes and the band spreading for each solute. Substituting Equation (12–10) into Equation (12–13) gives:

$$R_R = \frac{AZ(D_B - D_A)}{\sigma_A + \sigma_B} \qquad (12\text{–}14)$$

Even when there is sufficient difference between D_B and D_A, complete separation of A and B cannot occur if the spreading is too great.

Hamilton derived a complex expression relating the resolution ratio, R_R, to column parameters such as the flow rate, the resin particle diameter, the fraction of the column occupied by the mobile liquid, the column diameter, and the distribution coefficients of the two solutes. Thereby, he was able to predict the effect of altering experimental conditions on the resolution of any two amino acids. Hamilton[6] found experimentally that the resolution of glycine and alanine decreased as the flow rate increased from 0.02 to 0.40 cm/sec. This is to be expected for the equilibrium is less completely attained in the faster flowing solvents, and hence the efficiency of the column will decrease [see Equation (12–9)]. Peak widths increase, which means the resolution ratio decreases as the flow rate increases. The resolution ratio for the separation of glycine and alanine increased as the particle diameter decreased from 8.0×10^{-3} cm to 2.4×10^{-3} cm, which again is in accord with Equation (12–9). By means of his thorough study of the operational parameters of amino acid resolution, Hamilton was able to develop an instrument capable of resolving almost all amino acids.

ADVANTAGES AND LIMITATIONS

Ion exchange is one of many very widely used and powerful separation techniques, so it is worth asking the question "How does ion exchange compare to these other techniques?", which in practice means, "When should I consider using ion exchange as a separation method and when should I avoid using it?"

Ion-exchange chromatography is probably the best way of separating mixtures of ionic substances. This is especially true when the mixture contains many ions having closely related properties. Almost any separation technique will separate ions exhibiting a great difference in behavior. But ion exchange is superior for the separations such as of the platinum metals, the rare earth elements, the transuranium elements, and the amino acids.

Ion-exchange chromatographic behavior can be manipulated in various well-understood ways. Resins, solvents, temperatures, and operating parameters can all be selected to obtain maximum resolution ratios. The behavior of complex ion, pH, and distribution equilibria in aqueous solution is understood and predictable, in contrast to the behavior in most organic solvents. Thus, with ion exchange, the experimenter can manipulate the variables to produce a separation with a greater feeling of competence, and on a less empirical basis, than with other chromatographic techniques. In gas chromatography, many of these possibilities for varying D do not even exist.

Ion-exchange chromatography can be carried out in columns, using membranes and on thin layers. This variety enables separation in small amounts of sample as well as in large amounts.

Ion exchange, by the very nature of the process, is limited to solutions of ionic materials. While ion exchange can be used to separate ionic from nonionic materials, the applicability of the technique is much more restricted than partition or adsorption chromatographic methods.

Ion exchange can be used to concentrate dilute solutions. The ions are removed from the dilute solution and then eluted from the resin by a very small volume of solvent.

The eluents used in ion-exchange chromatography must be ionic solutions. The only solvents possible, therefore, are polar liquids.

Compared to gas-liquid chromatography, thin-layer chromatography, and paper chromatography, ion exchange is a slow process. The introduction of the new high-speed liquid chromatographs, which can be used for ion-exchange columns too, has shortened development times somewhat, but still not to times comparable to those of thin-layer separations on microscope slides. The time required for a solute to emerge from a column is given by:

$$t = \frac{Z(D + F_I)}{\bar{v}}$$ (12–15)

where Z is the column diameter and the other terms are the same as in Equation (12–10). The separation of amino acids by Hamilton's automatic analyzer requires a development time of about twenty-one hours.

The apparatus required for ion-exchange chromatographic separations is not expensive or complex. A 25-ml burette and separatory funnel are quite adequate for routine separations. Thus the equipment is less complicated and expensive than that needed for gas chromatography, is comparable to that needed for partition and adsorption column chromatography, but is more elaborate than that needed for paper and thin-layer chromatography. Still, it is common equipment found in every laboratory.

APPLICATIONS

Two of the most spectacular separations ever achieved were carried out by ion-exchange chromatography. The first of these was the separation of the rare earth elements as an outgrowth of the Manhattan Project during World War II and the second was the automatic separation of the amino acids by Hamilton.

Part of the Manhattan Project was the large scale production of plutonium. Before this could be undertaken safely, high-purity samples of the fission products of plutonium had to be obtained to study the chemical, physical and biological properties of these elements. These fission products included certain rare earth elements. Groups of workers under G. E. Boyd[10] and E. R. Tomkins[23,24] at Oak Ridge, and F. H. Spedding[20,22] at Iowa State University developed the vital separation processes using long columns of strong cation exchangers and 5% citric acid pH 3.3 buffers to elute the rare earth elements. This process was refined by Spedding[20] to a pilot plant scale on eight-foot-long columns of Amberlite IR-100 using 0.5% citrate buffered at 3.9.

The separation of the rare earth elements used today was also developed by Spedding.[21] It is a great improvement over the original one. A 90-cm-long column of Dowex 50-X8 is converted to the copper form. The sample of rare earth elements is placed on the column and then eluted at a flow rate of 0.5 cm/min with 2% ammonium EDTA buffered with a pH 8.5 NH_3–NH_4Cl buffer. The overall exchange reaction can be written as:

$$3(R^-)_2Cu^{2+} + 2MY^- + HY^{3-} \rightleftharpoons 2(R^-)_3M^{3+} + 3CuY^{2-} + H^+$$

The success of this separation is based on the differences among the ion-exchange and EDTA equilibria of each of the rare earth elements and copper.

Earlier in this chapter P. B. Hamilton's exploratory studies on the separation of the amino acids were described. In 1963, he utilized these to develop an automatic analyzer for amino acids,[7] which today is found in almost every biochemical and medical laboratory. The automatic amino acid analyzer is used routinely in protein research where knowledge of the nature and amount of each amino acid is essential. The automatic amino acid analyzer contains a long narrow column of 17.5-micron diameter Dowex 50-X8 beads. The separation process is programmed to change the temperature from 45 to 60°C during the column development and to change the pH of the eluent at discrete intervals. The eluent is a series of citric acid–EDTA–thiodiglycol buffers. For the first 460 minutes the eluent is buffered at pH 2.875, after which it is increased to a pH of 3.80 until 730 minutes. Then it is raised to 4.30 until 1210 minutes. At 1211 minutes the eluent is changed to a solution of pure EDTA in dilute sodium hydroxide until 1240 minutes. The eluent is treated with ninhydrin. From the retention volumes and the intensity of the ninhydrin colors, the identity and concentration of each of the amino acids is obtained.

Ion-exchange chromatography has been applied to a broad range of samples, for it is invaluable whenever metals need to be separated. It has been used to separate precious metals in meteorite samples, trace amounts of metals in sea water, beryllium in body fluids when checking for and studying beryllium poisoning, fluorides in dentifrices (on anion-exchange resins by separating the fluorophosphates (PO_3F^{2-}) from PO_4^{3-}), and impurities in zone refined zinc and ultrapure aluminum.

Because of the complexity of the mixtures involved, ion-exchange chromatography has been used extensively in establishing the chemistry of the transuranium elements and in separating these radioactive materials from other ionic and non-ionic substances. I. K. Kressin[12] separated plutonium from forty-six other ions on a column of Dowex-1-2X in the nitrate form. In 6 to 8 M HNO_3, plutonium forms an anionic complex, $Pu(NO_3)_6^{2-}$ which is held onto the anion-exchange column, whereas the other metal ions do not form this complex and hence pass through the column. An eluent of HF–HCl reduced the plutonium(IV) to the (III) state, destroyed the complex thereby, and quickly eluted it from the column.

S. M. Khopkar and A. K. De[11] separated barium from the lead, strontium, radium, lanthanum, uranium(VI), copper, mercury, cesium, zinc, and cadmium formed during fission reactions, on a column of Dowex 50-X8 in the hydrogen form using 1 M HCl as the eluent. They separated the barium from cerium(IV), zirconium (IV), bismuth(III) and thorium(IV) by using the EDTA complexes and then eluting with 4 M HCl. These separations take from three to four hours.

In a continuation of their separation of fission products, strontium was separated from copper, mercury, cesium, zinc, cadmium, and uranium(IV) by Majumdar and A. K. De[13] on Dowex 50-X8 in the hydrogen form by elution with 4 M HCl. It was separated from zirconium, thorium, iron(III), and bismuth by using an eluent of EDTA and citric acid at various pH values. In a study of radioactive fallout, strontium in urine has also been separated by ion exchange.

A very intriguing illustration of the power of ion-exchange chromatography to separate mixtures of extremely similar complex ions ions is provided by the work of L. P. Scott,[19] who separated the chromium complexes, $Cr(H_2O)_6^{3+}$; $Cr(H_2O)_5(Os(CH_3)_2)^{3+}$; $Cr(H_2O)_4(Os(CH_3)_2)_2^{3+}$; $Cr(H_2O)_3(Os(CH_3)_2)_3^{3+}$; $Cr(H_2O)_2(Os(CH_3)_2)_4^{3+}$; $Cr(H_2O)(Os(CH_3)_2)_5^{3+}$ and $Cr(Os(CH_3)_2)_6^{3+}$. Note, that in going through this series of complexes the charge on each ion is identical and the difference between any pair of members is merely the substitution for a water of hydration by the dimethyl osmium group. To effect this separation they used a Dowex 50W-X4 column thermostated at $-1°C$, a solvent of water-dimethyl sulfoxide, and a gradient elution technique in which the concentration of sulfuric acid in this solvent system was increased from 1 to 6 M during the elution.

Fritz[4] separated various groups of metal ions, such as Cd(II)–Zn(II), Mn(II)–Ni–(II), Zn(II)–Fe(III)–Cu(II)–Mn(II)–Ni(II), Fe(III)–Al(III), Bi(III)–Cd(II)–Zn(II), Zn(II)–Cu(II)–Co(II), In(III)–Fe(III)–Mn(II)–Ni(II), Ga(III)–V(IV), and Bi(III)–Cd(II)–V(IV) on a column of Dowex 50-X8 in the hydrogen form using eluents of acetone in water.

Blasius[2] has used weak ion-exchange resins to separate the platinum metals. He separated the chloro complexes of rhodium, palladium, and iridium on a weak base anion exchanger and rhodium, palladium and platinum as well as platinum, iridium and palladium on a weak (carboxylic acid) cation-exchange resin.

Practical uses of ion-exchange separations were made by Pollard[17] who separated magnesium, strontium, and calcium on Dowex 50-X8 using ammonium lactate as his eluent, followed by EDTA at a pH of 10 to remove the barium from the column. The eluate was analyzed by emission flame photometry. This separation of the alkaline earth metals was applied to minerals, limestone, dolomite, and barytes. Van Erkelens[22] used sulfonic acid cation-exchange resins to separate microgram amounts of cobalt from copper, iron, zinc and lead in cow's liver using an eluent of acetone–HCl–water. Bradley[3] studied the influence of potassium, calcium, and magnesium fertilization on the yield, the acidity, and the nature of the acid in tomatoes. His tomato purees were filtered, passed through a cation-exchange resin, and the eluates analyzed for the three metals. He reports that potassium showed a strong effect but that neither calcium nor magnesium influenced the growth.

EXPERIMENT 12–1
Separation of Cadmium and Zinc on an Anion-Exchange Resin *

The purpose of this experiment is to illustrate the technique of ion-exchange chromatography, showing how the anionic complexes of metal ions can be separated from one another by anion-exchange chromatography.

In a solution with a high chloride ion concentration both cadmium and zinc form complex anions.

$$Zn^{2+} + 4Cl^- \rightleftharpoons ZnCl_4^{2-} \qquad \beta_4 = 0.71$$

$$Cd^{2+} + 4Cl^- \rightleftharpoons CdCl_4^{2-} \qquad \beta_4 = 51$$

These chloro complexes are capable of being exchanged for other anions on an anion-exchange resin. Fig. 12–7 shows the change in the distribution coefficient for zinc and cadmium on Dowex 1-X8 as the chloride concentration in the solution increases. At 1.0 M HCl, D for $ZnCl_4^{2-}$ is 6.0×10^2 and D for $CdCl_4^{2-}$ is 2.2×10^3. These values are too high and too close together to enable a separation of them to to be made by ion exchange in a 1 M HCl medium. They can be separated with

---

* Taken from S. Kallmann, C. G. Stell, and N.Y. Chu, *Anal. Chem.*, **28**, 230 (1956).

0.01 M HCl; there the zinc does not exist as the anion complex, but cadmium does, with a D of 40. If the solution of zinc and cadmium contains both chloride and hydroxide ions, zinc will form mixed hydroxy-chloro complexes such as $ZnCl_3OH^{2-}$ or $(ZnCl_3)_2OH^{3-}$, whereas cadmium does not form mixed complexes. Some of the cadmium and some of the zinc will form the hydroxy complexes:

$$Zn^{2+} + 4OH^- \rightleftharpoons Zn(OH)_4^{2-} \qquad \beta_4 = 2 \times 10^{15}$$

$$Cd^{2+} + 4OH^- \rightleftharpoons Cd(OH)_4^{2-} \qquad \beta_4 = 1 \times 10^{12}$$

The sample containing zinc and cadmium is dissolved, and then the solution is made about 1.5 M in chloride ion, which will convert all of both metal ions to the chloro complexes. These complexes are then put onto the top of the column of Dowex 1-X8 where they exchange with the chloride ions. While the column is eluted with NaOH–NaCl, some of the zinc chloro complex is transformed to hydroxy and mixed hydroxy-chloro complexes, while some of the cadmium chloro complex forms hydroxy complexes only. The cadmium chloro complex is held more tightly onto the resin; the zinc hydroxy complexes are more stable. Therefore, the zinc is eluted from the column fairly rapidly, while the cadmium remains in the resin.

The cadmium can be removed from the column very rapidly by destroying its chloro complex. Therefore, after all of the zinc has been eluted, the eluent is changed to dilute nitric acid, which destroys the anionic cadmium complex, leaving only the positively charged metal ions in solution. These cations cannot be exchanged with the anion resin and hence elute immediately. The reactions for this separation are:

Sample addition

$$2R^+Cl^- + ZnCl_4^{2-} \rightleftharpoons (R^+)_2 ZnCl_4^{2-} + 2Cl^-$$

$$2R^+Cl^- + CdCl_4^{2-} \rightleftharpoons (R^+)_2 CdCl_4^{2-} + 2Cl^-$$

Elution of zinc

$$(R^+)_2ZnCl_4^{2-} + (R^+)_2CdCl_4^{2-} + 6OH^- \rightleftharpoons 2R^+OH^- + (R^+)_2CdCl_4^{2-}$$
$$+ Zn(OH)_4^{2-} + 4Cl^-$$

Elution of cadmium

$$(R^+)_2CdCl_4^{2-} + 2NO_3^- \rightleftharpoons 2R^+NO_3^- + Cd^{2+} + 4Cl^-$$

Preparation of the column.   Weigh about 15–20 g of Dowex 1-X8 in the chloride form into a 150-ml beaker, using the side-shelf scales. Add about 100 ml of deionized water and stir for a few minutes to wet the resin. Decant off the supernatant liquid as soon as the larger particles have settled. The volume of the wet resin should be about 25 ml. Add to the resin 50 ml of 0.5 M HCl, stir a few minutes, allow the resin to settle, and decant off the supernatant liquid. Repeat this washing process until the supernatant liquid is clear.

Into the bottom of a 50-ml burette or a narrow (~ 1.1 cm, i.d.) chromatographic column, tamp a small plug of glass wool. The glass wool should be tight enough and large enough to prevent any of the resin particles from passing through and clogging the stopcock or tip, but loose enough and small enough so as not to impede the flow of liquid through the column.

Using 0.5 M HCl as a wash liquid, transfer the wet resin slurry to the chromatographic tube. Rinse down the sides and allow the resin to settle under gravity alone. A 20-cm column of well-packed resin should result. If the column is shorter than this, add more resin. Wash the completed column once with 0.5 M HCl. Do not allow the level of the liquid in the column to fall below the surface of the resin bed. If it does, air will be entrained in the bed, surround the resin beads, prevent solution from coming in contact with the resin, and hence prevent ion exchange from occurring. Keep the liquid level about 1 cm above the resin bed when the column is not being used.

Wash the resin column with two 20-ml portions of 0.12 M HCl–10% NaCl eluent, draining the solution to about 0.5 cm above the top of the resin bed when finished.

Sample addition.   Pipette a 2.00-ml aliquot of the unknown cadmium–zinc solution onto the top of the column. This can best be achieved by holding the tip of the pipette about 1 cm above the resin bed and running the tip around the inner circumference of the chromatographic column while the sample is draining out of the pipette. Drain the sample to within 0.5 cm of the top of the resin bed. Use 5 ml of the HCl–NaCl eluent to wash down the walls of the column, draining the column down to within 0.5 cm of the top of the resin bed. Repeat the washing with a 2-ml aliquot of the eluent. The resin will change colors.

Development of the column.   Pass 150 ml of the 2 M NaOH–2% NaCl eluting solution through the ion-exchange column at a flow rate of about 3 ml/min, collecting the eluate containing the zinc in a 250-ml volumetric flask. (Why does a precipitate form and then redissolve?)

Wash the resin column with about 50 ml of water to remove most of the sodium hydroxide solution, discarding the solution collected from the bottom of the column.

Pass 150 ml of 1 M HNO$_3$ through the ion-exchange resin bed at a rate of about 3 ml/min, collecting the eluate containing the cadmium in a second 250-ml volumetric flask.

After removal of the zinc and cadmium from the column, the resin may be returned to the chloride form from the nitrate form by passing the HCl–NaCl eluent through the column. It is then ready for use in the analysis of another sample.

Analysis of the zinc eluate.   Dilute the eluate containing the zinc up to the mark on the volumetric flask with deionized water and mix the solution thoroughly by upending the flask at least ten times. Pipette a 50.00-ml aliquot of this solution into a 250-ml Erlenmeyer flask. Using 6 M HCl carefully adjust the pH of the solution to around 9. Titrate the zinc solution with 0.01 M EDTA according to the instructions given on p. 230 for the standardization of the EDTA solution, beginning with the addition of the NH$_3$–NH$_4$Cl buffer. Repeat the titration with a second and third aliquot.

Analysis of the cadmium eluate.   Dilute the eluate containing the cadmium up to the mark on the volumetric flask with deionized water and mix the solution thoroughly by upending the flask at least ten times. Pipette a 50.00-ml aliquot of this solution into a 250-ml Erlenmeyer flask. Titrate the cadmium solution with 0.01 M EDTA according to the instructions given on p. 230 for the standardization of the EDTA solution against zinc, beginning with the pH adjustment with NaOH. Repeat the titration with a second and third aliquot.

Calculation of the results.   The reaction for the titration with EDTA can be generalized as:

$$M(NH_3)_4^{2+} + HY^{3-} \rightleftharpoons MY^{2-} + NH_4^+ + 3NH_3$$

Therefore, from the titration data for each aliquot of each metal:

no. mmol of EDTA used to titrate = vol EDTA × molarity EDTA

and from the stoichiometry of the above titration reaction:

no. mmol metal titrated = no. mmol of EDTA used

The entire amount of eluate was not titrated, however, only an aliquot of it. Thus the entire amount of each metal ion in the eluate must be found by correcting for this.

$$\text{no. mmol metal in eluate} = \text{no. mmol titrated} \times \frac{250 \text{ ml}}{50.0 \text{ ml}}$$

Naturally, this is also the number of millimoles of each metal ion in the initial sample if the separation was accomplished successfully.

no. mmol of metal in sample = no. mmol of metal in eluate

We are interested in determining the weight of each metal ion present in the initial 2.00 ml of sample added to the top of the resin. This can be obtained readily, as surely you must remember, by multiplying the number of millimoles of the metal by its atomic weight.

no. mg metal in sample = no. mmol metal in sample × atomic wt

Summarizing all of this into a simple, handy equation:

$$\text{no. mg metal in sample} = \text{ml EDTA to titrate} \times M_{\text{EDTA}} \times \frac{250 \text{ ml}}{50.0 \text{ ml}} \times \text{atomic wt}$$

The relative standard deviation for each of the metal titrations should be five parts per thousand or less.

PROBLEMS

1. A column containing 1.694 g of air-dried, strong cation-exchange resin in the hydrogen form is eluted with 250 ml of 1.0 M KCl. Titration of the eluate required 63.72 ml of 0.0968 M NaOH to reach a phenolphthalein end point. Calculate the capacity of the air-dried cation resin.

2. In an experiment, 40.00 ml of 0.3636 M $Ba(ClO_4)_2$ is shaken with 15.63 ml of wet, strong cation-exchange resin in the hydrogen form until equilibrium is obtained. Analysis of the resultant solution by flame photometry showed that it was 0.1869 M in barium. The capacity of the wet resin is 2.218 mequiv/ml.

Calculate the separation factor, the selectivity coefficient, and the distribution coefficient for barium ion on this resin.

3. The selectivity coefficient, K_{Li}^{Ag}, for the cation-exchange reaction between silver and lithium of Dowex 50-X16 is 22.9. If 4.00 ml of wet resin in the lithium form having a capacity of 1.983 mequiv/ml is shaken with 50.0 ml of 0.111 M $AgNO_3$, calculate the concentration of silver ions remaining in solution at equilibrium.

4. How many grams of Dowex 1-X8 in the hydroxide form having a capacity of 3.14 mequiv/g are needed to remove 99.9% of the chloride ions from 125 ml of 0.0507 M HCl in a single equilibration? The selectivity coefficient, K_{Cl}^{OH}, is 8.9 × 10^{-2} and the density of the wet 8% cross-linked resin is 1.2 g/ml.

5. (a) A column of Dowex 50-X4 resin is 25.0 cm long and 1.00 cm in diameter. Two solutes A and B, each have a band width of 13.0 ml when eluted from this column. What is the minimum difference in distribution coefficients these two solutes can have and yet still be resolved on this column?

   (b) Which of the following pairs of ions from Table 12–2 could be separated under the stated conditions on this column? Na(I)–Cs(I); Mg(II)–Ca(II); Mg(II)–Sr(II); Mg(II)–Ba(II); Ca(II)–Sr(II); Sr(II)–Ba(II); Fe(III)–Ce(III); Fe(III)–La(III); Eu(III)–Ce(III); La(III)–Ce(III).

6. Using the information from Fig. 12–6 for the distribution coefficients of metal ions on Dowex 50-X4, devise conditions for the ion-exchange separation of each of the mixtures listed below:

   (a) calcium, barium, and zinc in HCl solutions
   (b) copper, cadmium, and manganese in HCl solutions
   (c) iron, aluminum, and indium in HCl solutions
   (d) iron, bismuth, and antimony in HCl solutions

7. The values of the distribution coefficients, D, between Dowex 50-X4 and 1 M HCl are: zinc = 23; manganese = 23; cadmium = 38; and calcium = 32. Referring to Fig. 12–9, explain why 0.02 M EDTA cannot be used as an eluent to separate a mixture of zinc and cadmium on Dowex 50-X4 at a pH of 8. Approximately what pH value would you suggest for attempting this separation using EDTA?

8. What are the three modes in which an ion-exchange resin can be used?

9. Sketch the structural formulas for:
   (a) a strong cation-exchange resin
   (b) a weak cation-exchange resin
   (c) a strong anion-exchange resin
   (d) a chelating resin

10. Arrange the following salts in the order that they will be eluted from a column containing a strong cation-exchange resin.
    (a) $Al_2(SO_4)_3$, K_2SO_4, $CdSO_4$, $Zr(SO_4)_2$
    (b) $Mg(NO_3)_2$, $Ni(NO_3)_2$, $Pb(NO_3)_2$, $Cu(NO_3)_2$
    (c) $AgNO_3$, NH_4NO_3, HNO_3, KNO_3

11. What is the order in which the following salts will be eluted from a strong anion-exchange resin?

    K_2SO_4, HNO_3, NaCl, NH_4OAc, CsBr

12. What effect does the concentration of HCl have on the exchange equilibrium of

barium(II), copper(II), and cadmium(II) on a strong cation-exchange resin? Account for these differences in behavior.

13. Explain why it is feasible to separate zinc and cadmium ions from one another using a strong anion-exchange resin.

14. What influence does the pH of the eluent have on the ion-exchange separation of a mixture of metal–EDTA chelates on a strong cation-exchange resin? Explain.

15. What influence does the pH of the eluent have on the ion-exchange separation of a mixture of metal ions when using a chelating resin? Explain.

16. Describe the mechanism of the exchange process.

17. What minimum difference in retention volume is required to separate two ions by ion-exchange chromatography?

18. Define the term resolution ratio, R_R, and give its meaning in your own words.

19. Compare and contrast ion-exchange and paper chromatography as a tool for separating mixtures of amino acids. Focus on:
    (a)   the complexity of the mixture that can be separated
    (b)   the length of time required for separation
    (c)   the apparatus needed
    (d)   the resolution which each method is capable of giving.

REFERENCES

1.   Adams, B. A. and Holmes, E. L., *J. Soc. Chem. Ind. (London)*, **54,** 1T (1935).
2.   Blasius, E. and Rexin, D., *Z. Anal. Chem.*, **179,** 105 (1961).
3.   Bradley, D., *J. Agr. Food Chem.*, **10,** 450 (1962).
4.   Fritz, J. S. and Fertig, T. A., *Anal. Chem.*, **34,** 1562 (1962).
5.   Glueckauf, E., *Trans. Faraday Soc.*, **51,** 34 (1955)
6.   Hamilton, P. B., *Anal. Chem.*, **32,** 1779 (1960).
7.   Ibid., **35,** 2055 (1963).
8.   Hamilton, P. B., Bogue, D. C. and Anderson, R. A., *Anal. Chem.*, **32,** 1782 (1960).
9.   Helfferich, F., *Ion Exchange*, McGraw-Hill Book Co., New York, 1962, p. 167.
10. Ketelle, B. H. and Boyd, G. E., *J. Amer. Chem. Soc.*, **69,** 2800 (1947).
11. Khopkar, S. M. and De, A. K., *Anal. Chim. Acta*, **23,** 441 (1960).
12. Kressin, I. K. and Waterbury, G. R., *Anal. Chem.*, **34,** 1598 (1962).
13. Majumdar, S. K. and De, A. K., *Anal. Chim. Acta*, **24,** 356 (1961).
14. Marcus, Y. and Kertes, A. S., *Ion Exchange and Solvent Extraction of Metal Complexes*, Wiley-Interscience, London, 1969, p. 300.
15. Nelson, F. and Kraus, K. A., *Proceedings of the First International Conference on the Peaceful Uses of Atomic Energy*, United Nations, New York, **7,** 113 (1955).
16. Nelson, F., Murase, T. and Kraus, K. A., *J. Chromatogr.*, **13,** 503 (1964).
17. Pollard, F. H., Nickless, G. and Spencer, D., *J. Chromatogr.*, **10,** 215 (1963).
18. Povondra, P., Pribil, R. and Sulcek, Z., *Talanta*, **5,** 86 (1960).
19. Scott, L. P., Weeks, T. J., Jr., Bracken, D. E. and King, E. L., *J. Amer. Chem. Soc.*, **91,** 5219 (1969).
20. Spedding, F. H., Fulmer, E. I., Butler, T. A., Gladrow, E. M., Gobush, M.,

Porter, P. E., Powell, J. E. and Wright, J. M., *J. Amer. Chem. Soc.*, **69,** 2812 (1947).

21. Spedding, F. H., Powell, J. E. and Wheelwright, E. J., *J. Amer. Chem. Soc.*, **76,** 2557 (1954).
22. Spedding, F. H., Voigt, A. F., Gladrow, E. M. and Sleight, N. R., *J. Amer. Chem. Soc.*, **69,** 2777 (1947).
23. Tompkins, E. R., Khym, J. X. and Cohn, W., *J. Amer. Chem. Soc.*, **69,** 2769 (1947).
24. Tompkins, E. R. and Mayer, S. W., *J. Amer. Chem. Soc.*, **69,** 2859 (1947).
25. Tremillon, B., *Z. Anal. Chem.*, **236,** 472 (1968).
26. Van Erkelens, P. C., *Anal. Chim. Acta*, **25,** 42 (1961).

CHAPTER 13

GEL CHROMATOGRAPHY

Gel chromatography sorts out molecules on the basis of their physical size. The gel consists of a network of carbon atoms supporting a film of liquid. The openings or pores in this network vary in size; small molecules will pass through them, but larger ones will not. So, in effect, the gel sieves the molecules according to their molecular volume. The size of the molecules excluded from the gel network depends upon the extent of the cross-linking of the carbon skeleton of the gel. If the degree of cross-linking is very large, only very small molecules can enter the gel. In general, gel chromatography is applied to macromolecular mixtures, such as polymers, or proteins, although some experiments have been performed with inorganic materials such as NaCl, $CaCl_2$, and Na_2SO_4.

The process of gel chromatography is similar to, and yet quite different from, the other forms of chromatography that have been discussed. A dried, highly cross-linked polymer, such as a dextran or polystyrene divinylbenzene, is soaked in solvent until the polymer has taken up as much solvent as is possible to form a gel. Then, a fairly large amount (100 g) of this gel is placed in a column, and the solvent is forced through the gel in a pulse-free manner. After the bed of gel has settled in the column to a volume of 80 to 100 ml, a sample of 1 to 5 ml of the unknown mixture is injected into the top of the column, without interrupting the solvent flow. The sample diffuses into the column where it immediately begins to be separated into its components on the basis of size. Those molecules too large to enter into any of the pores of the gel will remain outside the gel and be eluted immediately. Those molecules small enough to pass through all the pores in the gel, will be eluted with a volume of liquid that is equal to the volume of the gel bed. Molecules whose size lies between these two extremes pass through some of the pores but not all of them. The order in which these molecules are eluted depends upon the number of pores they can pass through. The eluate emerging from the bottom of the gel column, contains the solute molecules in order of decreasing molecular size—the largest molecules emerging first and the smallest molecules emerging last. The eluate is analyzed continuously either spectrophotometrically or by means of a differential refractometer.

484

Gel chromatography developed simultaneously in many different laboratories, producing different terminologies about the process. These variations more or less have been narrowed to only two different camps, or two schools of gel chromatography—gel filtration chromatography and gel permeation chromatography.

Gel filtration was introduced in 1959 by Porath and Flodin.[7] This school uses dextran gels as the molecular sieve. Because of the hydrophilic nature of dextran, the solutions are aqueous or highly polar. The members of this school are usually biochemists or natural-product chemists who separate mixtures of materials of natural origin such as proteins or viruses. The equipment used is identical to that of gel permeation but the detection of the components in the eluate is usually done spectrophotometrically.

Gel permeation was introduced in 1962 by Moore[5] who separated a mixture of polystyrene polymers on a polystyrene divinylbenzene gel using toluene as the eluent. This school uses hydrophobic gels (usually polystyrene divinylbenzene) as the molecular sieve. Therefore, the solvents are nonpolar organic liquids and the mixtures separated usually consist of synthetic macromolecules. The members of this school are usually polymer, analytical, or organic chemists. The equipment used is the same as that used in gel filtration, except that the components of the eluate are usually determined by differential refractometry.

Experimentally, mechanistically, and theoretically there really isn't any difference between gel permeation and gel filtration so that in order to avoid the inference that there may be, people recently have begun to speak merely of gel chromatography.

THEORY OF GEL CHROMATOGRAPHY

Since gel chromatography is the most recently invented chromatographic technique, an understanding of its operation and the development of a theoretical basis for its separating ability have not been formulated explicitly yet. Studies are still being carried out to obtain the necessary information and correlations in order to check theories and to prove or disprove hypotheses. Three different approaches or models have been used with moderate success as theoretical bases for gel chromatography. The first approach relies on steric exclusion; stating that the basis for the separation lies in the differences in the sizes of the pores of the gel and the sizes of the molecules being separated. This probably is the most widely accepted mechanism for gel chromatography. The second approach is based upon restricted diffusion—the difference in the times it takes different sized molecules to diffuse in and out of the gel. Friction and varying pore diameters cause the molecules to diffuse at different rates, according to their size. The third approach is a thermodynamic one, based on the enthalpy and entropy changes in transferring a solute from the mobile liquid to the gel phase. This theory is primarily concerned with calculating curves and comparing them with the experimentally obtained ones; it uses the statistics of the size distributions of pores and molecules. Because of these basically different approaches, there is no uniform explanation of how gel chromatography works or how separations can be improved.

THE EXPERIMENTAL VARIABLES

The similarities of chromatographic technique are so strong that a person watching an operator use a high-speed liquid chromatograph cannot tell whether partition, adsorption, ion exchange, or gel chromatography is being carried out. But gel chromatography has some striking differences from the other forms of chromatography that create its uniqueness. Relatively large volumes of sample mixture are separated. Short, broad columns often are used successfully. The stationary liquid and the mobile liquid are identical. The molecules in the sample mixture are eluted from the column in order of decreasing molecular size. The volume of eluting agent required to elute all sample components is less than the volume of the gel bed in the column. There is only a very small dilution of each sample component during the separation. The concentration of the solute in the gel is equal to or less than the concentration of the solute in the mobile eluent. The distribution coefficients for solutes range only from zero to one.

Apparatus

The apparatus used in gel chromatography can consist of merely a simple glass chromatographic column, a solvent reservoir from which the solvent flows by gravity, and a detector system. Usually, however, the more elaborate, high-speed liquid chromatographs discussed in Chapters 7 and 9 are employed. The basic apparatus for gel chromatography is shown in Fig. 13–1.

The pumps used to force solvent flow should give a constant and reproducible flow rate, one that does not have pulses of pressure and hence surges of flow. Often, in order to smooth out the pulses of the pumps, a ballast tank is included after the pump in the apparatus. The pumps should be able to function against a fairly strong back pressure, for it is not easy to force a liquid through a column of gel a meter long. The three pumps most commonly used are *peristaltic, syringe,* or *reciprocating piston* pumps.

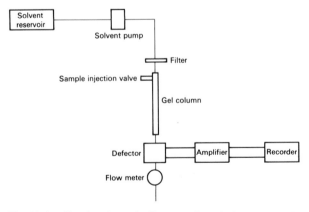

Fig. 13–1. Simple schematic diagram of a gel chromatograph.

Since the solvent is forced through the chromatographic system, it is not convenient to have to stop the solvent flow, open the system, and add the sample. Thus, the sample introduction system inserts the sample into the flowing eluent at the top of the column. This consists of an injection port which is usually an opening covered with a rubber septum through which the sample is injected from a hypodermic syringe, although other valve systems have been used.

The chromatographic column containing the gel must be made of a material capable of withstanding the high pressures and corrosiveness of the solvent system. Columns are usually made out of copper, glass, or stainless steel piping. Fig. 13–2

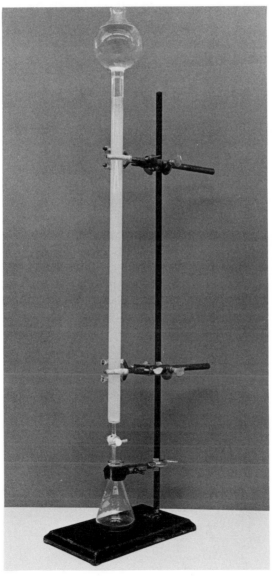

Fig. 13–2. A typical gel chromatographic column. (*Photograph by Stephen Daugherty.*)

shows a packed chromatographic column for gel chromatography. The columns used are straight, rather than bent or coiled, so as to have equal path lengths for diffusion.

The gels used to pack the columns contain a three-dimensional interwoven polymer skeleton. Throughout the skeleton are groups that will attract certain solvents, absorb them, and cause the gel to swell. The general mechanism of swelling is the same as that discussed in Chapter 12 for ion exchange. Chemically, the gels are either polymers of sugar molecules (dextrans, agaroses) or polymers of hydrocarbons (polystyrene, powdered rubber). The dextrans are polysaccharides composed of glucose units cross-linked with epichlorhydrin. Each epichlorhydrin reacts with a hydroxyl group on two different glucose chains forming 1,3 ether bonds. The resulting polymer can be very loose and soft, if the cross-linking is slight, or very rigid when the cross-linking is extremely high. As was mentioned in Chapter 10 when discussing paper, the glucose hydroxyl groups are capable of absorbing extremely large amounts of water. In dextrans, this solvent takeup continues until it produces a gel. The pore diameters within the gel depend upon the extent of cross-linking, which in turn determines the molecular weight limit of the molecules that will not pass through the pores.

a dextran   epichlorohydrin

Another gel used for separations is made by copolymerizing acrylamide with N,N'-methylenebisacrylamide. These polymers, with structures similar to those shown on p. 423 contain amide groupings that are capable of absorbing polar solvents and swelling.

acrylamide   N, N'—methylenebisacrylamide

The agar gels also are composed of sugar units, as are the dextrans; only in agarose gels the sugars are galactoses instead of glucoses. Again the polymer in attempting to dissolve in water or polar solvents forms a gel.

The structure of the polymer made from styrene and divinylbenzene is shown on p. 450. This hydrocarbon structure will absorb nonpolar or slightly polar liquids to produce nonpolar gels. Another nonpolar gel that swells in nonpolar or slightly polar solvents and will separate nonpolar or slightly polar mixtures is made from powdered rubber.

Unless very highly cross-linked, the above gels are soft and flexible. Gels with rigid structures have been prepared from powdered or porous glass and silica.

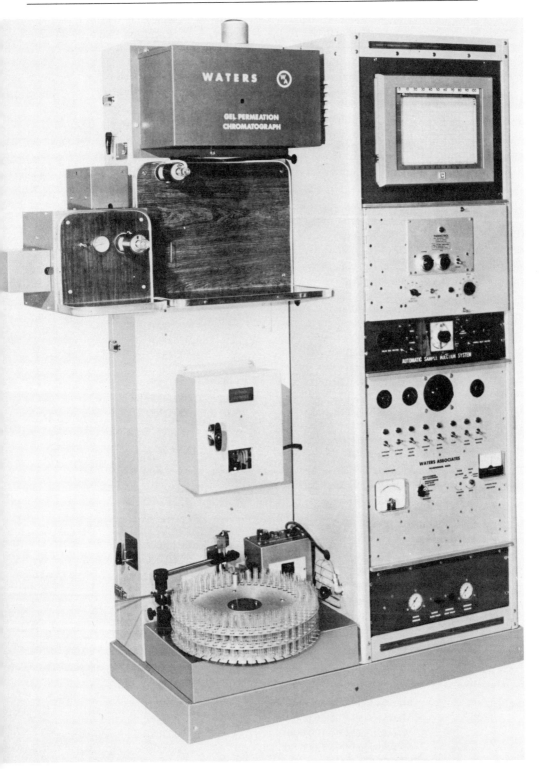

Fig. 13–3. Typical gel chromatograph. (*Courtesy of Waters Associates.*)

Table 13–1. COMMERCIALLY AVAILABLE COLUMN SUBSTRATES

Designation	Pore Diameter, Å	Molecular Weight Exclusion Limit	
1. Rigid materials			
A. Porous glass			
Bio-Glas 200	200	. . .	
Bio-Glas 500	500	. . .	
Bio-Glas 1000	1000	. . .	
Bio-Glas 1500	1500	. . .	
Bio-Glas 2500	2500	. . .	
CPG-10-75	75	28,000[a]	
CPG-10-125	125	48,000[a]	
CPG-10-175	175	68,000[a]	
CPG-10-240	240	95,000[a];	120,000[b]
CPG-10-370	370	150,000[a];	400,000[b]
CPG-10-700	700	300,000[a];	1,200,000[b]
CPG-10-1250	1250	550,000[a];	4,000,000[b]
CPG-10-2000	2000	1,200,000[a];	12,000,000[b]
B. Porous silica			
Porasil-60	. . .	60,000[b]	
Porasil-250	. . .	250,000[b]	
Porasil-400	. . .	400,000[b]	
Porasil-1000	. . .	1,000,000[b]	
Porasil-1500	. . .	1,500,000[b]	
Porasil-2000	. . .	2,000,000[b]	
Merck-o-gel Si-150	150	50,000[b]	
Merck-o-gel Si-500	500	400,000[b]	
Merck-o-gel Si-1000	1000	1,000,000[b]	
2. Semi-rigid gels			
A. Polystyrene gels			
Styragel 39720	. . .	60 Å[c]	
Styragel 39721	. . .	100 Å[c]	
Styragel 39722	. . .	350 Å[c]	
Styragel 39723	. . .	700 Å[c]	
Styragel 39724	. . .	2,000 Å[c]	
Styragel 39725	. . .	5,000 Å[c]	
Styragel 39726	. . .	15,000 Å[c]	
Styragel 39727	. . .	50,000 Å[c]	
Styragel 39728	. . .	150,000 Å[c]	
Styragel 39729	. . .	700,000 Å[c]	
Styragel 39730	. . .	5,000,000 Å[c]	
Styragel 39731	. . .	10,000,000 Å[c]	
Bio-Beads S-X8	. . .	1,000[b]	
Aquapak A-440	. . .	100,000[b]	
B. Polyvinylacetate gels			
Merck-o-gel-OR-750	. . .	750[b]	
Merck-o-gel-OR-1500	. . .	1,500[b]	
Merck-o-gel-OR-5000	. . .	5,000[b]	
Merck-o-gel-OR-20,000	. . .	20,000[b]	
Merck-o-gel-OR-100,000	. . .	100,000[b]	
Merck-o-gel-OR-1,000,000	. . .	1,000,000[b]	

(continued)

Designation	Pore Diameter, Å	Molecular Weight Exclusion Limit	
3. *Soft gels*			
A. *Dextran gels*			
Sephadex G-10	. . .	700[d]	
Sephadex G-15	. . .	1,500[d]	
Sephadex G-25	. . .	5,000[a];	5,000[e]
Sephadex G-50	. . .	10,000[a];	10,000[e]
Sephadex G-75	. . .	50,000[a];	70,000[e]
Sephadex G-100	. . .	100,000[a];	150,000[e]
Sephadex G-150	. . .	150,000[a];	400,000[e]
Sephadex G-200	. . .	200,000[a];	800,000[e]
Sephadex LH-20	. . .	[f]	
B. *Polyacrylamide gels*			
Bio-Gel P-2	. . .	2,000[e]	
Bio-Gel P-4	. . .	4,000[e]	
Bio-Gel P-6	. . .	5,000[e]	
Bio-Gel P-10	. . .	17,000[e]	
Bio-Gel P-30	. . .	50,000[e]	
Bio-Gel P-60	. . .	70,000[e]	
Bio-Gel P-100	. . .	100,000[e]	
Bio-Gel P-150	. . .	150,000[e]	
Bio-Gel P-200	. . .	300,000[e]	
Bio-Gel P-300	. . .	400,000[e]	
C. *Agarose gels*			
Bio-Gel A-0.5	. . .	500,000[e]	
Bio-Gel A-1.5	. . .	1,500,000[e]	
Bio-Gel A-5	. . .	5,000,000[e]	
Bio-Gel A-15	. . .	15,000,000[e]	
Bio-Gel A-50	. . .	50,000,000[e]	
Bio-Gel A-150	. . .	150,000,000[e]	
Sepharose B	. . .	3,000,000[a]	
Sepharose 2B	. . .	20,000,000[a]	
Sag (Ago-Gel)-10	. . .	250,000[e]	
Sag (Ago-Gel)-8	. . .	700,000[e]	
Sag (Ago-Gel)-6	. . .	2,000,000[e]	
Sag (Ago-Gel)-4	. . .	15,000,000[e]	
Sag (Ago-Gel)-2	. . .	150,000,000[e]	
D. *Polystyrene gels*			
Bio-Beads S-X1	. . .	3,500[b]	
Bio-Beads S-X2	. . .	2,700[b]	
Bio-Beads S-X3	. . .	2,100[b]	
Bio-Beads S-X4	. . .	1,700[b]	

SOURCE: Ref. 2. Reprinted by permission of *J. Chem. Educ.*
[a] Determined with soluble dextrans.
[b] Determined with polystyrene.
[c] Extended chain lengths of polystyrene. Multiply by 41 to convert these values to approximate molecular weight of polystyrene.
[d] Determined with polyethylene glycols (aqueous).
[e] Determined with peptides and/or proteins (aqueous).
[f] Exclusion limit depends upon solvent employed and resultant degree of swelling. Some solvents that can be used are water, methanol, ethanol, chloroform, *n*-butanol, dioxane, THF, DMF, acetone, ethyl acetate, and toluene.

Table 13–1 lists the gels commercially available, giving the diameter of the pores in the case of the rigid structure gels. In the softer gels, pore diameter varies within any one gel, so that a broad range of pore diameters exists. Molecules having molecular weights greater than those listed in column three of Table 13–1, will have distribution ratios of zero and will be eluted immediately from the column. For most of the gels there is also a minimum molecular weight, below which no separation is obtained because the gel is completely porous to such small molecules. This minimum molecular weight is one-tenth or less of the maximum molecular weight.

In selecting a solvent for use in gel chromatography, the prime consideration is that it dissolve the sample. A major difference between gel chromatography and partition chromatography is that the same liquid is both adsorbed on the polymeric framework and serves as the mobile eluent, so that gel chromatography involves only one liquid. The solvent, therefore, not only must dissolve the sample but it must swell the polymer to form the gel. Water is the most common solvent used with the dextran and agar gels. Solvents used with the polystyrene-divinylbenzene gels should not interfere with the detection of the separated components of the sample. This means that the solvent's absorption spectrum and refractive index should be different from those of the sample components. Solvents frequently used with these gels, listed in order of increasing refractive index, are: tetrahydrofuran, dimethylformamide, chloroform, dimethylsulfoxide, toluene, and benzene.

Any of the detection systems used in the high-speed liquid chromatographs that were discussed in Chapter 7 can be used to detect the separated components in the effluent of gel chromatography. As mentioned earlier, the two detectors most frequently used are differential refractometers and spectrophotometers. Fig. 13–3 shows a photograph of a typical gel chromatograph.

SEPARATIONS BY GEL CHROMATOGRAPHY

The recorder trace for the eluate from a gel chromatographic column may have the appearance shown in Fig. 13–4. Because gel chromatography developed independently of other forms of chromatography, the symbols and terminology used in gel chromatography are somewhat different from those encountered in the

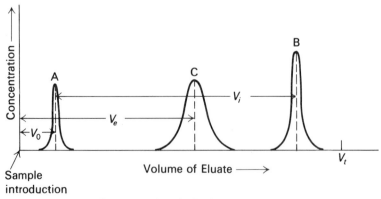

Fig. 13–4. A typical gel chromatogram.

other forms of chromatography, but the concepts are identical. Let us suppose that the mixture to be separated consists of three components, A, B, and C. A is a molecule so large that it is incapable of entering any of the pores in the gel. B is a molecule so small that it is capable of moving freely through all of the pores and solvent in the gel. C is a molecule of an intermediate size, capable of entering the solvent in the gel but only able to diffuse through some of the pores; C is too large to pass through all of the pores in the gel. Consider Fig. 13–4 as the elution curve of the mixture of A, B, and C. V_t is the total volume the swollen gel occupies in the chromatographic column. V_e is the volume of the eluent that is necessary to elute the sample component's maximum (or peak) concentration. V_e is identical to the term V_R, used in previous chapters and in other forms of chromatography. V_0, called the *outer volume of the gel*, is the volume of the solvent in the column that is not a part of the gel matrix. V_0 is identical to the volume of the mobile phase or the interstitial volume used in other forms of chromatography (V_m or V_I). V_i, called the inner volume, is the volume of the solvent that is in the gel. V_i is called the *volume of the stationary phase*, (V_s), in partition chromatography. The volume of the gel is the sum of the volume of the polymer skeleton, V_m (the *matrix volume*) and the volume of the imbibed solvent, V_i (the *inner volume*). The volume of the chromatographic column occupied by the packed gel is the sum of the three gel volumes.

$$V_t = V_0 + V_m + V_i$$

A solute such as A, that is totally incapable of entering into the gel because of its enormous size, will spend its entire time in the mobile solvent while passing through the chromatographic column. Thus the volume of the eluent needed to elute A from the column is merely the volume of the mobile phase that is contained in the packed column. The elution volume of A, V_e, is identical to the outer volume, V_0.

The solute B is so small that it can move freely throughout the gel, and is incapable of distinguishing between the stationary solvent and the mobile solvent, for it encounters no diffusion barriers. Since the solute will diffuse throughout all of the liquid that is in the column, the volume of the solvent that is required to elute it from the column will be equal to the sum of the volume of the stationary liquid phase, V_i, and the volume of the mobile liquid phase, V_0. For B, the elution volume, V_e, equals $V_i + V_0$.

The solute C can move freely in the mobile solvent, but its diffusion within the gel is restricted because its molecular size is larger than some of the pores in the gel structure. Thus the volume of solvent needed to elute C from the column is greater than that for solute A which can only move in the mobile solvent, but less than that of solute B which can move freely in both the stationary and mobile solvents. The larger the molecule C is, the fewer pores it can pass through and the smaller the volume of solvent required to elute it from the column. Fig. 13–5 shows these relationships schematically.

The difference between the elution volume for solute B and the elution volume of solute A, V_0, is the volume of the stationary liquid phase, V_i. The difference between the elution volume, V_e, for solute C and the elution volume of the solute A, is not the total volume of the entire stationary liquid phase, but the volume of

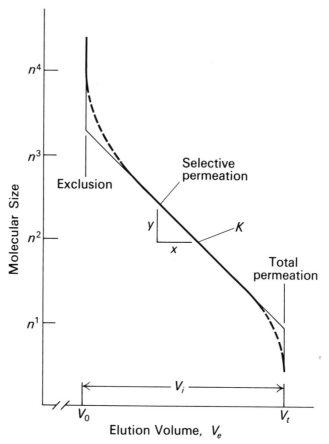

Fig. 13–5. Illustrative GPC calibration curve. (*Redrawn from Ref. 1, by permission of Marcel Dekker, Inc.*)

only that part of the stationary liquid phase through which B can diffuse freely. The fraction of the total volume of the stationary phase that is accessible to solute C is defined by the equation:

$$K_d = \frac{V_e - V_0}{V_i} \tag{13–1}$$

The term, K_d, in gel chromatography is called the *distribution coefficient*. Rearranging Equation (13–1) gives:

$$V_e = V_0 + K_d V_i \tag{13–2}$$

Compare Equation (13–2) with Equation (8–1), p. 357 (adsorption chromatography), Equation (9–1), p. 371 (partition chromatography), and Equation (14–10), p. 506 (gas chromatography). The form of these four equations is identical, only the symbols are different. Thus K_d, the distribution coefficient in gel chromatography can be considered to be an equilibrium constant representing the average equilibrium concentration of the solute in the gel divided by the average equilibrium concentration of the solute in the moving solvent.

From Equation (13–1) it is apparent that the maximum value that K_d can have is one, because when a solute (such as B) has complete access to all of the gel, $V_e - V_0 = V_i$. On the other hand, Equation (13–1) shows us that for a solute (such as A) which is excluded from all of the stationary liquid, $V_e = V_0$ so the value of K_d is zero. For solutes such as C, the values of K_d will be intermediate between zero and one. Note that this upper limit of one for the distribution coefficient is a distinguishing characteristic of gel chromatography, for there are no upper limits set upon the distribution coefficient in other forms of chromatography.

Occasionally values of V_e greater than $V_i + V_0$ are measured experimentally. When this occurs, the value of K_d calculated using Equation (13–1) is greater than one. This is an artifact and merely means that there is some other separating mechanism, such as ion exchange or adsorption, accompanying the molecular sieving in the gel column.

There is considerable uncertainty in determining the inner volume, V_i, for a gel. It is difficult to ascertain what portion of the solvent in the gel belongs to the stationary gel phase and what portion of the solvent is mobile. After all, remember that it is the same liquid. In determining V_i experimentally, one never can be absolutely sure that all of the stationary liquid phase is accessible to the diffusing molecule. To bypass this problem, another term has been defined that is based strictly upon readily measured values. K_{av} is called the *available diffusion coefficient* and is defined by the equation,

$$K_{av} = \frac{(V_e - V_0)}{(V_t - V_0)} \tag{13–3}$$

Comparison of Equations (13–1) and (13–3) shows that, instead of using the inner volume in the denominator, the difference between the total volume of the gel (which is readily measured) and the outer volume is the denominator. Since this latter contains V_m it is always going to be larger than V_i. The numerical values of K_{av}, consequently, are going to be smaller than those of K_d. K_{av} is measured readily. For a given molecule and gel column V_e and V_t are easy to measure. V_0 is measured by passing a very high molecular weight compound of large volume through the column. The molecule selected must have a molecular weight heavier than the maximum given in Table 13–1 for the particular gel used, so its elution volume is V_0. Blue dextran is used for dextran gels. K_{av} values for a given column are extremely reproducible. The more porous the gel, that is, the less the cross-linking, the smaller the numerical differences between K_d and K_{av}.

In order to resolve the components in a mixture, the solutes must have sufficiently different retention or elution volumes. The resolution of two chromatographic peaks depends upon the difference between the elution volumes as well as the width of the elution peaks, as has been stressed in discussing resolution in other forms of chromatography. The difference between the elution volumes of two components being separated by gel chromatography is called the *separation volume*, V_s. For components B and C of Fig. 13–4, we can write:

$$V_s = V_e^B - V_e^C$$

For component B, the K_{av} from Equation (13–3) is:

$$K_{av}^{B} = \frac{V_e^{B} - V_0}{V_t - V_0}$$

which when solved for V_e^{B} gives:

$$V_e^{B} = K_{av}^{B}(V_t - V_0) + V_0$$

Similarly, for component C, we can write:

$$K_{av}^{C} = \frac{V_e^{C} - V_0}{V_t - V_0} \quad \text{and} \quad V_e^{C} = K_{av}^{C}(V_t - V_0) + V_0$$

Substituting the values obtained for V_e^{B} and V_e^{C} into the equation defining the separation volume gives:

$$V_s = (K_{av}^{B} - K_{av}^{C})(V_t - V_0) \tag{13–4}$$

We have seen earlier that V_t is the sum of the inner, outer, and matrix volumes. Therefore, $V_t - V_0 = V_i + V_m$. Substituting into Equation (13–4) gives:

$$V_s = (K_{av}^{B} - K_{av}^{C})(V_i + V_m) \tag{13–5}$$

V_i and V_m depend upon the amount of gel packed into the column. Therefore, the greater the volume of the packing in the column, the larger the separation volume between the elution peaks of two solutes. The volume of solvent separating the concentration maxima for A and B depends not only on the difference between the available distribution coefficients of the two solutes, but also on the total volume of the gel packing. This is not as straightforward as it seems at first glance, for the elution peaks will broaden as they move down the gel column, as they do in other forms of chromatography, decreasing resolution somewhat.

Elution volumes, column efficiency, and separation power in gel chromatography are unaffected by many variables that influence separations by other forms of chromatography. This insensitivity to experimental conditions has both its advantages and its limitations. The reproducibility of any given separation is quite high, but when two solutes are not resolved completely under one set of experimental conditions, there is not much that can be done to improve the separation.

The elution volume is independent of the rate of solvent flow, provided that the flow rate is sufficiently slow that equilibrium is attained at all times. If this condition is not fulfilled, then the elution volume decreases, approaching V_0, as the solvent flow rate increases. Therefore, slowing down the rate of elution does not improve a separation and speeding it up makes things worse.

The elution volume is independent of the size of the sample placed on the column, provided that the sample is small enough so as not to overload the column capacity.

The presence of substances in the sample foreign to those that are being separated, does not alter the separation at all.

Changing the temperature of the column and solvent will change the viscosity of the solvent, and hence the flow rate, but the elution volumes of all of the solutes will change by the same amount, relatively. As a consequence, the actual separation power is not affected by the operating temperature.

The diameter of the gel particles does not influence the separation efficiency at all. Small particles, as we have seen before, will increase the resistance to liquid flow and thus decrease the flow rate. Small particles also provide a larger interface between the stationary and the mobile liquid phases, hence providing a better chance of attaining equilibrium.

The relationship between the elution volume of a solute and its molecular weight is an empirical one of the form:

$$V_e = k_1 - k_2 \log M \qquad (13-6)$$

where M is the molecular weight of the solute, and k_2, called the *separation sensitivity*, represents the slope of the line of the graph of log M vs. V_e. The greater the change in the elution volume for a given change in molecular weight, the greater the separation of two compounds. The separation sensitivity is related to the density of the gel particles.

Figs. 13–6 and 13–7 show typical elution curves for gel chromatography. Fig. 13–6 is the elution curve for a mixture of triglycerides and Fig. 13–7 is the elution curve for a mixture of straight-chain hydrocarbons. Fig. 13–8 shows the logarithmic relationship on the same column between the molecular weight of the compounds of Figs. 13–6 and 13–7 and their elution volumes.

A linear relationship exists between the molecular volumes of compounds and their elution volume. This relationship has led to the concept of *molecular partial volumes*, which, when added together to produce the total volume, predict the elution volume of the compound on a particular column. Hendrickson and Moore[4] used the effective volume of a carbon atom in a straight-chain molecule as the basic unit of volume. The effective volume of heteroatoms (oxygen, nitrogen, sulfur, fluorine, chlorine, bromine, iodine) computed in the same way, is expressed as a

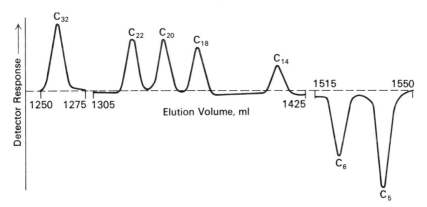

Fig. 13–6. High resolution GPC separation of triglycerides. Analytical/ operating conditions: columns, 160-ft × ⅜-in o.d. column of 500-Å gel; flow rate, 0.4 ml/min. Peak identification: 1, polystyrene; 2, triarachidin; 3, tristearin; 4, tripalmitin; 5, trimyristin; 6, trilaurin; 7, tricaprin; 8, o-dichlorobenzene. (*Redrawn from Ref. 1, by permission of Marcel Dekker, Inc.*)

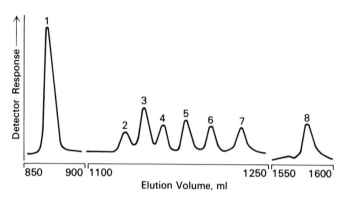

Fig. 13–7. High-resolution GPC separation of hydrocarbons. Analytical/operating conditions: see Fig. 13–6. (*Redrawn from Ref. 1, by permission of Marcel Dekker, Inc.*)

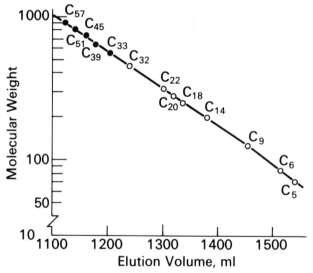

Fig. 13–8. High resolution GPC system: calibration curve ($V_0 = 883.0$ ml). Standards: *n*-hydrocarbon, ○; tristearins, ●. (*Redrawn from Ref. 1, by permission of Marcel Dekker, Inc.*)

fraction of the carbon volume. They developed *effective carbon numbers* which represent the effective volume in terms of carbon atoms occupied by the atoms in a molecule. Summation of these effective carbon numbers gives an effective volume for the entire molecule. From a previously prepared calibration curve relating effective carbon number and elution volume (see Fig. 13–9), the elution volume of an unknown can be estimated.

They measured elution volumes for 130 compounds and obtained a very straight line when they plotted elution volume against effective carbon number (see

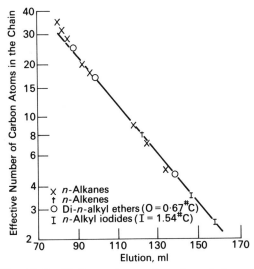

Fig. 13-9. Elution volume of nonbranched compounds as a function of 'effective" number of carbon atoms. (*Redrawn from Ref. 4, by permission of John Wiley & Sons, Inc.*)

Fig. 13–9). They studied saturated hydrocarbons (alkanes), unsaturated hydrocarbons (alkenes), ethers, and alkyl iodides. Branched hydrocarbons, aromatic compounds, cyclic compounds, alcohols, chloro compounds, and carbonyls all fell on the same straight line. Gel chromatography is insensitive to isomeric differences for n-heptane (CH_3—CH_2—CH_2—CH_2—CH_2—CH_2—CH_3), 1-heptene (CH_2= CH—CH_2—CH_2—CH_2—CH_2—CH_3), and 2,3-dimethyl pentane (CH_3— CH—CH—CH_2—CH_3) all eluted with the same volume of solvent.

CH_3 CH_3

    Gel chromatography has proven to be a rapid and valuable method for establishing molecular weights and molecular weight distributions in polymers. Because of the enormous number of closely related molecules present, mixtures of proteins, polysaccharides, oils, and synthetic polymers cannot be separated completely by gel chromatography. Fractions of the eluate are collected, the average molecular weight of each fraction determined, and a plot of the amount of material vs. molecular weight is drawn. Fig. 13–10 shows such a molecular weight distribution for a sample of asphalt. The resultant molecular weight curve is characteristic for a particular polymer.

    The relationship between the elution volume of a peak or a fraction on a particular gel column and the molecular weight causing that peak must be determined experimentally, using a graph or Equation (13–6). The problem, however, lies in calibrating or standardizing the curves, that is, in determining the constants k_1 and k_2 of Equation (13–6). This calibration requires that standards of accurately known molecular weights must be run through the column, and their elution volumes measured. From the resultant data, either a graph or a repeated use of Equation

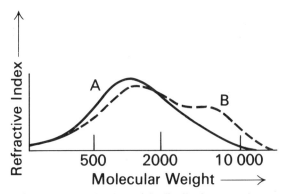

Fig. 13–10.   Molecular weight distribution curve for an asphalt. (*Redrawn from Ref. 8, by permission of the American Chemical Society.*)

(13–6) can be used to evaluate k_1 and k_2. Once this calibration of a particular column has been achieved, the molecular weights of unknown materials can be determined from their elution volumes.

The preceding description makes molecular weight determination and distributions sound easy. It is a misleading summary of the process. There is a major problem because the actual linear relationship is between molecular size and elution volume, not between molecular weight and elution volume. Although we have seen that elution volume is insensitive to isomeric differences for relatively small molecules, for high polymers the geometry of the molecule alters the molecular volume. Thus, depending upon coiling, branching, cross-linking, and other geometrical variations, polymer molecules of the same molecular weight have different sizes. The standards used in preparing the calibration curve should, therefore, be of the same physical and chemical identity as those of the sample to be analyzed. Polystyrene polymers of known molecular weights are available for use as standards, but these are about the only standards we have. As a consequence, experimenters frequently use these polystyrene standards for the establishment of calibration curves for other species, for example, proteins, or tars.

APPLICATIONS

Gel chromatography is used to separate mixtures of very large molecules, with molecular weights between 700 and 150 million (see Table 13–1). As was stated initially, the most frequent users of this technique are the medical scientists and the polymer chemists. Gel chromatography has been used to separate enzymes, hormones, sera and plasma proteins, nucleic acids, viruses, and carbohydrates.[3] Cazes[2] tabulates a wealth of systems studied by gel chromatography.

When synthetic polymers are passed through a gel chromatographic column, distinct elution peaks usually are not observed, but rather a very broad band covering the entire volume is obtained similar to Fig. 13–10, because of the enormously large number of molecules of different molecular weights found in polymer solutions. From the shape of this broad elution curve and by curve fitting

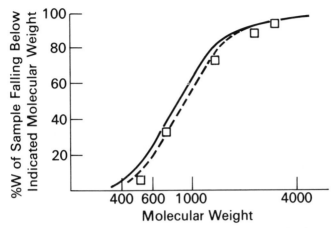

Fig. 13–11. Experimental asphalt molecular weight distribution. (*Redrawn from Ref. 8, by permission of American Chemical Society.*)

it is possible to obtain a distribution of the molecular weights present in a polymer solution as is shown in Fig. 13–11. Polymers that have been studied in this way include, asphalt, epoxy resins, polyester fibers and films, polyamide fibers and films, polyethylene, polypropylene, polystyrenes, polyvinyls, urea–formaldehyde resins, varnishes, and gelatins.

Determann[3] surveys the application of gel chromatography to clinical chemistry, the food stuffs industry, and beverage production.

Although gel chromatography is applied usually to organic polymers, some work has been done on the separation of inorganic salts and polymers. Neddermeyer and Rogers[6] used Sephadex gels to separate certain phosphate polymers. The order of elution is $Na_5P_3O_{10} < Na_2HPO_4 < KCl = LiCl < NaCl < HCl$, which is the order of decreasing molecular weight for these salts as well as of decreasing volume of the solvated salt. Inorganic separations are complicated by both adsorption and ion-exchange effects which accompany the molecular sieving of inorganic salts.

Because the equipment required is complex and elaborate, its cost usually prohibits its availability to teaching laboratories. Consequently, no experiments on gel chromatography are included in this chapter.

PROBLEMS

1. Distinguish clearly between gel filtration and gel permeation chromatography. Is this difference real or apparent? What is the physical principle upon which both are based?
2. In developing a theory for gel chromatography, three different physical models have been devised. What are these models?
3. Describe the chemical and physical structure of a dextran gel; of a styrene divinylbenzene gel.
4. What considerations must be taken into account when selecting the appropriate gel for a separation?

5. What is the dominant factor to be considered when selecting a solvent for gel chromatographic separations? List five commonly used solvents.

6. What techniques are used to analyze the effluent, both qualitatively and quantitatively, emerging from the bottom of a gel chromatographic column?

7. Define mathematically the distribution coefficient, K_d, as it is used in gel chromatography. Explain the meaning of this in your own words. How does this concept compare with the concept of a distribution coefficient as we encountered it in solvent extraction?

8. Between what numerical limits can the distribution coefficient, K_d, vary theoretically? Explain how it is possible for experimentally determined values of K_d to fall outside these limits.

9. Differentiate clearly between the concepts of distribution coefficient and available diffusion coefficient.

10. What is meant by the term separation volume, V_s? What does it represent?

11. How is the volume of eluent required to elute a particular solute from a gel column influenced by each of the following?
    (a) the rate of flow of the eluting agent
    (b) the size of the sample taken for separation—consider both volume and concentration
    (c) the diameter of the gel particles with which the column is packed
    (d) the molecular weights of the solutes to be separated
    (e) the temperature at which the column is operated

12. J. G. Hendrickson and J. C. Moore[4] report the following relationship valid for the separation of straight-chain hydrocarbons (n—C_nH_{2n+2}) on a 16-foot long column of Sephadex X8 gel, using tetrahydrofuran as the eluent at a flow rate of 1 ml/min:

$$V_{eluent} = 187 - 73 \log (\#C)$$

where V_{eluent} is the volume of the eluent required to elute one-half of the solute and ($\#C$) is the number of carbon atoms in the molecule. At what volume of tetrahydrofuran would you expect to locate the peak concentration of each of the following hydrocarbons?
    (a) n-pentane (C_5H_{10})
    (b) n-heptane (C_6H_{14})
    (c) n-nonane (C_9H_{20})
    (d) n-dodecane $(C_{12}H_{26})$

REFERENCES

1. Bombaugh, K. J., Dark, W. A., and Levangie, R. F., *Separation Sci.*, **3**, 375 (1968).
2. Cazes, J., *J. Chem Educ.*, **47**, A461, A505 (1970).
3. Determann, H., *Gel Chromatography—A Laboratory Handbook*, 2nd ed, Springer-Verlag, New York, 1969.
4. Hendrickson, J. G. and Moore, J. C., *J. Polymer Sci., Part A*, **4**, 167 (1966).
5. Moore, J. C., *J. Polymer Sci., Part A*, **2**, 835 (1964); *Part C*, **21**, 1 (1968).
6. Neddermeyer, P. A. and Rogers, L. B., *Anal. Chem.*, **40**, 755 (1968).
7. Porath, J. and Flodin, P., *Nature*, **183**, 1657 (1959).
8. Snyder, L. R., *Anal. Chem.*, **41**, 1223 (1969).

CHAPTER 14

GAS CHROMATOGRAPHY

Martin and Synge[20] proposed the technique of gas chromatography in their original 1941 paper on partition chromatography.

> The mobile phase need not be a liquid but may be a vapour .... Very refined separations of volatile substances should therefore be possible in a column in which permanent gas is made to flow over gel impregnated with a non-volatile solvent in which the substances to be separated approximately obey Raoult's Law.[20]

Since no one else followed up this suggestion, ten years later Martin returned to it himself. In 1952 Martin and James[19] published the first paper on gas chromatography, announcing the separation technique that has become so essential to organic and biochemists. The elegance and potentialities of gas chromatography were apparent now that Martin had pointed them out, so the method became exceptionally popular. It was introduced into research more rapidly and broadly than any other laboratory technique in recent history, The method is so powerful, so rapid, and so widely applicable that over 2600 articles on gas chromatography were published in 1971.

As is also the case for other forms of chromatography, the term *gas chromatography* (vapor phase chromatography) includes more than one experimental method. All that is required by the name is that the mobile phase be a gas at the temperature of operation of the column and detector. The stationary phase can either be a solid [gas–solid chromatography (GSC)] or a liquid film spread on the surface of a solid support [gas–liquid chromatography (GLC)]. As is shown in Table 7–1, the distribution process effecting a GLC separation is the partition of the solute between a stationary liquid and a mobile gas, whereas GSC separations depend upon the adsorption of the solutes from a mobile gas onto the surface of the stationary solid. GLC has been the more favored, studied, and applied, but interest in GSC is growing, with the realization that GSC has advantages. Most people intend the term *gas chromatography* to mean gas–liquid chromatography. Variations of operating parameters give rise to terminology such as *programmed-temperature gas chromatography*. Alterations in equipment have produced terms such as *capillary column* or *electron-capture gas chromatography*. The difference between *regular* and *preparative scale gas chromatography* depends on the size of the analyzed samples.

Why has gas chromatography become the most widely used of the separation techniques? The best reasons are: it almost always will separate mixtures; it will separate them in a short time; and it requires a minimum of effort. Unfortunately, many chemists believe the false conclusion that GLC always will separate complex mixtures.

The primary difference between GLC and the other forms of chromatography is that the mobile phase is a gas instead of a liquid. Since the viscosity of gases is considerably lower than the viscosity of liquids, the gas can be forced to flow through the column at extremely rapid rates. Flow rates between 50 and 100 cc/min routinely are used. Much faster than the 1 to 3 ml/min used in classical liquid chromatographic methods! Successful separations using such rapid flow rates are possible only because of the exceedingly rapid rate of establishment of partition equilibrium between a gaseous mobile and a stationary phase. In order to obtain a few milliliters of gaseous sample at the column temperature, only extremely small amounts of liquid are required. One milliliter of gaseous ethanol at 100°C weighs only 1.5 mg. To obtain this weight, only 1.2 μl of liquid ethanol at room temperature is needed. Therefore, for gas chromatography, the size of the sample used also is much smaller than that used in liquid column chromatography. Consequently, for microscale synthetic or identification processes, separation and identification of the components does not consume all of the material available. All of the solutes must exist as gases during the separation. The chromatographic column is operated at an elevated temperature that is maintained constant by an air thermostat. Because of this necessity of handling gases at elevated temperatures, the apparatus used for GLC is more complex and expensive than that routinely used for the other forms of chromatography. Yet the functions that the apparatus fulfill are the same.

The discussion in this chapter will be restricted to gas–liquid chromatography unless stated otherwise, with the distribution process being partition.

THEORY OF GAS CHROMATOGRAPHY

Retention of Solutes

Partition coefficients in gas chromatography are defined as the total concentration of the solute in the liquid phase, C_L, divided by the total concentration of the solute in the gaseous phase, C_G.

$$K_D = \frac{C_L}{C_G} \tag{14-1}$$

Since the amount of liquid phase in the chromatographic column is small, the total amount of sample that can be separated is limited. The amount of sample that a given GLC column can separate is determined by the capacity ratio, defined as:

$$k = \frac{C_L V_L}{C_G V_G} = K_D \frac{V_L}{V_G} \qquad (14\text{–}2)$$

$$= \frac{\text{no. moles solute in liquid phase}}{\text{no. moles solute in gas phase}}$$

where V_L is the volume of the liquid phase in the column and V_G is the volume of the gas phase (dead space).

In Chapter 7 it was shown that the retardation factor, R_f, can be thought as of either the time the moving solute spends in the mobile phase, the amount of solute in the mobile phase, or the fraction of the solute in the mobile phase. In gas chromatography,

$$R_f = \text{fraction of solute in gas phase} = \frac{C_G V_G}{C_G V_G + C_L V_L} \qquad (14\text{–}3)$$

Dividing numerator and denominator by $C_G V_G$ gives:

$$R_f = \frac{1}{k + 1} \qquad (14\text{–}4)$$

Equation (14–4) relates the partition coefficient and the retardation factor by an expression that is analogous to the expression encountered in liquid chromatography. Note that the more a solute favors the liquid phase (smaller K_D), the more it will be retarded during its passage through the column (smaller R_f). This retardation can be expressed more clearly if we consider the R_f value to represent the fraction of time a solute spends in the moving gas phase. Since the solute will move only when it is in the gas phase, and since the gas phase is flowing at a rate of F_C, the rate of movement of a solute, v_S, through a gas chromatographic column is:

$$v_S = R_f F_C \qquad (14\text{–}5)$$

substituting Equation (14–4) into Equation (14–5):

$$v_S = \frac{F_C}{k + 1} \qquad (14\text{–}6)$$

Measurement of R_f values in gas chromatography is not practical. The parameter used to identify solutes emerging from the column is the *retention time*, t_R. Retention time is defined as the time elapsed after the injection of the sample into the column until the maximum concentration of the solute emerges in the eluate. Retention time is also given by

$$t_R = \frac{L}{v_S} \qquad (14\text{–}7)$$

where L is the length of the chromatographic column. Substituting Equation (14–6) into Equation (14–7) gives:

$$t_R = \frac{L(k + 1)}{F_C} \qquad (14\text{–}8)$$

From Equation (14–8) the experimental variables that influence solute retention times are apparent: (1) column length, (2) amount of liquid phase present in the column, (3) volume of gas phase present in the column, (4) the partition coefficient, and (5) the carrier gas flow rate. While operating temperature is not stated explicitly in Equation (14–8), we know it will affect the value of the partition coefficient and hence the retention time, so temperature must be controlled. When air, or some other material such as methane that is not partitioned into the stationary liquid phase, is injected onto the column, this substance will move through the column at the rate of carrier gas flow because it is never stationary. Air commonly dissolved in gas chromatographic samples emerges at retention time, t_0, where:

$$t_0 = \frac{L}{F_c} \qquad (14\text{–}9)$$

Substituting Equation (14–9) into Equation (14–8) produces a relation between the measured retention time of a solute, the retention time of unretained gases, and the capacity ratio.

$$t_R = t_0 \, (k + 1) \qquad (14\text{–}10)$$

Comparison of Equation (14–10) with Equation (14–4) shows that

$$R_f = \frac{t_0}{t_R} \qquad (14\text{–}11)$$

which enables us to use retention times as a good indication of the extent to which a solute is retarded during its passage through the column. The longer the retention time, the more time the solute spends in the stationary phase, and hence the smaller its R_f value.

Resolution of Peaks

The success of a gas chromatographic separation is measured by the ability to resolve two components possessing nearly identical retention times. As we have seen in Chapter 11, resolution depends upon the difference between two chromatographic peaks and their base width. The difference between the two peak maxima can be expressed in terms of their retention times, while, as we have seen, peak width can be expressed in terms of the standard deviation. In Chapter 7, it was shown that the band (or peak) of a solute widens, the longer it remains within the column. This is true for gas chromatography, as can be seen clearly in Fig. 14–1, which gives the gas chromatogram of peppermint oil. Fig. 14–1 (a) shows that the width of the peaks (4σ) emerging increase as the retention time increases, whereas Fig. 14–1 (b) indicates that this increase in the standard deviation with retention time is linear. This is expressed by Equation (14–12), which relates the two:

$$\sigma = \frac{t_R}{\sqrt{n}} \qquad (14\text{–}12)$$

where n is the number of theoretical plates for that peak.

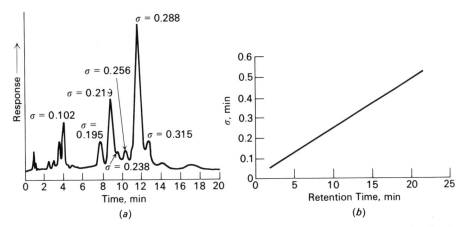

Fig. 14–1. Gas chromatographic peak widths: (*a*) gas chromatogram of peppermint oil; (*b*) relationship of σ, standard deviation, to retention time. (*Redrawn from Ref. 1, by permission of the National Research Council of Canada.*)

The resolution of two peaks is given by Equation (14–13):

$$\text{resolution} = R = \frac{t_{R_2} - t_{R_1}}{\dfrac{w_2 + w_1}{2}} \tag{14-13}$$

where w is the width of a peak at its base and is equal to four times the standard deviation of the peak. This equation is a bit awkward to use, so it is simplified usually by assuming that if two peaks are eluted with retention times that are very close to one another, their standard deviations will be nearly identical also, so that $w_2 = w_1$ (see Fig. 14–1 for an estimation of the error involved in this assumption). In order to compensate for any error, the value of the larger base width is used, w_2. Thus Equation (14–13) simplifies to:

$$R = \frac{t_{R_2} - t_{R_1}}{w_2} = \frac{t_{R_2} - t_{R_1}}{4\sigma_2} \tag{14-14}$$

Substituting Equation (14–10) into Equation (14–14) for the solutes 1 and 2:

$$R = \frac{t_0(k_2 + 1) - t_0(k_1 + 1)}{4\sigma_2}$$

And substituting Equation (14–10) into Equation (14–12) and that resultant equation into the above gives:

$$R = \frac{t_0(k_2 + 1) - t_0(k_1 + 1)}{\dfrac{4t_0(k_2 + 1)}{\sqrt{n}}}$$

Simplifying the above expression gives:

$$R = \frac{(k_2 - k_1)\sqrt{n}}{4(k_2 + 1)} \tag{14-15}$$

The relationship between resolution and purity is a complicated one. For components present in equal quantities, when there is only 0.1% impurity present in each component then R must be 1.5; for 0.5% impurity contamination R will be 1.25; for 2% impurity contamination R is 1.0; for 50% contamination R is 0.75.

Equation (14-15) shows that the ability to resolve two components will depend upon their capacity ratios (or partition coefficients) in the system selected. To illustrate how close these values can be and still have two peaks resolved, let us assume equal amounts of component 1 and of component 2, and separate them so that each is obtained with only 0.1% of the other as a contaminant. Thus R will have to be 1.5. If we use a column having a plate number of 2000 for the second component eluted, from Equation (14-15) the ratio of k_2/k_1 will be 1.13.

In Equation (14-15) k_1, k_2, and n all depend upon both the stationary and mobile phases, so that in order to improve the resolution of two closely eluted components, the nature of the mobile or stationary phase must be changed. Because of the detectors used, the mobile phase frequently cannot be changed. That leaves changing the stationary phase as the only means to improve a gas chromatographic separation. The value of the partition coefficient of a solute depends upon its activity coefficient in the liquid phase, the vapor pressure of the pure solute, the temperature, and the amount of the stationary phase. Thus, changing the stationary phase will cause differences in the activity coefficients of the two solutes which hopefully will enhance the desired separation. Alternatively, a chemical manipulation can be performed upon the mixture to convert the solutes into other chemical species having different vapor pressures (by bromination or formation of a derivative), in the hopes that the separation may be enhanced.

Separation Efficiency

One criterion used to measure the efficiency of a gas chromatographic column is called the HETP which is the height equal to a theoretical plate. (Remember the discussion in Chapter 12?) We can consider a theoretical plate as one stage of separation or equilibrium. For successful separations we want as many stages or equilibrium steps per unit column length as possible. Thus, for successful separations and efficient column operation we want as low a numerical value for HETP as is possible.

The value of the HETP is obtained by dividing the length of the chromatographic column (L) by the number of theoretical plates (equilibrium stages) in the column, n:

$$\text{HETP} = \frac{L}{n} \tag{14-16}$$

The number of theoretical plates required for a particular solute is given by the expression

$$n = 16\left(\frac{t_R}{W_b}\right)^2 \qquad (14\text{–}17)$$

where W_b is the width of the chromatographic peak at its base. This width is measured by extending the tangents to the inflection points on each side of the peak until each intersects the base line. The distance between the two intersections is W_b (see Fig. 14–2).

Substituting Equation (14–17) into Equation (14–16) gives

$$\text{HETP} = \frac{L W_b^2}{16 t_R^2} \qquad (14\text{–}18)$$

The efficiency of a column for separation of a solute having a retention time t_R is calculated readily from experimental data with Equation (14–18).

When attempting to separate mixtures by gas chromatography it is very important to know what experimental parameters and operating conditions can be adjusted to optimize the efficiency of the column operation (HETP). A relationship has been derived by van Deemter, Zuiderweg, and Klinkenberg,[26] but commonly is called the van Deemter equation:

$$\text{HETP} = A + \frac{B}{v} + Cv \qquad (14\text{–}19)$$

where v is the average velocity of the gas flow through the column, and A, B, and C are constants for a particular system. This three-term equation states that the efficiency of a gas chromatograph depends upon the length of the various paths along which the gaseous molecules move (A), the diffusion of the molecules within the gas phase (B), and the transfer of solute from the gas to the liquid phase and back again (C).

A, the multiple path length term, represents the effect on the column efficiency (peak spreading) due to each molecule traveling along its own pathway among the

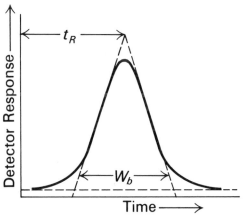

Fig. 14–2. A typical gas chromatographic peak.

particles packed in the column. Because of the enormous number of different routes molecules can travel through the column, there is an enormous number of different path lengths available, so that different molecules arrive at the outlet of the column at different times. A is independent of the velocity of the carrier gas, since the length of the path does not depend upon how slowly or rapidly it is traversed. A does depend, however, on how tightly and regularly the column is packed: $A = 2\lambda d_p$, where d_p is the average diameter of the solid particles and λ is a constant indicating the uniformity of the packing of the column. As particle size decreases, λ increases. For an average column, A varies between 0 and 1 mm.

B, the molecular diffusion term, represents the contribution to the column efficiency (peak broadening) from the diffusion of the solute molecules in the gas phase. This diffusion causes the spreading of a narrow band of solute because of the movements of the individual molecules. (See the section on band broadening in Chapter 7.) $B = 2\gamma D_g$, where γ is a constant representing the structure of the space in the column around the solid particles. It varies between 0.5 and 0.7 for the average column. D_g is the diffusion coefficient of the solute molecules in the carrier gas (in cm^2/sec). For an average column, B is about 10 cm^2/sec.

C, the mass transfer resistance term, represents the contribution to column efficiency (peak spreading) due to the physical process of crossing the gas–liquid phase boundary and diffusion within the liquid phase to that interface.

$$ C = \frac{8}{\pi^2} \left(\frac{k}{(1 + k)^2} \right) \frac{(d_l^2)}{D_l} $$

In this equation $(8/\pi^2)$ is a geometrical factor pertaining to the uniformity of the liquid film thickness on the particles, k is the capacity ratio, d_l is the thickness of the film of liquid phase, and D_l is the diffusion coefficient of the solute (in cm^2/sec) in the liquid phase. From this expression for C, it can be seen that thick liquid films produce less efficient separations than thin ones. Also the faster the molecules diffuse in the liquid phase, the more efficient the column operation. The term $k/(1 + k)^2$ reaches a maximum when $k = 1$. This occurs when the retention time of a solute is twice that of air. Most solutes elute later than this, so that the change in this ratio with k is slight and decreases with increasing k. For an average column, C is between 0.001 and 0.01 sec.

Although temperature of the column does not appear in the van Deemter equation, it does affect the efficiency of operation. D_g, D_l, and k are all temperature dependent. D_g and D_l increase with increasing temperature, whereas k usually decreases with increasing temperature. The net effect of these changes causes the HETP usually to be lower (the column is more efficient) when the temperature of operation is lower.

Both the second and the third term of the van Deemter equation contain the average gas velocity. A plot of HETP vs. v is a hyperbola, as is shown in Fig. 14–3. Fig. 14–3 also shows the contribution that each of the three terms of the van Deemter equation makes to the overall dependency of HETP on v.

Line A shows that the contribution to HETP from particle size and path lengths does not vary with gas velocity. Line B show that the contribution to the HETP by diffusional remixing of the solutes decreases as the velocity of the

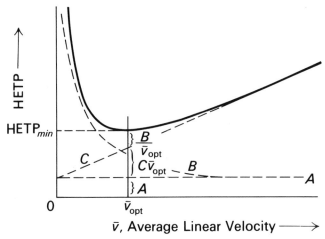

Fig. 14–3. Plot of the Van Deemter equation.

flowing gas increases. Line C shows that the contribution to the HETP by the partitioning of the solute between the two phases increases as the gas flows more rapidly.

As can be seen from Fig. 14–3, the sum of these three variations produces a minimum in the curve, that is, an optimum velocity exists at which the column operates most efficiently. This minimum HETP occurs when

$$\text{HETP}_{\text{opt}} = A + 2(BC)^{1/2} \tag{14–20}$$

or at a velocity of:

$$v_{\text{opt}} = \left(\frac{B}{C}\right)^{1/2} \tag{14–21}$$

This optimum velocity can be determined readily from experimental curves by ascertaining the position of the minimum HETP in the van Deemter plot. At low gas velocities the longitudinal diffusion becomes very important in limiting the efficiency obtainable, whereas at fast gas velocities the resistance to mass transfer limits the efficiency obtainable.

Operating Temperature. In the preceding discussion, it has been shown that the terms of the van Deemter equation are temperature dependent, so that the temperature at which the gas chromatographic column is operated plays an important role in establishing column efficiency and separations. The higher the operating temperature, the faster the diffusion of the solute in both the gas and the liquid phase. In general, the vapor pressure of the solutes will increase with increasing temperature, so the partition coefficient, as defined by Equation (14–1) decreases with increasing temperature. The capacity ratio, therefore, will also decrease with increasing temperature. Equation (14–8) shows that as the capacity ratio increases, the retention times increase. Therefore, lower column temperatures mean longer retention times. Equation (14–15) shows that as the capacity ratio increases, the resolution of two peaks also increases, so that lowering temperatures means increased resolution. The net result is that while lower temperatures will improve the resolution between closely spaced elution peaks, this is achieved at the price of increased time for the separation.

Sample Size. The size of the sample that can be separated is determined by the capacity ratio (k) of the column. When the sample is too large, the column becomes overloaded and is unable to establish a sufficient number of equilibrium stages before the solutes are eluted from the column. The capacity ratio is determined by the amount of liquid phase present in the column [see Equation (14–2)]. The amount of liquid phase depends upon the length of the column, the radius of the column, and the percentage of liquid phase coating the stationary support. Hence, these three factors establish the maximum sample size usable. Increasing the amount of liquid phase will increase the capacity of the column, but at the expense of other factors. As the amount of packing increases (longer and larger columns), the pressure drop along the column increases tremendously, so that unless the inlet pressure is raised considerably (and there are very practical limitations to this) the velocity of the gas will decrease. The van Deemter equation shows that increasing the thickness of the film of liquid phase decreases the efficiency of the column. The dilemma is that "lightly loaded" columns, having very thin liquid films (low percentage of liquid phase on the support), are not capable of separating very large samples. A compromise is necessary. The customary sample size is 1 to 10 μl for liquids, and 1 to 10 ml when the sample is a gas.

APPARATUS

Fig. 14–4 is a schematic drawing of a simple gas chromatograph. The essential components are: (1) carrier gas, (2) gas pressure and flow rate regulators, (3) injection port, (4) column, (5) detector, (6) thermostats, and (7) readout. For preparative work or when using additional methods for confirming the identity of the separated component, a sample collection device is added.

The properties and requirements of these components must be considered in their selection, control, and use during optimum operation of a gas chromatograph. Selection of many of these components is highly dependent upon the particular separation being attempted.

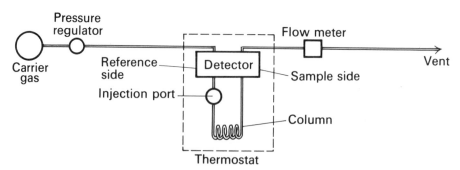

Fig. 14–4. Schematic diagram of a typical gas chromatograph.

Carrier Gas

Elution analysis is the normal mode of operation for gas chromatography. Since the eluting agent is a gas, it is called the *carrier gas*. The carrier gas must be inert to the column material, as well as the liquid and stationary phases. The sample must not interact chemically with the carrier gas (for example, hydrogenation or reduction). It should facilitate, not hinder, the detection of the eluted solutes. The most commonly used carrier gases are hydrogen, nitrogen, helium, and argon, all of which can be obtained commercially in adequate purity in pressurized cylinders.

To a large extent, the detection system used determines the carrier gas. The most widely used detector is thermal conductivity. Successful thermal conductivity requires that the thermal conductance of the carrier gas be greatly different from that of the solutes. Hydrogen and helium best fulfill this requirement. Because of the hazards of working with hydrogen, helium is the most widely used carrier gas when employing thermal conductivity detection. Economics also comes into play here. Helium is relatively cheap in America (a by-product from natural gas sources), but it is quite expensive in Europe, where argon is preferred. Although nitrogen is much cheaper than either, it cannot be used with thermal conductivity detectors. With flame ionization detectors hydrogen is desirable; however, because of its hazardous nature, nitrogen is more frequently used. Early chromatographic studies frequently used compressed air as the carrier gas. Since air is highly unsatisfactory for most detection devices, its use is quite uncommon today.

Pressure and Flow-Rate Regulators

Standard pressure reduction valves are used on the gas cylinders to regulate the pressure and flow of gas emerging from the tank. For theoretical studies manometers are inserted in the gas line before and after the column to measure the inlet and outlet pressures. Inlet pressures are determined by the desired flow rate and the density and amount of column packing. Since columns are open to the air after the detector, normal outlet pressure is the prevailing atmospheric pressure. Flow rates ranging between ten and two hundred milliliters per minute are used normally. The flow rate can be measured before the inlet to the chromatographic column, but more frequently it is done at the outlet. Either rotometer or orifice meters can be used. For routine work a simple soap bubble flowmeter is adequate.

Injection Port

Most gas chromatographic samples are liquids. It has been shown in Chapter 7 that for a clean chromatographic separation the sample must be introduced as a narrow concentrated band at the top of the chromatographic column. This holds true for gas chromatography but is complicated by the necessity of introducing the sample as a gas. Consequently, it is necessary to vaporize the samples completely and rapidly, before they enter the column. The sample injection port is designed for this job. It consists of a heated metal chamber of very small volume that is placed in the gas train just before the beginning of the column (see Fig. 14–4). The opening to the outside is capped by a self-sealing rubber septum, through which the sample is injected by means of a hypodermic syringe. The temperature of the injection port is usually set at or just slightly above the boiling point of the highest boiling component of the mixture to be separated. At this temperature the liquid is vaporized instantly. Since the injection port is in the gas train, the gaseous sample now is swept by the carrier gas onto the top of the column.

Columns

Gas chromatographic columns consist of long tubes filled with the solid packing. In order for the packed columns to fit conveniently into the air thermostats (ovens) they are coiled into spirals or bent into a U or W shape. U-shapes are used for columns up to ten feet in length, W-shapes for columns up to 20 feet long, and coils for columns of any length. Commercial gas chromatographs are designed for coiled columns, so the ovens can be smaller. Columns consist of 1/8 to 3/4'' o.d. stainless steel, glass, or aluminum tubing* connected to the detector and injection port by means of brass swagelock fittings.

Columns frequently are packed with the tubing straight and then bent or coiled, so as to prevent gaps and ensures a more uniform packing. To pack a column, the powdered solid is poured slowly through a funnel into the vertical tubing. During filling, the tubing either is tapped continuously with a pencil or on the floor or it is held against a mechanical vibrator. Ten-foot or longer columns are filled in stairwells usually. Thirty to one hundred-foot columns can be filled by standing on the roof of a multi-storied building with the tubing hung down the side of the building.

Supports

Gas chromatographic columns are filled with finely powdered solids. For gas-liquid chromatography, the sole function of this powdered solid is to provide a support for the thin film of liquid. The solid should exhibit the same properties and fulfill the same requirements as the supports discussed in Chapter 9 on partition chromatography. There are two significant differences from these general properties that pertain to supports for gas chromatography. Since gas chromatographic columns are run above room temperature, thermal stability of the support material is necessary. Porosity must be high in order to minimize the pressure drop as the carrier gas is forced rapidly through the packed columns. The most commonly used support is diatomaceous earth, although powdered glass, sand, graphite, powdered Teflon, detergent powders, and other inert materials can be used.

Sawyer and Barr[24] tried to determine whether or not the stationary support had any effect on performance of a gas chromatographic column. Crushed firebrick, Chromsorb W, Fluoropak, glass beads, carborundum, stainless steel, and nichrome were each coated with carbowax so that all were covered by the same amount of liquid. A mixture of nine ketones was injected into each of the columns and the chromatograms compared. Different performance behavior was

---

* Care must be exercised when considering copper tubing. It oxidizes appreciably above 130°C and is much more reactive than other tubings.

observed for each of the stationary phases. They concluded that adsorption was accompanying the solute partition—to different extents. Solute–liquid phase interactions are affected by the support, so it really is not inert.

Liquid Phases

Equation (14–15) states that the resolution of chromatographic peaks is determined by the differences between their capacity ratios (or partition coefficients). Thus, to improve, or even to effect a separation in the first place, the partition coefficients must be manipulated. One way of doing this is to change the stationary liquid. Selection of the proper liquid phase can make the difference between a successful and an unsuccessful separation.

Criteria for selection of liquid phases for partition chromatography were described in Chapter 9. A restatement of the solvent, thermal, and chemical properties the liquids must possess, slanted toward gas chromatography, follows.

The liquid selected for a given separation should have suitable solvent properties for the solutes to be separated. Generally, nonpolar liquids such as squalane or Apiezon grease are used for nonpolar solutes such as the hydrocarbons. Weakly polar liquids, such as the phthalate esters, are used as solvents when separating weakly polar solutes. Highly polar liquids such as succinate esters and polyglycols are used when separating polar solutes. The ability of the solvent to form hydrogen bonds with the solutes should also be considered as an additional factor for adjustment of partition ratios. In Chapters 9 and 10 the value of chemical reactions between a solute and reagents in the liquid phases in establishing the partition coefficient was stressed. Not too much gas chromatography has been done using chemical reactions in the liquid phase as a means of effecting separations. Solutions of silver nitrate in glycols have been found excellent for the separation of olefins; zinc stearate is a good liquid phase for amine separations. Silicone oils and greases seem to show little preference for molecules on the basis of their polarity and hence are broadly applicable. The vapor pressure of the solute is the determining factor in effecting a separation when silicones are used as the liquid phase.

Since many of the liquids used solidity at room temperature, the column is operated at temperatures above their melting points. The vapor pressure of liquids increases with increasing temperature. If the column is operated at a temperature too high over the melting point of the liquid, the liquid will evaporate from the surface of the solid (bleed) into the moving gas stream. In order to minimize loss of liquid from the column, the vapor pressure of the liquid should be less than 0.1 torr at the operating temperature of the column. Of course, the liquid should not decompose thermally at the operating temperature used.

The liquid selected should not react chemically with the support or the column tubing. Chemical reactions between the liquid and the solutes should be reversible so as not to alter their identity or destroy the compounds.

Table 14–1 is a selection of liquid phases frequently used for gas chromatographic separations. Included in Table 14–1 are the melting point of the liquid (or a temperature range when a family of compounds is indicated), the maximum temperature at which these liquids can be used (or a range of temperatures for a family

Table 14–1. TYPICAL LIQUID PHASES USED IN GAS CHROMATOGRAPHY

Liquid Phase	Melting Point, °C	Maximum Usable Temperature, °C	Components Separated
O ‖ ⬡—C—O—C$_9$H$_{19}$ —C—O—C$_9$H$_{19}$ ‖ O Dinonyl phthalate (and other phthalate esters)		175	Alcohols, aliphatic hydrocarbons, ethers, ketones, halides, methyl esters, substituted benzenes, sulfur compounds
CH$_2$OH | CHOH | CH$_2$OH Glycerol (polymeric glycols such as the Carbowaxes)	18.2	70–120 (125–250 for Carbowaxes)	Alcohols, aromatic ketones
CH$_3$(CH$_2$)$_9$—CH$_2$OH Hendecanol	19	150	Amines
C$_{20}$–C$_{34}$ alkanes, paraffins	51–55	100–200	Aldehydes, amines, aliphatic hydrocarbons, anilines, aromatic ketones, halides, methyl esters, substituted benzenes
Polymeric hydrocarbons (Apiezon oils and greases)		250–325	Phenols
CH$_3$ CH$_3$ | | —O—Si—O—Si—O— | | C$_6$H$_5$ C$_6$H$_5$ silicones (oils and greases)		175–400	Low-molecular-weight acids, alcohols, halides, methyl esters, steroids, organometallic compounds
CH$_3$—(CH$_2$)$_6$—COOH Stearic Acid	69.9	160	Low-molecular-weight acids
(⬡ PO$_4$ CH$_3$)$_3$ Tricresyl phosphate	77	120	Acetate esters, halides

of compounds), and some of the classes of organic compounds that have been separated using that liquid phase.

The thickness of liquid film on the surface of the solid affects a separation in the way described by the van Deemter equation. Liquid coatings between 10% and 30% by weight produce a film that is a satisfactory compromise between column efficiency and sample capacity. The "lightly loaded" columns, mentioned earlier, contain only 1 to 3%, by weight, liquid. To coat the solid with the stationary liquid, a weighed amount of the liquid is dissolved in a low boiling solvent, such as acetone. A weighed amount of the powdered solid is added and stirred to form a thin gruel. The solid is allowed to settle and the low-boiling solvent allowed to evaporate. Thus, the particles become coated uniformly with a thin layer of the liquid. The coated particles are free flowing so they can be handled easily.

Detectors

In their original paper on gas chromatography, Martin and James[19] point out that it is easier to detect changes in the composition of gaseous mixtures than of liquid mixtures. After separating a mixture of low-molecular-weight carboxylic acids, Martin and James monitored the concentration changes in the eluate by means of automatic acid–base titrations. Times have changed such that, of the twenty-three detectors listed by Hartmann[14] in a recent review, only two are based on chemical reactions; all the rest depend upon measurement of some physical property of the eluate.

The sensing device on a gas chromatograph ought to possess the following characteristics.

1. It must measure concentration changes in binary (or ternary) mixtures of gases, where the solute concentration is 0.01 M or less.

2. It should give a response that is linear with concentration, to enable calibration without unnecessarily elaborate procedures.

3. It should respond rapidly, since the eluate emerges from the column at fast flow rates. To facilitate quick response, the volume of the detector should be kept very small.

4. It should be versatile; that is, it should respond to as wide a variety of solutes as possible. Since the chemical identity of all components in mixtures separated by gas chromatography cannot be predicted in advance, the detector must be capable of responding to unsuspected components. If the detector is limited (such as Martin and James' acid–base titration) to only one or a few chemical species, much valuable information can be lost, because the presence of compounds other than those suspected will never be detected. To achieve versatility, detectors should respond to some general property of molecules, rather than to some functional group or specific property.

5. It should give a sensitive response, that is, it should be capable of giving a signal for extremely small quantities of solute. The signal produced should change appreciably for slight changes in concentration.

6. It should be stable. That is, the extent of the response should not change over either short or long periods of time. The signal obtained from a given amount of solute should be reproducible.

7. It should not destroy the sample or be destroyed by the sample. The detector should be capable of withstanding attack by a large number of chemically reactive substances.

Needless to say, there is no one detector that fulfills all of these characteristics, so that compromise is necessary. A very high excellence in one characteristic may more than balance out a shortcoming in another. For example, thermal conductivity detectors are not especially sensitive, but since they respond to all chemical compounds, they are the most widely used detectors.

Detectors may be classified according to the nature of the response they give to the concentration change. Differential detectors follow the change exactly, increasing and decreasing the signal as a solute peak emerges from the column. A typical differential curve is shown in Fig. 14–5(a). Integral detectors produce steplike curves, which are the integrated response of the detector to the concentration change. The height of the step is a measure of the area under the elution peak. A typical integral curve is shown in Fig. 14–5(b).

A second classification of detectors is based upon whether or not they destroy the sample. Some of the detection systems, such as flame ionization, consume the solute in detecting its presence. When the separated solute is needed for other purposes, this is a decided drawback. Other detection systems, such as thermal conductivity, merely measure a physical property of the solute, but do not alter it chemically in any fashion.

C. H. Hartmann[14] has written a review of six of the most widely used detection systems used in gas chromatography.

Thermal Conductivity Detector

The rate at which a hot object loses heat depends upon the gas which surrounds it. The object will cool off faster in air than in pure carbon dioxide. The thermal conductivity detector or katharometer is based on this difference in the ability of gaseous molecules to carry heat away from a hot wire. A typical thermal

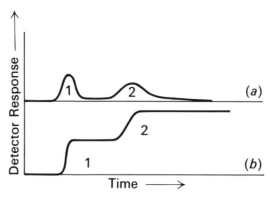

Fig. 14–5. Differential and integral detector responses.

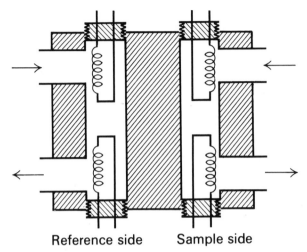

Reference side   Sample side

Fig. 14–6.   Thermal conductivity detector.

conductivity detector, drawn in Fig. 14–6, consists of four compartments, connected as the arms of a Wheatstone bridge. Each compartment is about 3.5 mm in
diameter, hollowed out of a solid metal block. Stainless steel, brass or aluminum
have all been used. Through the center of each compartment runs a spiral of fine
wire (about 10–20 microns in diameter) mounted under slight tension. Wires of
tungsten, platinum, platinum–iridium, tungsten–rhenium alloy are used. Either a
constant voltage is applied or constant current is passed through the four spirals to
heat them to some predetermined temperature (usually above 100°C). The metal
block is thermostated at a constant temperature lower than that of the wire.

When pure carrier gas, such as hydrogen or helium, flows through all four of
the compartments, the rate of transfer of heat from the wire to the metal block is
identical in all four compartments. Therefore, the temperature of each wire is the
same, which means that the electrical resistance of each wire is the same. Thus, the
voltage drop across each spiral of wire is the same, causing the four arms of the
Wheatstone bridge to be in balance. Since no signal of unbalance is produced, the
recorder pen is not deflected but draws a straight line at zero current on the pen-
and-ink recorder (the base line). During a gas chromatographic separation two of
the compartments always have pure carrier gas flowing through them (see Fig. 14–4).
These two form the reference portion of the detector. The eluate from the column
flows through the other two compartments. These two form the sample side of the
detector.

During elution analysis whenever a compound emerges from the column, a
binary gaseous mixture flows through the sample side of the detector, while a pure
gas flows through the reference side. Solutes have lower thermal conductivities
(conduct heat less rapidly) than the carrier gas. When a solute is present in the gas
flowing through the sample compartment, the amount of heat being carried away
from the heated wire to the metal block per unit time is less. Since the wire is
continuously heated, as less heat is lost the temperature of the wire rises. The

electrical resistance of metals increases with increasing temperature, so as the wire's temperature rises, the resistance of the wire increases. This resistance increase produces an increase in the voltage drop across the metal spiral. As a consequence, a voltage unbalance arises between the sample and the reference compartments. The Wheatstone bridge is out of balance, so the pen-and-ink recorder indicates current flowing because of this imbalance. The magnitude of the difference between the two halves of the detector depends upon the identity and amount of solute present in the eluent.

The response of a thermal conductivity detector depends upon the carrier gas used, the compounds being eluted, the temperature of the wire, and the temperature of the block. For maximum response, a carrier gas with a high thermal conductivity should be used. (Most organic compounds have low thermal conductivity so when they appear in the eluate the maximum difference will be obtained). Table 14–2 lists the thermal conductivities of a selected number of carrier gases and solutes.

Table 14–2.   THERMAL CONDUCTIVITIES OF GASES AT 100°C

Gas	Thermal Conductivity, cal/(cm sec °C)	Thermal Conductivity Relative to Helium = 100
Carrier gases		
Argon	5.2	12.5
Helium	41.6	100.0
Hydrogen	53.4	128.0
Nitrogen	7.5	18.0
Solutes		
Ethane	7.3	17.5
n-Butane	5.6	13.5
i-Butane	5.8	14.0
Benzene	4.1	9.9
Acetone	4.0	9.6
Ethanol	5.3	12.7
Chloroform	2.5	6.0
Ethyl acetate	4.1	9.9

SOURCE: Ref. 16.

Hydrogen has the highest thermal conductivity, so when hydrogen is used as a carrier gas the response is largest. Because of the hazards of hydrogen, helium, the second best gas, is used. Since hydrogen and helium conduct heat away from the heated wire better than any other compounds, solutes always have lower thermal conductivities which raise the resistance and voltage drop of the wire, so that the recorder traces a peak. Some solutes have higher conductivities than nitrogen and argon, some have lower. Consequently, when argon or nitrogen are used as carrier gases, the recorder tracing can show either a peak or a valley. Sometimes a W-shaped response which cannot be explained is obtained.

The heated wires in the compartments oxidize at these high temperatures until they are completely destroyed. As they do, the response characteristics of the filament are altered. To slow down this destruction, oxygen and air should be kept out of a thermal conductivity detector at all times when the wires are heated. In practice, this means that incorporating some air in the sample, so as to produce an air peak, is harmful and should be avoided. Carrier gas should flow continuously through the column and detector whenever the filaments are not at room temperature. The most common ways of burning out filaments are: (1) not to turn on the helium gas flow when the filament current is turned on prior to using a gas chromatograph; and (2) to turn off the helium gas flow immediately after using the gas chromatograph without waiting for the filaments to cool down. In concentrating upon saving helium because it is expensive, the damage to the detector is overlooked.

The response of the detector depends upon the difference in temperature between the heated filament and the metal block. As large a difference as possible is desirable because the sensitivity of the response is proportional to the three-halves power of the temperature difference. However, to prevent condensation of the solutes on the surface of the wire and metal block, which causes changes in the operating properties of the detector, not to mention destruction of the sample, the temperature at which the detector operates is higher than that of the column. A temperature difference of 50 to 100°C between the wire and the metal block gives a sensitive enough response without destroying the linearity of the response.

The thermal conductivity detector responds to all gases. For quantitative work, each solute needs its own calibration curve since the thermal conductivity of each solute is different. The peak area is proportional to the weight percentage of each solute and inversely proportional to the flow rate of carrier gas. For reproducible results the flow rate of the carrier gas must be constant, and the temperature fluctuations of the detector compartment must be less than $\pm$ 0.1°C. Thermal conductivity detectors are nondestructive and produce a differential signal. Thermal conductivity detectors have poor sensitivity, capable of detecting only 1 part of solute in 10^5 parts of carrier gas. Hartmann[14] states that "It is estimated that there are more TC detectors in service today than all others combined."

Flame Ionization Detector

When using the flame ionization detector, the gaseous eluate is mixed with hydrogen after it emerges from the chromatographic column. This mixture is burned in a metal jet. A metal ring or short tube is positioned a short distance above the top of the burner (see Fig. 14–7). Between the top of the metal burner and the collector ring, a voltage of 200 to 300 V is applied, with the collector positive with respect to the jet. A solute molecule combusts to ions, both positive and negative, in the flame. Because of the voltage drop, oppositely charged ions are attracted to the collector ring, causing a flow of current. The background current, arising from combustion of the hydrogen and pure carrier gas, is bucked out with a potentiometer, so that the flow of current measured is due solely to the presence of a solute in the eluent stream.

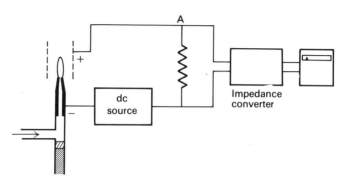

Fig. 14–7.   Flame ionization detector.

The main advantage of the flame ionization detector is its great sensitivity. It is capable of detecting as low as 2×10^{-12} g/sec of solutes. The response is linear over a 10^6 fold range of concentration. The presence of air or oxygen in the carrier gas does not affect the response or harm the detector. Moderate changes in the gas pressure or flame temperature and relatively large changes in the flow rate do not alter the current flow. Nitrogen, rather than hydrogen, is used as the carrier gas when a flame ionization detector is employed. Nitrogen is less hazardous to handle than hydrogen and cheaper than helium. Because a nitrogen–hydrogen flame burns at a lower temperature than a pure hydrogen flame, the background current is lower and more stable than when hydrogen is used as the carrier gas. The flame ionization detector is the most reliable of the ionization detectors.

The major drawback of flame ionization detectors is the lack of applicability to all compounds. Since the sensitivity for all hydrocarbons is the same, flame ionization is used primarily for detection of solutes containing only hydrogen and carbon. The detector does not respond to gases such as oxides of nitrogen, hydrogen sulfide, ammonia, carbon dioxide, or sulfur dioxide. The presence of oxygen, nitrogen, sulfur, phosphorus, or halogen atoms in the solute molecule reduces the sensitivity of the response considerably. Nevertheless, Hartmann[14] claims that the number of flame ionization detectors going into service today is greater than the number of new thermal conductivity detectors being introduced.

Other types of ionization detectors in use depend upon radioactive species to ionize the eluent gas. The resultant electric current is measured in the same fashion as for the flame ionization detector. The helium ionization detector uses tritium to ionize the eluate, the argon detector uses strontium-90 and the β-ray detector uses either these two or radium-226. Photoionization detectors use ultraviolet light to ionize sensitive compounds. The alkali flame detector depends, in some unknown way, upon the presence of CsBr in the flame to produce ions of halogen or phosphorus containing compounds. Lovelock[18] has written an extensive analysis of ionization detectors.

Electron Capture Detector

Although the electron capture detector has a very restricted applicability, it

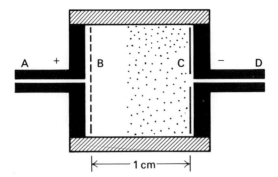

Fig. 14-8.   Electron capture detector.

has an extremely high sensitivity. Fig. 14–8 is a schematic diagram of this detector. The carrier gas, usually nitrogen or argon containing methane as a quencher, is passed into the cell at A, through a diffuser, B, and into the cavity of the cell. C contains the source of ionizing radiation, usually tritium or nickel-63. The gas leaves the cell through the outlet, D. The anode of the collector system is A, and D is the cathode. Ionization of the carrier gas by the β-rays in the chamber produces electrons near the radiation source. The voltage of 10–50 V applied between the electrodes is just enough to cause a current of about 10^{-9} to 10^{-8} amp to flow across the chamber.

$$\beta^- + N \rightarrow N^+ + e^- + \beta^-$$

where N is a molecule of carrier gas.

When an eluate (E) that has a high electron affinity enters the chamber, it combines with the electrons present:

$$E + e^- \rightarrow E^-$$

to produce negatively charged ions. These eluate ions combine with the positive carrier gas ions:

$$N^+ + E^- \rightarrow N + E$$

and thereby reduce the current flowing between the electrodes. This current decrease is measured and used to establish the concentration of solute in the eluate. The detector design of flowing the carrier gas against the flow of ionizing radiation gives a high sensitivity to the detection process.

The success of the electron capture detector rests on the readiness of a compound to capture or take on an electron, that is, its electron affinity. Molecules containing oxygen, sulfur, phosphorus, or halogen give excellent response in the electron capture detector. Halogenated and aromatic compounds have the lowest limits of detection, about 2×10^{-14} g/ml. Thus, electron capture is an excellent detector for pesticides, lead alkyls, and phosphates. There is almost no response for hydrocarbons and only a slight response for aliphatic fluorocarbons. Since the detector responds very readily to oxygen, extreme precautions must be taken to preclude air or oxygen from the eluate stream. Each chemical compound has its own electron affinity, so that each must have its own calibration curve. An equation resembling Beer's law has been used to relate the current decrease to the solute concentration

$$I = I_0 e^{-kc} \tag{14--22}$$

where I is the current flowing in the detector circuit in the presence of a concentration, c, of a solute; I_0 is the current flowing in the absence of a solute, and k is called the *response factor*.

There are many other methods used to detect the presence of solutes in gas chromatographic effluents. These methods are based on density changes in the effluent, light absorption, electrolytic conductivity, or other chemical and physical properties. Some of these are usable only for specific classes of compounds. Gough and Walker[12] have written an excellent article on how to select the appropriate detector for a particular analysis.

Readout Devices

The signal from most gas chromatographic detectors is an electrical current or a voltage. As we have seen, these currents are usually exceedingly small. The signal is usually amplified and then fed to a readout or printout device.

The most commonly used readout device is the *pen-and-ink* or *strip chart recorder*. This recorder is a self-balancing potentiometer. When the amplified signal from the gas chromatographic detector is fed to the potentiometer, it causes an imbalance. This imbalance is marked with the pen on chart paper, giving rise to the familiar peaks (for a differential detector). For most chromatographic recorders, a response time (the length of time it takes the pen to travel the width of the paper) of one second is perfectly adequate.

For quantitative analysis the area under the peaks in the elution curve must be measured. One way of doing this is to integrate the signal from the detector. An integrator can be connected to the recorder either electrically or mechanically. Both *ball-and-disc integrators* and *electromechanical integrators* have been used quite successfully in gas chromatography with an accuracy between 0.2 and 2.0%, depending upon the method used. A second integration technique does not use a recorder at all but connects the detector output directly to the integrator. Integrating amplifiers or digital counters are used commercially in this technique. A third method feeds the detector signal directly onto a magnetic tape, which is then fed into a computer for integration. All three of these integration methods are expensive, so that manual integration methods (see below) are used more commonly, especially in academic laboratories.

QUALITATIVE ANALYSIS

Retention Parameters

The major use of gas chromatography is separation and identification of mixtures of organic and inorganic components obtained from an almost infinite variety of sources. The identification process requires that each peak on the strip recorder be attributed to a specific chemical compound. In the other forms of chromatography, R_f values are used for identification purposes (see above), but R_f values are not very practical in gas chromatography [see Equations (14–4) and (14–11)]. At constant flow rate, the length of time elapsed before a solute emerges from the column (retention time, t_R) or the volume of carrier gas required to elute the solute (retention volume, V_R) is related to the R_f value of a solute. Thus, either is used for qualitative analysis by gas chromatography. Equations (14–7), (14–8), or (14–10) define the retention time. Fig. 14–2 illustrates how this is measured experimentally. On the recorded chromatogram, t_R is the distance from the injection point of the sample to the maximum in the elution peak. The measured distance in centimeters multiplied by the rate at which the chart paper moves through the recorder is the retention time of a solute:

$$t_R = \text{(distance from injection to peak)} \times \text{(rate of movement of chart paper)} \tag{14–23}$$

Alternatively, retention volumes, V_R, are used to characterize solutes. The retention volume is easily obtained from the retention time by multiplying t_R by the rate which the carrier gas passes through the column.

$$V_R = t_R \times F_c \tag{14–24}$$

where F_C is the flow rate of the carrier gas at the outlet of the chromatographic column (hence at atmospheric pressure and the temperature of the column).

As has been discussed in Chapters 7 through 9, within any chromatographic column a certain volume is not filled with the solid support containing the liquid phase. In gas chromatography, this empty space is known as the *dead space* of the column, or the *gas holdup*. A column's dead space is measured by determining the retention volume of some substance, such as air or methane, that is not partitioned into the liquid phase, but passes directly through the column (k is extremely small, so $R_f = 1$). The dead space is what has previously been called the volume of the mobile phase in the column, V_G [see Equation 14–2)].

$$V_G = t_A F_C \tag{14–25}$$

where t_A is the retention time for the unpartitioned solute (air or methane).

To obtain the volume of the carrier gas used to elute a partitioned solute from the column, it is necessary to subtract from the measured retention volume for a solute, the volume of gas normally contained in the column. The volume so obtained represents the volume of carrier gas required for the partitioning of the solute within the column. This volume is called the *adjusted retention volume*, V_R'.

$$V_R' = V_R - V_G \tag{14–26}$$

Remember that the eluent is a gas. As it is forced to flow at rapid speeds through tubing packed with powdered solid, this gas will be compressed. The extent to which the gas is compressed is not the same throughout the length of the column. At the inlet of the column the compression is greatest, after which the gas expands throughout the column until it reaches its maximum volume at the column outlet, where the pressure is atmospheric. As a result, when determining the volume of gas used to elute a solute, a correction must be made for this change in gas volume throughout the column. This correction, called the *pressure correction term, j,* was first derived by James and Martin[19]

$$j = \frac{3(P_i/P_0)^2 - 1}{2(P_i/P_0)^3 - 1} \qquad (14\text{--}27)$$

from the ideal gas law, gas density, flow rates, and average pressure drops. The volume, corrected for the compression within the column, is called the *net retention volume, V_N.*

$$V_N = j \times V_R' \qquad (14\text{--}28)$$

V_R, V_R', V_G, and V_N vary with the temperature of the column and the amount of the liquid phase on the solid support. In order to eliminate these experimental factors so as to obtain a retention volume that different workers using different equipment could compare, Littlewood, Phillips, and Price[17] introduced a term, V_g, which they called the *corrected retention volume/gram of liquid phase* but which since has been renamed the *specific retention volume*. The specific retention volume, V_g, is defined as the net retention volume of a solute at 0°C per gram of liquid phase. V_g is calculated from the net retention volume, V_N:

$$V_g = \frac{V_N \times 273}{w_L \times T} \qquad (14\text{--}29)$$

where w_L is the weight of the liquid phase in the column.

Example. As an illustration of the calculation of these retention volumes and to show how they differ, let us consider the elution of a solute from a 6–ft chromatographic column that contains 2.8 g of stationary liquid phase. The air peak is eluted after 0.030 min, and the solute peak is eluted after 4.78 min. The temperature of the column was 85°C, while room temperature was 23°C. The flow rate was measured with a soap bubble counter at the end of the column and found to be 63.0 ml/min. Atmospheric pressure was 759 torr while the measured pressure at the inlet of the column was 900 torr. Calculate (a) F_c, (b) V_R, (c) V_g, (d) V_R', (e) V_N, and (f) V_g.

(a) The flow rate measured by the soap bubble counter is not the flow rate used in Equation (14–24). F_c is the flow rate at the column temperature and atmospheric pressure. When using a soap bubble counter the gas pressure is less than atmospheric because the measured gas is saturated with the water vapor from the counter. Assuming that the ideal gas law can be applied to the emerging gas, then:

$$F_c = \text{measured flow} \left(\frac{T}{T_{room}}\right)\left(1 - \frac{p_w}{p_0}\right)$$

At 23°C the vapor pressure of water is 21.1 torr.

$$F_c = 63.0 \text{ ml/min} \left(\frac{358°\text{K}}{279°\text{K}}\right)\left(1 - \frac{21.1 \text{ torr}}{759 \text{ torr}}\right)$$

$$= 74.0 \text{ ml/min}$$

(b) The retention volume, V_R, of the solute is [Equation (14–24)]:

$$V_R = 4.78 \text{ min} \times 74.0 \text{ ml/min} = 354 \text{ ml}$$

(c) The retention volume, V_G, of air is [Equation (14–25)]:

$$V_G = 0.03 \text{ min} \times 74.0 \text{ ml/min} = 2.2 \text{ ml}$$

(d) The adjusted retention volume, V_R', is [Equation (14–26)]:

$$V_R' = V_R - V_G = 354 - 2.2 \text{ ml} = 352 \text{ ml}$$

(e) From the measured inlet and outlet pressures, j is calculated to be 0.90. Therefore the net retention volume, V_N, is [Equation (14–28)]:

$$V_N = j \times V_R' = 0.90 \times 352 \text{ ml} = 316 \text{ ml}$$

(f) Finally, the specific retention volume, V_g, is [Equation (14–29)]:

$$V_g = \frac{V_N \times 273°\text{K}}{w_L \times T} = \frac{316 \text{ ml} \times 273°\text{K}}{2.8 \text{ g} \times 358°\text{K}} = 86.2 \text{ ml/g}$$

Operating conditions, (T, P, F_C), of chromatographic columns may vary from run to run, especially where there is a considerable length of time between two runs. The change in conditions will produce differences in the retention volumes, so that corrections can be very necessary. To avoid these corrections, it is more accurate and ultimately more simple to use *relative retention volumes* or *times*. That is, the retention time or volume of a solute is measured relative to that of some standard substance added to the sample mixture, hence run under identical experimental conditions. The relative retention volume or time is given the symbol, $\alpha_{1,2}$.

$$\alpha_{1,2} = \frac{V_{R_1}'}{V_{R_2}'} = \frac{V_{N_1}}{V_{N_2}} = \frac{V_{g_1}}{V_{g_2}} = \frac{t_{R_1} - t_0}{t_{R_2} - t_0} = \frac{k_1}{k_2} \qquad (14\text{–}30)$$

where 1 signifies the sample component and 2 signifies the added internal standard. It is recommended that the internal standard be a normal-alkane whenever possible. When this is not possible, the standard should be something that can be related to a normal-alkane by a relative retention time or volume. The internal standard selected should have a retention volume reasonably close to that of the unknown.

Identification of Chromatographic Peaks

The measurable properties of each elution peak on the recorder printout are the height of the peak, the base-width of the peak, and the retention time or volume of the peak. From these pieces of data, the chemical identity of the compound giving rise to each peak must be deduced. Crippen and Smith[5] have written an excellent review of the methods used to identify peaks on gas chromatograms.

Two components of a mixture may have identical or nearly identical retention volumes producing only a single peak. Therefore, before attempting to identify them, one must make certain that each of the peaks obtained is caused by only a single component. Simple inspection of the shape of the peak may give some indication: an exceptionally broad peak or one with shoulders is usually caused by more than one solute. One excellent way to establish the number of components present in an unknown mixture is to chromatograph the sample on two different columns. A nonpolar column should be used first since components are eluted from it in order of increasing boiling points. In selecting the column, choose one for which there are a lot of data available in the literature. For the second column choose one that is moderately polar, so that properties of the solutes other than just vapor pressure will affect the separation of the compounds. The same number of peaks should be obtained on both columns, for each solute should produce a completely resolved elution peak on both columns. When this occurs, it is very unlikely that two components will be giving rise to any of the peaks.

When it has been established that each of the elution peaks in the gas chromatogram is caused by a single compound, the next problem is the identification of each of the compounds in the mixture. While Equations (14–2), (14–8), and (14–24) show how retention volumes can be calculated from solute concentrations and column parameters, there is nothing in any of these equations that reveals the identity of the solute. Therefore, retention times or volumes *per se* are insufficient for identification purposes. They are, however, the tools used to discover what compound causes the peak. If the retention time or volume of a compound causing a peak on a gas chromatogram is identical to that of a known compound on the same column under identical experimental conditions, then it is reasonably certain that the two compounds are identical. Identification of the compounds giving rise to elution peaks is done by matching retention times or volumes of the unknown substance with retention times or volumes of known substances, measured under identical conditions. If you have no idea about possible compounds to try as knowns, you are in for trouble. What must be done is to guess what compound causes a peak, then inject it onto the same column under identical conditions and measure its retention volume.

It shouldn't be too surprising to realize that frequently pure samples of possible solutes are not available to the experimenter. After all, it is not probable that each laboratory will have a stock of thousands of compounds! This does not mean that certain peaks must remain unidentified, although many times chromatographic peaks do remain unidentified because the experimenter cannot guess possible compounds. When the needed known compound is not at hand, empirical, graphical relationships may be used to obtain the necessary retention time or volume. The vapor pressure of similar molecules usually varies only because of size or weight differences. Thus the relationship for similar compounds between retention time and boiling point, or molecular volume, or the number of carbon atoms in the compound, or some other property is a linear one. If enough compounds are available to establish the line, then a graph can be used to obtain the needed retention time or volume from the known molecular weight, boiling point, or other identifying property. Fig. 14–9 is an example of such an experimental graph. Fig. 14–9 gives the relationship between retention time and the number of carbon atoms present in the methyl esters of a series of monocarboxylic acids. Notice that there are different lines for the different isomers. Saturated straight,

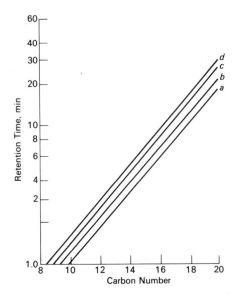

Fig. 14-9. Retention time for methyl esters of mono-carboxylic acids as a function of the number of carbon atoms in the molecule: (*a*) normal saturated chains, (*b*) branched saturated chains, (*c*) chains with one double bond, (*d*) chains with two double bonds. (*Redrawn from Ref. 5, by permission of J. Gas Chromatogr.*)

chain esters fall on line *a*, saturated branched-chain esters fall on line *b*, esters containing only one double bond fall on line *c* and esters containing two double bonds fall on line *d*. These lines can be drawn using data from a small number of compounds. If it is believed that the unknown is a member of a particular class of compounds and its retention time or volume matches one of the points on the line, then it can be assumed to be that compound.

One excellent method for insuring that the unknown peak is caused by a particular compound is to add a small amount of the compound to the unknown. If the area of the unknown peak increases while no new peaks appear, then the two compounds are identical.

When the identity of the material causing a chromatographic peak cannot be obtained after comparing retention parameters with standards, other identification techniques should be used. As it emerges from the column, the recalcitrant compound should be collected so that mass spectroscopy, infrared spectrophotometry, nuclear magnetic resonance spectroscopy, or chemical reactions (for example, functional group analysis) can be used as auxiliary techniques for its identification.

When comparing the retention time (or volume) of an unknown with that of a standard, the reproducibility of the numerical value becomes critical. Goedert and Guiochon,[9] in a study of retention time measurements, found that pressure changes, temperature changes, and time measurement errors caused the greatest uncertainty in the numbers obtained for t_R. To measure retention time with precision of $\pm 1\%$: (1) The inlet pressure to the column must be controlled to within $\pm 0.5\%$. Since the outlet pressure is sufficiently constant over short periods of time, it need not be controlled. In actuality this means F_C, the flow rate is being controlled reproducibly. (2) The column temperature must be held steady within $\pm 0.4°C$. In the usual air thermostat (oven) this control is very difficult to achieve. (3) The time between sample injection and the elution peak maximum must be measured within $\pm 0.5\%$. They insist that when measuring the distance along a sheet of chart paper with a ruler and pencil, this accuracy cannot be obtained. The conclusion of their study is that commercially available gas chromatographs cannot reproduce retention times within $\pm 1\%$.

QUANTITATIVE ANALYSIS

Measurement of Peak Areas

After identifying each of the components present in the unknown mixture, frequently the concentration of each component is wanted. The amount of each solute present in a mixture is represented by the area under the gas chromatographic peak for that solute or by the number obtained from an integrator. Some people merely use the height of a chromatographic peak when determining the concentration of the solute, but this is very risky and at best, is only approximate, so the use of peak heights is not recommended and will not be discussed. Before considering the various methods used to obtain solute concentrations from the measured peak areas let us evaluate the methods most commonly used to measure the area under an elution peak. Fig. 14–10 illustrates the four most common techniques: (1) height vs. half-width; (2) triangulation; (3) cut out and weigh; and (4) planimetry.

(1) Height vs. Half-Width

When the shape of an elution peak is symmetrical and Gaussian (as theoretically all are) its area is given by the relationship:

$$A = \frac{2.507}{2.354} h \times w_{h/2}$$

where h is the height of the peak and $w_h/2$ is the width of the peak at a distance half-way up its height. In order to measure the height a base line must be drawn underneath the peak. The base line is drawn from the beginning of the rise of one peak to the beginning of the rise of the next peak. The accuracy of this base line is determined by the stability of the detector. Since both the peak height and width can be measured very simply and accurately, this method is a good one. When the peaks are extremely narrow (t_R is very low) large errors are obtained by this technique for there are extreme errors in measuring the peak height. Most people tend to ignore the initial factor, assuming that it is one. Areas calculated neglecting this factor are less than those obtained by methods (2), (3), (4). When all peaks in both the standard and the unknown are calculated without the factor, no error is introduced. The method will only give accurate results for symmetrical peaks.

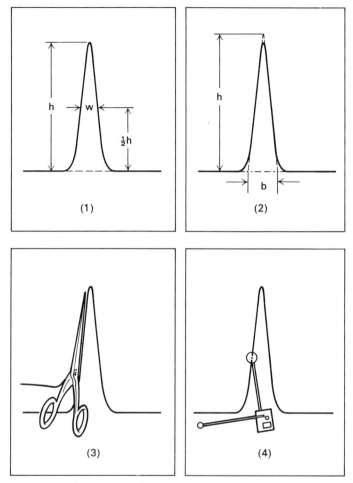

Fig. 14-10. Methods of integrating peak area.

(2) Triangulation

The shape of a Gaussian peak approximates that of a regular triangle. Assuming that each peak is a triangle, its area can be computed from the equation $A = 1/2\ BH$, where H is the height of the triangle (not of the peak) and B is the width of the base of the triangle (not the peak). To construct the proper triangle extend the base line under the peak. Draw lines tangent to the inflection point in each side of the peak. The triangle is created by the points where the tangents intersect each other and the extended base line (see Fig. 14-10). The area calculated for this triangle is not the exact area of the elution peak, but again if all peaks in both the standards and in the unknown are measured by triangulation, no errors are introduced. Triangulation is very subject to the human error in drawing the tangents. The magnitude of the error resulting from incorrect tangents will depend upon the width of the peak—increasing as the peaks become narrower. Since the peaks in a chromatogram vary in width, measurement of areas by triangulation will have different accuracy. Very narrow peaks (spikes) have very large errors.

(3) Cut and Weigh

In the cut and weigh method, after the base line is extended underneath the peak, the peak is cut out of the chart paper with a pair of scissors and weighed on an analytical balance. The weight of the piece of paper is a measure of the area under the peak. The method assumes that the chart paper has a uniform density and constant moisture content. In actuality, these can vary by over a percent. The major disadvantages of the cut and weigh method are that it is very difficult to correct any errors made in cutting out the peak and the cutting process destroys the original chromatogram. If a Xerox copy of the chromatogram is made and cut, these disadvantages are overcome, for the original is preserved and Xerox paper has a greater uniformity than chart paper.

(4) Planimetry

The use of a planimeter to measure the area of a chromatographic peak takes a fair degree of skill. Best results are obtained if the outline is traced several times and the measured areas averaged. The technique is an excellent one for irregularly shaped peaks.

Comparison of Methods

Several groups of people have tried to find out which of the methods used to measure peak areas is the most reliable. Mefford, Summers, and Clayton[21] studied the accuracy and precision of several methods of peak area measurement, including the preceding four. All of the methods they investigated gave essentially identical areas and had nearly identical standard deviations for repeated measurements. Scott and Grant[25] investigated the preceding four methods for repeatability by the same operator using the same method and reproducibility using different operators and equipment but the same methods. According to their results, the peak height times half-width method has the best repeatability and reproducibility while planimetry gives the poorest repeatability and reproducibility. Planimetry is poor because of the deviations made by the operator in tracing the outlines of the peaks. Gill and Tao[8] also compared these four methods. They report that the cutting and weighing of Xerox copies of ten chromatograms gives the most precise measurement of peak area. Both planimetry and triangulation give the poorest precision. From all of these studies, considering the cost of a planimeter and the operator errors involved, planimetry is not recommended for measuring peak areas. Cutting and weighing of the original chromatogram is also undesirable. The peak height-half-width method of arriving at peak areas is a rapid, accurate, and suitable method. Tall, thin peaks (spikes) and short squat peaks—peaks where one dimension is very small yet the perimeter of the peak is large—cannot be measured with an accuracy as high as more uniform peaks.

Methods of Analysis

Once the areas of the peaks have been measured, the concentration of a solute in the sample can be calculated. The area of a peak is related to the concentration of the solute causing that peak by the expression:

$$\text{area} = R \times C \qquad (14\text{--}31)$$

where R, called the *response factor*, is nothing more than the proportionality constant between the concentration and the area. The numerical value of the response factor depends upon the nature of the sample, the nature of the detector, and experimental conditions. Each chemical compound, each detector, and almost each analysis have their own response factors. The response factor varies with sample size, sample matrix, detector sensitivity for the compound, detector response to the compound, bridge current or voltage (for thermal conductivity detectors), carrier gas flow, column temperature, detector temperature, and injection-port temperature. Figs. 14–11, 14–12, and 14–13 show the variation in response

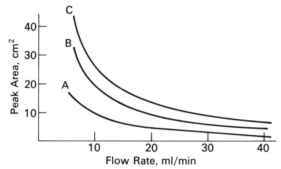

Fig. 14–11. Effect of flow rate on response factor: (A) ethyl formate, (B) ethyl acetate, (C) ethyl propionate. (*Redrawn from Ref. 6, by permission of John Wiley & Sons, Inc.*)

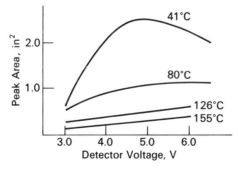

Fig. 14–12. Effect of detector voltage on response factor. (*Redrawn from Ref. 2, by permission of the American Chemical Society.*)

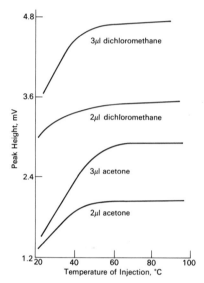

Fig. 14–13. Effect of injection-port temperature on response factor. (*Redrawn from Ref. 23, by permission of C. J. Hardy.*)

factor (as peak height and area changes) with changes in the carrier gas flow rate (Fig. 14–11), the voltage applied across the wire in a thermal conductivity detector, the temperature of the detector (Fig. 14–12), sample size and the injection-port temperature (Fig. 14–13). Fig. 14–11 shows that for a given class of chemical compounds (esters in this case) the change in the response factor will be essentially of the same nature, although different esters produce a different magnitude of response. Fig. 14–12 shows that the variation in the response factor is different at different detector cell temperatures. It also shows that the response factor increases with increasingly applied voltage (except at 41°C). There are two features of Fig. 14–13 to focus on—sample size and injection-port temperature. Acetone boils at 56.2°C and dichloromethane boils at 40.2°C. In order to obtain a constant response factor, the injection port-temperature must be well above the boiling point of the solute so complete vaporization is instantaneous. The effect is essentially the same for both compounds. The larger the sample size the higher this temperature must be.

Because the response factor is not a constant, in order to obtain quantitative results in gas chromatography, either all experimental factors must be controlled and reproduced rigorously or analysis techniques which circumvent these variations must be used. Both approaches are used, as can be illustrated by the four most commonly used quantitative techniques.

Peak Area Normalization Method

The peak area normalization method is independent of experimental conditions because data from only one gas chromatographic separation are used. The method is based on the assumption that the response factors for all of the components in a sample are identical. This is not a valid assumption, as illustrated by Figs. 14–11 and 14–13. When determining the concentration of a mixture by the peak area normalization method, the areas of all the elution peaks on the chromatogram are measured and then summed. Since it is assumed that all response factors are identical, the percentage of the total peak area made up by the area of the peak of the desired component is equal to the percentage weight of the component in the sample mixture.

$$\text{weight percent of component} = \frac{\text{area of component peak}}{\text{total area of all peaks}} \times 100$$

For a method that gives only semiquantitative results at best, there are stringent restrictions on it. Accurate measurements of the areas of all of the peaks on the chromatogram must be made. This implies that for the method to be used, all of the peaks must be resolved completely so that their areas can be measured. When dealing with complex mixtures, often only a few peaks are of interest and resolution of all peaks is not attempted because it is not necessary. Under these conditions this method would not work. Any error in measuring the area of any peak creates an error in the result since all areas are used in the summation. Even though it is widely used, the method is not recommended.

The error of this method is about ten percent relative. The accuracy can be improved by using standards to evaluate the response factor of each component present in the mixture. This negates the advantage of being independent of experimental conditions. In order to determine response factors all components in the mixture must be identified. For complex mixtures this is frequently impossible and it is time-consuming at best. Other quantitative methods are used to circumvent this identification process.

Relative Response Factor Method

This method avoids the complications caused by changes in response factors by using relative rather than absolute values. A measured amount of a known compound (standard) is added to the unknown sample. This added standard must be some compound not originally present in the sample. The response factors for only those components of the unknown to be determined are measured. This measurement is achieved by obtaining samples of the pure compound, adding a known amount of the standard compound to it, separating the mixture on the chromatograph, and then measuring the area of each peak. On the standard samples, the absolute response factor for each peak is calculated by Equation (14–31) from the measured peak area and the known component concentration. The ratio of each response factor to the response factor of the added standard is calculated. This ratio is called the *relative response factor*. That is to say, for each peak in the known:

$$R_c = \frac{\text{area of peak for component, } C}{C_c} \tag{14–32}$$

$$R_S = \frac{\text{area of peak for standard, } S}{C_S}$$

where R_c is the absolute response factor of the sample component, and R_S is the absolute response factor of the added standard. C_c is the concentration of the sample component in the known, and C_S is the concentration of the standard in the known. The ratio of R_c to R_S is the relative response factor.

$$\text{relative response factor} = \frac{R_c}{R_S} \qquad (14\text{--}33)$$

The standard material also is added to the unknown sample in known concentrations, after which the chromatogram of the mixture is obtained. The peak areas of each component are measured. From its peak area and known added concentration, the absolute response factor of the added standard is calculated. Do not be too surprised to find that it differs slightly from the value calculated from the known mixture. From the relative response factor for each component, the absolute response factor for the standard in the unknown; and Equation (14–33), the absolute response factor for each component in the unknown is calculated. Again don't be surprised to find these values differ slightly from those calculated in the known solution. Knowing the response factor for each compound in the unknown sample, the concentration of each can be calculated by means of Equation (14–32).

The use of relative response factors circumvents the problem of reproducing experimental conditions. Any changes in conditions are assumed to affect all components equally, so that any changes in the response factors of the unknown components and the standard will be the same. When this is so, the relative response factor will remain constant from one run to the next; from chromatogram of the known solution to the chromatograms of the unknown sample.

This method gives quite good results, although, as Figs. 14–11 and 14–13 show, the changes in response factors for different compounds are not identical. This method also has the advantage that peak areas and response factors need only be calculated for those components of interest in the sample. The main disadvantage lies in having to add a suitable standard compound in known concentrations to all known and unknown mixtures.

Calibration Curve Method

In this method a series of solutions containing the desired component in different concentrations is prepared. Each solution is injected into the gas chromatograph, and the peak area on the recorder trace is measured. The peak area is graphed as a function of solute concentration as is shown in Fig. 14–14. The unknown sample is then injected into the chromatograph and the area of the peak of the desired component on the chromatogram is measured. From this area, by means of the calibration curve, the concentration of the desired component in the unknown is determined easily.

As can be seen from Fig. 14–14, each component of a mixture will require its own calibration curve, since it has a unique response factor. When using a calibration curve, it is absolutely essential that all of the factors mentioned earlier be controlled—not only be held constant but also be reproducible over extended periods of time (from run to run). One extremely difficult operation to reproduce is

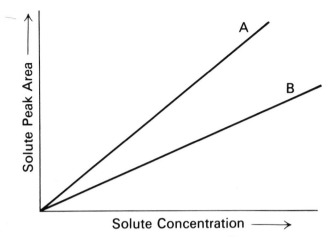

Fig. 14-14. Gas chromatographic calibration curve.

sample injection. The art of sample injection regulates sample size. Injection of a small volume of a liquid sample through a rubber septum from a hypodermic syringe is extremely difficult to perform and to reproduce exactly. Sample injection has been shown time and time again to be the largest source of error when using a method dependent upon reproduction of sample size.

One advantage in using a calibration curve is that only the peaks of interest need to be measured in this method. Resolution of all component peaks is not necessary. Nonlinear response by the detector is taken into consideration since the actual detector response as a function of concentration is measured. This method is capable of giving results that are within 1% relative of the correct concentration.

Internal Standard Method

The internal standard method is the most accurate of the quantitative gas chromatographic methods, capable of giving results accurate to 0.3%. The method is also very complex—a combination of the relative response factor and calibration curve methods. As in the relative retention factor method, a known amount of some compound, called the internal standard, is added to all solutions—knowns and unknowns. The calibration curve is prepared from a series of standard solutions containing different concentrations of the desired component, yet a constant concentration of the internal standard. After each solution is injected into the chromatograph, the peak areas of the component and the internal standard are measured. The ratio of the peak area of the desired component to the peak area of the internal standard for each solution is calculated. These ratios are graphed as a function of the concentration of the desired component in each solution, to produce a calibration curve such as Fig. 14–15. The same concentration of internal standard is added to the unknown solution, and its chromatogram run. The peak areas of both the internal standard and the desired component are measured, their ratio calculated and the desired concentration read at this ratio from the calibration curve.

Not everything can be used as an internal standard. The compound selected as

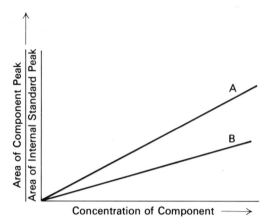

Fig. 14–15. Typical calibration curve for internal standard method.

the internal standard must satisfy certain conditions: (1) the compound must not be present naturally in the unknown; (2) the peak of the standard on the chromatogram must be cleanly resolvable from all others; (3) the compound should have a retention time close to that of the desired component; (4) the ratio of the peak area of standard to that of the desired component should be close to one.

The internal standard method possesses two advantages. First, the size of the sample is not at all critical; and second, the operating conditions need not be kept constant. The drawbacks of the method are: (1) each component must have its own calibration curve; (2) the standard must be added in known amounts to all solutions used; (3) two peak areas must be measured which limits the precision of the method; and (4) the method is only applicable to mixtures where the peaks can be resolved easily.

Temperature Programming

Frequently a mixture contains both low-boiling and quite high-boiling components. Equations (14–8) and (14–15) show that lower column temperatures produce longer retention times and better resolution of solute peaks. If the gas chromatographic column temperature is set so as to elute the low-boiling components with good separation, then it will require an inordinate length of time to elute the high-boiling components. If the column is operated at a temperature so as to elute the high-boiling components in a reasonable length of time, then the low-boiling components come off so early that they are not separated from one another. An obvious solution to this dilemma is to raise the temperature of the column during the elution process, which is exactly what is done during *temperature programming*. In a way, temperature programming can be considered as a form of gradient elution analysis (see Chapter 7) since the elution conditions are changed continuously throughout the elution process.

In temperature programming, the temperature is set initially at some value that is lower than the constant temperature one would use. Throughout elution the

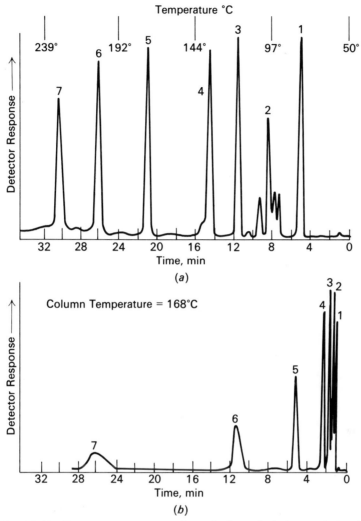

Fig. 14–16. Temperature-programmed vs. isothermal elution analysis of a mixture of C_5–C_{14} n-hydrocarbons. (*Redrawn from Ref. 6, by permission of John Wiley & Sons, Inc.*)

column temperature is increased gradually (usually linearly) to some value higher than the constant temperature value. Not only does this technique improve the resolution of the peaks and shorten the analysis time, but it also lengthens the lifetime of the liquid phase. Fig. 14–16 shows the difference between a constant-temperature column separation of a mixture of normal C_5–C_{14} hydrocarbons and a temperature-programmed separation of the same mixture. n-Tetradecane (peak 7) boils at 252°C. As Fig. 14–16(b) shows, when the operating temperature of the column is held constant at a value of 168°C, n-tetradecane is eluted after about twenty-six minutes, which is not too unreasonable. The lower hydrocarbons, however, elute in about two minutes with quite poor resolution. Fig. 14–16(a) shows that resolution is improved tremendously and analysis time not lengthened appreciably when the temperature is raised from an initial value of 50°C to a final one of 239°C during elution.

The air thermostat of a regular gas chromatograph does not respond to temperature changes rapidly. Consequently, the column in a chromatograph used for temperature programming is wound with a low-mass heating wire. The temperature of the heating wire can be changed very rapidly, which in turn changes the column temperature quite rapidly. When a heating wire is used, the column temperature changes according to the temperature programming as long as the rate of change is less than 30°C/min.

Capillary Columns

In order to separate and analyze extremely small samples, the diameter of the gas chromatographic column must be reduced to a small value. Moreover, a packed chromatographic column often does not operate at its theoretical efficiency. Golay[10] first separated microsamples using a very long capillary coated on the inside with a thin film of the stationary liquid. Capillary columns operate at a much greater efficiency, making them excellent for difficult separations. Capillary columns are made from glass, stainless steel, or nylon capillaries with an inner diameter between 0.25 and 1.0 mm and lengths from 6 to 300 meters. The thickness of the liquid film is between 0.4 and 2 microns.

Coating capillary columns is an art. Enough of the appropriate liquid phase is dissolved in a low-boiling solvent to form a ten percent solution. The capillary is filled with the solution for a length of about 30 cm. Air is slowly blown through the capillary, moving the liquid through it, coating the walls as it moves. After the solution has passed down the length of the column, air is passed continuously through the coated column to evaporate the volatile solvent, leaving the stationary liquid on the capillary wall. Naturally, these columns having only very small amount of liquid phase on them, can only separate very small samples. Liquid sample sizes used with capillary columns range about 10^{-6} g or 10^{-7} ml. These very small samples require different injection techniques from those ordinarily used. Smaller amounts of solutes place more restrictive requirements on the detectors—they must respond faster than regular detectors and to amounts of solute on the order of 10^{-8} mg/ml. Thermal conductivity detectors cannot be used, so flame or other ionization detectors are used. Analysis times in many cases range between 5 and 25 sec.

Evaluation of Gas Chromatography

The major advantages of gas–liquid chromatography are: (1) Separations can be effected very rapidly. The normal analysis time is about fifteen minutes. (2) Very complex mixtures, that is, mixtures containing a very large number of components, components that chemically are extremely closely related to one another, or both, can be separated. (3) Only small amounts of sample are required for the separation. (4) A very wide variety of compounds can be separated. The only restriction is that the compound must exist as a gas at the operating temperature of the column.

The chief disadvantages of gas chromatography are: (1) Relatively expensive and often sophisticated apparatus is required. (2) Only small samples can be separated, so that the technique is restricted for preparative work. (3) The compounds must be gases at the column temperature in order to be separated. Inorganic and high-molecular-weight organic and biochemical compounds frequently cannot be separated. (4) The compounds must be stable thermally at the elevated temperatures. Not only must they not decompose, they must not react at the column, detector and injection-port temperatures. (5) Only the liquid phase can be altered to change the distribution ratio of solutes. Because of detector requirements the mobile gas phase is not readily changed.

The advantages decidedly outweigh the disadvantages, and many ways have been devised to circumvent disadvantages. Repeated separation of small volumes of the same sample is practiced in the preparative gas chromatographs in use. High-boiling compounds are converted chemically (often by fairly elaborate procedures) into volatile derivatives which can be separated by gas chromatography.

Gas chromatography has been applied more broadly and is more rapid than liquid–liquid chromatography. Because the distribution equilibrium can be shifted in either of the two phases, liquid–liquid chromatography has more flexibility for effecting separations. Liquid–liquid chromatography is capable of separating larger volumes of solutions because of the higher capacities of its columns. High-speed liquid chromatography is as rapid as gas chromatography as well as being capable of handling temperature-sensitive compounds.

Gas chromatographic separations are faster than most paper chromatographic separations. Neither technique can separate large volumes of sample. Paper chromatography is used to separate mixtures that cannot be separated conveniently by gas chromatography because of high temperature instability. Thin-layer chromatography is as rapid as gas chromatography and uses equally small samples, so these two techniques have advantages (or disadvantages) in common. Thin-layer chromatography can be used to separate mixtures of sensitive or unstable compounds. Liquid–liquid, paper, and thin-layer chromatography all use apparatus that is much simpler and less expensive than that needed for gas chromatographic separations of comparable quality. All three of these techniques operate at room temperature.

APPLICATIONS

Because of the speed with which it operates, the smallness of the sample size required, and the resolving power and efficiency of its separations, gas chromatography has been applied to the separation of all classes of organic compounds. It also has become a routine analytical tool in all kinds of laboratories. Not only is it an essential piece of analytical equipment in research laboratories, but it is also used for product control, for analysis of commercial products, and in forensic chemistry. As has been mentioned before, the only restriction placed on the samples to be analyzed is that the components of the mixture be sufficiently volatile to enable enough of all components to be in the gas phase during separation. The compounds to be separated should not be temperature sensitive at the operating temperature of the separation. These restrictions, as we have seen, usually can be circumvented, so that gas chromatography can be used for almost all separation purposes.

The petroleum industry uses gas chromatography extensively for the analysis of the enormously complicated mixtures of hydrocarbons that comprise gasolines and petroleum fractions. Liquid phases are nonpolar with the hydrocarbons eluted from the column in order of increasing boiling point. Gas chromatography can separate straight-chain hydrocarbons from their branched-chain isomers containing the same number of carbons. In general, a branched-chain hydrocarbon will be eluted before the straight-chain isomer with the same number of carbons but after the straight-chain compound containing one fewer carbon. Examples of hydrocarbon applications are the separation of mixtures of the isomers of pentanes, of hexanes, of heptanes, of octanes, of nonanes, of olefins, and of aromatic hydrocarbons.

Mixtures of organic halogen compounds, of esters, of ethers, and of organic sulfur compounds can be separated on either polar or nonpolar stationary liquid phases. Mixtures of aldehydes can be separated on poly(ethylene glycol) columns. Aldehydes, very reactive compounds, are widely used in the chemical and plastics industries. Aldehyde mixtures also are obtained during the oxidation of fats and oils. Formaldehyde is too reactive to be separated. Since ketones are widely used as solvents in industry, separation of mixtures of them frequently is necessary. Either polar or nonpolar columns have been used to separate ketones successfully. Alcohols are widely used industrial products. Alcohols also are obtained during the isolation of chemicals occurring in natural products. Mixtures of alcohols containing up to six carbons are separated on columns of phthalate esters. The alcohols are eluted roughly in order of increasing boiling point. Phenols may be separated on nonpolar columns. Carboxylic acids containing up to five carbon atoms can be separated successfully on silicone oil columns. If there are more than five carbons in the acid molecule, the volatility is too low, so the acids are converted to their methyl esters before separating. Amines containing up to twelve carbon atoms can be separated successfully on nonpolar columns, with the order of elution that of increasing boiling point. Carbohydrates are not sufficiently volatile to be separated by gas chromatography. After conversion to their volatile trimethylsilyl derivatives, the mono- and disaccharides can be separated.

During the separation of very polar organic molecules, such as acids and alcohols, some adsorption of solutes onto the solid support accompanies the partition equilibrium. This adsorption causes the peaks to tail. Temperature programming alleviates this tailing to a considerable extent. The hydrogen bonding that occurs in the liquid phase with these very polar compounds alters the order of elution so it is not that of increasing boiling point, as is found with non- and weakly polar molecules.

Although gas chromatography is widely used in biochemistry, the complications caused by low volatility and temperature sensitivity are very prevalent. Because of these difficulties, paper and thin-layer chromatography remain routine tools for biochemical separations and analysis. Gas chromatography can be used to separate mixtures of fatty acids containing up to twelve carbon atoms. Since amino acids are not sufficiently volatile to be separated by gas chromatography they must be converted to their volatile methyl esters. These methyl esters can be separated at about 140°C on silicones. Most steroids are not volatile, although those that are can be separated by gas chromatography. To separate mixtures of steroids, they must be converted to volatile derivatives. The terpenes found in the essential oils of trees, bushes, plants are unsaturated hydrocarbons containing alcohol, ester, keto, and ether functional groups. Their separation is extremely tricky for they are quite unstable. Chemical change or isomerization during the separation process is encountered frequently.

The list of applications of gas chromatography to the separation of commercial products is exceedingly long. It is used for the separation of aminoglucoside antibiotics, and for the separation of tranquilizers in blood and urine samples. Gas chromatography is used for the analysis of herbicide and pesticide residues, for the detection of atmospheric pollutants, for the separation of adulterants and food additives, as well as to analyze cosmetics and other commercial products.

Gas chromatography has become the standard, routine method for the separation prior to the analysis of mixtures of gases. The carbon dioxide, oxygen, and nitrogen in air are separated on molecular sieves by either gas–liquid or gas–solid chromatography. A thin coating of dioctyl sebacate on molecular sieve packings separates hydrogen, oxygen, nitrogen, carbon monoxide, carbon dioxide, and methane from one another. Nitrogen, nitrous oxide, nitric oxide, carbon monoxide, and carbon dioxide can be separated from each other on silica columns. The gases emitted from petroleum refineries (the C_1 to C_5 hydrocarbons) can be separated from one another using columns of deactivated alumina and a flame ionization detector.

The high boiling points of most inorganic compounds prevent the widespread application of gas chromatography to separation of mixtures of them. Special equipment has been designed to separate compounds having boiling points up to 1000°C. Inorganic gas chromatography, therefore, is limited normally to the separation of the volatile hydrides, halides, and acetonylacetone complexes. Organic liquids make poor stationary phases for the separation of inorganic mixtures, so that the 240°C eutectic of $BiCl_3$–$PbCl_2$ frequently is used. The boron hydrides and alkyl boron compounds have been separated on silicones, the volatile phosphorus compounds on poly(chlorotrifluoroethylene) waxes supported on Teflon. Fluorosulfur compounds have been separated on phthalate esters. Mixtures of hydrogen sulfide, carbonyl sulfide, and carbon disulfide can be separated at room temperature.

Parker, Fontan, Yee, and Kirk[22] have used gas chromatography for the separation and determination of the amount of ethanol in blood. The sample of blood is diluted with ethyl acetate (which serves both as a solvent and as the internal standard) and then injected onto a poly(ethylene glycol) column. Quantities of ethanol as high as 0.3% were determined in blood samples with an error less than two percent. J. R. Harris[13] separated and determined the amount of ethanol in cough syrups, food flavorings (almond, vanilla, and orange), and toiletries on columns of molecular sieves at 160°C using a flame ionization detector. J. J. Bennett and M. Hertzlinger[3] used gas chromatography in their analysis of the heavy duty cleaner used by the New York City Transit Authority. Cresylic acids

($\sim 50\%$), methylene chloride ($\sim 40\%$), potassium soaps (under 5%), and per-chloroethylene (under 5%) were determined with a precision of 1% using temperature programming and a thermal conductivity detector.

Gas chromatography is the natural separation technique to consider for studies of air pollution. Bethea and Meador[4] attempted to find a single column and set of experimental conditions for the separation of mixtures of nitrogen dioxide, nitrous oxide, nitric oxide, ammonia, sulfur dioxide, hydrogen sulfide, carbon dioxide, chlorine, hydrochloric acid, and hydrofluoric acid. After a very exhaustive study, they found the goal impossible to achieve so they were forced to use several columns to separate these reactive gases. The particular combination of columns used depends upon the mixture of gases that one is interested in studying.

To separate mixtures containing only nitrogen oxides two columns are needed. The chromatogram obtained when using a column of poly(chlorotrifluoroethylene) grease on a diatomaceous earth support contains two peaks—a single peak for air, NO and N_2O; the second peak due to NO_2. A second column containing a chlorinated hydrocarbon on mixed diatomaceous earths must be used to separate the N_2O from the NO. In order to separate the acidic gases NO, CO_2, N_2O, H_2S, HCl, SO_2, NO_2, and Cl_2 three columns were required. The first, poly(chlorotrifluoroethylene) grease on diatomaceous earth, separates the gases into three groups. The first group contains air, NO, CO_2, N_2O, H_2S, and HCl; the second, SO_2 and Cl_2; and the third is pure NO_2. A column composed of a silicone oil on a diatomaceous earth support separated the SO_2 from Cl_2. The third column, containing a mixture of molecular sieves, separated the components of the first group. When they used a thermal conductivity detector, they could detect only as low as 200 p.p.m. of each gas, but with an electron capture detector they were able to detect as low as 2.2 p.p.m. of sulfur dioxide, 0.3 p.p.m. of chlorine, but only 200 p.p.m. of nitrogen dioxide. The relative error in analyses of air samples was $\pm 10\%$ for chlorine and sulfur dioxide at 10 p.p.m., and 50% for nitrogen dioxide.

Goodwin, Goulden, and Reynolds[11] separated pesticide residues using a column consisting of silicone oil on kieselguhr and an electron capture detector. Samples of apples, broccoli, cabbage, carrots, grapes, lettuce, potatoes, Swedes (turnips), tea, and tomatoes were macerated and then extracted with acetone. Because acetone is too volatile, the initial extract was, in turn, extracted with hexane. The hexane solution was injected into the gas chromatograph. Amounts of lindane, heptachlor, aldrin, telodrin, dieldrin, and endrin as low as 0.1–0.25 p.p.m. were detected. Traces of DDT down to 1 p.p.m. could be detected.

Hoffmann and Rothkamp[15] analyzed cigarette smoke for the amount of nitrobenzenes present. Nitrate in tobacco leaves is believed to inhibit the production of the carcinogen, benzopyrene, during combustion. The nonvolatile particulate matter from cigarette smoke was steam distilled, after which an aliquot of the distillate was injected into a gas chromatographic column. When using a column of a silicone gum on diatomaceous earth, operated at $200°C$, and a flame ionization dector, eight nitrobenzenes were found in the smoke from regular cigarettes. The percentage of each of these was determined using the internal standard method with an error estimate to be $\pm 10\%$.

The elegance of gas chromatography can be illustrated by Genty and Schott's[7] gas chromatographic separation of mixtures of H_2, HD, D_2, DT, T_2, and HT. A three meter column of activated alumina coated with ferric hydroxide and then deactivated with carbon dioxide was used for the separation. Thermal conductivity was used to detect the nonradioactive compounds but an ionization detector was needed for the tritium compounds. Because of the equilibria among all these species when present together their results are considered quite satisfactory.

Although gas chromatography *per se* provides no information about the nature or concentration of any substance present in a mixture, when used in conjunction with appropriate qualitative and quantitative techniques, it is one of the most powerful separation, identification, and determination tools available today.

EXPERIMENT 14-1
Separation and Determination of a Mixture of Aliphatic Alcohols *

The purpose of this experiment is to use gas–liquid chromatography to separate a series of closely related compounds—members of a homologous series. Not only will the identity of the compounds present be ascertained, but also a quantitative determination of the amounts of each component present in the mixture will be made. Because of the probability of fluctuations in operating conditions between sample runs, the relative response factor method is used for the quantitative analysis.

The lower-molecular-weight aliphatic alcohols have the following boiling points: methanol (CH_3OH)—64.7°C; ethanol (CH_3CH_2OH)—78.4°C; 2-propanol (CH_3CH_2OH—CH_3)—82.4°C; n-propanol ($CH_3CH_2CH_2OH$)—97.2°C; isobutanol [($CH_3)_2$—CH_2—CH_2OH]—108.1°C; and n-butanol ($CH_3CH_2CH_2CH_2OH$) —118.0°C. The experimentally measured retention times of these alcohols on a column of Carbowax 20 M [a poly(ethylene glycol)] supported on a diatomaceous earth, relative to the internal standard isobutanol, are: methanol—0.38 ± 0.03; ethanol—0.43 ± 0.04; 2-propanol—0.42 ± 0.03; n-propanol—0.76 ± 0.02; isobutanol—1.00; n-butanol—1.39 ± 0.04. Since members of an homologous series are eluted from a gas chromatographic column in order of increasing boiling point, the observed sequence—methanol, ethanol, n-propanol, n-butanol is also the predicted one. Branched-chain alcohols usually are eluted before their straight-chain homologs, but follow after the straight-chain alcohol containing one less carbon, which explains the orders of ethanol, 2-propanol, n-propanol; and n-propanol, isobutanol, n-butanol. Thus, the entire sequence observed is that predicted. (Note: This is not immediately apparent because of the simultaneous elution of ethanol and 2-propanol.)

In this experiment the gaseous alcohols are partitioned at 85°C, between the flowing solvent, helium, and the stationary solvent, Carbowax 20M [a poly-(ethylene glycol) with a maximum usable temperature of 220–225°C] held on the diatomaceous earth solid support.

Any gas chromatograph with a thermal conductivity detector can be used for

---

* Developed by L. C. Hall and C. Holyoke from material presented by F. Urone and R. L. Pecsok, *Anal. Chem.*, **35**, 837 (1963).

the separation. The detector response is fed to a 1.00 mV full scale response recorder. The column is a 6-ft × 1/4-inch stainless steel tube, packed with 10% (by weight) Carbowax 20M on 70 to 80 mesh ABS Chromosorb P. The helium carrier gas flow rate is regulated at some chosen rate between 40 and 70 cc/min. The injection port is heated to 150°C, the column oven operated at 85°C, and the detector-block temperature set at 150°C.

Qualitative identification of the unknown. In order to obtain meaningful and reproducible quantitative results, the art of sample injection must be mastered. The 10-microliter Hamilton hypodermic syringe must be handled carefully and knowledgeably. In handling the syringe, be sure that the needle is not bent and that the plunger slides freely.

Inject a 1-μl sample of each of the pure alcohols through the rubber septum into the injection port of the gas chromatograph. To accomplish this, fill the microliter syringe that is kept with each instrument with the sample solution to be injected as follows: Place the syringe tip into the solution; gently slide the plunger up slowly and down rapidly to dislodge air bubbles; and finally draw the plunger up easily so as to withdraw 3 μl. Invert the syringe so its tip points up and slowly push the plunger to the 1-μl mark. Wipe off the excess solution that has run from the tip. The injection process should be effected with decisiveness and as rapidly as possible. Quickly insert the point of the needle through the rubber septum of the sample injection port and without hesitation inject all of the sample quickly into the port. Rapid, but continuous and gentle pressure should be used. Instantly withdraw the point of the syringe after all of the sample has been injected (Note 1). The sample, as was indicated in Chapter 7, should be introduced at the top of the column in as concentrated a space as possible. The recorder paper should be moving before injection of the sample; mark on the recorder paper the point of injection of each sample.

Inject each of the six alcohols separately. Adjust the attentuation so that the top of each peak is on scale and is of a reasonable height.

Inject a sample of the unknown onto the column, again marking the chart paper at the time of injection.

On each of the seven chromatograms measure the distance between injection of sample and the maximum in the elution peaks. From the rate of movement of the chart paper and this distance, calculate the retention time, t_R, for each of the standard alcohols using Equation (14–23). Similarly, calculate the retention time for each of the peaks present in the unknown. The internal standard to be used is isobutanol. Calculate the retention time of each of the standard alcohols and of each of the peaks in the unknown relative to that of isobutanol [Equation (14–30)].

$$\text{relative retention time} = \frac{\text{retention time of alcohol}}{\text{retention time of isobutanol}}$$

From the relative retention time of each of the peaks present, determine which alcohols are present in the unknown mixture.

Quantitative analysis of the unknown mixture. After ascertaining the alcohols present in the unknown, approximate visually the area under each of the peaks on the elution curve of the unknown mixture. Do this crudely and quickly, since its sole purpose is to allow selection of that standard mixture most closely approximating the composition of your unknown. Isobutanol is present in all standards and unknowns in a concentration of 25.00 percent by weight. From the concentration of the isobutanol present in the standards, the rough area of the isobutanol peak, and the rough areas of the peaks present in the unknown, estimate the concentration of each of the components present in the unknown sample. From this crude estimation of the concentrations of the unknown, select the standard mixture whose concentrations most closely approximate those in the unknown.

The relative response factor method is now used to obtain accurately the concentration of each of the alcohols present in the unknown. To measure the area of each elution peak with maximum accuracy, the peak should have the largest area possible. Thus while eluting each alcohol the attenuator of the thermal conductivity detector is set to produce the maximum peak area. Each peak may have a different setting. The attenuator is set at the appropriate value each time the recorder pen returns to the base line. Record the setting of the attenuator dial used for each alcohol. Probably two injections of the sample will be necessary—one to determine the appropriate attentuator setting for each alcohol and the second to produce a measurable chromatogram.

Inject the standard alcohol mixture selected onto the gas chromatographic column, adjusting the attenuation of the detector during elution so as to draw the maximum area for each of the peaks. For each peak, be sure to write its attenuator setting on the chart paper. Perform a duplicate analysis of the standard if time permits.

Inject a sample of the unknown mixture onto the gas chromatographic column, adjusting the attenuation of the detector during elution so that each peak has its maximum area. For each peak, record the attentuator setting. Perform a duplicate analysis of the unknown mixture if time permits.

Determination of the concentration of the unknown. Accurately measure the area of each of the peaks on the two standard curves by any of the methods discussed (see above). Multiply each measured area by the appropriate attentuator setting, so as to obtain all areas on a common basis. True area = measured area × attenuator setting.

Calculate the thermal conductivity response factor for each alcohol present in the standard:

$$\text{area} = \text{response factor} \times \text{weight percent alcohol}$$

Thus, for each alcohol, divide the true area by the concentration of the alcohol present in the standard. Since the response factor of the detector varies slightly with experimental conditions and time, all response factors are measured relative to that of the internal standard, isobutanol.

$$\text{relative response factor} = \frac{\text{response factor of alcohol}}{\text{response factor of isobutanol}}$$

Calculate the relative response factors for each of the alcohols present in the standard for both aliquots of the standard. Average the two values of the relative response factor for each alcohol.

Accurately measure the area of each of the peaks on the two unknown elution curves by the same method used for the standard. Multiply each measured area by the appropriate setting of the attenuator so as to obtain all areas on a common basis, as above.

In order to calculate the weight percentage of each alcohol present in the unknown it is necessary to know the absolute response factor for that alcohol when present in the unknown.

$$\text{weight percentage} = \frac{\text{true area}}{\text{response factor}}$$

Since relative response factors are independent of experimental conditions, the absolute response factor can be calculated from the relative response factor calculated for the alcohol when present in the standard and the absolute response factor of isobutanol in the unknown mixture (Note 2).

response factor for alcohol in the unknown = relative response factor × response factor for isobutanol in unknown

Using these two equations, calculate the weight percentage of each alcohol present in both aliquots of the the unknown mixture. Average the weight percentages for each alcohol (Note 3).

Report the relative retention time of each standard alcohol, the relative retention time of all alcohols present in the unknown, the relative response factors and the weight percent of each of the alcohols present in the unknown (Note 4).

NOTES

1. The student should consider possible repercussions of leaving the syringe needle in the injection port for longer than is absolutely necessary—both before and after injection of the sample. Remember that the temperature of the injection port is higher than the boiling point of all of the sample components.
2. Do not be surprised to find that the absolute response factor for each alcohol may be different between the unknown and the standard alcohol mixtures. After all, that is why the relative values must be used.
3. The total percentage of all alcohols present in the unknown should be very close to one hundred percent. If it is not, an error has been made somewhere.
4. The total time elapsed during this experiment will be from two and one-half to three hours, provided that all equipment functions properly and the student is prepared.

PROBLEMS

1. How does the fact that the mobile phase is a gas, rather than a liquid, change the operating parameters and equipment needed for gas chromatography from that used in liquid chromatography?
2. Define the capacity ratio, k. Why is the capacity ratio used in gas chromatographic theory instead of the partition coefficient?

3. Define the retention time in your own words. How is the retention time related to the capacity ratio?

4. How does the retention time of a specific solute change when each of the following experimental parameters is altered?
   (a) the carrier gas flow is increased from 70 to 90 cc/min
   (b) a six-foot-long column is used instead of a ten-foot-long column
   (c) the liquid coating on the solid support is increased to 15% from 8%
   (d) the operating temperature of the column is increased from 150 to 195°C

5. What is meant when we say that two chromatographic peaks can *just* be resolved? What features of the two peaks determine whether or not they can be resolved? State the equation that relates resolution, *R*, with capacity ratio. In order to just resolve two chromatographic peaks, what is the minimum value that *R* must assume?

6. How is the efficiency of a gas chromatographic column determined empirically?

7. (a) State the van Deemter equation, defining all terms and indicating in your own words what each term represents.
   (b) Graph this equation, indicating on the graph the contribution from each term.

8. (a) Isobutyl alcohol is eluted from a 10.0 ft, 10% Carbowax column on Chromasorb with a retention time of 12 min 43 sec. The base width of the peak on the chart paper is 8.23 cm. The chart paper was emerging at a rate of 1.00 in/min. Calculate the efficiency of this column for isobutyl alcohol in cm/plate.
   (b) *n*-Butyl alcohol is eluted from the same column with a retention time of 16 min 10 sec. The peak has a base width of 9.45 cm. Can a mixture of about 20% *n*-butyl alcohol and about 30% isobutyl alcohol be resolved with 99.9% purity of each alcohol using this column and these operating conditions?

9. Why are some gas chromatographic separations effected using helium as the carrier gas whereas nitrogen is used as the carrier gas for others? Why are carbon dioxide or oxygen not used as carrier gases?

10. Compare and contrast the column used for gas chromatography with those used in regular column chromatography. Do the same with those used in high-speed liquid chromatography.

11. List five materials commonly used as supports in gas–liquid chromatography. Why are powdered cellulose and silica gel not included in this list?

12. How does one establish the temperature at which a gas–liquid chromatographic column should be operated? How does one establish the temperature at which to set the injection port? Why are these two temperatures not identical; or are they?

13. Why are the nonpolar liquid phases used in gas–liquid chromatography high-molecular-weight hydrocarbons such as squalene rather than octane or benzene?

14. In order to be used as a detector for gas chromatography, what properties must an instrumental technique possess?

15. Explain how a thermal conductivity detector functions.

16. Explain how a flame ionization detector functions.

17. Explain how an electron capture detector functions.

18. What factors must be considered when selecting a detector for a gas–liquid chromatographic separation? Explain each of the following:
(a) a thermal conductivity detector is used for separations of alcohols, amines, and steroids
(b) a flame ionization detector is not used for the separation of chlorinated hydrocarbons, such as insecticides
(c) an electron capture detector is used to detect pesticide residues on fruits and vegetables

19. Define each term below and distinguish it clearly from each of the others:
(a) retention volume   (c) specific retention volume
(b) net retention volume   (d) relative retention volume

20. One of the primary uses of gas–liquid chromatography is in separating mixtures of closely related compounds. How are the identities of the compounds causing the peaks on the chart paper established?

21. Given the chromatogram in Fig. 14–17, calculate the percentage of benzene present in the mixture by the peak area normalization method.

22. Consider the cyclohexane peak in the chromatogram in Fig. 14–17 to be the peak for the internal standard, which is present at a concentration of 6.00%. In a known mixture, cyclohexane has a response factor of 0.000300 g/% and benzene has an absolute response factor of 0.000372 g/%. Calculate the percent benzene present in the mixture by the relative response factor method.

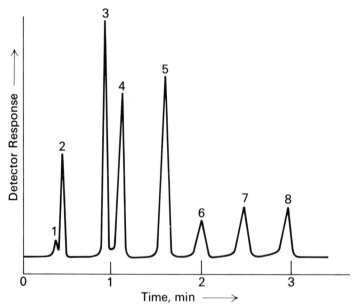

Fig. 14–17. Separation of C_5–C_7 hydrocarbons on a micro packed column: (*1*) isopentane, (*2*) *n*-pentane, (*3*) 1-hexene, (*4*) *n*-hexane, (*5*) benzene, (*6*) cyclohexane, (*7*) 1-heptene, (*8*) *n*-heptane. $t_c = 50°C$, $L = 1$ m, i.d. $= 0.9$ mm. Chromosorb W coated with 15% by weight squalane. Carrier gas: nitrogen.

23. For a series of standard benzene solutions it is determined that the peak area is 0.442 cm^2 for 10.0% benzene, 0.655 cm^2 for 15.0% benzene, 1.100 cm^2 for 25.0% benzene, and 1.323 cm^2 for 30.0% benzene. Again referring to the chromatogram in Fig. 14–17, calculate the percent benzene present in the mixture by the calibration curve method.

24. What is a response factor? How is the numerical value of a response factor changed, if at all, when each of the following is done?
   (a) the rate of flow of carrier gas is increased
   (b) the operating temperature of the column is decreased
   (c) the temperature of the injection port is increased
   (d) a larger size sample is injected
   (e) the sample injected is *n*-butanol instead of dichloromethane

25. What is meant by the term temperature programming? How is this accomplished in the laboratory? What are the advantages and the disadvantages of temperature programming?

26. What are the two major limitations on the compounds that can be separated successfully by gas–liquid chromatography?

27. Compare and contrast gas–liquid chromatography and high-speed liquid chromatography with respect to:
   (a) the apparatus required for a separation
   (b) the size of sample that is capable of being separated
   (c) the time required for a separation
   (d) the effectiveness of the separations
   (e) the kinds of samples that can be separated

28. Repeat the comparison stated in Problem 26 for gas–liquid chromatography and thin-layer chromatography.

REFERENCES

1. Bartlett, J. C. and Smith, D. M., *Can. J. Chem.*, **38**, 2057 (1960).
2. Bennet, C. E., Dal Nogare, S., Safranski, L. W. and Lewis, C. V., *Anal. Chem.*, **30**, 898 (1958).
3. Bennett, J. J. and Hertzlinger, M., *J. Chromatogr. Sci.*, **9**, 63 (1971).
4. Bethea, R. M. and Meador, M. C., *J. Chromatogr. Sci.*, **7**, 655 (1969).
5. Crippen, R. C. and Smith, C. E., *J. Gas Chromatogr.*, **3**, 37 (1965).
6. Dal Nogare, S. and Juvet, R. S., Jr., *Gas-Liquid Chromatography*, Interscience, New York, 1962.
7. Genty, C. and Schott, R., *Anal. Chem.*, **42**, 7 (1970).
8. Gill, J. M. and Tao, F. T., paper presented at the ASTM E-19 Committee on Gas Chromatography Meeting in St. Louis, 1967.
9. Goedert, M. and Guiochon, G., *Anal. Chem.*, **42**, 962 (1970).
10. Golay, M. J. E., *Gas Chromatography*, V. J. Coates, *et al.*, Eds., Academic Press, New York, 1958, p. 1.
11. Goodwin, E. S., Goulden, R. and Reynolds, J. G., *Analyst*, **86**, 697 (1961).
12. Gough, T. A. and Walker, E. A., *Analyst*, **95**, 1 (1970).
13. Harris, J. R., *Analyst*, **95**, 158 (1970).
14. Hartmann, C. H., *Anal. Chem.*, **43**, (2), 113A (1971).

15. Hoffmann, D. and Rothkamp, G., *Anal. Chem.*, **42,** 1643 (1970).
16. Lawson, E. and Miller, J., *J. Gas Chromatogr.*, **4,** 273 (1966).
17. Littlewood, A. B., Phillips, C. S. G. and Price, D. T., *J. Chem. Soc.*, **1955,** 1480.
18. Lovelock, J. E., *Anal. Chem.*, **33,** 162 (1961).
19. Martin, A. J. P. and James, A. T., *Biochem. J.*, **50,** 679 (1952).
20. Martin, A. J. P. and Synge, R. L. M., *Biochem. J.*, **35,** 1358 (1941).
21. Mefford, R. B., Jr., Summers, R. M. and Clayton, J. D., *J. Chromatogr.*, **35,** 469 (1968).
22. Parker, K. E., Fontan, C. R., Yee, J. L. and Kirk, P. L., *Anal. Chem.*, **34,** 1234 (1962).
23. Pollard, F. H. and Hardy, C. J., *Chem. Ind.*, **1955,** 1145.
24. Sawyer, D. T. and Barr, J. K., *Anal. Chem.*, **34,** 1518 (1962).
25. Scott, R. P. W. and Grant, D. W., *Analyst*, **89,** 179 (1964).
26. van Deemter, J. J., Zuiderweg, F. J. and Klinkenberg, A., *Chem. Eng. Sci.*, **5,** 271 (1956).

APPENDIXES

APPENDIX 1a. DISSOCIATION CONSTANTS FOR WEAK ACIDS

Acid		K_a	pK_a
Acetic, CH_3COOH		1.754×10^{-5}	4.7560
Acetylacetone, $CH_3COCH_2COCH_3$		1.8×10^{-9}	8.75
Alanine, $H_2N-CH-COOH$	(1)	4.37×10^{-3}	2.340
$\quad\quad\quad\quad\;\; \mid$			
$\quad\quad\quad\quad CH_3$			
	(2)	1.35×10^{-10}	9.870
Arsenic, H_3AsO_4	(1)	6.5×10^{-3}	2.19
	(2)	1.1×10^{-7}	6.94
	(3)	3.2×10^{-12}	11.50
Arsenous, $HAsO_2$		5.08×10^{-10}	9.294
Barbituric, $HNCONHCONH$		9.23×10^{-5}	4.035
$\quad\quad\quad\quad \diagdown \quad \diagup$			
$\quad\quad\quad\quad\;\; CH_2$			
Benzoic, C_6H_5COOH		6.320×10^{-5}	4.1993
Boric, HBO_2		5.80×10^{-10}	9.237
Bromoacetic, $BrCH_2COOH$		1.4×10^{-3}	2.86
n-Butyric, $CH_3CH_2CH_2COOH$		1.515×10^{-5}	4.8196
Carbonic, H_2CO_3	(1)	4.45×10^{-7}	6.352
	(2)	4.69×10^{-11}	10.329
Chloroacetic, $ClCH_2COOH$		1.378×10^{-3}	2.8607
Chlorous, $HClO_2$		4.9×10^{-3}	2.31
Chromic, H_2CrO_4	(1)	9.6	-0.98
	(2)	3.2×10^{-7}	6.49
Citric, $C_3H_4(OH)(COOH)_3$	(1)	7.45×10^{-4}	3.128
	(2)	1.73×10^{-5}	4.761
	(3)	4.03×10^{-7}	6.395
Cyanic, $HCNO$		3.4×10^{-4}	3.47

(*continued*)

Appendix 1a (Continued)

Acid		K_a	pK_a
1,2-Diaminocyclohexanetetraacetic, $(HOOCH_2C)_2NC_6H_{10}N(CH_2COOH)_2$	(1)	4.00×10^{-3}	2.40
	(2)	2.82×10^{-4}	3.55
	(3)	7.25×10^{-7}	6.14
	(4)	2.00×10^{-12}	11.70
Dichloroacetic, $Cl_2CHCOOH$		5.0×10^{-2}	1.30
Diethylenetriaminepentaacetic, $(HOOCH_2C)_2NCH_2CH_2NCH_2CH_2N(CH_2COOH)_2$ $\quad\quad\quad\;\; \mid$ $\quad\quad\quad CH_2COOH$	(1)	1.39×10^{-2}	1.86
	(2)	1.62×10^{-3}	2.79
	(3)	5.13×10^{-5}	4.29
	(4)	9.78×10^{-9}	8.01
	(5)	3.32×10^{-11}	10.48
Dimethylglyoxime, $C_4H_6N_2(OH)_2$		2.2×10^{-11}	10.66
Ethylenediaminetetraacetic, $(HOOCH_2C)_2NCH_2CH_2N(CH_2COOH)_2$	(1)	1.0×10^{-2}	1.99
	(2)	2.1×10^{-3}	2.67
	(3)	6.9×10^{-7}	6.16
	(4)	5.5×10^{-11}	10.26
Formic, $HCOOH$		1.772×10^{-4}	3.7515
Glycine, NH_2CH_2COOH	(1)	4.464×10^{-3}	2.3503
	(2)	1.661×10^{-10}	9.7796
Hydrazoic, HN_3		1.9×10^{-5}	4.72
Hydrocyanic, HCN		6.04×10^{-10}	9.22
Hydrofluoric, HF		6.8×10^{-4}	3.17
Hydroselenic, H_2Se	(1)	1.3×10^{-4}	3.89
	(2)	1×10^{-11}	11.0
Hydrosulfuric, H_2S	(1)	1.0×10^{-7}	6.99
	(2)	1.3×10^{-13}	12.89
8-Hydroxyquinoline, C_9H_6NOH	(1)	1.7×10^{-4}	3.76
	(2)	6.5×10^{-12}	11.19
8-Hydroxy-2-methylquinoline, $CH_3C_9H_5NOH$	(1)	2.47×10^{-6}	5.608
	(2)	6.91×10^{-11}	10.161
8-Hydroxy-4-methylquinoline, $CH_3C_9H_5NOH$	(1)	2.1×10^{-5}	4.67
	(2)	2.4×10^{-12}	11.62
8-Hydroxyquinoline-5-sulfonic, $C_9H_5NOHSO_3H$	(1)	7.88×10^{-5}	4.104
	(2)	1.75×10^{-9}	8.757
Hypobromous, $HBrO$		2.5×10^{-9}	8.60
Hypochlorous, $HClO$		3.0×10^{-8}	7.53
Iminodiacetic, $HN(CH_2COOH)_2$	(1)	1.0×10^{-3}	2.98
	(2)	1.3×10^{-10}	9.89
Iodic, HIO_3		1.42×10^{-1}	0.848

(continued)

Appendix 1a (Continued)

Acid		K_a	pK_a
Lactic, $CH_3CHOHCOOH$		1.387×10^{-4}	3.8579
Malonic, $CH_2(COOH)_2$	(1)	1.4×10^{-3}	2.85
	(2)	2.1×10^{-6}	5.67
Nitrilotriacetic, $N(CH_2COOH)_3$	(1)	2.24×10^{-2}	1.650
	(2)	1.15×10^{-3}	2.940
	(3)	4.64×10^{-11}	10.334
Nitrous, HNO_2		5.1×10^{-4}	3.29
Oxalic, $HOOCCOOH$	(1)	5.6×10^{-2}	1.25
	(2)	5.19×10^{-5}	4.285
1,10-Phenanthroline, $C_{12}H_8N_2$		1.39×10^{-5}	4.857
Phosphoric, H_3PO_4	(1)	6.73×10^{-3}	2.172
	(2)	6.15×10^{-8}	7.211
	(3)	4.37×10^{-13}	12.360
Phthalic, $C_6H_4(COOH)_2$	(1)	7.2×10^{-4}	3.14
	(2)	4.0×10^{-6}	5.40
Picric, $(NO_3)_3C_6H_2(OH)$		0.196	0.798
Propionic, CH_3CH_2COOH		1.336×10^{-5}	4.8742
Salicylic, HOC_6H_4COOH	(1)	1.1×10^{-3}	2.97
	(2)	4×10^{-14}	13.4
Selenic, H_2SeO_4	(2)	4.37×10^{-2}	1.88
Succinic, $(CH_2COOH)_2$	(1)	6.214×10^{-5}	4.2066
	(2)	2.31×10^{-6}	5.636
Sulfuric, H_2SO_4	(2)	1.3×10^{-2}	1.89
Sulfurous, H_2SO_3	(1)	1.72×10^{-2}	1.764
	(2)	6.24×10^{-8}	7.205
Tartaric, $(CHOHCOOH)_2$	(1)	9.20×10^{-4}	3.036
	(2)	4.31×10^{-5}	4.366
Telluric, H_2TeO_4	(1)	2.0×10^{-8}	7.70
	(2)	1.1×10^{-11}	10.95
Thiocyanic, $HSCN$		1.4×10^{-1}	0.85
Thiosulfuric, $H_2S_2O_3$	(1)	2.0×10^{-1}	0.60
	(2)	1.9×10^{-2}	1.72
Tiron, $Na_2C_6H_2(OH)_2(SO_3)_2$	(1)	2.5×10^{-8}	7.60
	(2)	3.3×10^{-13}	12.48
Trichloroacetic, Cl_3CCOOH		2.0×10^{-1}	0.70

SOURCE: Values taken from G. Kortum, W. Vogel, and K. Andrussow, *Dissociation Constants of Organic Acids in Aqueous Solution*, International Union of Pure and Applied Chemistry, Commission on Electrochemical Data, Butterworths, London, 1961; and L. G. Sillen and A. E. Martell, *Stability Constants of Metal-Ion Complexes*, Special Publication No. 17, The Chemical Society, London, 1964.

APPENDIX 1b.   DISSOCIATION CONSTANTS FOR WEAK BASES

Base	K_b	pK_b
Ammonia, NH_3	1.7×10^{-5}	4.76
Aniline, $C_6H_5NH_2$	4.2×10^{-10}	9.38

(continued)

n-Butylamine, $C_4H_9NH_2$			5.1×10^{-4}	3.29
Dimethylamine, $(CH_3)_2NH$			7.2×10^{-4}	3.14
Ethanolamine, $HOC_2H_4NH_2$			3.148×10^{-5}	4.5020
Ethylamine, $C_2H_5NH_2$			4.7×10^{-4}	3.33
Ethylenediamine, $H_2NCH_2CH_2NH_2$	(1)		9.1×10^{-5}	4.04
	(2)		1.5×10^{-7}	6.82
Hexamethylenetetramine (urotropine) $(CH_2)_6N_4$			1.4×10^{-9}	8.87
Hydrazine, $(NH_2)_2$	(1)		9.8×10^{-7}	6.01
	(2)		1.9×10^{-14}	13.73
Hydroxylamine, NH_2OH			9.1×10^{-9}	8.04
Methylamine, CH_3NH_2			5.5×10^{-4}	3.26
N-Methylaniline, $C_6H_5NHCH_3$			6.0×10^{-10}	9.22
Nicotine, $C_{10}H_{14}N_2$	(1)		7×10^{-7}	6.15
	(2)		1.4×10^{-11}	10.85
Novocain, $C_{13}H_{20}O_2N_2$			7×10^{-6}	5.15
Piperidine, $C_5H_{11}N$			1.33×10^{-3}	2.877
n-Propylamine, $C_3H_7NH_2$			3.9×10^{-4}	3.41
Pyridine, C_5H_5N			1.5×10^{-9}	8.82
Quinoline, C_9H_7N			8.7×10^{-10}	9.06
Strychnine, $C_{21}H_{22}O_2N_2$	(1)		1×10^{-6}	6.0
	(2)		2×10^{-12}	11.7
Trimethylamine, $(CH_3)_3N$			8.1×10^{-5}	4.19
Urea, NH_2CONH_2			1.5×10^{-14}	13.82

SOURCE: Values taken from G. Kortum, W. Vogel, and K. Andrussow, *Dissociation Constants of Organic Acids in Aqueous Solution*, International Union of Pure and Applied Chemistry, Commission on Electrochemical Data, Butterworths, London, 1961; and L. G. Sillen and A. E. Martell, *Stability Constants of Metal-Ion Complexes*, Special Publication No. 17, The Chemical Society, London, 1964.

APPENDIX 2. α_{0H} FOR EDTA AT 20°C AS A FUNCTION OF pH

pH	α_{0H}	pH	α_{0H}
0.00	8.26×10^{-22}	7.00	4.81×10^{-4}
0.50	8.06×10^{-20}	7.50	1.66×10^{-3}
1.00	7.57×10^{-18}	8.00	5.38×10^{-3}
1.50	6.17×10^{-16}	8.50	1.71×10^{-2}
2.00	3.72×10^{-14}	9.00	5.21×10^{-2}
2.50	1.30×10^{-12}	9.50	0.148
3.00	2.51×10^{-11}	10.00	0.355
3.50	3.30×10^{-10}	10.50	0.633
4.00	3.61×10^{-9}	11.00	0.847
4.50	3.66×10^{-8}	11.50	0.943
5.00	3.55×10^{-7}	12.00	0.980
5.50	3.12×10^{-6}	12.50	0.990
6.00	2.25×10^{-5}	13.00	1.00
6.50	1.19×10^{-4}		

APPENDIX 3. α_{OH} FOR AMMONIA AT 25°C AS A FUNCTION OF pH

pH	α_{OH}	pH	α_{OH}
0.00	5.55×10^{-10}	6.50	1.76×10^{-3}
0.50	1.76×10^{-9}	7.00	5.55×10^{-3}
1.00	5.55×10^{-9}	7.50	1.73×10^{-2}
1.50	1.76×10^{-8}	8.00	5.24×10^{-2}
2.00	5.55×10^{-8}	8.50	0.149
2.50	1.76×10^{-7}	9.00	0.356
3.00	5.55×10^{-7}	9.50	0.637
3.50	1.76×10^{-6}	10.00	0.848
4.00	5.55×10^{-6}	10.50	0.948
4.50	1.76×10^{-5}	11.00	0.983
5.00	5.55×10^{-5}	11.50	0.994
5.50	1.76×10^{-4}	12.00	0.997
6.00	5.55×10^{-4}	12.50	1.00

APPENDIX 4.   SOLUBILITY PRODUCT CONSTANTS FOR SLIGHTLY SOLUBLE SALTS AT 25°C AND ZERO IONIC STRENGTH

Salt	K_{sp}°	Salt	K_{sp}°
Aluminum		CaF_2	2.7×10^{-11}
$Al(OH)_3$	3.1×10^{-34}	*Cerium*	
$AlPO_4$	3.9×10^{-11}	Ce_2S_3	6.0×10^{-11}
Barium		*Chromium*	
$BaCO_3$	5.1×10^{-9}	$Cr(OH)_3$	6×10^{-31}
$BaCrO_4$	1.2×10^{-10}	*Cobalt(II)*	
BaF_2	1.0×10^{-6}	$CoCO_3$	1.4×10^{-13}
$Ba(IO_3)_2$	1.5×10^{-9}	$Co_2Fe(CN)_6$	6.6×10^{-17}
$BaMnO_4$	2.5×10^{-10}	$Co(OH)_2$	1.3×10^{-15}
$BaSO_4$	1.1×10^{-10}	$Co_3(PO_4)_2$	2×10^{-35}
Bismuth		CoS	7.9×10^{-23}
$BiPO_4$	1.3×10^{-23}	*Cobalt(III)*	
Bi_2S_2	1×10^{-96}	$Co(OH)_3$	3×10^{-41}
Cadmium		*Copper(I)*	
$CdCO_3$	5.3×10^{-12}	CuI	1.1×10^{-12}
$Cd_2Fe(CN)_6$	9.6×10^{-16}	Cu_2S	7.2×10^{-49}
$Cd(OH)_2$	5.9×10^{-15}	$CuSCN$	4.8×10^{-15}
$Cd(IO_3)_2$	2.3×10^{-8}	*Copper(II)*	
$Cd_3(PO_4)_2$	3×10^{-33}	$CuCO_3$	2.3×10^{-10}
CdS	9.3×10^{-27}	$CuCrO_4$	3.6×10^{-6}
Calcium		$Cu_2Fe(CN)_6$	2.1×10^{-16}
$CaCO_3$	4.5×10^{-9}	$Cu(OH)_2$	2.2×10^{-20}
$Ca(OH)_2$	9.1×10^{-6}	$Cu(IO_3)_2$	7.33×10^{-8}
$Ca(IO_3)_2$	7.1×10^{-7}	$Cu_3(PO_4)_2$	1×10^{-37}
$Ca_3(PO_4)_2$	2.0×10^{-29}	CuS	4.0×10^{-36}
$CaSO_4$	9.1×10^{-6}		

(*continued*)

Appendix 4 (Continued)

Salt	K_{sp}°	Salt	K_{sp}°
Gallium		$Ni(DMG)_2$	2.2×10^{-24}
$Ga(OH)_3$	8.0×10^{-40}	$Ni_2Fe(CN)_6$	1.3×10^{-15}
Indium		$Ni(OH)_2$	6.2×10^{-16}
In_2S_3	5.8×10^{-74}	$Ni_3(PO_4)_2$	5×10^{-31}
Iron(II)		NiS	2×10^{-21}
$FeCO_3$	2.1×10^{-11}	*Silver*	
$Fe(OH)_2$	1.4×10^{-15}	AgBr	4.9×10^{-13}
FeS	4.2×10^{-17}	Ag_2CO_3	8.1×10^{-12}
Iron(III)		AgCl	1.78×10^{-10}
$Fe_4[Fe(CN)_6]_3$	3.0×10^{-41}	Ag_2CrO_4	1.3×10^{-12}
$Fe(OH)_3$	3.7×10^{-40}	AgCN	2.3×10^{-16}
Lanthanum		$Ag_4Fe(CN)_4$	7.1×10^{-28}
$La(OH)_3$	1.7×10^{-19}	AgOH	1.9×10^{-8}
$La(IO_3)_3$	6.2×10^{-12}	$AgIO_3$	3.0×10^{-8}
La_2S_3	2.0×10^{-13}	AgI	8.30×10^{-17}
Lead		Ag_2MoO_4	2.8×10^{-12}
$PbBr_2$	3.9×10^{-5}	Ag_3PO_4	1.4×10^{-16}
$PbCO_3$	7.4×10^{-14}	Ag_2SO_4	1.46×10^{-5}
$PbCl_2$	1.7×10^{-5}	Ag_2S	6.3×10^{-50}
$PbCrO_4$	2.8×10^{-13}	AgSCN	1.0×10^{-12}
$Pb_2Fe(CN)_6$	3.5×10^{-15}	Ag_2WO_4	5.5×10^{-12}
$Pb(OH)_2$	1.1×10^{-20}	*Strontium*	
$Pb(IO_3)_2$	2.6×10^{-13}	$SrCO_3$	1.1×10^{-10}
PbI_2	8.7×10^{-9}	SrF_2	2.5×10^{-9}
$Pb_3(PO_4)_2$	8.0×10^{-43}	$Sr(IO_3)_2$	3.3×10^{-7}
$PbSO_4$	1.7×10^{-8}	$SrSO_4$	3.5×10^{-7}
PbS	7.1×10^{-28}	*Thallium(I)*	
Magnesium		TlBr	3.8×10^{-6}
$MgCO_3$	3.5×10^{-8}	TlCl	1.88×10^{-4}
$Mg(OH)_2$	1.8×10^{-11}	Tl_2CrO_4	9.8×10^{-13}
Manganese(II)		$TlIO_3$	3.1×10^{-6}
$MnCO_3$	5.0×10^{-10}	TlI	6.5×10^{-8}
$Mn_2Fe(CN)_6$	8.0×10^{-13}	Tl_2S	7.1×10^{-20}
$Mn(OH)_2$	1.9×10^{-13}	TlSCN	1.6×10^{-4}
MnS	2.3×10^{-13}	*Thallium(III)*	
Mercury(I)		$Tl(OH)_3$	6.3×10^{-21}
Hg_2Br_2	5.8×10^{-23}	*Tin(II)*	
Hg_2Cl_2	1.3×10^{-18}	$Sn(OH)_2$	3.4×10^{-26}
Hg_2CrO_4	2.0×10^{-9}	SnS	1.1×10^{-27}
$Hg_2(IO_3)_2$	1.9×10^{-14}	*Zinc*	
Hg_2I_2	4.5×10^{-29}	$ZnCO_3$	2.1×10^{-11}
Hg_2SO_4	6.8×10^{-7}	$Zn_2Fe(CN)_6$	4.1×10^{-16}
Mercury(II)		$Zn(OH)_2$	8.9×10^{-18}
$Hg(OH)_2$	3.0×10^{-26}	$Zn(IO_3)_2$	3.9×10^{-6}
HgS	1.9×10^{-53}	$Zn_3(PO_4)_2$	9.1×10^{-33}
Nickel		ZnS	1.5×10^{-24}
$NiCO_3$	1.3×10^{-7}		

SOURCE: Values taken from L. G. Sillen and A. E. Martell, *Stability Constants of Metal-Ion Complexes*, Special Publication No. 17, The Chemical Society, London, 1964.

APPENDIX 5. STABILITY CONSTANTS FOR METAL AMMINE COMPLEXES AT 25°C

Metal Ion	$\log \beta_1$	$\log \beta_2$	$\log \beta_3$	$\log \beta_4$	$\log \beta_5$	$\log \beta_6$
Ammonia, NH_3						
Ag^+	3.315	7.230				
Cd^{2+}	2.54	4.78	6.08	7.26		
Co^{2+}	2.1	3.7	4.7	5.5		
Co^{3+}						32.51
Cu^{2+}	4.27	7.86	10.86	13.05		
Fe^{2+}	1.4	2.2				
Hg^{2+}	8.8	17.5	18.5	19.3		
Mg^{2+}	0.23	0.08	−0.34	−1.0		
Ni^{2+}	2.36	4.26	5.81	7.04	7.89	8.31
Zn^{2+}	2.59	4.91	6.92	8.62		
Ethylenediamine, $NH_2-CH_2-CH_2-NH_2$						
Ag^+	6	7.4				
Cd^{2+}	5.63	10.22	12.29			
Co^{2+}	5.93	10.66	13.96			
Co^{3+}	18.7	34.9	48.69			
Cu^{2+}	10.72	20.03	21.03			
Fe^{2+}	4.34	7.65	9.70			
Hg^{2+}	14.3	23.3				
Ni^{2+}	7.51	13.86	18.28			
Zn^{2+}	5.92	11.07	11.93			

SOURCE: Values taken from L. Meites, *Handbook of Analytical Chemistry*, McGraw-Hill Book Co., New York, N.Y. 1963; and L. G. Sillen and A. E. Martell, *Stability Constants of Metal-Ion Complexes*, Special Publication No. 17, The Chemical Society, London, 1964.

APPENDIX 6. LOGARITHMIC VALUES FOR α_{NH_3} FOR METAL AMMINE COMPLEXES AT VARIOUS pH VALUES*

Metal Ion	C_{NH_3}, M	2	3	4	5	6	7	8	9	10	11	12	13	14
Ag(I)	1.0				0.1	0.8	2.6	4.6	6.4	7.2	7.4	7.4	7.4	7.4
	0.1					0.1	0.8	2.6	4.4	5.2	5.4	5.4	5.4	5.6
	0.01						0.1	0.8	2.4	3.2	3.4	3.4	3.4	5.1
Cd(II)	1.0					0.1	0.5	2.3	5.1	6.7	7.1	7.1	8.1	12.0
	0.1						0.1	0.5	2.0	3.0	3.6	4.5	8.1	12.0
	0.01							0.1	0.6	1.4	2.0	4.5	8.1	12.0
Co(II)	1.0						0.2	1.2	3.7	5.3	5.7	5.8	7.2	10.2
	0.1							0.2	1.0	1.8	2.9	4.9	7.2	10.2
Cu(II)	1.0				0.2	1.2	3.6	7.1	10.6	12.2	12.7	12.7	12.7	12.7
	0.1					0.2	1.2	3.6	6.7	8.2	8.6	8.6	8.6	8.6
	0.01						0.2	1.2	3.3	4.5	4.9	4.9	5.1	5.8
Hg(II)	1.0	2.7	4.7	6.7	8.7	10.7	12.7	14.9	17.6	19.1	19.4	19.4	20.0	21.9
	0.1	0.9	2.7	4.7	6.7	8.7	10.7	12.7	14.6	15.7	16.2	17.9	19.9	21.9
	0.01		0.9	2.7	4.7	6.7	8.7	10.7	12.5	14.0	15.9	17.9	19.9	21.9
Ni(II)	1.0					0.1	0.6	2.8	6.3	8.3	8.8	8.8	8.8	8.8
	0.1						0.1	0.6	2.5	3.8	4.5	4.5	4.5	4.5
	0.01							0.1	0.5	1.3	1.8			
Zn(II)	1.0						0.4	3.6	7.1	8.7	9.1	9.2	11.8	15.5
	0.1							0.4	3.2	4.7	5.6	8.5	11.8	15.5

SOURCE: Values taken from A. Ringbom, *Complexation in Analytical Chemistry*, Wiley-Interscience, New York, 1963, pp. 352–359.

* All values are $-\log \alpha_{0_{NH_3}}$.

APPENDIX 7. STABILITY CONSTANTS FOR COMPLEX IONS FORMED BETWEEN METAL IONS AND VARIOUS INORGANIC AND ORGANIC LIGANDS AT 25°C

Metal Ion	$\log \beta_1$	$\log \beta_2$	$\log \beta_3$	$\log \beta_4$	$\log \beta_5$	$\log \beta_6$
Acetylacetone, CH_3—CO—CH_2—CO—CH_3						
Cd^{2+}	3.83	6.65				
Ce^{3+}	5.29	9.27	12.65			
Co^{2+}	5.40	9.54				
Cu^{2+}	8.27	15.06				
Fe^{3+}	11.4	22.1	26.7			
Mg^{2+}	3.65	6.28				
Ni^{2+}	5.92	10.49				
UO_2^{2+}	7.70	14.16				
VO^{2+}	8.68	15.79				
Zn^{2+}	5.03	8.92				
Chloride, Cl^-						
Fe^{3+}	0.61	0.79				
Pt^{2+}				16		
Ag^+		5.24	no complex	6.14		
Hg^{2+}	6.74	13.22	14.07	15.07		
Sn^{2+}	1.05	1.76	1.14	1.14		
Citric acid, $C_3H_4OH(COOH)_3$, all complexes contain only the hydroxyl proton						
Ca^{2+}	4.90					
Cd^{2+}	3.98					
Co^{2+}	4.16					
Cu^{2+}	3.95					
Fe^{2+}	3.08					
Fe^{3+}	11.85					
Mg^{2+}	3.29					
Ni^{2+}	5.11					
Pb^{2+}	5.74					
Sr^{2+}	2.85					
Tl^+	1.04					
UO_2^{2+}	7.40					
Zn^{2+}	4.71					
Cyanide, CN^-						
Fe^{2+}						24
Fe^{3+}						31
Co^{2+}						19.09
Co^{3+}						64
Ni^{2+}	no evidence for lower complexes			30.1		
Ag^+		19.85				
Zn^{2+}				16.76		
Cd^{2+}	5.48	10.62	15.18	18.76		
Hg^{2+}		35.21	38.85	41.47		
Tl^{3+}				35		
Fluoride, F^-						
Ag^+	0.38	no evidence of anionic complexes				
Al^{3+}	6.13	11.15	15.00	17.74	19.37	19.84

(continued)

Appendix 7 (Continued)

Metal Ion	$\log \beta_1$	$\log \beta_2$	$\log \beta_3$	$\log \beta_4$	$\log \beta_5$	$\log \beta_6$
Cr^{3+}	4.36	7.70	10.18			
Fe^{3+}	5.21	9.16	11.86			
Mg^{2+}	1.82					
Glycine, NH_2—CH_2—$COOH$						
Ag^+	3.51	6.89				
Cd^{2+}	4.80	8.83				
Co^{2+}	5.02	8.99				
Cu^{2+}	8.29	15.90				
Mg^{2+}	3.45	6.46				
Ni^{2+}	6.18	11.14				
Pb^{2+}	5.47	8.86				
Zn^{2+}	5.52	9.96				
8-Hydroxyquinoline, C_9H_6OHN, all constants determined in 50% dioxane						
Cd^{2+}	9.43	17.11				
Ce^{3+}	9.15	17.13				
Co^{2+}	10.55	19.66				
Cu^{2+}	13.49	26.22				
Fe^{2+}	8.71	16.83	22.13			
Fe^{3+}			38.00			
Mg^{2+}	6.38	11.81				
Ni^{2+}	11.44	21.38				
Pb^{2+}	10.61	18.69				
UO_2^{2+}	11.25	20.89				
Zn^{2+}	9.96	18.86				
Oxalic acid, $HOOC-COOH$						
Cd^{2+}	4.00	5.77				
Co^{2+}	3.72	6.03				
Cu^{2+}	6.19	10.23				
Fe^{3+}	9.84	16.06	19.74			
Mn^{2+}	3.82	5.25				
Ni^{2+}	5.16	6.51				
Pb^{2+}		6.54				
Zn^{2+}	5.00	7.36				
1,10-Phenanthroline, $C_{12}H_8N_2$						
Ag^+	5.02	12.07				
Cd^{2+}	5.93	10.52	14.30			
Cu^{2+}	9.08	15.76	20.94			
Fe^{2+}			21.15			
Fe^{3+}	6.5	11.4	23.5			
Mn^{2+}	3.88	7.04	10.11			
Ni^{2+}	8.60	16.70	24.25			
VO^{2+}	5.47	9.69				
Zn^{2+}	6.36	12.00	17.20			
Salicylic acid, HO—C_6H_4—$COOH$						
Fe^{3+}	15.81	27.48	35.30			

(continued)

Appendix 7 (Continued)

Metal Ion	log β_1	log β_2	log β_3	log β_4	log β_5	log β_6
Th^{4+}	4.25	7.60	10.05	11.60		
UO_2^{2+}	4.91					
Tartaric acid, HOOC—CHOH—CHOH—COOH						
Ba^{2+}	2.54					
Ca^{2+}	2.80					
Cu^{2+}	3.00	8.15				
Fe^{3+}	7.49					
Zn^{2+}	2.68	8.32				
Thiocyanate, CNS^-						
Ag^+		8.39	9.62	9.90		
Cd^{2+}	1.36	2.09	2.38	2.48	2.22	1.72
Co^{2+}	1.01					
Cr^{3+}	1.87	2.98				
Cu^{2+}	1.74	2.54	2.69	2.99		
Fe^{3+}	2.14	3.45				
Ni^{2+}	1.50					
Hg_2^{2+}		17.26	19.97	21.69		
Pb^{2+}	0.78	0.99	0.97	0.92	0.86	0.63
Zn^{2+}	−0.14	0.90	1.20	1.29	1.29	0.63
Thiosulfate, $S_2O_3^{2-}$						
Ag^+	8.87	13.73				
Ba^{2+}	2.21					
Ca^{2+}	1.91					
Cd^{2+}	2.82	4.57	6.39			
Co^{2+}	2.05					
Cu^{2+}		12.29				
Fe^{3+}	1.98					
Hg^{2+}		29.86	32.26	33.61		
Mg^{2+}	1.79					
Ni^{2+}	2.06					
Pb^{2+}	2.56	4.88	6.34	6.23		
Sr^{2+}	2.04					
Zn^{2+}	2.40					
Tiron (4,5-Dihydroxybenzene-1,3-disulphonic acid), $(HO)_2$—C_6H_4—$(SO_3H)_2$						
Cd^{2+}	10.29					
Co^{2+}	10.78					
Cu^{2+}	15.62					
Fe^{3+}	20.78					
Ni^{2+}	11.24					
Pb^{2+}	14.77					
Sr^{2+}	4.55					
UO_2^{2+}	15.90					
VO_2^{2+}	15.88					
Zn^{2+}	11.68					

SOURCE: Values taken from L. Sillen and A. E. Martell, *Stability Constants of Metal-Ion Complexes*, Special Publication No. 17, The Chemical Society, London, 1964.

APPENDIX 8. STABILITY CONSTANTS FOR METAL CHELATES OF AMINOPOLYCARBOXYLIC ACIDS AT 20°C

Metal Ion	Iminodiacetic Acid $\log K_{st}$		NTA $\log K_{st}$	EDTA $\log K_{st}$	DTPA $\log K_{st}$	DCyTA $\log K_{st}$
Ag^+				7.2		
Al^{3+}				16.68	18.40	18.63
Ba^{2+}		1.67	5.875	7.78	8.62	8.64
Bi^{3+}				27.94	35.6	24.11
Ca^{2+}		3.41	7.608	10.59	9.98	13.15
Cd^{2+}	β_1	5.35	9.80	16.46	18.9	19.88
	β_2	9.51				
Ce^{3+}			10.83	15.98	20.40	16.76
Co^{2+}			10.38	16.31	18.4	19.57
Co^{3+}				40.7		
Cr^{3+}				23		
Cu^{2+}	β_1	10.55	13.16	18.80	21.03	21.95
	β_2	16.20				
Eu^{3+}			11.49	17.35	22.39	18.62
Fe^{2+}			8.84	14.33	16.55	
Fe^{3+}			15.87	24.23	28.6	27.48
Ga^{3+}			13.6	21.10	25.54	23.10
Hg^{2+}				21.67	26.59	23.59
La^{3+}			10.37	15.50	19.98	16.91
Mg^{2+}		3.66	7.00	8.69	9.0	10.97
Mn^{2+}			7.44	14.04	15.5	17.43
Ni^{2+}	β_1	8.26	11.54	18.62	20.2	19.4
	β_2	14.61				
Pb^{2+}			11.39	18.04	18.6	20.33
Pr^{3+}			11.07	16.40	21.07	17.31
Sc^{3+}				23.10		
Sn^{2+}				22.1		
Sr^{2+}			4.98	8.63	21.85	10.54
Th^{4+}			16.9	23.20	28.78	29.25
Tl^{3+}			32.5	37.8	46.0	38.3
VO^{2+}				18.77		19.40
Zn^{2+}	β_1	7.03	10.66	16.50	18.8	19.32
	β_2	12.17				

SOURCE: Values taken from L. G. Sillen and A. E. Martel, *Stability Constants of Metal-Ion Complexes*, Special Publication No. 17, The Chemical Society, London, 1964; G. Anderegg, *Helv. Chim. Acta*, **50**, 2333, 2341 (1967); G. Anderegg and E. Bottari, *Helv. Chim. Acta*, **50**, 2341 (1967); A. R. Selmer-Olsen, *Acta Chim. Scand.*, **15**, 2052 (1961); and T. Moeller and S. K. Chu, *J. Inorg. Nucl. Chem.*, **28**, 153 (1966).

APPENDIX 9a. LOGARITHMIC VALUES OF STABILITY CONSTANTS OF METALLOCHROMIC INDICATOR CHELATES

Metal Ion	Alizarin[a] Red S	Chrome[b] Azurol S	Xylenol[c] Orange		Methylthymol[d] Blue	Pyrocatechol[e] Violet
H^+ k_{a1}		11.79	12.58	OH	13.4	11.73
k_{a2}	6.07	4.88	10.46	OH	11.15	9.76
k_{a3}	11.1	2.37	6.40	COOH	7.2	7.82
k_{a4}		− 4.8	3.23	COOH	3.24	
k_{a5}			2.58	COOH	2.60	
k_{a6}			1.15	COOH	1.13	
Al^{3+}	β_2 7.5	4.32				16.50
Be^{2+}	10.96	4.67				
Bi^{2+}			5.52			27.1
Cd^{2+}		9.0				
Ce^{3+}					6.16	
Cr^{3+}	4.7					
Cu^{2+}	5.65	4.23				
Fe^{3+}	3.73		5.70			
Hg^{2+}					K' 5.5 at pH 6	
La^{3+}	β_2 8.5	4.6			6.09	
Ni^{2+}		9.26	K' 6.78 at pH 6			
Pb^{2+}	4.78					
Sc^{3+}	β_2 9.0	5.5			3.9	
Th^{4+}	β_2 8.23	4.84				23.4
Tl^{3+}			4.90			
UO_2^{2+}	4.22	4.94				
V^{5+}	β_2 8.6					
Zn^{2+}			6.15			

SOURCE: Values taken from L. G. Sillen and A. E. Martell, *Stability Constants of Metal-Ion Complexes*, Special Publication No. 17, The Chemical Society, London, 1964; L. Meites, *Handbook of Analytical Chemistry*, McGraw-Hill Book Co., New York, 1963; and A. Ringbom, *Complexation in Analytical Chemistry*, Wiley-Interscience, New York, 1963.

[a] M. Bartusek and J. Zelinka, *Collection Czech. Chem. Commun.*, **32**, 992 (1967); D. P. Joshi and D. V. Jain, *J. Indian Chem. Soc.*, **41**, 33 (1964); K. N. Munshi, S. N. Sinha, S. P. Sangal, and A. K. Dey, *Microchem. J.*, **7**, 473 (1963); S. P. Sangal, *Microchem. J.*, **9**, 26 (1965); S. P. Sangal, *J. Prakt. Chem.*, **30**, 60, 314 (1965); and R. L. Seth and A. K. Dey, *J. Prakt. Chem.*, **19**, 229 (1963).

[b] S. T. Sangal and A. K. Dey, *Bull. Chem. Soc. Japan*, **36**, 1347 (1963); P. Sanyal and S. P. Mushran, *Chim. Anal.*, **49**, 231 (1967); and S. N. Sinha, S. P. Sangal, and A. K. Dey, *J. Indian Chem. Soc.*, **44**, 203 (1967).

[c] F. J. Langmyhr and P. E. Paus, *Acta Chem. Scand.*, **20**, 2457 (1966); B. Rehak and J. Korbl, *Collection Czech. Chem. Commun.*, **25**, 797 (1960); and L. Sommer and V. Kuban, *Collection Czech. Chem. Commun.*, **32**, 4355 (1967).

[d] M. K. Akhmedli and D. G. Cambarov, *Zh. Anal. Khim.*, **22**, 1183 (1967); N. Iritani and T. Miyahara, *Bunseki Kaga Ku*, **12**, 1183 (1963); and L. S. Serdyuk and V. S. Smirnaya, *Zh. Anal. Khim.*, **20**, 161 (1965).

[e] I. S. Mustafin, L. A. Molor, and A. S. Arkhangel'skaya, *Zh. Anal. Khim.*, **22**, 1808 (1967).

APPENDIX 9b. LOGARITHMIC VALUES OF STABILITY CONSTANTS OF METALLOCHROMIC INDICATOR CHELATES

Metal Ion	Murexide as MH_4L Chelates[a]	Erio- chrome Black T[b]	Calmagite	Calcon	Erio- chrome Blue Black B	Zincon	PAN in 20% Dioxane[c]	PAR[d]	TAR[e]
H^+ k_{a1}	14	11.50	12.35	13.5	12.5	8.3	12.2	13.70	13.07
k_{a2}	13.5	6.91	8.14	7.36	6.2	4.5	1.90	7.08	7.61
k_{a3}	10.28			1.0				2.31	1.65
k_{a4}	8.70								
Ba^{2+}	2.0	3.0							
Ca^{2+}	2.6	3.72	3.67	5.58					
Cd^{2+}	4.15	12.74			5.7			β_1 11.5 β_2 21.6	
Co^{2+}	2.48						> 12		β_1 12.28 β_2 23.74
Cu^{2+}	4.36	21.98		21.2			β_1 15.5 β_2 23.9	β_1 14.8 β_2 23.9	14.42
Mg^{2+}		5.75	5.69	7.64					
Mn^{2+}	2.1	9.6			7.4		β_1 8.5 β_2 16.4	β_1 9.79 β_2 18.92	β_1 9.66 β_2 18.46

Ni²⁺	3.38		15.4	β_1 14.0 β_2 27.5	β_1 13.2 β_2 26.0	β_1 13.15 β_2 25.22
Pb²⁺	4.4	13.19	13.2	β_2 6.919	β_1 12.9 β_2 26.6	
Th⁴⁺			19.8		7.17	
Tl³⁺				2.29	β_1 9.8 β_2 19.6	
UO₂²⁺			18.9		β_1 12.5 β_2 20.9	
Zn²⁺	3.0	12.76	12.5	13.0	β_1 11.2 β_2 21.7	β_1 12.4 β_2 23.5	β_1 11.31 β_2 21.62

NOTE: PAN = 1-(2-pyridylazo)-2-naphthol, PAR = 4-(2'-pyridylazo)-resorcinol, and TAR = 4-(2'-thiazolylazo)-resorcinol.

SOURCE: Values taken from L. Meites, *Handbook of Analytical Chemistry*, McGraw-Hill Book Co., New York, 1963; A. Ringbom, *Complexation in Analytical Chemistry* Wiley-Interscience, New York, 1963; and L. G. Sillen and A. E. Martell, *Stability Constants of Metal-Ion Complexes*, Special Publication No. 17, The Chemical Society, London, 1964.

[a] G. Geier, *Ber. Bunsenges. Physik. Chem.*, **69**, 617 (1965); G. Geier, *Helv. Chim. Acta*, **50**, 1879 (1967); and V. M. Tolmachov and A. K. Khukhryanskii, *Uch. Zap. Khak'kovsk. Gos. Univ.*, **133**, Tr. Khim. Fak i Nauchn.-Issled. Inst. Khim., No. 19, 158 (1963).

[b] M. Kodama and H. Ebine, *Bull. Chem. Soc. Jap.*, **40**, 1857 (1967); and M. Kodama and C. Sasaki, *Bull. Chem. Soc. Jap.*, **41**, 127 (1968).

[c] A. Corcini, I. M. L. Yih, Q. Fernando, and H. Freiser, *Anal. Chem.*, **34**, 1090 (1962); G. Nakagawa and H. Wada, *Nippon Kagaku Zasshi*, **84**, 639 (1963); G. Nakagawa and H. Wada, *Nippon Kagaku Zasshi*, **85**, 549 (1964); and D. Negoiu, A. Kriza, and L. Baloiu, *Analele Univ. Bucuresti, Ser. Stiint. Nat.*, **13**, 165 (1964).

[d] W. J. Geary, G. Nichless, and F. H. Pollard, *Anal. Chim. Acta*, **27**, 71 (1962); M. Hnilickova, and L. Sommer, *Collection Czech. Chem. Commun.*, **26**, 2189 (1961); and R. W. Stanley and G. E. Cheney, *Talanta*, **13**, 1619 (1966).

[e] R. W. Stanley and G. E. Cheney, *Talanta*, **13**, 1619 (1966).

ANSWERS TO SELECTED PROBLEMS

Chapter 1

1. (a) 2.0 mg.   **(b)** 1.4 mg.   **(c)** 85 min.   **2. (a)** 29.4986 g.
(b) 28.9071 g.   **(c)** 0.5915 g.   **5.** 14.274 g.

Chapter 4

1. (a) 2.8 p.p.t.   **(c)** 20.0 p.p.t.   **(e)** 3.3 p.p.t.   **2. (b)** $+$ 10.2 p.p.t.
(d) $-$ 0.3 p.p.t.   **4. i (b)** $\pm$ 0.34 mg.   **(d)** 9.1 p.p.t.   **(e)** $\pm$ 0.62 mg.
iii **(b)** $\pm$ 0.04%.   **(d)** 16.1 p.p.t.   **(e)** $\pm$ 0.05%.   **5. (a)** $t = 8.24$, so the
difference is meaningful.   **(c)** 0.0108%.   **6. (a)** 4.36×10^{-4}, rel. std. dev. $=$
55.1 p.p.t.   **(d)** 0.1003 N, rel. std. dev. $= 0.7$ p.p.t.   **(e)** 0.4066, rel. std.
dev. $= 0.3$ p.p.t.   **7. (a)** $m = 6.11 \times 10^{1}$, $b = 0.003$.   **8. (a)** 2.   **(c)** 2.
(e) 4.   **(g)** unknown.   **(i)** 3.   **9. (a)** 12.4.   **(c)** 0.0413.   **(e)** 76.3.
(g) 227.   **(i)** 7.92.   **10. (a)** 1.68.   **(c)** 5×10^{-4}.   **(e)** 1.68 mequiv/ml.
(f) 3.9×10^{-2}.

Chapter 5

Activity Coefficients

1. (a) 0.745.   **(c)** 0.570.   **(e)** 0.149.   **2. (b)** 1.00.   **(d)** 2.7×10^{4}
3. (a) 1.884×10^{-5}.   **(c)** 2.87×10^{-5}.   **(d)** 2.85×10^{-5}.

4. (a) $\log K_a = \log \mathbf{K}_a + 2\left(\dfrac{0.511 \sqrt{\overline{\mu}}}{1 + \sqrt{\overline{\mu}}} - 0.15\mu \right).$

(d) $\log K_b = \log \mathbf{K}_b - \left(\dfrac{2.044 \sqrt{\overline{\mu}}}{1 + \sqrt{\overline{\mu}}} + 0.60\mu \right).$

7. (a) 3.33×10^{-8} M.   **(c)** 7.43×10^{-7} M.

Electroneutrality

1. (b) $[H^+] + [Na^+] = [ClO_4^-] + 2[SO_4^{2-}]$, $1.745 = 1.745$.   (d) $2[Mg^{2+}] + [H^+] = [NO_3^-] + [Cl^-]$, $2.125 = 2.125$.   2. (a) $C_{Cl^-} = [Cl^-] = 0.250\ M$.
(c) $C_{CN^-} = [HCN] + 2[Ag(CN)_2^-] + [CN^-] = 0.598\ M$.   (e) $C_{en} = [en] + [enH^+] + [enH_2^{2+}] = 0.0645\ M$.   3. (a) $[H^+] + [NH_4^+] = [Cl^-]$.   (c) $[H^+] + [Na^+] = [HCO_3^-] + [CH_3COO^-]$.   (e) $3[Fe^{3+}] + 2[Cu(NH_3)_4^{2+}] + 2[Cu^{2+}] = [ClO_4^-] + 2[SO_4^{2-}] + [OH^-]$.   4. (b) $C_{en} = [en] + [enH^+] + [enH_2^{2+}] = 0.0500\ M$.   (d) $C_{CN^-} = 4[Ni(CN)_4^{2-}] + [CN^-]$, $C_{Ni} = [Ni(CN)_4^{2-}] + [Ni^{2+}]$.

Acid–Base

1. (a) pH $= 3.9080$, $[H_3O^+] = $ [propionate] $= 1.236 \times 10^{-4}\ M$, [propionic acid] $= 1.143 \times 10^{-3}\ M$.   (c) pH $= 11.06$, $[OH^-] = $ [piperidinium ion] $= 1.16 \times 10^{-3}\ M$, [piperidine] $= 2.59 \times 10^{-3}\ M$.   (e) pH $= 2.29$, $[H_3O^+] = [HSO_3^-] = 5.1 \times 10^{-3}\ M$, $[H_2SO_3] = 1.53 \times 10^{-3}\ M$, $[SO_3^-] = 6.24 \times 10^{-8}\ M$.
2. (a) $K_a = 5.0 \times 10^{-2}$.   (c) $K_b = 9.4 \times 10^{-9}$.   3. (a) pH $= 3.98$.
(c) pH $= 3.45$.   (e) pH $= 4.91$.   4. (b) pH $= 4.38$.   (d) pH $= 8.57$.
5. (a) $3.38 \times 10^{-5}\ M$.   (c) $7.04 \times 10^{-4}\ M$.   6. (b) $1.05 \times 10^{-4}\ M$.
(d) $1.81 \times 10^{-3}\ M$.   7. (a) 57.5 g.   (c) $0.147\ M$.   (e) 89.8 ml.
8. (b) 5.11.   (c) no change.   9. (a) pH $= 7.44$.   (c) between 4.36 and 7.88.

Solubility

1. (a) 35 mg.   (c) 0.32 mg.   (e) 0.13 mg.   2. (b) 1.3×10^{-15}.
(d) 5.5×10^{-12}.   3. (a) $CdS < NiS < Tl_2S < MnS < La_2S_3$.
(c) $Ni_3(PO_4)_2 < Ca_3(PO_4)_2 < AlPO_4 < Ag_3PO_4$.   4. (a) 7.06×10^2 mg.
(b) 1.37 mg.   (c) 3.92 mg.   5. (a) 0.083 mg.   (b) 0.0064 mg.
(c) 7.4 mg.   6. (a) 12.41.   (c) 9.2.   (e) 8.53.   7. (b) $7.9 \times 10^{-4}\ M$.
(d) $1.7 \times 10^{-4}\ M$.   8. (b) $5.7 \times 10^{-4}\ M$.   (d) $4.2 \times 10^{-4}\ M$.
9. (a) $7.3 \times 10^{-10}\ M$.   (c) $6.67 \times 10^{-2}\ M$.   (e) $1.8 \times 10^{-4}\ M$.
10. (a) 6.7×10^{-5} ml.   (b) 22.7 ml.   11. $[Cl^-] = 2.11 \times 10^{-5}\ M$, $[H^+] = 1.16 \times 10^{-4}\ M$, $[NO_3^-] = 9.45 \times 10^{-5}\ M$, $[Hg_2^{2+}] = 3.0 \times 10^{-9}\ M$.
12. (b) $1.7 \times 10^{-7}\ M$.   13. $3.53 \times 10^{-2}\ M$.   16. (a) yes, $[Ag^+] = 9.68 \times 10^{-12}\ M$ when thallium iodide begins to form.   (c) no $[Pb^{2+}] = 7.4 \times 10^{-6}\ M$ when $MnCO_3$ begins to form.   17. (b) pH must be between 2.96 and 5.13.
(d) pH must lie between 4.22 and 5.52.

Complex Ion

1. (a) $\alpha_{0NH_3} = 0.68$.   (c) $\alpha_{0NH_3} = 5.3 \times 10^{-13}$.   2. (b) $\bar{n} = 0.34$.
(d) $\bar{n} = 3.99$.   5. $3.9 \times 10^{-6}\ M$.   6 (a) $4.4 \times 10^{-3}\ M$.   (b) $1.14 \times 10^{-2}\ M$.
7. $[Co^{2+}] = 4.1 \times 10^{-4}\ M$, $[Co(NH_3)^{2+}] = 1.2 \times 10^{-3}\ M$, $[Co(NH_3)_2^{2+}] = 9.9 \times 10^{-4}\ M$, $[Co(NH_3)_3^{2+}] = 2.2 \times 10^{-4}\ M$, $[Co(NH_3)_4^{2+}] = 3.1 \times 10^{-5}\ M$.
8. $4.00 \times 10^{-7}\ M$.   9. pH $= 7.29$.   10. (a) $6.34 \times 10^{-8}\ M$.   (c) $2.3 \times 10^{-5}\ M$.
(e) $1.6 \times 10^{-11}\ M$.   11. between pH 0.04 and 1.02.
12. (b) $3.52 \times 10^{-5}\ M$.   (d) $7.2 \times 10^{-4}\ M$.   13. (a) $K' = 2.4 \times 10^5$.
(c) $K' = 6.8 \times 10^{13}$ (e) $K' = 1.3 \times 10^1$ 14. $2.0 \times 10^{-10}\ M$.

15. 0.091 moles.   **17.** separation is feasible between pH 3.14 and 4.15.
19. (b) $pH_{min} = 3.11.$ **(d)** $pH_{min} = 4.00.$

Distribution

1. $K_D = 7.75.$ **2.** 0.777 g.   **3. (a)** 42.3 ml.   **(c)** 463 ml.   **0. (b)** 8.55 $\times$ 10^{-4}.   **(d)** 1.09 $\times$ 10^{-8}.   **6.** $K_{assoc} = 5.84 \times 10^2$.   **8. (a)** 3.04 $\times$ 10^{-2}. **(c)** 3.04.   **(e)** 304.

Chapter 6

1. 0.00335 g Br_2 in CCl_4, 0.00061 g Br_2 in water.   **3.** 16.2, or 17 to get at least 99.9%.   **4. (a)** 79.9%.   **(c)** 43.3%.   **d.** $pH_{\frac{1}{2}} = 3.98.$ **9.** pH = 2.36, Cu is in benzene, Co in water.   **10.** 5.92 $\times$ 10^{22}.   **12.** pH = 4.30. **13.** 3.7 $\times$ $10^{-2} = D.$ **10.** pH = 6.81.

Chapter 8

6. (a) pentane.   **(b)** water.   **(c)** hexane or benzene.   **(d)** aqueous phosphate buffers.

Chapter 10

17. (a) phenol–water or n-butanol–acetic acid–water.   **(b)** and **(c)** n-butanol–acetic acid–water.   **(d)** i-propanol–ammonia–water.   **(e)** i-butanol–HCl.

Chapter 11

1. the thin layer of powdered stationary phase. **3.** adsorption, partition, ion exchange, gel filtration.   **4. (a)** ethanol–water–NH_3.   **(b)** diethyl ether. **(c)** methanol or diethyl ether.   **(d)** water or pyridine–water.   **(e)** acetic acid. **12.** size and location (R_f); 0.33, 0.06.

Chapter 14

8. (a) 1.24 cm/plate.   **(b)** no, since R is only 0.99.   **20.** 26.2%. **22.** 22.2%.   **23.** 22.2%.

INDEX